CONT]

PREFACE

Biblical quotations in Creation's Mutiny
The King James Bible (an English translation from the Hebrew, Aramaic and Greek) was chosen as the source for the biblical quotations, because it is a very accurate translation and has widespread availability. However, it has limitations today mostly regarding the ability of a modern audience to understand the English used yet remains an excellent study Bible. M. W. Seymour advises the use of this Bible along with a more modern translation to improve understanding.

About the footnotes
Although M. W. Seymour has made every attempt to interpret Scripture from the perspective of the entire Bible, the presented biblical references for each comment are not always all the considered references; only the most relevant are often listed. Biblical text has been quoted from the King James Bible (widely known as the King James Version). Regarding each comment that is not directly related to the Bible, the nonbiblical references on which he comments are not always an exhaustive list regarding the subject. The footnotes are vital accompaniments to the main text and in many cases are more important. The book should never be sold without the footnotes, select bibliography, timeline, glossary and select index.

Cross-referencing
When a single page number is given, this denotes where the relevant passage starts and may continue on to the next page or pages.

About the author
M. W. Seymour is a preacher, medical doctor and graduate of Cambridge University.

Acknowledgements

I would like to express my sincere gratitude to all those individuals who have loyally guarded and/or faithfully translated the Bible over the centuries. I owe a great debt to them. I also acknowledge the authors and, where relevant, the translators of the nonbiblical sources referenced in Creation's Mutiny.

Understanding can be likened to the creation of a necklace. The beads are called Science, Mythology, History, Religion, Supernatural, Future and Meaning of Life. The Bible is the string that fits into each bead, and without it they remain scattered and unfathomable.

M. W. Seymour 2008.

Some time in the near future . . .

Chapter 1　　　**Origins**

I'm Sol Amos. That's not my real name. I'm one of the seven chief advisers of the House of Hodaviah. My other responsibility is to record events connected with the House. Sol is an abbreviation of Solomon and has nothing to do with the ancient Roman sun gods who have the same name.[1] All of our first-name aliases are Solomon, because, like him, our wisdom comes from God.[2] This may seem immodest to you, but the sound advice that we've given over the last twenty years is proof enough. The outcomes of actions committed to this counsel are unrivalled. Furthermore, to questions embedded in future's eternity we've provided answers that will be forever trustworthy. Our boast is in God and not in ourselves, because it is He who provides us with the necessary insight to deliver such counsel. The very origin of wisdom is clearly spelt out, yet most choose to ignore it. The root of wisdom is the fear of God.[3] Wisdom brings knowledge and understanding of the visible, the invisible, the past, the present and the future, which together are the determinants of good decisions.

---

[1] Two so-called gods with the name Sol were worshipped: one, also known as Elagabalus, was brought from Syria to Rome in 218 AD; and the other, identified with the Greek sun god, Helios, was established in Rome at an earlier time. Tacitus' Annals Book 15 *chapter 74*, Tertullian's De Spectaculis *chapter 8*, Ovid's Metamorphoses Book 4 *lines 166-255*, Book 14 *lines 1-36*, Hesiod's Theogony *lines 371-374, 956-962*, Herodian's History of the Empire Book 5 *section 3:1-6*, Dio Cassius' Roman History Epitomes of Book 79 *chapter 31:1-2* and Book 80 *chapter 11:1-2*, Historia Augusta: Antoninus Elagabalus *chapters 1:4-7, 3:4-5, 17:8-9* and The Deified Aurelian *chapters 25:3-6, 35:3*.

[2] 1 Kings 3:7-14.

[3] Job 28:28, Psalms 111:10, Proverbs 1:7, 9:10.

I was once asked if there was life anywhere else in the universe. My answer was, "Yes, in Heaven, the home of God."

The question that followed was, "Is Heaven much different from Earth?"

"No, it's similar, but there are some important differences," I replied.

In Heaven there are a mountain and clouds. On the mountain are a temple and peculiar flaming stones. There is a sea, but instead of holding water, it's a sea of glass that can be stood upon.[1] In the sky talking beings fly, proclaiming the sovereignty of God.[2] They can talk, because they're angels. The angels were created with different forms and for diverse purposes. Some angels resemble what we on Earth would call animals, some look like men and some have both bestial and human features.[3]

You may ask what the relevance of this place called Heaven is to Earth. I would answer that events have occurred in Heaven that influence each and every day of our lives. To explain this I shall first tell you about Earth and the rest of the universe (excluding the home of God). I shall then follow with Heaven (the home of God) and go on to illustrate how Heaven and Earth are connected.

In the beginning God created the entire universe, including a very special planet, Earth. In just six days He'd completed this great work. These days were like present days and don't represent billions of years, for it's made clear that each day had an evening and a morning. After each day, a phase in His

---

[1] Isaiah 14:12-14 (mountain and clouds); Ezekiel 28:14-17 (mountain and stones of fire); Revelation 4:1-6 and 15:1-2 (sea of glass); Isaiah 6:1, 14:12-14, 57:15, Revelation 7:15, 11:19 and 16:17 (combining these references—temple on mountain).

[2] Isaiah 6:1-3, Revelation 4:6-9.

[3] 2 Kings 6:14-18, Isaiah 14:12-16, Ezekiel 1:5-25, Daniel 9:21, Revelation 4:6-9, 9:2-11, 12:9, 16:13-14.

creation was finished.[1] He fashioned the Earth in a mature state, so that an abundance of life could thrive there once created.[2] The days were as follows.

On the first day God created space[3] and the Earth. The surface of the Earth was covered with water.[4] He then created light and separated it from the darkness.[5]

On the second day God divided the water with an expanse (the firmament), so that some water remained on the Earth, while the rest of the water was elevated above the expanse. He called the expanse "heaven". In the Old Testament of the Bible the word heaven (often shamayim in Hebrew) can mean one of three things: sky, space (the universe beyond the Earth's atmosphere) or home of God. The context in which the word heaven is found reveals its meaning. Regarding the second day, heaven means sky. In other words, God positioned a layer of water above the atmosphere to surround the entire Earth.[6] This layer of water no longer encompasses the Earth above our sky. I shall reveal more about it later.

---

[1] Genesis 1:1-2:1. No time period other than a day can have both an evening and a morning: not a thousand, a million or a billion years!

[2] Genesis 1:1-31.

[3] In Genesis 1:1 the King James Version uses the word heaven (a translation of the Hebrew word shamayim) instead of space; however, in this instance the word heaven is more precisely translated as space given its context. See further on for the explanation.

[4] Genesis 1:2 contains the first biblical reference to water: "And the earth was without form, and void; and darkness *was* upon the face of the deep. And the Spirit of God moved upon the face of the waters." It wasn't until the third day that God made dry land appear.

[5] Genesis 1:1-5. God made the light before creating the celestial bodies such as the sun and other stars. This would explain why light-emitting celestial bodies that are millions of light years away can be observed; God created their light to reach the Earth before they themselves were created.

[6] Genesis 1:6-9—these four verses can be clarified according to the text of Creation's Mutiny. The explanatory words (which are

FOOTNOTE CONTINUED ON THE NEXT PAGE

On the third day God gathered the water under the sky into one place, so that dry land would appear. He created grass, herbs and trees to exist on the land.[1]

On the fourth day God created the sun, the moon and the stars, and set them all in the expanse of space.[2]

On the fifth day God created the creatures of the sea and the winged birds.[3] Like the plants already present and the other living beings yet to come, these sea creatures and birds were created to multiply after their kind.[4]

CONTINUED FOOTNOTE PRESENT

---

alternative translations) are in brackets. "And God said, Let there be a firmament (expanse) in the midst of the waters, and let it divide the waters from the waters. And God made the firmament (expanse), and divided the waters which *were* under the firmament (expanse) from the waters which *were* above the firmament (expanse): and it was so. And God called the firmament (expanse) Heaven (sky). And the evening and the morning were the second day. And God said, Let the waters under the heaven (sky) be gathered together unto one place, and let the dry *land* appear: and it was so."

[1] Genesis 1:9-13.

[2] God placed the sun, moon and stars in the "firmament of heaven", now referring to space: Genesis 1:14-19.

[3] God created some winged birds to fly in the "firmament of heaven", now referring to sky: Genesis 1:20. The translation of the Hebrew word "shamayim" in Genesis 1:26 is "air" to permit the series of words "fowl of the air" instead of "fowl of the heavens". (Air is still one of the three meanings of "shamayim": in this instance "sky".) A valid translation of the series of words would also be "fowl of the sky".

[4] Genesis 1:11-25 demonstrates that although there may be diversity within a species, ultimately the members of that species retain the ability to reproduce with one another. The strict definition of species is a group of organisms that can reproduce with one another and the offspring (males and females) are capable of reproduction. Domestic dogs and cats are different species, as they cannot

FOOTNOTE CONTINUED ON THE NEXT PAGE

On the sixth day God created every animal that walks or crawls on the Earth.[1] On this same day He also created a man and a woman.[2] Their appearance would have been unlike most

CONTINUED FOOTNOTE PRESENT

---

produce offspring together. Horses and donkeys are different species; although they can mate to produce mules, the majority of these animals are sterile, i.e., they can no longer produce offspring after their kind. Despite the different behaviours and appearances of wolves, jackals, dingoes, coyotes and domestic dogs, they can all breed with one another and the offspring are capable of reproduction, and therefore these dogs are all one species; hyenas and foxes are incapable of breeding with the dogs mentioned earlier and with each other, and so are different species.

Various individuals are much more liberal with the use of the word species. They distinguish many creatures as different species that can in fact breed with one another and the offspring are capable of reproduction. Their aim is to differentiate creatures according to behaviour and/or mating preference and/or appearance and/or geographic location; however, this is not in accordance with the strict definition of species.

Diversity within a species (strict definition) can be brought about by: God or mankind choosing certain breeding pairs; by the effect of the environment promoting certain breeding pairs; chance; and by spontaneous mutations (almost always with a negative effect). However, the resultant descendants remain members of the species, which can breed with one another, and the offspring are capable of reproduction. There is no conclusive scientific evidence that one species changes into another species, i.e., there is no mechanism here to support the theory of evolution. Example: It has been proposed that Darwin's finches found on the Galapagos Islands have become different species because of their differing habitats; however, according to the strict definition, these finches remain the same species, as they can and do mate with one another to produce offspring that are capable of reproduction.

[1] Genesis 1:24-31.
[2] Genesis 1:26-31, 2:20-25.

humans on the Earth today, although similar in overall form. The first man and woman would have had features of all the different races combined together. Imagine a male and a female offspring of a half-Swedish-half-Kenyan father and a half-Indian-half-Chinese mother, and you may have an approximation of how Adam and Eve might have appeared.

Therefore, from the third to the sixth day inclusive all of Earth's species were created.[1] Humans were the last creation—a

---

[1] That all of Earth's species were created at a discrete point in time (to be precise from the 3rd day to the 6th day of creation inclusive, i.e., over 4 days) is evidenced by the fossil record. The number of extinct species so far discovered makes up only a small fraction of those currently in existence on the Earth. The theory of evolution assumes that there has been progressive change from one species to another over billions of years, and furthermore those who adhere to this theory believe that many of the changing paths have not been successful. If the theory of evolution is correct, then the number of species currently in existence would be a tiny fraction of those that are extinct, i.e., a reverse of what we observe but to an even greater extent. It isn't possible for one species to change into another, but for argument's sake there would be well over a million times more extinct species than those still in existence today. To explain this massive deficiency of species, advocates of the theory of evolution suggest that there have been distinct times in which cataclysms have caused large extinctions with the conditions amenable to fossiliza-tion, and therefore we are witnessing only occasional periods during which certain species thrived (e.g., Jurassic). However, at the same time the advocates propose that there have been many of these fossil-generating extinction episodes to explain the supposed many different periods. This still means that we should have found a vastly greater number of extinct species, recorded as fossils, than species still in existence today.

Various individuals are constantly trying to affirm that certain species are links between others, because the theory of evolution depends on the demonstration of change from one species to another. Owing to their fruitless search for genuine missing links

FOOTNOTE CONTINUED ON THE NEXT PAGE

CONTINUED FOOTNOTE PRESENT

and the realization that, according to their theory, there are vast numbers of unaccounted species, they erroneously state that there are gaps in the fossil record. They are not gaps but huge uncrossable chasms that ruin the theory and point to a fixed number of species coming into existence collectively at a distinct time and that since then a modest fraction have become extinct.

Related to the above, mathematical probability destroys the theory of evolution, because if the theory is correct, then we should be regularly finding links between species rather than repeatedly finding previously identified species, which is most often the case.

Adherents of the theory of evolution often put forward the similarities (such as eyes, red blood cells, insulin, etc.) between species as evidence that one species changed into another. This is an argument that in itself proves nothing and lacks awareness as to the theory of evolution's main opposition, which is that God has created all life on Earth over 4 days. God, the supreme inventor, doesn't need to reinvent the fundamental mechanisms by which He allows each species to live; He has clearly used many of these mechanisms repeatedly. (Compare this to how we construct buildings. Whether a simple house or multi-storey skyscraper, they will have many similarities, from the construction materials to the rooms that make it function—bedrooms, toilets, kitchens, etc.) Regarding DNA, the genetic information that encodes these mechanisms, similarities between species don't mean that one species has led to another but instead point to a single, brilliant economical creator, for if the mechanisms are similar, so will be their blueprints.

Sometimes a species is so closely designed to another that they are able to mate to produce offspring that are sterile or only the offspring of one gender are fertile. This does not mean that the two different species share a common ancestor or that one evolved from the other. There is no conclusive proof of a common ancestor to horses and donkeys, although unsurprisingly smaller extinct animals have been proposed by evolutionists; however, these supposed ancestors simply represent distinct species that no longer exist. The Bible can shed some light on this. In relation to the period between

FOOTNOTE CONTINUED ON THE NEXT PAGE

species separate from all others, because although we are also made from the elements of the Earth, the man was made in God's own image and the woman complementary to the man.[1]

Adam and Eve were placed in the Garden of Eden and were given control over the entire Earth and every living thing in it.[2] The couple were meant to live an idyllic life. The only work that they needed to do was maintain the Garden of Eden and collect fruits and vegetables for sustenance.[3] Adam and Eve were both naked and innocent. Despite this innocence, it's important to note that they were created as adults with the ability to speak.[4] They were not created as babies, who need to be taught how to behave as adults as they develop to maturity. In a similar way, the animals and plants were created in a mature state, as were the world and the rest of the universe.[5] The whole of God's creation wouldn't have been able to function unless He'd made it this way, and sadly it's this fact that's so often overlooked by individuals who therefore incorrectly assume that the world is a

CONTINUED FOOTNOTE PRESENT

2166 BC and 1876 BC horses, donkeys (asses) and mules are mentioned. This demonstrates that horses and donkeys were known as distinct species at that time. Furthermore, the mule, the in most cases sterile product of a horse and donkey, was also recognized (Genesis 12:16—asses; Genesis 36:24—mules and asses [the next mention of a mule is around 1000 BC—2 Samuel 13:29]; Genesis 47:17—horses and asses). The situation 4,000 years ago is the same as today.

[1] In the main text "elements of the Earth" is used to convey the modern essence of the word "dust" in the Bible: Genesis 1:26-27, 2:7, 3:19, 9:6, Job 10:9, Psalms 103:14, 1 Corinthians 11:7.

[2] Genesis 1:26-28.

[3] Genesis 1:29, 2:15-17. See Dispensations (1).

[4] Genesis 1:27-30 (and created with the ability to understand speech), 2:19-20, 2:23-3:13.

[5] 2 Peter 3:5. See Chapter 4 pg 100 and footnote regarding incorrect conclusions based on assumptions.

million times older than it truly is. Because God made the Earth in a mature state, it's futile to radiometrically date rocks to determine its age. I shall explain this further. Over time radioactive atoms within rocks are converted to stable atoms. Radiometric dating is a method used to determine the age of rocks by measuring the proportion of radioactive atoms to their stable atoms of conversion: the younger the rock, the greater the proportion of radioactive atoms there will be; and the older the rock, the lesser the proportion of radioactive atoms there will be. Put plainly, the world appears to have very old rocks. However, the assumption of this method is that there were no stable atoms of conversion in the beginning. The Bible demonstrates that this couldn't have been the case, because if God created the Earth with vast quantities of rocks that emitted large amounts of harmful radioactivity (ionizing radiation), then the life that He'd placed here would have been destroyed from the outset. The rocks were created old.

In the middle of the Garden of Eden there were two unique trees: the Tree of Life and the Tree of the Knowledge of Good and Evil.[1] The fruit of the Tree of Life had special healing and rejuvenating properties that would make those who ate it live forever.[2] Adam and Eve were free to eat from this tree, as it was God's intention that they should live eternally. They needed this special fruit, because Adam and Eve were made from the elements of the Earth, and consequently without the Tree of Life they would eventually grow old and die. Presumably, they would need to eat from this tree at certain times to maintain their youthfulness and if they became injured or sick. Consumption of the fruit from the Tree of the Knowledge of Good and Evil was forbidden. If this one law was broken, then death was the intended punishment.

---

[1] Genesis 2:9.
[2] Genesis 3:22.

I confess that in my studies I've not yet discovered when the home of God, Heaven, was created. It may be that at the present time we're simply not supposed to know. Even so, I imagine that Heaven was created by God at a time long before the creation of the Earth and the rest of the universe, because He pre-existed these eternally. However, the Bible shows us that Heaven is a physical place and has now been positioned within the universe.[1]

Within the mountain temple in Heaven are a throne and an altar.[2] God rules from this temple, and angels gather there to meet with Him.[3] He is seated on the throne, yet at the same time He is omnipresent.[4] He is the Living God and the author of all life. The laws of science that bind the universe together were created by Him. By continually preserving these laws, God maintains everything.[5]

The angels were created before the Earth, because they were present at its creation, celebrating the event.[6] There are so many

---

[1] Heaven's physical attributes have already been described in this chapter: possessing a mountain, clouds, a glass sea, etc. Heaven is positioned in the universe, because the Bible states that it is "the heaven of heavens". Deuteronomy 10:14, 1 Kings 8:27, 2 Chronicles 2:6 and 6:18 all mention the three heavens. Along the lines of translating the Hebrew word shamayim (heaven) explained earlier in this chapter, Deuteronomy 10:14 can be clarified as follows with the alternative translations in brackets. "Behold, the heaven (sky) and the heaven (home of God) of heavens (space) *is* the LORD'S thy God, the earth *also,* with all that therein *is.*" The other verses can be similarly clarified.

[2] Isaiah 6:1, 14:12-14, 57:15, Revelation 7:15-17, 8:2-5, 9:13, 11:19, 16:17.

[3] 1 Kings 22:1-29, Job 1:6-12, 2:1-7, Isaiah 14:13.

[4] Deuteronomy 4:7, 1 Kings 22:19, 2 Chronicles 2:6, Psalms 103:22, Revelation 4:2-5, 5:6.

[5] Colossians 1:12-17, Hebrews 1:1-3.

[6] Job 38:4-7 (see Timeline). In this passage angels are referred to as both "morning stars" and "sons of God". For explanations see

FOOTNOTE CONTINUED ON THE NEXT PAGE

misconceptions about angels that I feel that it's necessary to explain the truth to you at this early stage in my narrative. Unlike mankind, all angels were created knowing the difference between right and wrong.[1] When descriptions of their appearances include gender, they are always portrayed as males in the adult form. There is a possible exception to this: in one biblical passage two flying women are described with wings like those of storks, but it is not explicitly stated that they are angels.[2] There are multitudes of angels. All are supernatural beings. They can be divided into four groups.

Firstly, there are regular angels. They have a variety of different roles, including that of messengers, guardians, carers, rescuers and punishers.[3]

Secondly, there are high-ranking angels. They generally have authoritative roles. Some are chief princes elevated above other angels. Michael, one of the chief princes, has the unique position of archangel, for he is the only one with this rank mentioned in the Bible. Moreover, the word archangel is always used in the singular, even when not in conjunction with the name Michael. Therefore, although there may be many chief princes, there is only one archangel, and that individual is Michael. This position includes the duty of being a leader of an army of angels. Michael is also the prince assigned to protect the Israelites.[4] Gabriel

CONTINUED FOOTNOTE PRESENT

---

respectively further on in this chapter pg 24 with footnote regarding what Lucifer said in his heart and Chapter 3 pg 59 with footnote regarding the sons of God.

[1] The angelic rebellion was not preceded by angels eating the fruit from the Tree of the Knowledge of Good and Evil or any equivalent.

[2] Zechariah 5:9-10.

[3] Genesis 19:1-29, 2 Kings 6:8-18, Matthew 4:11, 13:41-50, Revelation 7:1-11.

[4] Archangel is a New Testament word (1 Thessalonians 4:16, Jude 1:9). In the Old Testament Michael is referred to as "one of the chief princes" (Daniel 10:13), but of these princes he is designated

FOOTNOTE CONTINUED ON THE NEXT PAGE

should be mentioned here, because he is another angel who is specifically named in the Bible. He is customarily regarded as an archangel, but this is incorrect. Nonetheless, he is a vital heavenly messenger who has the honour to stand in the presence of God. Gabriel has the appearance of a man.[1]

The third group are the cherubim. They are frequently described in the Bible as being in close physical proximity to God.[2] Their roles appear to be that of guardians in Heaven and on Earth, and as occasional means of transport for God when visiting the Earth.[3] Some of the cherubim are portrayed as having wings and multiple faces. Four of them are described in great detail in the book of Ezekiel; each has two pairs of wings and four different faces (that of a man, a lion, an ox and an eagle).[4]

CONTINUED FOOTNOTE PRESENT

---

as "the great prince" (Daniel 12:1). Daniel 10:21 and 12:1 illustrate that Michael stands up for Daniel's people (meaning the Hebrews, who after the kingdom split were divided into Judah and Israel, and now come under the universal title of Israel—see Timeline).

[1] Daniel 8:16, 9:21, Luke 1:19-22, 1:26-38.

[2] 2 Kings 19:15, Isaiah 37:16, Ezekiel 1:5-2:4, 10:1-22.
The word cherubim is a plural Hebrew word; singular is cherub.

[3] Genesis 3:24, 2 Samuel 22:7-16, Psalms 18:6-10, Ezekiel 1:5-2:4, 9:3, 10:1-22, Revelation 4:1-9.

[4] Ezekiel 1:1-28 (cherubim presented in the main text), 10:1-22. The cherubim in Ezekiel chapter 10 were identified as the same group described in chapter 1 seen by the River Chebar, although observed at a later time. Furthermore, it is explicitly stated that their faces were identical to the cherubim observed previously. However, the later cherubim's faces are as follows: that of a cherub, a man, a lion and an eagle. Therefore, the appearance of these cherubim's cherub-face is that of an ox. As a consequence of this deduction, one should not generally infer that when a cherub is mentioned in the Bible without a description of his appearance, then his face (or one of his faces) has the aspect of an ox. Other cherubim described in the Bible have different semblances. In Revelation 4:6-9 four beings are described. Each has a single face and three pairs of wings. Although

FOOTNOTE CONTINUED ON THE NEXT PAGE

The fourth group are the seraphim. They are mentioned in only a single passage of the Bible. Each has three pairs of wings and flies above the throne of God.[1]

For centuries scholars have placed the cherubim and seraphim at the top of an angelic hierarchy; however, this is neither expounded nor refuted in the Bible. On the other hand, Michael and the other chief princes are described as having leadership roles, thus are high-ranking. The cherub Lucifer is a complicated exception and will be dealt with separately. Angels cannot die.[2] It's not that God cannot extinguish them but rather that it's His will that they're eternal. Angels are spirits[3] but can also take on solid form. They can eat and drink as we do, amongst other things![4]

The most important angel of all is "the Angel of the LORD", also known as "the Angel of God". There are many passages related to Him in the Old Testament. I have deliberately not included Him with the other angels, because He is in fact God.

CONTINUED FOOTNOTE PRESENT

---

not directly stated, they are almost certainly cherubim. Each of three of the beings has a body that corresponds with the face; the first being resembles a lion, the second a calf (this one does have the face of an ox) and the third an eagle. The other has a face like a man. His body is not described but cannot be humanlike, as he, like the others, is described as bestial.

[1] Isaiah 6:1-6.
The word seraphim is a plural Hebrew word; singular is seraph.
[2] Luke 20:34-36.
[3] Psalms 104:1-4, Matthew 8:16, Hebrews 1:7. See Soul and Spirit.
[4] Genesis 6:2-4, 18:1-19:3, Psalms 78:24-25, Hebrews 13:2. Genesis 18:1-19:3 starts with the LORD (God) and two other beings, all having the appearance of men, meeting Abraham. The LORD remained with Abraham, and the other two beings went to Sodom. At the end of this passage these two beings are referred to as angels.

The word angel in Hebrew[1] means messenger. This "Messenger of the LORD" was different from the other angels, since one or more of the following three are present in each of the detailed Old Testament Scriptures related to Him: He proclaimed that He was God; He was identified as God by those to whom He appeared; and the author of the relevant book of the Bible stated that He was God. Other angels did not state that they were God, and neither were they recognized as such. The Angel of the LORD carried out the following tasks in the Old Testament: herald, saviour and punisher. He appeared to Abraham, Jacob, Moses, David, Zechariah and others.[2]

God made a cherub called Lucifer. Although Lucifer has the ability to change form,[3] his created appearance was that of a man, because in the future he will have this semblance in his conquered state when deprived of his power.[4] He was brought into

---

[1] Singular is malach; plural is malachim.

[2] In the King James Version this supernatural individual is named "the angel of the LORD" and "the angel of God"; note that angel starts with a lowercase a. Therefore, the main text, which uses an uppercase (capital) A, is not quoting directly but rightly reflects His status as God. Genesis 16:7-13, 21:1-21, 22:11-18, 31:11-13, Exodus 3:1-22, 14:1-31, Numbers 22:22-35, Judges 2:1-5, 6:11-23, 13:3-23, 1 Kings 19:1-7, 2 Kings 19:32-35, 1 Chronicles 21:7-30 (see also 2 Samuel 24:1-18), Zechariah 1:1-21, 3:1-10, 12:8.

The following Old Testament passages briefly mention the Angel of the LORD without expanding on His nature: Judges 5:23, 2 Kings 1:1-18, Psalms 34:7, 35:5-6, Isaiah 37:21-38.

In Genesis 32:24-30 the Angel of the LORD is not specifically named, but Jacob wrestled with a supernatural being who had the appearance of a man but was God. The supernatural being was certainly the Angel of the LORD.

[3] 2 Corinthians 11:14.

[4] Isaiah 14:12-17. In this passage Lucifer is observed in the semblance of a man. He is being incarcerated in Hell: to the "sides of the pit" (that is, the Abyss). This is a future event and will be

FOOTNOTE CONTINUED ON THE NEXT PAGE

existence perfect in wisdom and beauty. All angels and humans have some measure of these two attributes, but Lucifer filled up the entire sum of both; moreover, his wisdom was unquestionably accompanied by extreme intelligence. He was the anointed cherub, which means that he'd been chosen by God from all the cherubim for a leadership role in sacred duties.[1]

Lucifer's true name is Heelel, which means radiant. He is also called "son of the morning".[2] He was the guardian cherub of the mountain of God[3] and not an archangel, as has been incorrectly ascribed to him. On the same day that he was created he was clothed, because, unlike the first man, Lucifer would have known that he was naked. His apparel is gold armour adorned with a variety of precious jewels such as emeralds, sapphires and

---

CONTINUED FOOTNOTE PRESENT

---

dealt with further on in Creation's Mutiny, as will his other major semblance.

[1] Ezekiel 28:12-19. This passage starts by referring to the king of Tyre and then identifies this character with the anointed cherub, an angel who, based on further description, is none other than Lucifer. The true human king of Tyre is referred to earlier in the same chapter as the prince of Tyre (Ezekiel 28:2-11). He is described as being merely a man, but, like Lucifer, he fancies himself to be a god. The angel Lucifer and the human king of Tyre are deliberately compared in this manner, because their existences have features in common. Lucifer's sacred duties included being the guardian of the holy mountain of God in Heaven and walking up and down between the "stones of fire" (perhaps a pathway lined by burning stones leading to the throne of God).

[2] Isaiah 14:12-14. Heelel, a Hebrew word, has been translated as Lucifer, which means light-bearing. The two names have similar meanings.

[3] Ezekiel 28:12-14. See footnote earlier in this chapter pg 23 regarding the anointed cherub.

diamonds.[1] Lucifer is described as having "traffic".[2] Undoubtedly, a combination of handsomeness, intelligence and an
elevated position means that his traffic is influence. Power and
persuasion are his to wield—tools of a first-rate guardian. He
even had access to the Garden of Eden on Earth.[3]

Lucifer remained perfect until the day that sin was found in
him. On that day, because of his handsomeness, he was filled
with conceit, and this unbalanced his wisdom. His conceit gave
him ambitions beyond his station. He became jealous of his
creator's power and coveted the throne of God. This was the first
sin. To smoulder against God when you walk in the presence of
His unlimited power is an almost inconceivable thing, but this
was an incomparable and all-consuming vanity. The Almighty
God knows everything, even the innermost thoughts of His
creations. Lucifer said in his heart, "I will ascend into heaven, I
will exalt my throne above the stars of God: I will sit also upon
the mount of the congregation, in the sides of the north: I will
ascend above the heights of the clouds; I will be like the most
High."[4]

---

[1] Ezekiel 28:12-19. In the King James Version the word *was* of
"*was* thy covering" in verse 13 is in italics, meaning that it is an
additional word that was not a direct translation but represents an
interpretation; in this case the word was probably incorrectly added.
Therefore, what is described is still his covering (or remains one
that he can select).

[2] Spelt "traffick" in the King James Version: Ezekiel 28:18. The
Hebrew word "rekula", which has been translated as traffick, has
also been translated as "merchandise": Ezekiel 28:16.

[3] Ezekiel 28:12-19.

[4] Isaiah 14:12-14. As in this case, angels are sometimes referred to
as stars in the Bible. Where relevant, each passage in which the
word stars appears reveals that they are not celestial bodies but
angels. Other examples: Job 38:7 (angels referred to as "morning
stars" in this passage—see earlier in this chapter pg 18 and footnote
FOOTNOTE CONTINUED ON THE NEXT PAGE

With Lucifer's very core contaminated, his wisdom and insight were lost, and his power filled him with violence. With his intelligence and handsomeness retained, his burning rage focused on convincing the other angels to revolt with him. He used his remarkable influence to tremendous effect. The result was that a guardian cherub, the one who'd been exalted by God through anointing, became the leader of at least a third of the heavenly hosts, all opposed to the will of their creator.[1] Lucifer was then cast out of Heaven with his rebel angels—all demons.[2] It's a commonly held mistake that demons no longer have access to Heaven. This is not supported by the Scriptures. They've lost their posts in Heaven, but they still have right of entry to meet with their creator, one aim being to make accusations against humans who are faithful to God.[3] When not being a menace in Heaven, Lucifer, now additionally called Satan, occupies much

---

CONTINUED FOOTNOTE PRESENT

---

regarding angels celebrating the creation of Earth), Revelation 1:20, 12:4-9.

[1] Revelation 12:4. This passage is regarding events around the time of Jesus' birth and reveals that at this time Satan commanded a third of the angels (stars—see immediate previous footnote); some angels had already been removed from his authority (made clear further on in Creation's Mutiny).

[2] Luke 10:17-20. Although this passage mentions only Satan falling from Heaven like lightning, without doubt he would have been accompanied by the other angels who had rebelled, as he is their leader. This is evidenced by the fact that in this passage Satan and his demons are collectively mentioned as opponents of the followers of Christ who do His work on Earth, indicating that the demons followed their master to this planet. Not surprisingly, Satan and his demons' ultimate destination, the Lake of Fire, will be the same: Matthew 25:41, Revelation 20:10.

[3] 1 Kings 22:1-29, Job 1:6-12, 2:1-7, Revelation 12:1-17.

of his time roaming the Earth, the reasons for which I shall go on to explain.[1]

The ambition of Satan is still to be like God. Satan knows that ultimately he cannot take God's place, hence his heart's resolution: "I will be like the most High." Satan realizes that an achievable goal is to take the place of God in the minds of other created intelligent beings. Satan will divert their worship from God to himself. Short of that he will distract them from following God, so that they too will share his own eventual fate in the Lake of Fire.[2] Satan is also jealous for territory and authority, and will usurp these gifts if able. His first target was Earth and whom better to attack than those who'd been given rule over it, Adam and Eve.[3]

Satan will use any means to achieve his end. On this occasion he chose a subtle deception. Satan possessed the serpent.[4] There are two accounts in the Bible of Satanic possession, as opposed to possession by one or more of his demons. The other occasion was the possession of Judas Iscariot, the betrayer of Jesus.[5] When Satan himself possesses another being, it's for a great malevolent purpose, which, because of its pivotal importance to the future, can be left to no other. In the Garden of Eden Satan convinced Eve that if she ate the fruit from the Tree of the Knowledge of Good and Evil, not only would she continue to live, but she would ascend to a greater plane of existence by becoming like God, knowing both good and evil. With Eve convinced, she ate from the tree, then gave some to Adam. He also ate the fruit.[6]

---

[1] Job 1:6-12, 2:1-7, 1 Peter 5:8.

[2] Revelation 20:10 (see Timeline).

[3] Genesis 1:26-28.

[4] Genesis 3:1-6. In Revelation 12:9 and 20:2 Satan is referred to as "that old serpent", identifying him with the serpent who was in the Garden of Eden.

[5] Luke 22:1-6, John 13:1-2.

[6] Genesis 3:1-6, Revelation 12:9.

The consequences of this event were manifold. Adam and Eve instantly had the knowledge that was promised. They realized that they were naked and covered themselves with fig leaves. But instead of gaining the promised power, they were filled with fear and hid from God when He walked in the Garden of Eden to meet with them. Although they'd been bested by Satan, God had mercy on them and did not put them to death. However, He instituted some changes. Eve no longer had equal power with Adam on the Earth, childbirth was to be painful and man would have to work hard for a living. God made clothes for them out of animal skins, so for their offence living things died. This was the first sacrifice for the sins of humans.[1] Adam and Eve were driven out of the Garden of Eden. A flaming sword that moved and cherubim were placed at the east of the Garden of Eden to prevent humanity from returning to eat from the Tree of Life, their way to eternal life.[2] Therefore, with this special gift withdrawn and humans dispossessed of their original office, Satan has become the temporary ruler of the Earth.[3]

Satan and his fellow demonic mutineers are operating in the world that we were meant to have ruled over. Demons still have access to Heaven, although this will one day be permanently prevented in the last days of our age. At that time Michael and his angels will fight against Satan and his demons in Heaven. This is the Battle of Heaven, which many mistakenly think has already taken place. The battle is a future event. Satan and his demons will be overcome and their movements restricted to the Earth. What a wretched place the world will be at that time, because Satan's anger will increase, knowing that he has but a little time left,[4] for the end of our age signals the end of his.

---

[1] Genesis 3:7-21.

[2] Genesis 3:22-24.

[3] Luke 4:4-8, 2 Corinthians 4:1-6, Ephesians 2:2, 6:12.

[4] Revelation 12:7-12.

You may ask, if God knows the future, then why did He create Lucifer. I would answer that God in His wisdom never intended to create machines that would mindlessly obey and worship Him. His intention is for us, the created intelligent beings, to come to Him voluntarily. Worship can only be truly expressed by individuals who give it willingly. This is also true for love. We and the angels were created with the ability to rebel. Satan is both the initiator and director of the universal rebellion. He is the greatest of all God's opponents. The name Satan means adversary. He is a liar, a tempter and a murderer.[1] He is not in Hell, as is often erroneously thought. He is known as the prince of the power of the air, not the prince of the bowels of the Earth.[2] However, he is well aware that his eventual destination will be the eternal Lake of Fire.[3] Although Satan has been in existence for thousands of years, he knows that his time is running out. He will never show remorse for his actions and ask God for forgiveness. Satan will hold on to his power for as long as angelically possible. His desire is that multitudes of other created intelligent beings will be with him in his ultimate doom. God's desire is for humans to turn away from their rebellion and willingly come to Him. It is they who will be with God forevermore, along with the angels who remained faithful to Him.

Humans face a trial called "life". Where they place themselves during this test determines their eternal fates. This is the story of one such trial.

---

[1] Matthew 4:1-11, Mark 1:13, Luke 4:1-13, John 8:44, 1 Corinthians 7:5.
[2] Ephesians 2:2.
[3] Satan's ultimate destination is the Lake of Fire: Matthew 25:41, Revelation 20:10.

The fishing boat slowly made its way eastward along the fjord. Samuel March was sat on the deck at the bow. He was watching the gently wind-swept water that was about to be severed while he thought about the task ahead. As the middle-aged skipper piloted the vessel from the lofty cabin, he occasionally glanced in Sam's direction. The other Norwegian fishermen took little notice of their passenger.

It was Sam's third day in Norway. He'd arrived by plane in Oslo early on Thursday morning, the 22nd of May. After a brief appointment at the meteorological institute with one of the country's experts on weather patterns, Sam had taken a short internal flight westward to the city of Bergen. From there he'd begun his search.

Sam was fighting the fatigue that had followed the exams that had delayed the start of the mission. He should have waited at least another day to catch up on sleep, but how much rest would his mind allow, knowing that there were others who'd already started the task that he'd been set? His mental numbness had drowned the course noise of the boat's diesel engine to a faint hum. He looked around him. Given his current focus and exhausted state, he could scarcely appreciate the splendour of Sogn Fjord. The towering, grey walls of this the deepest and longest fjord in Norway were almost vertical, and the boat had already passed countless small waterfalls cascading from fertile, green sources. In places the walls were the sheer buttresses of expansive, snow-capped mountains. In some areas the walls were less steep but still prohibited a landing. However, once in a while the boat passed isolated pockets with flat bays, some of which supported small human settlements. The water on that day was deep blue, and in the deepest regions, almost black. In a number of places, some of which were close to the water's edge, a dead weight would plunge to depths of over a kilometre. The mid-afternoon sun was obscured by thick, ill-defined clouds. The only indication of its position was an uncomfortable warmth that it created on Sam's retinas as his eyes occasionally searched the sky above.

Sam March was a sinner. He'd become a Christian in his early teens. The realization of his sin, the fear of Hell, the desire to go to Heaven and the knowledge that Jesus is God the Messiah (Christ), who'd died for his sins and from whom he could receive both forgiveness and salvation, had disquieted his mind. Why disquieted? Because he hadn't acted on these universal truths immediately, but instead a mental battle had ensued, the opponents having been a life in subjection to his creator versus a future that he thought that he could control. After seven months of shark-like thrashing, he calmly put his trust in Jesus and changed the direction of his life.[1] This truly transformed Sam. Having put his trust in Jesus, the Holy Spirit followed and lived inside of him, assuring him of his salvation, that his eventual destination was Heaven.[2] Sam had turned away from actively seeking sin and felt God's forgiveness.[3] Yet even with the

---

[1] Advice to those seeking salvation: believe that Jesus is God; admit that you're a sinner and express a desire to God to turn away from sin; believe that Jesus died for your sins and seek forgiveness from Him; and put your trust in Jesus. John 3:13-21, 14:1-11, Acts 3:1-26, 4:10-12, 5:29-31, 13:33-38, 26:15-18, Ephesians 1:2-14, Colossians 1:12-14, 1 Peter 1:3-4.

[2] The Holy Spirit (Spirit of God, Holy Ghost) enters a person after he or she has accepted Jesus as his or her personal saviour: John 1:29-34, Acts 1:1-8, 2:38, Ephesians 1:1-14.
The Holy Spirit can also do many other things. Two examples are: by the power of the Holy Spirit, Stephen was able to see the glory of God (Acts 7:1-60); and the Holy Spirit can convict people of their sin who haven't yet put their trust in Jesus (John 16:7-16).

[3] Through Jesus' sacrifice forgiveness for sin can be received by all who seek Him: John 14:1-6, Acts 5:30-31, 13:36-39, 26:14-18, Colossians 1:13-14, 1 John 1:1-10.

influence of the Spirit, who granted a heightened sense of right and wrong along with divine guidance, Sam remained a sinner.[1] Yes, he sinned less, and yes, he desperately strove to do what was right, for Christ had given him the ability to not lead a life ruled by sin;[2] however, like all those who put their trust in Jesus, only his eventual presence in Heaven after death would forever free him from mankind's sinful nature.[3] My Lord had been good to Sam. In the same way that his inheritance of salvation through

---

[1] On Earth the Holy Spirit (Spirit of God) communes with the human spirit to deliver a greater awareness of the correct action to take given the circumstance: John 16:13, Acts 16:6, Romans 8:1-16, Galatians 5:16-26, see Soul and Spirit.

The person cannot become completely without sin. If we say that we are without sin, we lie, for only Jesus is without sin. However, Jesus wants us to not be ruled by sin but to live righteous lives. John 8:1-36, Romans 7:18-25, 1 John 1:1-10.

True guidance by the Holy Spirit does not contradict the Bible, which is the Word of the Living God. Beware of those who claim to be led by the Spirit but what they say and their actions contradict the Bible; their guiding spirit is not the Holy Spirit. Matthew 7:15-28, Ephesians 5:6-17, 1 Timothy 4:1-11, 6:3-5, 2 Timothy 3:7-17, 1 John 3:1-10 (this passage should be balanced by the rest of Scripture, for to be wholly without sin is impossible, but righteousness is possible; sin in this passage is ultimately referring to individuals ruled by sin, their flesh, living unrighteous lives—see above and next immediate footnote), 1 John 3:23-24, 4:1-3, 2 John 1:6-11.

[2] Christ can free us from being ruled by sin whilst on Earth, thereby allowing us to lead righteous lives: John 8:1-36, Romans 3:21-26, 5:1-6:23, 8:10-15, 10:4, 1 Corinthians 1:28-32, 2 Corinthians 5:20-21. See Dispensations (5).

[3] Romans 7:18-25, 1 John 1:1-10, 1 Corinthians 15:42-58, Revelation 21:1-27.

Christ was an unearned gift,[1] so was each and every ability that my Lord had given him. Despite the fact that Sam was now twenty-two years old and a maturing Christian, one of his ongoing sins was that he took for granted what the Lord had done for him. Nevertheless, my Lord used him anyway.

Sam's father was English, and mother Guyanese.[2] To describe how Sam looked, I might say that he was a mulatto, except this may conjure up the wrong image in your head, especially for those not acquainted with many mulattos. These people display tremendous physical diversity. This may be due to the dark-complexioned parent, who although appearing to be African, is often in fact a mixture of mostly this race, which therefore visually predominates, and also many possible other races, including English, Chinese, Dutch, Spanish, Portuguese, Amerindian and eastern Indian. Mulattos can appear Hispanic to Middle Eastern, and anything in between. Sam March looked mostly like an Arab from the southern Arabian Peninsula and was often mistaken as such. He was of medium height and slim but with a muscular build that could be deceptively concealed by a suit. He was clean-shaven. He had brown skin and dark-brown, deep-set eyes. His nose was long and straight. Those like himself could easily recognize his true origin from structural clues: his high cheekbones and strong jaw line. He enjoyed those moments when he and one of those like himself acknowledged one another.

Sam secretly hated the word mulatto. He also disliked the term mixed-race, although he often declared himself as such. To him it expressed not being completely one or another. He possessed a combination of many traits that have been controversially

---

[1] A person cannot earn a place in Heaven. Salvation is a gift from Jesus the Messiah. Romans 3:23-25, Ephesians 1:1-13, 2:1-9. See Dispensations (5).

[2] Guyana, a country located in the north of South America, borders Brazil, Venezuela and Suriname.

assigned to different racial groups, some of which were not even part of his near ancestry. Sometimes the traits blended well. At other times they clashed. Yet Sam always felt utterly whole. As I've explained already, all humans are descended from two people: Adam and Eve. There is only one human race. I suspect that Sam's internal feelings of wholeness were a reflection of this fact. The world attempts to box each person into one racial group, but for Sam to be subject to this he would have to deny one of his parents—a thing that he would never do. However, for the purpose of this account I shall still refer to races, ethnicities and cultures, as they are human terms that are inescapable in this age and have been for millennia before.

One thing that transcends race is faith. It's sometimes perceptible to us but is a thing that only God can fully see and measure. Even with my imperfect human wisdom, I observed that Sam had been given faith in abundance, and it was this above all else that was his greatest earthly gift.

Sam was in the middle of his medical school training at Cambridge University. The recently completed exams represented the exact halfway point, and if he passed them, he would be awarded with a degree, the first of two required to conclude his studies to become a doctor. Before the beginning of the Easter term,[1] he'd been contacted by the Norwegian National Consortium of Museums, who'd asked him to meet with one of their senior staff about a potential job. This was all the letter had declared—not unusual in Sam's second vocation. Many of his clients preferred to discuss the assignments face to face. He'd arranged to meet their man in a small café in Cambridge.

I learnt how to read eyes, because I thought that it was a useful skill. Sam needed to read eyes to survive, and therefore his ability in this regard was far superior to mine. After just a glance, Sam knew exactly how someone felt about him. He rarely got it

---

[1] Final term (late April to mid-June) of the academic year. During this term most students sit exams.

wrong, and most people stayed true to form, at least on their first meeting with him. Klaus Remer had surprised Sam. The café was quiet, and Sam had arrived on time. Remer was already there, sat at a table and smartly dressed in a cream linen suit that was inappropriate for the season in England. He was thirty-five years old and bespectacled. He had light-brown hair and a square jaw. He'd seen Sam walk into the café and hadn't for one second thought that the new arrival was the man with whom he had his meeting. Sam confidently strode up to Remer.

"Klaus Remer?" Sam asked, knowing the answer to his own question.

Remer's blue eyes initially showed astonishment that Sam had dark skin. Remer had known that Sam was British but hadn't been told about his background. Then what was that? It lasted for such a tiny fraction of a second that it was difficult to interpret. If Sam was forced to guess, he would have said that it was hate. Yet his reading was cast into doubt by the eyes' generous approval that immediately followed, accompanied by a smile and an outstretched hand. This outward appearance persisted. The fact that the Norwegian Consortium's representative was an Austrian was another surprise, though a lesser one, as there was considerable migration in Europe and the man was far from being the first person to hold an important public-company position as a foreigner.

In perfect English Klaus Remer described the assignment in detail. The aim was to find the hammer of Thor, Mjollnir.[1] The

---

[1] The Elder Edda (otherwise known as the Poetic Edda)—Hymiskvida (The song of Hymir) *stanzas 23-36*, Lokasenna (Loki's home-truths) *stanzas 57-63*, Thrymskvida (The song of Thrym) *stanzas 11-32*; The Prose Edda (otherwise known as the Younger Edda)—Gylfaginning (The deluding of Gylfi) *chapters 21, 42, 44*, Skaldskaparmal (Poetic Diction) *3, 4, 5*.
The Eddas are the most informative sources of Germanic mythology still in existence.

item had been part of the private collection of a Norwegian baron who'd died the year before. Very few people had known that the baron had possessed the hammer, but somehow the Consortium had found out. Remer didn't mention how. The baron had left no heir, and the hammer was not in his will. When his properties had been searched, although many priceless objects had been found, the hammer hadn't been among them. Regarding the assignment, the most useful items that had been recovered were his memoirs and journal. The baron had been obsessed with Germanic mythology. Whilst in his forties, he'd inherited Mjollnir from his father. The baron had then spent the last thirty years of his life excavating ancient sites in almost every county of Norway. The memoirs revealed that he'd excavated twenty-five sites in total, and in the journal were sketches of a host of artefacts, many of which were now on display in various Norwegian museums. The journal didn't mention the hammer. The memoirs did but only in relation to Thor (the Germanic god of thunder[1]), whom the baron had greatly revered. Indeed, there was nothing found in writing that stated that the baron had had Mjollnir in his possession. The Consortium was convinced that Mjollnir had been hidden somewhere in Norway and most likely at one of the baron's archaeological sites.

Sam explained that he couldn't attempt the mission until two months had passed on account of his exams. Remer simply shrugged his shoulders and continued by relaying some of the more practical aspects of the assignment. He then stated the finder's reward. On accepting the mission, Sam was handed

---

[1] Thor is generally referred to as the Germanic god of thunder. The name Thor means thunder. In both Eddas, Thor is referred to as a god*, but he is not specifically referred to as one who controls thunder. *The Elder Edda—Völuspá (The prophecy of the seeress) *stanzas 25-26*, Thrymskvida (The song of Thrym) *stanzas 1-2, 17*; The Prose Edda—Gylfaginning (The deluding of Gylfi) *chapters 21, 42*.

photocopies of the journal, the memoirs and the Consortium's schematics of all twenty-five archaeological sites. The documents were written in Norwegian.

A warning from Remer followed, "I know of at least one other person who's looking for the hammer—a ruthless man. He has many people in his employ. So when you arrive in Norway, keep your eyes open. You'd do well not to run into them."

"Who is he?" Sam asked.

"I'd prefer not to say," there was fear in Remer's voice. If Sam was given the name, would he spread it abroad and make trouble for Klaus. "Let's just say that I know how he operates. Watch your back!"

It was just after Sam had left the meteorological institute in Oslo that he gathered that he was being watched. He noticed a man in his late twenties standing on the opposite side of the street. The watcher was tall with short, naturally white-blond hair. His eyebrows were the same colour. Sam stared back at the person observing him, and despite this the tall man didn't avert his gaze. Sam could tell the difference between simple curiosity and work. He walked on and executed some countermoves to avoid being followed, which had the desired effect.

Bergen is the wettest city in Norway. Even as the plane from Oslo approached its destination, Sam observed a dense, shapeless mist over and around Bergen and extending westward to obscure the land before the sea. Through a singular break in the mist he glimpsed part of a road-bridge meandering dreamily across one of the many fjords that surround the city. As the plane descended into the mist, Sam realized that it was in fact a vast rain cloud when large droplets spattered against his window. That same day Sam hiked 15 miles to an area outside the city where an ancient temple had been excavated by the baron and his team ten years previously. The temple had been dedicated to Odin.[1] Tools of human sacrifice had been discovered and removed, leaving the site barren. The voidness didn't deter Sam, who, under the cover of darkness and rain, performed a little digging of his own. He didn't find the hammer there or in the remains of Thor's temple on the outskirts of the village of Brekke, the wettest single location in Norway. Brekke had occupied his second sodden day in Norway.

As the boat thumped its way through the fjord, Sam checked the working order of the sophisticated electrical gear in his backpack. His most prized piece of kit was the tiny Global Positioning System (GPS) receiver that he'd bought in New York two years previously. Since then he'd used it on three missions, and it had performed admirably. He was a good map reader but that took time. The GPS receiver enabled him to forge ahead without stopping. He also had a satellite phone. The international travel and remoteness of some of his jobs meant that an ordinary mobile phone was mostly useless. The last device, a small, old metal detector, was not his own but borrowed from the archae-ology department in Cambridge. He was dressed for wet weather. He wore a raincoat, waterproof trousers and rubber-soled hiking boots, the leather uppers of which, bar the toes, were covered by his trousers. The skipper gave the helm to one of the other fishermen and joined Sam on the deck. As it happened, the skipper was also a Christian, and each recognized the other's faith after only a few minutes of conversation. They shared a few of their lives' Christian experiences before the skipper returned to the cabin.

Leikanger is one of the few natural bays of Sogn Fjord, and rarer still it's large enough to support a small town. As the boat pulled into the harbour and its people observed the newcomers,

[1] A Germanic god of war: The Elder Edda—Völuspá (The prophecy of the seeress) *stanzas 28-30;* The Prose Edda—Gylfaginning (The deluding of Gylfi) *chapter 36.*

Sam once again noticed the conspicuous clatter of the diesel engine. The fishermen weren't known in Leikanger. This town was Sam's destination. The fishermen lived in Kaupanger, a village further to the east. Even before they'd docked and despite the overcast sky, Sam had been able to make out the mountain range that bears the enormous Jostedals glacial ice cap. The mountain range was over ten miles away to the north. He tried to pay the skipper for the trip. The skipper refused any money, and a grateful Sam left the boat and made his way on a gentle upward slope through the town toward its northern border. As Sam passed a hostel on the outskirts of the town, it started to rain heavily.

The gradient steepened after the border, and Sam was now ascending through slanted fields, which were demarcated by natural terrain rather than artificial barriers. The various hues of green were spotted with simple wooden farm buildings painted bright red, each of which had a corrugated-iron roof. He wasn't alone. Besides the cows, there were plenty of tourists hiking, some of whom were descending to Leikanger after a long day's trek in and around the Jostedals Glacier National Park. Looking into the distance, he observed branches of the glacier spilling down slopes between peaks of the mountain range. He progressed northeast toward his goal whilst occasionally glancing at his GPS receiver.

Sam thought about the preceding two unproductive days and questioned his method to locate the hammer. After meeting with Remer, Sam had had the journal and the memoirs translated. He'd slowly and meticulously read the translations whilst also revising for his exams. On completion of his study of the translated documents, it had dawned on him that the best way to approach the task was to think about Mjollnir from the perspective of those who had possessed an absolute belief in Germanic mythology—not just the baron but also the similarly minded Germanic ancestors of the Norwegians. To this he would add to the equation his own rational explanation of the mythology, which has religious aspects. It was his belief that the mythology had to be based on some fact, however thin. Before Sam had left for Oslo, Klaus Remer had confirmed over the phone that to his knowledge the hammer remained undiscovered, and hence whatever method or methods that their rivals had so far been using had failed. If the next site, a burial mound, bore no fruit, Sam would have to come up with a different plan.

The farmlands abruptly ended with a dense forest, which Sam entered. Although it instantly felt unsafe, at least he was now undetectable to distant prying eyes. Even the ever-present mountain range to the north was no longer visible. Whilst he journeyed through the forest, he saw no one.

After walking for over an hour, the forest slowly petered out as the ground became harder. Having been significantly sheltered by the leafy cover, Sam now met worse rain than before entering the forest. Despite this, he could see that half a mile further north the steady slope that he was currently ascending was met by the steep, grey stone of a mountain, part of the range. However, before this, while the land remained green, was the burial mound, also known as a barrow. It was an unusual place for a barrow. Most of the barrows that Sam had visited in England were in locations where they could be seen from a distance from practically any direction—earthen mausoleums built to honour dead men. This barrow was hidden by the forest below and the mountains above, and furthermore was stunted by the latter. Perhaps the forest had grown long after the barrow had been created, and before this the mound would have been visible from Leikanger as an offering to the mountains, Sam thought. He reached the barrow as the sun set—perfect timing.

The barrow had been excavated to preserve its overall appearance. Instead of digging from the summit downward to expose what lay beneath, the archaeologists had entered from the side. What Sam met was a grass-covered hillock, which was roughly 40 metres in diameter and 15 metres high. The entrance was a tunnel that had been hollowed out of the northern face by the baron's team. The tunnel had been strengthened by wooden supports, visible on the walls and ceiling. Sam entered using a battery-powered lantern to guide the way. He could immediately see that the earthen tunnel extended for a few metres before leading to a crypt. He entered the crypt, a rectangular chamber, through an opening, which, like the rest of the tunnel, was a metre wide and almost two metres high. The opening was in the centre of one of the crypt's two walls of least breadth. The walls, floor and ceiling of the chamber were made entirely of stone. The crypt had been buried centuries before without any intended access, and the stones that would have blocked the relatively recent opening had been removed during the excavation. The ceiling was made of large slabs that spanned the width of the chamber. A few of the slabs were broken, and in places wooden supports, clearly recent additions, held the damaged areas of the ceiling in position. In comparison, the floor was completely intact and was made up of many much smaller-sized slabs. The baron's team must have met the crypt in a collapsed state and partly filled with earth, Sam thought. The journal stated that the crypt had been found containing an unremarkable stone sarcophagus of a 4th century king and some of his life's precious possessions. The crypt was now empty except for a few items of rubbish scattered on the floor.

From the schematic of the barrow Sam had known that the barrow's interior would be simple, but he'd not predicted the inspiration-suppressing effect that it would have upon him firsthand. Although they were open archaeological sites, almost flat in comparison with the barrow, each of the two temples possessed multiple corridors and chambers, which had inspired ideas of where to look for the hammer. Moreover, at both sites he'd generated potential clues from the shapes of the chambers themselves, their possible previous functions and the artefacts tallied in the journal that had been found in them. The temples' complexities had given Sam the notion that the baron had cleverly hidden Mjollnir, so that it would eventually be found by someone worthy of possessing the artefact. If the baron had hidden the hammer in the barrow, then its blandness suggested that his desire had been for the hammer to be lost forever. As before, Sam was aware that any area marred by his digging would have to be faultlessly restored—this was part of his contract with the Consortium—and therefore he would keep his excavating to a minimum.

Sam started by clearing the rubbish. He packed the various bits into a polythene bag, which he placed into a corner. He surveyed the chamber with the metal detector, and, as in the two temples, there were no significant signals. This hadn't deterred him before and wouldn't do so now, because for even substantial solid-metal objects, the device had a maximum detection depth of just eighteen inches. He then examined the chamber's floor for signs of resetting of slabs. There was uniformity throughout. He measured the lengths of the walls and compared the dimensions with those stated in the schematic. Perhaps a false wall had been added with something hidden behind. The chamber matched the schematic. At each temple he'd selected a single spot to dig, which had been based on hours of careful consideration. There was therefore a chance that he could have missed something at those sites. He dismissed this from his mind. He was one man and had been employed for precision. If the Consortium were allowed to comprehensively dig up all twenty-five sites, then they would have done so and well before he'd entered Norway. In the absence of any apparent clues, he chose the exact centre of the chamber to perform his excavation—the precise location where the king's sarcophagus had been found. He used a small collapsible spade to lever the stone slabs and dig the earth beneath. An hour and a half later he'd satisfied himself that the hammer wasn't hidden in that spot.

It was one o'clock in the morning, and Sam hadn't eaten a thing since snacking on board the fishing boat. His fatigue reminded him of its ongoing neglected presence. He'd already filled the hole and had replaced the stone slabs. He drank some water from his canteen. That was now three specially chosen archaeological sites completed—twenty-two more to go. He decided to camp inside the barrow and later that morning return to Bergen, where he would determine his next course of action. Before making camp, he examined the schematic again. It focused on the crypt rather than on the barrow. The crypt and the recently created tunnel had been expertly drawn, and the barrow itself was represented by a large, perfect circle, whose centre was aligned exactly with the centre of the rectangular chamber. However, this arrangement didn't quite feel right to Sam. He left the barrow to be met by a starless night and light rain. He climbed up the nearest mountain until he was 20 metres higher than the barrow's summit and confirmed, using the lantern's light, that the perimeter of the mound was indeed very close to being a perfect circle. From the schematic he noted the radius. But could that be trusted? There was only one way to be sure. By repeatedly using his tape measure, he determined the circumference of the barrow. He then calculated the radius. Curiously, the actual dimensions were different from those in the schematic. He returned to the crypt and established that the area within this chamber that was directly below the summit of the barrow was approximately three metres south of where he'd excavated. Therefore, neither were the schematic's dimensions of the barrow nor its diagrammatic perfect alignment of the centre of the barrow with the centre of the crypt correct.

Sam removed four stone slabs and started digging again. On reaching a depth of three feet, he struck dark metal. Initially excited, he cleared the earth around the object, but the dull metal became ever wider, so that he decided that the object couldn't be a hammer. He soon needed to remove another four stone slabs and the earth that had been beneath them to properly expose the superficial edges of the metal. He then dug further down, and before long he was thrilled and perplexed to find that he'd uncovered an unusually large hammer.

It was half-past three. Sam stood at the entrance to the barrow. He'd left the lantern inside the chamber, and the droplets of rain that hung on his curls glistened, reflecting the faint yellow light. He held the satellite phone tightly to his right ear.

"Mr Remer, it's March. I've found them."

"Them?"

"Yes, there are two hammers. They're huge."

"Really?"

"If they're made of iron, then I estimate that the larger of the two weighs around three hundred kilograms. I'm at site two in Sogn Og Fjordane. I don't know how you're going to get here. It's pretty inaccessible—maybe some kind of heavy-duty four by four. You'll need a lifting device as well—or a few strong men."

"Good, Mr March."

"If it's going to take a long time for you to get to me, then I'll bury them again."

"That won't be necessary."

Remer hung up.

Sam briefly looked at the silent phone, then returned to the crypt. He stood with his back to the entrance, hands on hips, staring at the exposed hammers, which remained in the large, newly created hole. Taking no notice whatsoever of Remer's instruction, Sam started to carefully bury the hammers. Twenty minutes later and halfway through the task, Sam stopped to rest. He sat on the floor near to the edge of the hole, facing the hammers, and started to eat a sandwich.

Sam turned his head toward the entrance to see the man with white-blond hair looming over him from a distance of just two metres. The fair-haired man was six feet six inches tall and broad throughout his frame: a thick-necked bull. He had the appearance of a northern European. His clothes were damp and his boots filthy with mud from his climb. Sam wasn't a trained fighter but had experienced more than his fair share of scuffles, mostly against opponents who'd reckoned themselves more than a match for him. One thing that he always tried to do was employ his brains: simply relying on speed and strength rarely sufficed. The burly man's approach had been unannounced: the prelude to a hostile act, especially considering that he must have known that Sam had spotted him in Oslo. It would be vital that Sam not get caught in the burly man's grip. Keep your distance, Sam recommended to himself.

"Have you contacted anyone yet?" the burly man asked loudly in an accent that Sam was unable to place.

Questions that were racing through Sam's mind were answered. The man has only just arrived. His footsteps were masked by the patter of rain from outside. Positioned behind me the man has probably seen only one hammer and thinks that it's in the process of being uncovered.

"I don't know what you mean," Sam answered.

The burly man lunged forward to seize Sam. Still sat, Sam grabbed the handle of the lantern with his right hand and threw it at his opponent's face. As the lantern struck the burly man's nose, Sam was already on his feet with the spade held in both hands. At the same time as leaping toward the burly man, Sam raised the spade high to his right, aiming to bring the spade down onto the left side of his opponent's head, thereby bringing the fight to a swift conclusion. The burly man caught the mid-shaft of the spade in his left hand. For a fraction of a second Sam was held aloft, clinging to the spade. The burly man released a punch, every inch of his twisting body incorporated into the effort. The cube-shaped right fist, a hammer of flesh and bone, hit Sam in the centre of his chest and threw him through the air. Sam landed on his back in an area beyond the hole and slid four feet on the undisturbed stone slabs before coming to a halt.

Sam wasn't quite sure what hurt the most: the front of his chest or back. Either way, he was winded and let out a subdued groan. The burly man had an unintelligent appearance yet was anything but. Sam had hoped that his bulky foe would be unfit, but he was in shape, a skilled fighter and fast to boot. As the burly man started to circumvent the hole, Sam watched his assailant briefly glance inside at the two incompletely buried hammers. The burly man, bleeding from a laceration of his nose below the bridge, stopped and looked toward Sam, who was still incapacited. Now ignoring Sam, the burly man stepped into the hole and with both hands he grabbed the 16-centimetre-diameter handle of the largest hammer. He manoeuvred the handle to the vertical position, the movement shifting loose earth from around the head. With a deep grunt, he strained to lift the hammer. He managed to raise the head from the base of the hole by just two inches for only three seconds before being forced to give up. He tried again with even less success. He aborted any further attempts on noticing that Sam was now able to raise his head and upper torso from the stony floor. The burly man jumped out of the hole and ran toward Sam.

"Who else knows?" the burly man shouted.

Still only partially recovered from the massive strike, Sam feebly thrust forward his left foot in the direction of his opponent's right kneecap. The burly man dodged in the manner that Sam expected. Sam immediately put all his strength into a swiping movement that connected his right foot with the outer side of the burly man's left knee. The burly man's unsupported weight, carried by his own momentum, fell toward Sam, who wriggled backward out of the way. The burly man crashed to the ground at Sam's feet. Despite the burly man's fall, he was unfazed, and from a position on all fours he leapt onto Sam and started to throttle him with both hands.

The burly man wanted an answer to his question, but he was enraged and was gripping too tightly for any to be forthcoming. He'd lost control. Sam struck at the thick arms, then punched the heavy jaw, which was the only part of the large head within reach. With Sam's neck fixed, he could only use the movement of his eyes to look right and left for potential weapons. There was nothing within reach. He fought the emerging thought of death's inevitability. He physically wrestled but to no avail. His legs were useless beneath the weight of his assailant.

The chamber was still lit by the lantern, which was lying on its side near the west wall. Tenuous shadows and then a dense fog of dark grey invaded Sam's vision. The hands relaxed except only a little. Sam struggled to breathe. Did any air enter his lungs? It didn't feel so. His eyes were open but now provided no sight. The back of Sam's head was being banged over and over again against the stone below, and the seemingly distant words "Do they know?" were being repeated.

Then there was another noise—directionless and repetitive. It echoed off the walls and slapped at Sam's failing consciousness. The yellow light was visible again—faint at first but slowly increasing. With his senses improving, he recognized the noise to be the sound of two hands clapping. And did he hear a new male voice say the word "Enough"? The bull of a man stood up, releasing his grip from around Sam's neck. Sam spluttered.

The intensity of the clapping reduced and then stopped, which allowed another sound to be registered by Sam: the muffled beat of decelerating helicopter blades.

Klaus Remer stood near the entrance; his hands were still united after his applaud. He wore dry hiking gear, which was flawlessly clean. His spectacles were absent. He held an umbrella—barely wet from the raindrops that had fallen onto it within the 20-metre distance between the helicopter and the barrow's entrance—in his left hand. "Bargsten, don't bear the man such a grudge! He found them before you, but at least it's over. Yes, well done, Mr March."

Sam was gasping for air. After a minute, he slowly sat up while clutching his neck as if returning his lost head. He looked around the chamber. He could see Bargsten limping toward the lantern and Remer peering into the hole.

Bargsten righted the lantern. Remer turned his attention to Sam. "March, you've been here for only three days, and not just one hammer but two. And, Bargsten, you've been to sixteen sites over the last two months. You were even here once before, were you not?"

Bargsten glowered at Sam. Because this one really needs goading, Sam thought. Sam gradually rose to his feet.

"How did you know that it would be here?" Remer asked.

Sam patted himself off. "Call it an educated guess," his voice was hoarse. "The counties of Hordaland and Sogn Og Fjordane are the wettest in Norway, and so I figured that they would have the highest frequency of rainbow sightings. Rainbows are caused by drops of water in the air dispersing and reflecting light from . . ."

"I know how rainbows are formed. Go on."

The beat of the blades had stopped, and Sam could hear that there were several men at work outside the barrow. He wondered about the size of the helicopter. "These regions must have been especially sacred to the ancient Norwegians who believed that the bridge to Asgard, the home of the gods, was a rainbow.[1] There are three sites in the memoirs that are located within the two counties. Two of the sites are temples. Because of that, I went to them first. This is simply the last site of the three."

"Rainbows! Here that, Bargsten, rainbows." Remer was almost laughing. His relief at achieving his own goal had lessened his envy.

"And why Bargsten?" Sam asked.

"Competition, Mr March: I think this helps progress, yes?" Now Remer was laughing.

---

[1] The rainbow bridge is known as Bifrost (also called Bilrost): The Elder Edda—Grímnismál (The lay of Grímnir) *stanza 44*, Fáfnismál (Fáfnir's lay) *stanza 15*; The Prose Edda—Gylfaginning (The deluding of Gylfi) *chapters 13, 15, 17, 27, 51*.
The main text refers to the Asgard that was believed to be a part of heaven (not Asgard the Old, which was reportedly a city on Earth, Troy*): The Elder Edda—Hymiskvida (The song of Hymir) *stanzas 5-7*, Thrymskvida (The song of Thrym) *stanza 18*; The Prose Edda—Gylfaginning (The deluding of Gylfi) *chapters 2, 15, 17, 27*.
*The Prose Edda—Gylfaginning (The deluding of Gylfi) *chapter 9*.

So this is humour for you, Sam thought.

"And I was right," Remer added.

Sam wanted to tell Remer where he could go with his warped ideas about competition but could hear the footfalls of men entering the barrow. The job had gone awry enough already. Sam also knew, deep down in the recesses of his own mind, that Remer had a point.

"Even in a helicopter, how did you get here so quickly?" Sam asked Remer.

"We've been triangulating your position from your phone signal. We checked in at the nearest hotel with a helipad earlier this night. It's about fifty miles from here. Oh, Bargsten's been working independently. I'm trying him out. In fact, Bargsten, you're in—but no reward."

"You're the man who you warned me about, and you're keeping the hammers for yourself," Sam accused.

"He's quick, isn't he, Bargsten?" Remer finished with a self-satisfied smile.

There was no reply from Bargsten.

And you're a fine actor, Sam thought.

"No hard feelings, Mr March. After all, our deal still stands," Remer said.

"Because I'm all about the money, right?" Sam replied.

Chapter 3   **The House of Hodaviah**

"So did you find the hammer of Thor?" Edward asked Sam. Edward was reclined comfortably on a sofa. His bare feet rested on a leather bean bag.

The two men were in the lounge of Sam's college quarters, which that year were on campus in Emmanuel College (one of the thirty-one Cambridge colleges). Sam had a separate lounge and bedroom. He shared the use of the kitchen and bathroom with only one other person. It was Sunday night, and the room was poorly lit by a single light bulb that hung centrally from a thick wooden beam.

"I'd prefer not to talk about it," Sam replied.

Edward's exams were over as well. He was a very different person from Sam, both in character and appearance. Edward was tall and wiry. Both his parents were white and English. He had blond hair, which, although tidily swept back, was longer than he usually kept it on account of the exams. His light-blue eyes were clear and bright, even in the low light of the room. He'd read modern languages, focusing mostly on Spanish and German, and had just finished the final year of a three-year degree. Sam and Edward had first met each other at school in GCSE classes and had maintained their friendship despite divergent A levels. The men had chosen Cambridge University independently of one another. Edward had been accepted at Trinity College, which is approximately a third of a mile from Emmanuel. Each of the men had deferred their entry to the university for a year. Edward had travelled to the Far East, where he'd toured from country to country with two other friends. Sam had journeyed to Africa alone. He'd spent the majority of the year in Zambia, working in a public hospital. At first he'd been given basic tasks, but because the staff had known that he'd been about to start training to be a doctor, his responsibilities had been gradually increased. By the

time he'd left, he'd been assisting in major operations in theatre
and had even been performing minor procedures on his own.

Sam didn't entirely trust Edward. In their second year Sam had
considered dating Monica, a Brazilian overseas history student in
his own college. Sam felt that an individual would always be on
shaky ground dating "internally" rather than with a person from
another college. Instinct told him this, not personal experience.
This was later reinforced by his observations of others; the
internal relationships often ended badly with private information
subsequently disseminated and groups of friends parting
acrimoniously. His policy was that if he dated internally, the
woman would have to have a very individual character and be
exceptionally discreet.

Therefore, the second year found Sam uncharacteristically
tentative about asking out a woman to whom he was attracted.
He'd decided to gather as much information about Monica from
chance meetings in the college grounds before making his move.
She was keen on him. Anyone would have been able to tell by
the way she always stopped to say hello, even if she was with
friends and in the middle of a conversation. However, she hadn't
taken much notice of him the first time they'd met on Freshers'
Night, in the first week of the first year, and neither had he of
her, although he'd acknowledged her beauty. She'd then dated
another history student—in college—who, to Sam, had the
appearance of a weasel. The relationship had ended after only
two weeks. She'd broken it off. One night in the dining hall a
whole year later, in the Lent term[1], Sam and Monica locked eyes
as he sat down on his bench. He read her gaze. She was sat on the
opposite side of the hall, dining with friends. Her eyes became
momentarily still and serious. He could see her desire ignite then
flourish. He realized that he was staring and felt warmth behind
his own eyes. After that, their brief exchanges started. There was
an unsaid connection. They were both checking each other out as

---

[1] Middle term (mid-January to mid-March) of the academic year.

to whether they should risk dating. Sam remained instinctively cautious and Monica now apprehensive from having had her fingers burnt. Sam mentioned the situation to Edward, who at that stage knew Monica as a faceless name, not being in her college nor studying the same subject.

As it happened, Edward was acquainted with a Trinity English student called Felicity, who knew Monica through the adc theatre. The women were both amateur actresses. Sam and Edward were walking through Great Court in Trinity on a Saturday afternoon when they bumped into Felicity. The three of them talked together. This was the first time that Felicity had met Sam but recognized him by face and name. She mentioned that she was going to see Monica. As Sam also knew her, Felicity suggested that they all go.

A few minutes later they were in Monica's room in a house owned by Emmanuel, off campus. Edward instantly understood Sam's interest in Monica. Sam could tell this, as could everyone else in the room. Edward noticed an archery bow in a corner and made a passing remark about the weapon. Monica explained that she was a member of the Cambridge Archery Society. And sure enough Edward turned up, bow in hand, at the next class that the society held in the grounds of Selwyn College. Not the most subtle tactic ever but it gave him the opportunity to ask her out. Sam could have only presumed that a rejection followed, as he heard no reports that Edward and Monica were subsequently seen together. Furthermore, Edward seemed unusually disappointed when he and Sam met a few days later. Nevertheless, the code had been broken. One never made a play for a friend's aspiration. The Lent term drifted into the break period, then a hard academic Easter term followed—at least for medical students. Sam forgot about Monica, and they met only once in the grounds of Emmanuel College that summer after their second-year exams. Their dialogue was short and the enchantment gone. Why? I imagine that I shall never know.

Besides this one failing, Edward was a good friend, but Sam harboured a reservation. At the end of their second year Sam had even considered letting their friendship fade. However, he'd decided to give Edward another chance. A year had then passed.

"You got paid didn't you?" Edward was undeterred by Sam's response.

"Yes, I found the hammer and got paid."

"What does it look like?" Edward probed further.

"I really don't want to talk about it," Sam's tone was more decisive.

"All right, all right, but everyone in Cambridge is going to know that you found it."

"Only if you tell everybody. The hammer isn't going to be displayed publicly, and there are no pictures. I didn't even get a chance to do that."

"How much did you earn?" Edward asked.

"Forty thousand pounds." Sam sat down on a chair opposite the sofa with a bowl of soup in hand. Edward had declined an offer for some earlier.

"Muchos dólares," Edward's voice was not envious. He already had a job lined up at a bank in the City of London.

Not a lot considering what I went through and what I found, Sam thought. "What it means is no summer job required—thank goodness. I need a break. This term really took it out of me: what with the exams, the sevens[1] tournaments and the prep for the job. And the summer's shorter this time."

Sam's first degree had been preclinical medicine. His next would be a clinical medical degree. This would involve seeing patients on the wards. It also meant that there would be no more terms: just three years punctuated by a few short breaks. The next phase of his training would start in September rather than in October as before.

---

[1] Each match of the tournaments is a game of Rugby played on a full-size pitch with 7 players on each side rather than 15.

"Maybe I'll smarten up the chariot," Sam said.

"With that kind of money, you could buy a new car."

"I guess so, but I've got other things that I want to spend it on. In any case, it's not forty thousand pounds anymore. Before I left, there was an eight thousand-pound hole in my bank account that had to be filled: the money I paid to Prof."

"You're too generous," Edward remarked.

"He spent two entire weekends translating the documents. They were a little rough but good enough."

"Did you tell him that? 'Thanks for the ropy translation, Prof!'"

Sam laughed. "He admitted it himself."

Edward smiled. "Anyway, I think it's time for you to come back to planet Cambridge . . . The King's Event[1] . . . three days away. And guess who are going? Katy & Co. And when I say 'Co.', I mean Rachel—well, you know, amongst others." Sam's face couldn't conceal his interest. He needed to work on that. "Yeh, that's right. I thought you'd like the sound of that."

Rachel was the woman whom Sam now fancied. He'd taken more care to hide facts such as this from his duplicitous friend since Monica. Rachel was also a medical student. Edward had surmised that Sam must like her: she was she, he was he and they'd both been to the same lectures. Edward had also correctly guessed that Sam knew about his attempt at Monica. There had been a cooling of the men's friendship for a few weeks. At the time Edward thought that he wouldn't try anything like that again. In reality, he would, only when he was surer of a positive outcome. On this occasion Sam hadn't actually stated that he was interested; therefore, officially there was no code to break. But that didn't matter. Edward felt that Rachel was the kind of medic who would date only other medics, so he probably didn't stand a chance. That was her track record, which had been confirmed by an air of aloofness that she'd displayed when she

---

[1] A large party held at King's College.

and Edward had been introduced many months ago. But damn it, she's a glorious female, he thought. Maybe still worth going for despite the rejection that would likely follow. Her olive-complexioned, seductive Mediterranean face framed by thick, curly, black hair and her shapely figure, which complimented her full, sensual lips, had made an indelible impression on him. And why was it that when Sam was interested in a woman, she became so much more attractive to Edward? Sam hadn't once liked anyone whom Edward was keen on—or so Edward thought.

At exactly eight o'clock in the morning Sam's tired sleep was interrupted by the first rap of a harsh triple knock on his door. He'd stayed up late talking with Edward and some more friends who'd joined the two at eleven o'clock. The additions had included Sanjeev, the budding stand-up comic. Sam's friends had all left at two in the morning. He still hadn't properly caught up on sleep since his exams. He got up from his bed, put on a winter coat and walked through the lounge to the main door. He opened the door at the start of the intended third triple knock. A FedEx delivery woman stood at the door.

"Are you Mr March?"

"Yes, that's me," Sam replied.

"I have a package for you, sir. If you could just sign here, I'll be on my way."

Sam signed the screen of a flat electronic device after a quick glance at the large, brown, A4-sized envelope tucked under the woman's left arm. He wasn't expecting a delivery. It isn't really much of a package, he thought; they probably use that term to describe all of their deliveries.

"Thank you," Sam said as he accepted the envelope.

"You have a nice day, sir."

"I'll try my best." Sam shut the door.

Sam could feel that the envelope was reinforced internally with cardboard. He sat down at the table in the lounge and immediately opened the envelope. He found and removed another envelope, which was white. The flap was straight and fixed with seven red wax seals. His first thought was of the book of Revelation, except he couldn't remember the event that occurred after each seal was broken. Whoever sent this had a flair for the dramatic. Sam smiled, then made sure that the lounge's curtains, which he'd not yet opened, had no gaps. The curtains weren't thickly lined, and the penetrating morning sun provided more than enough light to read. He broke each seal separately. He slowly pulled out a folded white piece of paper, on which was written a short message.

Dear Mr March

Congratulations on your recent success in Norway. We would like to discuss an assignment with you. If you are interested, go to the public telephone box on Marshall Street W1 this Tuesday at 1300 hours. You will receive a call and then be given further instructions.

May God be with you.

The House of Hodaviah.

Sam sat at the table and read the letter again. He began to think deeply. How did the House know about Norway? What do they need my help for? The House is an organization that gives advice. He then considered how the world perceived him. His jobs had included roles as a detective, treasure seeker and general problem solver. Which one do they want to hire?

Even though Tuesday was a clear, sunny day, it was still only late May and not yet hot. Sam was on the Cambridge to London train in an economy-class seat. It was eleven thirty and well after the peak. There were only a handful of people in his carriage. He used the time to read from his handheld computer, onto which he'd loaded the Bible and a huge encyclopaedia. He also had a special program that allowed the user to find the location(s) of a chosen word throughout the entire Bible. It could also display words in their original Hebrew if Old Testament[1] and Greek if New Testament, and explain, where possible, how these Hebrew and Greek words were derived.

Sam already knew a few things about us, most of which were known to the general public. He knew that the House of Hodaviah was initiated by seven founding members, whom some believe to be Christian fundamentalists. Fundamentalism was a term first used over a hundred years ago to describe Christians who believed in the literal interpretation of the Bible (except where symbolism is indicated by the text) and intelligently applied it to their lives for the betterment of themselves and those around them. If this was still the definition, then we would gratefully receive the label, but fundamentalism now describes irrational extremism of any religion, and therefore the designation no longer applies to us. I prefer the simple term "Bible-believing Christians".

Sam was accurate that the House's advisory service started on the internet. Individuals left their problems in writing on a secure site. We answered each problem within twenty-four hours. When each reply was sent, the charge was debited to the relevant individual's account. At first the responses were provided by only the seven founding members. Now there are fifty additional advisers, all trained by the original seven, although the fifty have never met us in person. Of the fifty there are junior and senior advisers. People now phone and the answers are given immediately. To obtain an answer from one of the original seven, the callers pay extra. Some of the money earned is used to keep the organization running (this includes salaries), secure and growing. The House offers advice on a wide range of matters: from faith to

---

[1] Note that a small proportion of the Old Testament is written in the Aramaic language but with Hebrew letters.

defence; and from personal relationships to financial issues. The clients themselves range from ordinary men to politicians.

The House has always courted controversy since it started twenty years ago. Recently, most of the criticisms have been connected with the fact that the House has expanded and continues to do so and is already receiving related problems to which solutions are being sought, sometimes from opposing sides. Therefore, these presented problems could be collated, and if two or more sides are following counsel from the same source, then the resultant outcome could be manipulated. The fact is that although opposing sides may be seeking advice, the responses are given straightaway and are based on the information imparted at the time. All is treated confidentially. If an adviser receives a problem that is related to a previous problem fielded by him or her, then the call is transferred to another adviser. On a difficult call an adviser may put the caller on hold and seek guidance from a more-experienced adviser. However, if the problem appears to be related to a previous call answered by the latter adviser, then the less-experienced adviser is instructed to seek help from another more-experienced colleague. I will concede that we record and store in our database the counsel provided by us, some of which is reviewed after a year in order to provide an internal judgement as to the quality of our service. This internal database is secure and not connected to the internet.

Sensationalist sections of the media feel that the advice given has a deep underlying religious purpose that is not in the interest of the general public. For this and other reasons the House of Hodaviah has generated many enemies. Sol Hodaviah, the head of the House, had predicted this would happen and therefore kept the seven founding members' real names and other aspects of their identities hidden from the outset.

Sam had also heard two rumours on his travels that were not generally well known. Firstly, the seven founding members have never met one another in the flesh. Secondly, three of the founding members are Jewish believers in Jesus. At this stage I won't comment on either of these rumours.

It was quarter to one when Sam arrived at the Oxford Circus tube station, which was as busy as ever. On reaching Marshall Street, he immediately saw the only public telephone box located there. He walked into the kiosk, lifted the handset and placed his index finger to depress the cradle. At exactly one o'clock he heard the phone start to ring and released his finger.

"Hello, it's Samuel."

"Meet me in the V&A[1] in exactly thirty minutes," the voice on the other end of the line showed no surprise at the rapidity of Sam's answer. "Go to the statue of Neptune,[2] one of the Nephilim. Wait there and I'll approach you."

"And who are you?" Sam inquired. He heard a click, then a long tone.

Sam hung up the phone. He knew that the V&A is in South Kensington, not far away—a short underground-train journey. The caller's instructions were clear, but there was an additional piece of information in the directions that was superfluous— Nephilim. This was a word that Sam hadn't heard for a long time, and he'd never heard it used in association with anything outside of the Bible.

Once Sam was on the underground train heading toward South Kensington station, he investigated the word Nephilim on his computer. It's a plural Hebrew word that has been translated into English as giants; the singular is Nephil. Other translations of Nephilim are tyrants and fellers (for example, of trees). The word is related to the Hebrew verb lipol, which means to fall. Sam

---

[1] Victoria and Albert Museum.

[2] Roman god of the sea, identified with the Greek god Poseidon, who was one of many Greek gods, the most notable of whom was his brother Zeus: Ovid's Metamorphoses Book 1 *lines 274-292,* Virgil's Aeneid Book 1 *lines 125-141,* Hesiod's Theogony *lines 1-21, 453-458,* Apollodorus' The Library Book 1 *chapters 1:5-2:1, 4:5.*

found the passage where the Nephilim are first mentioned. He started to read from the first verse of chapter six in Genesis.

And it came to pass, when men began to multiply on the face of the earth, and daughters were born unto them, That the sons of God saw the daughters of men that they *were* fair; and they took them wives of all which they chose. And the LORD said, My spirit shall not always strive with man, for that he also *is* flesh: yet his days shall be an hundred and twenty years. There were giants (Nephilim) in the earth in those days; and also after that, when the sons of God came in unto the daughters of men, and they bare *children* to them, the same *became* mighty men which *were* of old, men of renown.

Sam's knowledge of the Bible was good enough to place this passage between the expulsion of Adam and Eve from the Garden of Eden and the worldwide Flood. Sam confirmed that the "sons of God" is a very specific term that exclusively refers to angels in the Old Testament.[1] In the Genesis passage the

---

[1] The term occurs five times in total in the Old Testament: twice in Genesis (6:2-4) and thrice in Job (1:6-7, 2:1, 38:4-7). Job 1:6-7 and 2:1 demonstrate that God has regular meetings with the "sons of God", and Satan, being one of them, attends. Job 38:4-7 demonstrates that when God was laying the foundations of the Earth, the "sons of God" were rejoicing. They cannot be human, as man was created at a later time. The "sons of God" (bene Elohim in Hebrew) are therefore angels.
The term in the New Testament "sons of God" means something entirely different: that through accepting Christ (the Messiah), the Son of God, we can be adopted by God the Father, and being therefore brothers and sisters, we can have a special relationship with one another. Moreover, we should no longer live lives ruled by sin but be those who live righteous lives and tell others about Christ. John 1:10-18, Romans 8:11-28, Philippians 2:11-18, 1 John 3:1-24.

angels were doing something that God never intended them to do, that is, fathering children with human women. And as for the Nephilim, an indication of their origin is in the name. The Nephilim were the offspring of fallen angels.

Sam arrived at the museum on time. He quickly looked for signs that would lead him to the rendezvous point. He'd been to the V&A only once before. His last visit was at the age of thirteen before he became a Christian. He now entered the V&A with a less naïve view on the numerous idols that he would view within its walls.

Sam found Neptune on the ground floor. The so-called god was standing on a five-foot-high pedestal. The figure itself had to be about eight feet tall and was carved from white marble. Neptune's face was bearded and had a heavy brow. Deep shadows beneath his eyebrows covered his orbits, accentuating his stern expression. Both hands held a trident. His right arm was drawn back, contorting his muscular torso, while his left hand guided the trident downward to direct a fatal thrust. Incorporated into this sculpture was another figure, called Triton, who was meant to have been a son of Neptune.[1] Triton was portrayed as a merman blowing a conch. Sam stood beneath the statue and waited. People passed by. A group stopped to admire the statue. An old, white Englishman with salt-and-pepper hair and a short, neatly trimmed beard remained as the group left. He turned to face Sam. There was no one within a five-metre radius of the two men.

"Hello, Samuel, I'm Sol Hodaviah."

"I wasn't expecting to see you—maybe one of the senior advisers. From what I've heard, you're taking quite a risk meeting me yourself." There are many who would want to be in my position right now just to kill you, Sam thought.

---

[1] Hesiod's Theogony *lines 930-932*, Apollodorus' The Library Book 1 *chapter 4:5*, Hyginus' Theogony *18*.

"I know, but meeting you in person was a calculated risk. It serves many purposes. Anyhow, I'm not worried about you. I know that you became a Christian at the age of fifteen and were baptized by complete immersion that same year. Since that time at least three people have become Christians due to you—and at least one more person indirectly: from an association with one of the three. Incidentally, that last person, whom you've never met, now goes to the same Baptist church as you. Your friend Edward has yet to see the Light though."

"I won't ask how you know all of that." Sam took a close look at Sol Hodaviah's face. Sam noticed mismatches: between the colour of Sol Hodaviah's skin and the colour of his eyes; and between the texture of his skin and the age of his eyes. The discrepancies drew Sam's attention, willing him to look even closer. "What does Hodaviah mean?"

"Let's sit." Together they walked over to a bench that was located in a recess. There they could talk without disturbance and not be overheard. "It means 'majesty of God'," the Sol replied.

"Ostentatious."

It was a name that we'd chosen, for the House and its leader, to honour God rather than our own endeavours; however, Sol Hodaviah decided not to challenge Sam at that moment. Hodaviah was also a little surprised that Sam hadn't known the meaning, as many did, yet made no change in facial expression to signal this emotion. "Perhaps, but we are still on Earth, and the House of Hodaviah is a business, and one that has to sustain itself." Sol Hodaviah paused. "You're talking to me as you would a young man."

"Because you are young. Your eyes are not a day over forty."

"So you can tell that I have a mask on. That's for my own protection and yours. If someone knew that you could identify me . . . Well, I'm sure you get the picture." The mask had been expertly applied as for a film, with blended edges, but couldn't withstand close scrutiny, especially from someone with a medical background.

"I will ask you how you found out about my job in Norway though?"

"You're a wary man."

"A trait that keeps me breathing."

"For that and other reasons you're here talking with me, although you'll need to drop your guard a little for us to proceed. You'll be amazed at what we know, Sam." Sol Hodaviah hadn't provided Sam with an answer. "Now let's see what you know. Tell me about the clue that I left you in my phone call."

"I suppose that you're associating the Nephilim with all these statues of Greco-Roman gods in here, not just Neptune."

"Correct and more so. Tell me about the job."

"I thought you knew everything about it?"

"We know that you were in Norway and that you found the hammer. The details we don't know. Obviously, it goes without saying that I'll treat whatever you tell me in confidence, as if you were one of my clients seeking advice."

"I think I know where this is headed." Sam proceeded to give an account of his assignment in Norway. First of all, he related how he'd been recruited, naming the deliverer of the documents. Sam then explained why he'd chosen the three sites. After that, he briefly mentioned Bargsten and followed with a description of the barrow and the size of the two hammers. "No normal human can effectively use either hammer. And they're not ornaments, I can tell you. The handles are made of iron as well, but at one time they were bound with thick leather for grip. All that's left are rags hanging near the heads. I found bone fragments embedded in the leather of both. The hammers were used as weapons."

Sol Hodaviah didn't seem surprised at all by what Sam had said. "Were there any clues as to where they were originally from?"

"Good question! There was writing engraved on the head of the largest hammer near the handle—cuneiform characters: an ancient Mesopotamian script I suppose.[1] I can recognize cuneiform, but I can't read it. I expect that it means that the hammer was forged in the area that we would consider today as Iraq—a far cry from the fjords of Norway."

"Iraq is a significant part of Mesopotamia, which is where all humans originated," Sol Hodaviah added, also making it clear that the hammer might have come from another part of Mesopotamia.[2]

"They're obviously giants' hammers. Perhaps the lighter one belonged to a giant of smaller stature. I'd not previously thought of connecting them to anything in the Bible. Hmm . . . So the

---

[1] Cuneiform is an ancient writing system that was used by several languages. Cuneiform was mostly used within Mesopotamia.

[2] Mesopotamia in the broadest sense comprises the following modern-day countries in whole or in part: Turkey (part), Jordan (whole), Syria (whole), Lebanon (whole), Iran (part), Iraq (whole), Kuwait (whole), Israel (whole), Saudi Arabia (part) and Egypt (part). Iraq is at the centre of Mesopotamia.

In the pre-Flood era Adam and Eve lived in the Garden of Eden before they were expelled by God. Regarding the location of the Garden of Eden, within its bounds there was a river that separated into four rivers. Genesis 2:8-3:24. Two of these four derivative rivers were and are identifiable in the post-Flood era: Hiddekel (Daniel 10:4—now known as Tigris) and Euphrates (Genesis 15:18), although their courses run differently. Both rivers' origins are still close, located in Turkey, but are no longer the same. Even well into the post-Flood era the courses of both rivers have changed. Eden was positioned in any (one or more) of the above locations of Mesopotamia. It is difficult to be more precise than this because of the Flood and the resultant change in the Earth's topography.

After the Flood, the people moved as a single group from Ararat (today in Turkey) and settled in the land of Shinar (today in Iraq). God brought their construction of the City and Tower of Babel in Shinar to a halt and scattered the people across the face of the Earth. Genesis 11:1-9. See Timeline.

wielders of the hammers were Nephilim. Do you think one of them was called Thor?"

"Who knows? The crucial thing is that he existed, and there's evidence for this fact. Furthermore, I strongly suspect that he was a post-Flood rather than a pre-Flood giant, given that his weapon has been located." Sol Hodaviah looked thoughtful. The mask conveyed his emotions well.

"A post-Flood giant? I read the first part of Genesis six on the way here. From that I thought that all the giants were born before the Flood. Surely the ones who were alive when the Flood started must have of all drowned? They weren't immortal like their demon-fathers."

"Yes, they were all drowned. But if you look closely at the passage again, you'll see that it reads: 'There were giants in the earth in those days; **and also after that** when the sons of God came in unto the daughters of men'. So there were additional waves of giants after the Flood. They too are recorded in the Bible. Examples of post-Flood giants who were individually named are Arba, King Og of Bashan and Goliath."[1]

"Is this anything to do with gigantism? It's caused by over-production of brain growth hormone from childhood, which makes the person grow excessively."

"I thought that you might ask that. The Nephilim did not have gigantism. As you said, gigantism is a disease—one that I have great sympathy for. In adulthood people with gigantism can develop a range of problems, including heart failure, visual defects, diabetes and muscle weakness. Their excessive height doesn't give them genuine advantages over humans of normal stature. In fact, they're weakened by their disease. They're hardly the champion fighters that the Nephilim were known to have been. Also, people with gigantism rarely ever grow to a height of

---

[1] Arba: Deuteronomy 2:10-11, Joshua 14:15, 15:13-14, 21:11.
Og: Numbers 21:33-35, Deuteronomy 3:1-13, Joshua 12:4, 13:12.
Goliath: 1 Samuel 17:1-58.

over eight feet. According to the biblical accounts, Goliath was over nine and a half feet tall and Og of Bashan was about thirteen feet tall."[1]

"Yes, of course, you're right," Sam replied.

Sam wondered about Sol Hodaviah, whose answer had been relayed with the confidence and care of a doctor rather than a lay person relaying medical facts that he'd read.

Sol Hodaviah deepened his explanation: "What's fascinating is that the Bible tells of many giants who were in fact the descendants of giants. Arba, who had a city named after him because he was an exceptionally powerful giant, was the father of Anak, who was also a giant.[2] Anak had three giant sons called Sheshai, Talmai and Ahiman.[3] The three sons of Anak and their numerous giant descendants, many of whom settled in various mountainous cities throughout the land of Canaan, were collectively known as the Anakim.[4] The Anakim were almost completely wiped out from Canaan in the early phases of the Hebrew conquest of that land. Some of the Anakim remained in three Philistine cities, one of which was Gath.[5] The giants Goliath and his brother Lahmi

---

[1] Goliath's height was six cubits and a span. A cubit is the standardized distance from the elbow to the tip of the middle finger, which is 18 inches (45.72 cm). A span is half a cubit. Goliath was 9 feet 9 inches tall (2.97 metres). His brass coat of mail weighed 5,000 shekels (57.5 kg) and his iron spearhead weighed 600 shekels (6.9 kg). A shekel is 11.5 grams. 1 Samuel 17:4-7.
Og's iron bedstead was nine cubits long and four cubits wide. The bed was 13½ feet long (4.11 metres). Deuteronomy 3:11.

[2] Deuteronomy 2:10-11, Joshua 14:15, 15:13-14, 21:11.

[3] Numbers 13:22, 13:28-33, Deuteronomy 9:2, Joshua 15:13-14.

[4] Numbers 13:17-22, Deuteronomy 1:28, 2:10-11, 2:20-21, 9:2, Joshua 11:21-22, 14:12-15.
Because the word Anakim always refers to giants, it also means giants. Even Arba is described as one of the Anakim (in Joshua 14:15), although he was the father of Anak.

[5] Joshua 11:21-22.

were possibly descendants of one or more of the Anakim, as both were born in Gath, were the sons of an unnamed giant and died between three hundred and four hundred years after the demise of the three sons of Anak.[1] I strongly suspect that Arba's father was a demon."

---

[1] The origins of Goliath and Lahmi: 1 Samuel 17:4, 1 Chronicles 20:5, 20:8 (for further comment see [α]). To estimate the time between the deaths of the three sons of Anak and the deaths of Goliath and Lahmi one should first approximate the year of the deaths of the three sons of Anak. Soon after the death of Joshua, the warriors of the tribe of Judah fought against the three sons of Anak and slew them at the city of Arba—Judges 1:1-10 (for further comment see [β]). So what year did Joshua die? Joshua died at the age of 110 years (Joshua 24:29, Judges 2:8). Near the beginning of the Hebrews' 40-year desert wandering (between the 15th day of the second month after the Exodus from Egypt and the third month after the Exodus—Exodus 16:1, 17:1, 19:1-2) Joshua was recruited by Moses to lead a force against the Amalekites at Rephidim (Exodus 17:8-13). Although old enough to lead this force, Joshua was still considered to be a young man (Exodus 33:11). If one deduces that Joshua was 21 years old (for further comment see [γ]) at the time of the Exodus from Egypt, then he would have died in 1357 BC (see Timeline). David killed Goliath around 1025 BC (1 Samuel 17:1-58 and see Timeline). Therefore, approximately 330 years separate the deaths of the three sons of Anak from the death of Goliath. Lahmi was killed after Goliath during David's reign as king (1 Chronicles 20:1-5 and see Timeline).

Goliath's relatively short height in comparison with Og (purely a height comparison—no implication that they were related*) would support the view that Goliath was indeed an approximately 300-year-distant descendant of one or more of the Anakim: his lesser height owing to his giant ancestors coupling with regular humans over the many generations, resulting in dilution of the genes that determine gigantic height. Alternatively, the giants of Gath at the time of Goliath could have been unrelated to the Anakim and

FOOTNOTE CONTINUED ON THE NEXT PAGE

"Why?"

"Because no giant ancestor is declared for Arba in the Bible."

"Do all the giants whom you've just mentioned come under the term Nephilim?"

"Yes, Nephilim is a word that doesn't refer only to the first-generation giants, who were the direct offspring of demonic-

---

CONTINUED FOOTNOTE PRESENT

---

therefore the ultimate result of a different demonic-human pairing or of different demonic-human pairings.

Furthermore, Og was possibly a distant descendant of one or more first-generation Nephilim and therefore, assuming ancestral coupling with normal humans, of lesser height than his ancestors, because he is referred to as a remnant of the giants who lived at Ashtaroth and Edrei (both cities within Bashan). *Note that Og was not evidently a relative of the Anakim. Deuteronomy 3:10-11, Joshua 12:4, 13:12, 13:30-31.

[α] After the death of Goliath, a number of his brothers (they all had the same father) were later killed in battle by the Hebrews. These events are recorded in 2 Samuel 21:15-22 and 1 Chronicles 20:4-8. The list of Goliath's brothers, once the passages are aligned, is as follows: Ishbibenob, Saph (Sippai), Lahmi (already mentioned) and an unnamed giant with an excess of fingers and toes. Therefore, their father had at least 5 giant sons in total.

[β] Caleb had previously driven the three sons of Anak out of the city of Arba while Joshua was alive, but they had clearly returned in defiance of the Hebrews: Joshua 14:6-15, 15:13-14.

[γ] Joshua would not have been less than 20 years old, because the Bible makes it clear that he was one of two men who were 20 or over at the time of the start of the Exodus and were permitted to enter the Promised Land after the 40-year wandering in the desert; the rest of the Hebrews who were 20 or over at the time of the start of the Exodus were prevented by death from entering the Promised Land: Numbers 14:1-35, 32:1-13.

human pairing. Nephilim also refers to the giant descendants within the subsequent generations."[1]

"On the way here I read that the Bible also collectively refers to the giants as 'Rephaim',"[2] Sam added. "What's more, I can tell that God detested the Nephilim."

"Indeed," Sol Hodaviah replied. "They were abominations in His eyes. They were one of the reasons why He destroyed the Earth with the Flood.[3] Then long after the Flood, God had to deal with them again. In various parts of Canaan and some of the surrounding areas[4] God used the Hebrews to destroy the

---

[1] Genesis 6:1-4, Numbers 13:33 (the sons of Anak were at least third-generation giants and are referred to as Nephilim).

[2] Deuteronomy 2:10-11, 2:20, 3:11, 3:13, Joshua 18:16.

[3] Genesis 6:1-8.

[4] Amorites were both inside and outside of the land of Canaan. They too had giants amongst them. These giants were defeated by God on behalf of the Hebrews. Amos 2:2-10*.
Being east of the River Jordan, Bashan and Heshbon were both Amorite kingdoms outside of the land of Canaan: Deuteronomy 4:46-47, Joshua 2:10. The king of Heshbon, Sihon, initiated and commanded an unprovoked attack on the Hebrews. The Hebrews defeated the Kingdom of Heshbon. Sihon was slain. The king of Bashan, Og the giant, did the same thing, and the Kingdom of Bashan was defeated. Og was slain. The Hebrews then possessed these lands. Numbers 21:21-35, 32:33, Deuteronomy 2:24-37, 3:1-21, 29:7-8, 31:4, Joshua 2:10, 12:1-6, 13:12, Judges 11:19-23, Nehemiah 9:22.
See next immediate footnote, which mentions the giants in the land of Canaan.
*The heights of the Amorite giants were compared to the heights of cedar trees. These trees can grow to well over 100 feet tall. The heights of the giants in this passage are difficult to comment on as an actual measurement is not given. However, there is a distinct possibility that the comparison is literal. Interestingly, giants over fifty feet tall are found in texts of mythology and nonbiblical

FOOTNOTE CONTINUED ON THE NEXT PAGE

Nephilim. Their destruction was necessary for the Hebrews to inherit the Promised Land.[1] The Nephilim were spread across the

CONTINUED FOOTNOTE PRESENT

---

religion (see footnote later in this chapter pg 73 regarding Neptune having been the father of colossal giants and footnote in Chapter 13 pg 285 regarding Buddhism).

[1] Numbers 13:17-33, Joshua 11:21-23, 12:7-24 (amongst the Amorites were lots of giants—Amos 2:2-10), 14:12-15, 15:13-14, Judges 1:10, 1 Samuel 17:1-58, 2 Samuel 21:15-22, 1 Chronicles 20:1-8, see earlier in this chapter pgs 65-67 and footnotes regarding the Anakim and the giants of Gath, see also immediate previous footnote. The Nephilim were often mixed with the normal humans.

The inhabitants of the land of Canaan also practised idolatry and child sacrifice, which were the other two reasons why God wanted them removed at this specific period in history (see Timeline and Dispensations [4]). The gods of the inhabitants of Canaan included two female deities, Ashtaroth and Asherah, and two male deities, Baal and Baal-Zebub. The latter is identified with Beelzebub, who is declared in the New Testament to be Satan, the prince of demons. Judges 2:8-13, 1 Kings 16:30-33, 18:19, 21:25-26, 2 Kings 1:2, Psalms 106:34-40, Mark 3:22-27, Luke 11:14-20. One can note from the above passages within Judges, 1 Kings, 2 Kings and Psalms that we learn about some of the transgressions of the inhabitants of Canaan, because they were also criticisms directed at the Hebrews after they had settled in the land. Specifically, the Hebrews had adopted the worship of the same idols and child sacrifice. However, there is no record of Nephilim being born among the Hebrews. The fact that the Hebrews turned away from God caused them to be later removed from the Promised Land.

Interestingly, one particular group of the inhabitants of Canaan, the Rechabites (who were descended from the Kenites, of whom there is no evidence of their women giving birth to Nephilim), joined the Hebrews and were an example of a people whom God acknowledged as being faithful to Him at a time when many of the Hebrews had rejected Him. 2 Kings 10:23-28, 1 Chronicles 2:55, Jeremiah 35:2-19.

FOOTNOTE CONTINUED ON THE NEXT PAGE

CONTINUED FOOTNOTE PRESENT

Note references that the land of Canaan was promised (Genesis 17:1-8, Exodus 12:25, Deuteronomy 19:8, Joshua 23:5, Nehemiah 9:23) but not inherited by the Hebrews until the original people of the land had been given a chance to turn away from their sins (Genesis 15:1-16).

There is often controversy surrounding the slaying of the inhabitants of the land of Canaan by the Hebrews. However, this was the will of God against those particular inhabitants at that specific time for the above reasons. The Hebrews were given contrary instructions when they confronted other peoples. The specific rules that God set out against the inhabitants of the Land of Canaan are not applicable to any other situation or time (see Dispensations [4]). However, this does not mean that we can mimic the inhabitants of Canaan with impunity. For we may still be judged adversely, receiving punishment in our lifetimes and when we eventually die. The inhabitants of Canaan were exceptionally wicked people. Furthermore, they had been given a chance to repent: over 400 years. The Jebusites, one of the many different peoples who together made up the inhabitants of the land of Canaan, even had a very special individual called Melchizedek in their presence. Melchizedek was the king of Salem and priest of the Most High God. Salem was the Jebusite city, which became Jerusalem. Melchizedek's priesthood is the prototype of Jesus the Messiah's priesthood. Being both the city's priest and king, Melchizedek would have undoubtedly preached righteousness and had secular influence. However, Melchizedek's message was clearly rejected, for if accepted, God's judgement wouldn't have fallen on the people of Salem. Genesis 14:18-20, 15:13-16, Deuteronomy 7:1-8, 9:1-5, 20:1-18, Joshua 15:8, 15:63, Judges 1:21, 19:10-11, 2 Samuel 5:1-10, Psalms 110:1-7, Hebrews 5:5-10, 6:20, 7:1-28.

The inhabitants of Canaan included Amorites, Jebusites, Hivites, Girgashites, Hittites, Sidonians, Canaanites, Giblites, Philistines, Geshurites, Maachathites, Perrizites, Kenezzites, Amalekites, Kenites, Rephaim and Kadmonites: Genesis 15:18-21, 36:2, Exodus

FOOTNOTE CONTINUED ON THE NEXT PAGE

world at that stage; however, this is a well-documented instance of how they were removed from a specific region."[1]

Sam was inspired by Sol Hodaviah's understanding of these matters.

Sol Hodaviah continued to impress: "While we've been talking, I've been performing some calculations. If the largest hammer is three hundred kilograms, then for a man to skillfully wield such a weapon in battle, he would have to weigh a minimum of three metric tons (3,000 kilograms) and therefore be at least nineteen feet tall, assuming that he had similar proportions to a twenty-first-century fighting champion—I've chosen a professional heavyweight boxer for my math."[2]

Sam delved into his memory of Germanic mythology, augmented by recent events and now sharpened by Sol Hodaviah's profound biblical knowledge. "Thor was portrayed as a god rather than a giant.[3] Yet he was reportedly descended from a giant—his great-grandfather who was called Bolthorn.[4] I'd say

CONTINUED FOOTNOTE PRESENT

3:8, 3:17, 13:5, 33:2, 34:11, Numbers 13:29-30, 33:40, Joshua 9:1, 13:1-33, 24:11, Judges 1:10, Nehemiah 9:8, Zephaniah 2:5.

[1] See Timeline.

[2] Equations for calculating the heights of Nephilim based on their weights (or vice versa): Nephil's Height = Normal Man's Height X $\sqrt[3]{Nephil's\ Weight/Normal\ Man's\ Weight}$ or Nephil's Weight = Normal Man's Weight X (Nephil's Height/Normal Man's Height)^3.
In this example: 6-foot-tall (1.83 m) typical professional heavyweight boxer weighing 95 kg (209.4 lb); weight of Nephil is 3,000 kg (6,613.8 lb), so height of Nephil is 18.96 feet (5.78 m).

[3] See Chapter 2 pg 35 and footnote regarding Thor (the Germanic god of thunder).

[4] The mythology reports that the giant Bolthorn had a daughter called Bestla. She married Bor and gave birth to Odin, who was the father of Thor. Odin and Thor were both believed to be gods. The Elder Edda—Völuspá (The prophecy of the seeress) *stanza 4,* Grímnismál (The lay of Grímnir) *stanza 54,* Hymiskvida (The song

FOOTNOTE CONTINUED ON THE NEXT PAGE

that even in the absence of my recent discovery, given that normal human beings recognized Thor as a god and because he had what is evidently Nephilic ancestry, the mythology points to him having been a giant as well. And so the legends that describe Thor slaying giants are actually telling us that he slew giants like himself!"[1]

"Did you get to see the Jotunheimen Mountains?" Sol Hodoviah asked.

"No, but I was close. I remember seeing the name on my map. They're about fifty or sixty miles east of the barrow."

"Do you know what Jotunheimen means?"

"No, but you're about to tell me." Sam lifted his eyebrows.

"It means 'home of the giants'. I believe that Thor had many peers and wouldn't have been short of giant skulls to smash with that hammer of his. Interestingly, the Bible tells us that the giants

---

CONTINUED FOOTNOTE PRESENT

---

of Hymir) *stanzas 28-35*; The Prose Edda—Gylfaginning (The deluding of Gylfi) *chapters 6, 20, 21.*

Also, Thor reportedly had a son, Magni, with a giantess called Jarnsaxa: The Prose Edda—Skaldskaparmal (Poetic Diction) *3.*

[1] The Elder Edda—Hárbardsljód (Grey-beard's poem) *stanza 19*, Thrymskvida (The song of Thrym) *stanzas 11-32* (in one evening at a wedding feast, Thor reputedly ate an entire ox and eight salmon before he massacred the others at the event, who were giants); The Prose Edda—Gylfaginning (The deluding of Gylfi) *chapters 21, 42*, Skaldskaparmal (Poetic Diction) *3.*

Giants varied in height. Regarding the giants whom Thor killed within the above references, only the last reference suggests that his opponent was larger than him. Furthermore, a giant called Skrymir, whom Thor was unable to kill despite repeated attempts, was portrayed as much larger than Thor! The Prose Edda—Gylfaginning (The deluding of Gylfi) *chapter 45.*

were once so numerous in some areas that the populaces of those lands were regarded as being made up mostly of them."[1]

Sam looked toward the now diminutive-appearing statue of Neptune and wondered just how massive he'd really been; after all, he was reportedly a son of a Titan[2] and the father of some

---

[1] The Emim and the Zamzummim (each is a plural word) were two different groups of giants who once possessed lands that later belonged to the Moabites and the Ammonites respectively: Deuteronomy 2:9-11, 2:19-21.

[2] Cronus (a Titan) was reportedly the father of Poseidon (Neptune): Hesiod's Theogony *lines 453-462, 729-733, 850-852,* Apollodorus' The Library Book 1 *chapter 1:4-6.*

Today we take it for granted that the Titans were giants. In mythology the Titans are indeed reported to be giants (The Fall of Troy by Quintus Smyrnaeus Book 2 *lines 203-207*). In one of the earliest existing records of the Titans, although not stating directly that they and those whom they fought against were all giants, Hesiod describes a conflict between the Titan gods (Titans) fathered by Uranus and the Olympian gods fathered by Cronus (along with their allies), during which despite there being only a few opponents on either side, the battle was able to make both a mountain and the deep earth shake, and create a fearsome noise from the ocean: Hesiod's Theogony *lines 664-686* (from this book one can determine that 12 Titans* fought against 6 Olympians, the 3 multiple-armed brothers and Styx with her 4 progeny[‡] [i.e., 12 vs. 14]—*lines 132-210, 337-403, 453-506, 617-735*).

*12 Titans (all reportedly the direct offspring of Uranus and Gaea): Mnemosyne, Theia, Rhea, Themis, Phoebe, Tethys, Ocean, Coeus, Hyperion, Crius, Iapetus and Cronus.

[‡]6 Olympians (all reportedly the direct offspring of Cronus and Rhea): Hestia, Demeter, Hera, Poseidon, Hades and Zeus.

3 multiple-armed brothers: Briareus, Cottus and Gyges (full brothers of the Titans but not called Titans).

Styx's 4 progeny: Bia, Cratos, Nike (Victory) and Zelus. (Reportedly, Styx was the direct offspring of Ocean and Tethys.)

truly colossal giants.[1] Sam's thoughts returned to Norway. When he'd found the hammer, the cuneiform had surprised him. He'd expected an early Germanic runic script or some kind of precursor to this writing. He wondered if Thor had migrated from Mesopotamia to northern Europe or if the cuneiform represented a previous owner, maybe even an ancestor. Sam considered asking Sol Hodoviah what he thought but decided instead to test my associate's knowledge of things more recent. "Do you know anything about Klaus Remer—if that's even his real name?"

---

[1] Poseidon (Neptune) was reportedly the father of: Polyphemus the Cyclops (a giant with a single eye), who ate some of Odysseus' companions; Orion the hunter; and the Aloadae (the brothers Otus and Ephialtes), who attacked the so-called gods of Olympus. Homer reported that the Aloadae were 9 fathoms tall (54 feet) and 9 cubits wide (13.5 feet)—is this correct or an exaggeration? See earlier in this chapter pg 68 regarding God dealing with the Nephilim in the land of Canaan—one of the footnotes contains a comment on the heights of the Amorite giants. Homer stated that the Aloadae were shorter than Orion.

Polyphemus: Apollodorus' The Library Epitome *chapter 7:4-9*, Homer's Odyssey Book 9 *lines 161-412* (all the Cyclopes on the island where Polyphemus lived were reportedly sons of Poseidon).

Orion: *Apollodorus' The Library Book 1 *chapter 4:3* (father Poseidon; mother Euryale).

The Aloadae: Homer's Odyssey Book 11 *lines 305-320*, Apollodorus' The Library Book 1 *chapter 7:4*, Hyginus' Fabulae *28*.

There is an alternative origin proposed for Orion in the same Apollodorus reference above*, which is just one of many testaments to the fallibility of Greek mythology: Orion having been earth-born (i.e., offspring of the supposed goddess Gaea). The Hyginus reference above mentions that the Aloadae were reportedly either sons or grandsons of Poseidon. Despite the unreliability of Greek mythology, there is clearly a pattern present throughout that makes it seem unlikely that the accounts of the various individuals are derived completely from the imagination of men.

"He is called Klaus Remer, and he is an employee of the Norwegian National Consortium of Museums—in a round about way," Sol Hodaviah answered.

"What do you mean?"

"He's one of the Consortium's leading sponsors and is also listed as a senior member of staff. They don't pay him anything though."

"You think that the letter was legitimate?"

"What's more likely is that he used his position in the Consortium as his cover to get you on board and that they know nothing of the discovery of these priceless relics—which makes you an accomplice."

"But an innocent one."

"You'd have to prove that."

Sam paused to think about the many ways that an inquest could turn out—some not so good for him. "Well, I'm just going to keep quiet about it. Oh, no . . . And I'm going to have to persuade a friend to keep his big mouth shut."

"And the Professor?"

"He just translated the documents. He didn't know what I was looking for. I really thought that if I found the hammer, it would end up in a museum."

"Yes, but did Remer actually say that."

"No, he didn't."

"There's more," Sol Hodoviah said. "I hadn't planned on telling you this: Bargsten wasn't the only one watching you. For a while we've had you in mind for the mission that I'm going to tell you about. We've been observing you, particularly how you perform on assignment. I suppose that you've already guessed as much. After you, Remer and the hammers were flown from the site, another of his helicopters arrived with a new team of men. This helicopter was larger than the first. Together with some of the men who'd initially arrived with Remer yet stayed at the site they put up a huge, green tent near to the barrow. In fact, the tent was connected to and covered the barrow's entrance. The men seemed to be working in the tent and inside the crypt. Twenty-four hours later another wooden crate emerged—a good deal bigger than the ones that held the hammers."

"Did your person see what it contained?"

"No, she didn't. I have an idea though. It was shaped like a simple rectangular coffin. I suspect that the tomb of Thor was near the hammers—probably much deeper within the barrow. I imagine that it was either his bones or the entire sarcophagus that they hoisted into the helicopter. The baron must have discovered Thor's tomb but deliberately left it undisturbed. One of the hammers had to belong to Thor, so the baron buried them both there. The man was clearly a fanatic. He knew, according to the myths, that when Thor awakens at the end of time, he will need to fight his archenemy, the evil serpent Jormungand, and most likely benefit from his trusted weapon.[1] The baron probably hoped to be rewarded for this deed of his in the afterlife."

"How big was the crate?"

"About twenty-two feet long and nine feet wide!"

"How could I have missed that? I was so focused on the hammer. Then there were two. I didn't stop to think that there could be more. Remer knew that the tomb would be near the hammer, and I led him right to it."

"Where did your helicopter take you?" Sol Hodoviah asked.

"Damn! I should have twigged that there could be more there: the hammers were in a burial mound, not a temple. If it was his

---

[1] Also known as the Midgard Serpent. The following references relate to Jormungand's purported origin (offspring of a god!) and Thor's previous fight with this serpent: The Elder Edda—Hymiskvida (The song of Hymir) *stanzas 21-24*; The Prose Edda—Gylfaginning (The deluding of Gylfi) *chapters 34, 48*.
The following references relate to Thor's predicted future fight with the serpent: The Elder Edda—Völuspá (The prophecy of the seeress) *stanzas 50, 55-56*; The Prose Edda—Gylfaginning (The deluding of Gylfi) *chapter 51*.

entire sarcophagus, then they must have literally torn the barrow apart to get something that size out of there." Sam then answered the question: "The helicopter dropped me off in Oslo. I don't know where they went after that. Maybe back to his residence in Austria."

"Klaus is quite the character, isn't he? And I wonder what he's truly planning to do with those hammers. We'll be keeping a close eye on him from now on." Sol Hodaviah passed a small carved object to Sam. "Take a look at this. Its last owner was Armenian. What do you think?"

The object was disc-shaped. Sam took a minute to examine it before answering. "It's crudely fashioned from wood with an ankh carved onto one surface. The hole here is for leather string, so that it can be worn around the neck with the ankh facing outward. It's an amulet of sorts. I expect that its owner thought that it would ward off evil." Sam extended his right arm to give back the amulet to Sol Hodaviah.

An ankh is a cross that has a loop, which resembles a handle, instead of an upright upper bar. The ankh can be found in stone engravings of the ancient Egyptians, often in the hands of their deities, and represents life. The ankh has also been used by the Coptic Church (also known as the Coptic Orthodox Church[1]), a religion that resembles Eastern Orthodoxy, although not officially part of it.[2]

Sol Hodaviah declined the return. "Take a closer look at the wood. I'll give you an extra clue. I paid ten thousand dollars for that thing at an auction in Los Angeles."

---

[1] The Coptic Church has been additionally known as the Coptic Orthodox Church since the 19th century.

[2] The main difference between the Coptic Orthodox Church and Eastern Orthodoxy is that the former believes that Jesus is fully divine (rather than fully divine and fully human, which is correct) despite recognizing that the Messiah God has taken on a human body—a doctrine known as Monophysitism. See Dispensations (6).

Sam persisted, "It's blackened in places—on only this side." He was referring to the side with the ankh. "It seems to be a type of tar. There's no odour though. This object is clearly very old. The ankh is a later addition; it's been engraved so that the tar has been removed. I haven't trained myself to differentiate types of wood, so I really can't tell you any more."

"It's possibly gopher wood. What does that mean to you?" Sol Hodaviah asked.

"Gopher wood! Are you saying that it's made of wood from Noah's Ark? Have you had it analysed? Gopher wood is an ancient name. No one knows what tree it was."

"That amulet is made from a type of pine. The problem is that the term gopher wood may not be a specific wood at all but a general term for any resinous wood. It could even simply mean sliced wood for building purposes."

"But how do you know if the amulet is genuine?" Sam asked.

"I don't. And that's where you come in. I need you to go to the site where the dealers claim that it was originally from."

"You mean Mount Ararat, don't you?"

"That's correct. Your mission is to go to Turkey, scale Mount Ararat and find and photograph the Ark of Noah with a camera that uses film. Don't bother with digital: the pictures can be manipulated, and nobody will verify them as being truly authentic."

"Photograph the Ark. What? As if it's still standing after over four thousand years. I know a little about this already. Others have tried to find the Ark. Some came back with just wood fragments—most with nothing!"

Sol Hodaviah had patiently waited until Sam had finished talking. "Actually, around thirty years ago an American group found large, ancient boards of tar-coated wood—wood coated with pitch, to be precise—together with similarly aged metal rivets near a small village at the base of Mount Ararat. Boards are something, but as a three-dimensional structure is how people want to see the Ark. We have reason to believe that a substantial section of the Ark may still be present on the mountain itself."

"And how do you know this?"

"I can't reveal my source; however, we wouldn't be financing you if we didn't value this information highly. Above four thousand metres the mountain is always covered by snow and ice. It's remarkable what those kinds of conditions can preserve."

"Keep on talking." Sam was interested but wanted to maintain a look of coolness.

"Near the summit are two prominent glaciers: one north of the peak and the other south of the peak. Our source tells us that the northern glacier is of particular interest. In the last decade Turkey has experienced some particularly hot summers, and in the last two years two straight ridges, perpendicular to one another, have become noticeable on the surface of the glacier. They're visible only at certain times of the year: when there's been no snowfall for a while and the glacier has had time to shift. They're extremely subtle, especially because of the uneven surface of the glacier itself—and the ridges are ice themselves. The maximum height of each one is never more than four centimetres. Neither is long: the shortest is just five feet and the longest only double that."

"Do they touch?"

"Not quite, but if you extended each ridge by a few feet, then they would. In fact, they'd meet at exactly ninety degrees."

"To look like a tick."

"Exactly. Or I'd prefer to say: like a corner. There's something inside that glacier that's making those ridges on the surface. We think that it's the Ark."

"Sounds reasonable—not a bad start. But what about Little Ararat, which stands next to Great Ararat? The Bible says that the Ark came to rest on the 'mountains of Ararat', so which one?[1]

---

[1] Genesis 8:4.

From a biblical perspective Mount Ararat is two mountains rather than one mountain with two peaks."

"We've not heard of any clues there. The taller and bigger mountain, Great Ararat, is the target. As well as the pictures, we still need one of those wood fragments that you mentioned, although try and retrieve a decent-sized piece. A board would be good. Your reputation will add to the authenticity of the evidence that you bring back. This is a sad age. So many need signs before they can believe instead of listening to what their souls are telling them."

"Proof can also encourage those with faith, who already believe," Sam added.

"That's true." Sol Hodaviah was pleased with Sam's insight.

"Some, of course, will refuse to believe, no matter what I bring back from that mountain."

"Also true. If they allow themselves to believe, then they'll have to search for more answers, and they already know where those answers will take them. Putting your trust in God is a place where most people don't want to go."

"It was a place that at one time I didn't want to go to either. I knew that it would change my life forever."

"Samuel, I must tell you that this is a mission that involves maximum danger. For decades the legend of the Ark resting on Mount Ararat as the Flood was regressing was one of the attractions promoted by the Turkish tourist industry. Street vendors even used to sell miniature models of the Ark in the local towns and villages. This was despite the fact that Turkey was, and still is, an Islāmic country and the Koran stating that the Ark came to rest on a different mountain, called Mount Judi, which is almost two hundred miles south of Mount Ararat.[1] For the last ten years there have been changes in Turkey. The promotion of Mount Ararat as the resting place of the Ark is

---

[1] The Koran 11 Hud (Hūd):44. Mount Judi (Cudi Dağı) is located in Southeast Turkey.

forbidden. The background checks for Ararat climbing permits are now much more extensive, and excavation on the mountain is absolutely prohibited. The Turkish military trains soldiers on the mountain, and I'm sure that that's not the only reason why they're there. We know of two groups who've entered Turkey in the last five years with the secret intent of finding the Ark on Mount Ararat: a team of three Americans was discovered and deported, and a team of two British men is still missing—they're presumed dead. Neither group was sent by us. And there are other things going on, such as numerous excavations throughout Turkey that are wholly independent of the government and the universities. We've just started looking into this, so I can't say any more at this stage."

"I've completed missions where death was a potential outcome."

"There are things worse than death." Sol Hodaviah looked at Sam, expecting a reaction. Hodaviah could see that Sam understood. "At least you don't need to learn how to climb. I read about your trip to the Peruvian Andes."

"In search of the secret gold forge of the Inca kings," Sam said bitterly. "A failed attempt. That was an expensive trip with nothing to show for it except malaria. I suppose that I should be pleased that I came back with my life. Finding Noah's Ark would certainly be my most significant discovery. I think that the potential gains outweigh the risks."

"You don't know all the risks yet. There's also a second objective—even more significant than the first. It's also in Turkey. The second objective can't be achieved without an attempt at the first."

"Now you're speaking in riddles."

"If you find the Ark and present the world with irrefutable evidence of its existence, then you'll be permanently branded as a bearer of truth. Reprisals may occur well after completion. If you complete the second objective, your situation will be worse. You may need to go underground for a long, long time."

"I can't study medicine underground. That puts the matter in a different light."

"We also can't guarantee that we'll provide you with more work, although it would be my intention to do so. That said, I can't even be sure of our continued existence as an organization."

"What is the second objective?"

"For your own safety I can't reveal it to you now. The magnitude of the first objective should be enough to inform your decision. If you choose to accept the mission, I'll contact you when you're in Turkey at the relevant time to tell you what the second objective is."

"You have a formidable reputation for being able to predict the outcomes of endeavours—even placing percentages on different outcomes coming to fruition. You must clearly rate my chance of success favourably?"

"The mission must go ahead. I'm sorry to say that it's more that I rate your likelihood of success over that of any other potential candidates, than the actual prospect of a fully completed mission."

"Great! So what chance do I have?"

There was an uncomfortable pause. "There are so many variables, so it's difficult to say. Let's put it this way, if you didn't have a hope, we certainly wouldn't be backing you. And there are unseen entities involved whom I find difficult to factor in. You'll come up against the principalities who reign on this Earth. They'll try to defeat you in any way they can. But remember, they're not omnipotent or omnipresent and God can protect the steps of those he chooses."[1]

"That I understand. Can I think about it?"

"Aren't you doing that now?"

"I mean can I have more time?"

"You've got two minutes."

"Thanks," Sam replied.

---

[1] Psalms 5:12.

Sam thought about the possible outcomes and their consequences. Failure of the first and therefore the second objective. Success of the first and failure of the second. Success of both. Death. Life. He knew that he had to base his decision on full completion of both, regardless of how remote the likelihood of that was. Lack of full commitment to each objective spelt doom. He loved the thought of becoming a doctor. He'd been working toward that goal since he was thirteen and was loath to give it up. No matter how much money the House was willing to offer him, he had to imagine that he was doing the mission for free. The first objective was exactly what he would want to do. Even though he didn't know what the second objective entailed, something told him that it was of great significance. He tried to ignore the veiled flattery that he was the person who stood the best chance.

Sam spoke, "Mount Ararat borders Armenia and Iran. Obviously, Iran's out of the question, but why can't I get to Ararat via Armenia?"

"For both objectives to be completed, you'll have to approach Mount Ararat through Turkey. Just trust me on this."

"What are you planning to pay me?"

"Three hundred thousand pounds and all expenses paid for on top of this figure. If you accept, we'll give you a third straightaway. If you die, the other two-thirds will go to whomever you designate, whether you're successful or not. You'll have to trust us on that second part, as you definitely shouldn't discuss this with anyone and we're not putting it in writing."

"I accept, and I designate my parents as the beneficiaries. Can I ask you: why is the House financing this?"

"We don't just give people advice. The House has other functions. One of these functions is to preserve the Bible. For centuries its opponents have tried to destroy it and prevent its translation. If they can't manage these, then they corrupt the words within it, so that it's no longer the truth.[1] Despite all their efforts, through the toil of people of different nations the original Hebrew[2] and Greek words have persisted and have been faithfully translated into almost all languages. Many have died for these causes. In our time we together with other groups have taken up the mantle of the preservation of the Bible. Another function of the House is to reveal the truth of the Bible to the world. These two functions are interconnected."

"I get it."

"Here, take this envelope. There's some extra information and things that you'll need inside. You'll receive the down payment tomorrow in cash as well as a little extra to get underway—Royal Mail this time."

"Thank you," Sam said. They were about to shake hands. "Oh . . . the amulet."

"Keep it. It won't ward off evil, but it might help you to know that you're on the right track. In truth, it's worthless unless you verify its authenticity." They then shook hands. "Goodbye, Sam. I'll be praying for your success."

---

[1] An example of a corrupted Bible is the Roman Catholic Douay-Rheims Bible. An example of how this deviates from biblical correctness is the frequent use of the word penance (Leviticus 5:5, 3 Kings 8:33 [1 Kings 8:33], Matthew 3:2, 4:17, and many more). Penance means inflicting harm or discomfort on oneself to show regret for sin. This word should not be found in any Bible, because no word in the Bible in the original languages means penance and penance is not a biblical teaching.

[2] Note that a small proportion of the Old Testament is written in the Aramaic language but with Hebrew letters.

Adam and Eve had been expelled from the Garden of Eden.[1] The human race multiplied on the Earth. Although people no longer had access to the beneficial fruit of the Tree of Life, unless their lives were cut short by disease, accident or violence, they lived for almost a thousand years before eventually dying of old age. A man of 300 years probably had the appearance of a 30-year-old by today's standard.[2] This meant that many generations lived on the Earth together. Adam would have seen the consequences of his sin in Eden. He lived for 930 years.[3] One of the factors that maintained this longevity was probably the ongoing presence of the layer of water that surrounded the entire Earth above the atmosphere.[4] It is very likely to have been a protective shield acting as a barrier that prevented the majority of harmful forms of radiation from space (cosmic rays)[5] from bombarding and thus damaging the life-forms' fragile DNA.[1]

---

[1] Genesis 3:22-24. See Dispensations (1-2).

[2] Similarly, a 400-year-old woman probably had the physical appearance of a contemporary 40-year-old woman and had the potential to have babies up to her 500th year. This is evidenced by the fact that Adam and Even had one of their sons, Seth, when they were both 130 years old (Genesis 4:25-5:4). Adam and Eve were the same age, as they were created on the same day: Adam being only slightly older than Eve (Genesis 1:26-31).

[3] Genesis 5:5.

[4] Genesis 1:6-9 (see Chapter 1 pg 11 and footnote regarding the same topic), 2 Peter 3:5-6.

[5] Cosmic rays, like other forms of ionizing radiation, are impeded by matter. The more dense and thicker the matter, the more the cosmic rays are hindered. In other words, a much smaller thickness of lead (a very dense metal that makes an excellent radiation shield) compared with water is required to block the same amount of cosmic rays. Therefore, there is still a certain thickness of water that

FOOTNOTE CONTINUED ON THE NEXT PAGE

Human thoughts became continually evil, and soon corruption and violence reigned on the Earth. The situation was compounded by the presence of the tyrannical giants. God regretted His creation of mankind.[2] He would have destroyed all humans if it wasn't for one man, Noah. This man found favour in God's eyes. There were three reasons for God's favour. Firstly, Noah "walked with God", which means that he had a good relationship with Him. Noah was also an honest, faithful man, who tried to do the right thing despite the conditions of his time. The last reason was that none of his ancestors were demons: the Bible states that he was perfect in his generations. Each one of these three had to be present or God wouldn't have saved Noah and his family from what happened next. God spoke with Noah about His plan to start afresh by means of a global flood. Of mankind, only Noah, his wife, his three sons and their three wives would be saved.[3]

There was no rain during the era before the Flood (4174–2518 BC).[4] The entire land was watered by a mist that rose from the Earth.[5] This mist probably came from vents connected to colossal

CONTINUED FOOTNOTE PRESENT

---

will block a large proportion of the cosmic rays from space. Air, which is much less dense than water, will also hinder cosmic rays, but a much greater thickness is required to produce the same effect. Today our atmosphere does block some of the cosmic rays from space.

[1] In humans and many other life-forms their genes are made up of sequences of deoxyribonucleic acid (DNA).

[2] Genesis 6:1-6. See also Dispensations (2).

[3] Genesis 6:7-22.

[4] See Timeline.

[5] Genesis 2:5-6. The amount of atmospheric water vapour, relative to temperature, required for rain was nowhere present. Therefore, neither could the rainbow manifest, which is a feature of the post-Flood era (see further on in this chapter pg 92). Rainbows occur because of the refraction and reflection of the sun's light by drops of water in the air. The water shield (the layer of water that

FOOTNOTE CONTINUED ON THE NEXT PAGE

chambers of water that were deep beneath the ground.[1] Regarding the layer of water above the atmosphere, given the freezing temperatures in space and the requirement for light to pass through, this water would have undoubtedly been solid ice in the form of a transparent shell.[2] Although making no contribution to the Earth's natural irrigation and even though clear ice will absorb some sunlight passing through, the amount depending on the ice's thickness, the layer of ice above the atmosphere might have assisted the world's fertility by acting as a heat collector and diffuser respectively by retaining and spreading some of the sun's radiance reflected off the surface of the planet, thereby making the climate more uniform, which is probably why both the Arctic and Antarctic regions once sustained dense forests.[3] In

CONTINUED FOOTNOTE PRESENT

---

surrounded the Earth above the atmosphere) and the colossal chambers of water beneath the ground (fountains of the great deep—Genesis 7:11 and 8:2) are likely to have had something to do with the atmospheric conditions that prevented rain.

[1] Genesis 7:11, 8:2. See also further on in this chapter pg 89 and relevant footnote regarding the deep chambers of water.

[2] The layer of water (ice) above the atmosphere would have had to have been a transparent shell to allow enough light from the celestial bodies (sun, moon and stars) to illuminate the Earth and to permit them to be visible from the surface of the planet: Genesis 1:14-18. If in the form of a layer made up multiple ice particles, even if each piece had been transparent, too much light would have been scattered. It is unknown how far the layer of water (ice) was above the Earth's atmosphere. Without bubbles of air, ice is transparent. The bubbles make ice opaque. Being above the atmosphere of Earth, the layer of ice would not have contained air bubbles. Incidentally, regarding another planet in our solar system, the particles of Saturn's rings are believed to be partly made of ice.

[3] It is also possible that the lands that today constitute the Arctic and Antarctic regions were further from the poles before the continents shifted (see further on in this chapter pg 94 and footnote regarding

FOOTNOTE CONTINUED ON THE NEXT PAGE

this era many of the continents that we consider as separate today were indistinct parts of one united land mass.[1] Furthermore, it is very likely that there was a larger surface area of land—dry land—on the Earth for reasons that will become evident further on. There were 1,656 years from the time of Earth's creation to the Flood.[2] Mankind could have travelled huge distances in that time, and it is unknown where Noah lived before the Flood; however, he lived amongst other people (besides his own family), for he preached to them during the pre-Flood era.[3]

Noah was given instructions on how to build a refuge called an ark.[4] In essence, the Ark was a large wooden box intended to just float and not to sail. In modern-day dimensions it would be 137 metres long (450 feet), 23 metres wide (75 feet) and 14 metres high (45 feet)—equivalent to a medium-sized cruise ship except with no space lost for the propulsion mechanism and fuel. The Ark had three floors, a door and ventilation in the form of a window. The vessel was made waterproof by smearing it with pitch inside and out. One male and one female of every kind of unclean animal, such as pigs and eagles, were to be brought into

CONTINUED FOOTNOTE PRESENT

Peleg—the one united land mass was later followed by the separation of the continents).

[1] Genesis 1:9-10. The so-called Pangaea, postulated in the early 20th century, was already described in the Bible. These two verses demonstrate that the water beneath the sky was gathered into one place, and therefore the land would have also been located in one place. The only way that this wouldn't have been the situation was if the water had been a ring that circled around the Earth, there being a body of land on either side. Unlikely in itself, but also Genesis 10:25 demonstrates that after the Flood the land was initially still one body, and then during the lifetime of Peleg the land was divided.

[2] Genesis 5:1-7:6. See Timeline.

[3] 2 Peter 2:5.

[4] Genesis 6:14-16.

the Ark. Of the clean animals, such as sheep and chickens, seven of each kind were to be saved. Therefore, of each type of clean animal it is likely that there were three pairs and an unmatched single. "Clean" meant that an animal was fit to be sacrificed to God.[1]

Noah did exactly as God had instructed. With the Ark complete, God told Noah to assemble the animals inside. On the 17th day of the 2nd month in the 600th year of Noah's life the Flood began. Noah and his family then entered the Ark, and God closed the sanctuary. The water came from two places. Firstly, from the colossal chambers of water that were deep beneath the ground. The Bible says: "were all the fountains of the great deep broken up". Every one of these chambers of water was destroyed, which meant that there would have been immense shifts of subterranean rocks that forced the water upward. On the surface this would have manifested as tremendous earthquakes and enormous fountains. The second source was from the layer of water, in the form of ice, positioned above the atmosphere of the Earth in space. This layer of ice started to collapse inward, which is why the Bible says: "the windows of heaven were opened." The ice would have reached the Earth as liquid water, and for the first time in Earth's history it rained. It rained continuously, without respite, for 40 days and nights. The rain persisted after that for another 110 days, although intermittently. The water ejected from the deep chambers, like the rain, lasted for a total of 150 days. The volume of water within the layer that had been present above the Earth's atmosphere is unknown, but it was clearly a vast amount, because together with the first source of water they caused the Earth to be entirely covered, including all the mountains. The highest point on the Earth was 7 metres (22.5 feet) beneath the surface of the water. Outside of the Ark every

---

[1] Genesis 6:19-20, 7:2-3, 8:20-21.

human and every animal that either moved on the Earth or flew over it died. God then forced the water to regress.[1]

A fossil is the detectable impression and/or remains of a deceased life-form that is found embedded in matter, usually rock.[2] As most fossils are found in rock in the form of impressions (rather than remains), I shall comment on these fossils. In short, the life-forms are buried in fine sediment, then converted to solid rock. The process, fossilization, must take place over a very short period of time—a matter of days to a few weeks. One reason for this is that feathers and soft tissues of animals can be represented within fossils in addition to the harder structures such as bone. Plants have also been fossilized and even bacteria. The impression of soft tissues would not be present in fossils if the life-forms had had time to decompose. Fossils found in rock were generated in a water environment and required simultaneous rapid burial, high pressure and the presence of fine sediment. Bony structures would also have had to have been fossilized over a short period of time, because the pressure that helped create the fossil of the encased organism would be increasing as further sediment and water collected above and would otherwise crush the bones unless they had already been replaced by solidified sediment. This is the other main reason why fossilization must be rapid, for even though soft tissues can be preserved for hundreds of years in a muddy environment and bones for longer, if the life-forms are not speedily converted to rock, then they would be obliterated by the increasing downward pressure, thereby leaving no impression. The Flood possessed the ideal conditions needed for fossilization. This combined with the fact that vast numbers of different living things were killed during the Flood is the

---

[1] Genesis 7:1-8:19.

[2] Other examples of relevant matter are ice and amber. The remains of life-forms in ice can be remarkably well preserved. Insects are the common life-forms found in amber.

reason for these fossils, which are found in abundance throughout the world.[1]

---

[1] It stands to reason that the lower the stratum (layer) of rock, the earlier it was laid. It has been proposed: (i) that different rock strata (layers) are from different eras, some strata separated by millions of years, and (ii) that each stratum represents a cataclysmic phase in the Earth's history. The observation that led to these theories is that although species of creatures that exist today can be found in the lowest levels, there is a general pattern of more extinct species at the lower levels than at the higher levels. However, in addition to species types alive today found at the lowest levels, the pattern is further broken—examples as follows: the fact that although certain strata were suspected to be from vastly different eras, these strata were then found to contain fossils, such as trees, that spanned through them all; and in the same stratum considered to be from one era, there are then found fossils considered to be from an entirely different era, yet the characteristics of the rock are the same.

One might suspect that on account of the Flood, the fossils would be completely mixed up, but this is unlikely to be the case. The entire world wasn't flooded in a second; the Bible states that the water took 150 days to reach its maximum extent (Genesis 7:24-8:2). Different species would have thrived in different locations before the Flood, resulting in diverse ecosystems. The different ecosystems would have been influenced by altitude, proximity to or location within bodies of water and many other factors. This would mean that although some mixing would have occurred at the time of the Flood, what is likely to have happened is different species would have been engulfed earlier than others, the order depending on their pre-Flood location, thus creating certain patterns within the strata.

Therefore, according to all the above, the principle of the lower the stratum the earlier it was laid remains correct, but periods of only minutes to months separate one stratum from the one that followed, and indeed many strata were clearly laid in approximately a year.

Hard parts of organisms (e.g., bone, shell), although most often replaced by minerals, may be preserved within fossils found in rock.

FOOTNOTE CONTINUED ON THE NEXT PAGE

As the water was regressing, the Ark came to rest on the mountains of Ararat. The family remained inside, because the majority of the Earth was still submerged. It wasn't until a year and 10 days had passed from the start of the Flood that the Earth was dry. God told Noah to leave the Ark with his family and the animals.[1] Noah built an altar and sacrificed one of every kind of clean animal.[2] God accepted the sacrifice and set up a covenant with Noah and his sons. This pact had a number of components: a blessing for each of them, an announcement that all animals will fear mankind, instructions on the eating of meat, a proclamation regarding the importance of human life, God's plan of punishment for the killing of a human by another human, the extension of the pact to the four men's offspring and a promise that God will not destroy the Earth again with a flood.[3] The Earth then witnessed a new phenomenon, the rainbow, set by God as an intermittent sign of the new deal.[4] The three sons of Noah (Ham,

CONTINUED FOOTNOTE PRESENT

Preservation of some soft tissue has also been recorded, although exceptionally rare. This indicates the lack of time that has passed since the creature's death and some truly exceptional conditions by which even a creature fossilized in rock approximately 4,500 years ago has soft parts partly preserved, i.e., some soft tissue was not decomposed, nor was it obliterated by pressure as the proportion of it compared with supportive rock was clearly small enough to be protected by the rock.

[1] Genesis 7:11-8:19.

[2] Which is probably why there were seven of every type of clean animal—so that three pairs were left after the sacrifice: Genesis 7:2, 8:20.

[3] Genesis 8:21-9:12. See Dispensations (3).

[4] Genesis 9:13-17. Rainbows were not a feature of the pre-Flood era. They are a consequence of the changes to the distribution of water around (beyond the atmosphere), on and inside the Earth owing to the Flood, resulting in increased atmospheric water vapour relative to temperature and periodic precipitation in the form of

FOOTNOTE CONTINUED ON THE NEXT PAGE

Shem and Japheth) are the human male ancestors of all people living on the Earth today.[1] The animals were now able to repopulate the Earth.[2]

Noah's family and the animals that left the Ark would have met a changed Earth. Movements of parts of the Earth's crust would have occurred at the time of the Flood, because all the vast subterranean chambers of water had been broken up. Furthermore, the crust's movements would have caused earthquakes and volcanic eruptions. These movements of the crust, the turbulence of the water during the Flood and the increased volume of water present on the surface of the Earth would have altered the topography of the Earth.[3] Higher mountains, deeper oceans, less dry land, icy polar regions and immense deserts—and one shouldn't forget the destruction of the Garden of Eden—are

CONTINUED FOOTNOTE PRESENT

---

rain. The cloud has its first mention in association with the rainbow (verse 13).

[1] Genesis 6:9-18, 7:1-13, 8:15-18, 9:1, 9:18-19. Even though Nephilim have a demonic component to their ancestry, ultimately they would not exist if not descended also from mankind, that is, descended from Adam before the Flood and from Ham, Shem and Japheth (themselves descendants of Adam) after the Flood.

[2] Genesis 6:7-9:15. See Timeline.

[3] Therefore, three types of rocks would have been freshly formed: igneous—the result of volcanic activity; sedimentary—the result of deposition of matter from weathered pre-existing rocks (which is probably one of the reasons why we sometimes see this rock type sandwiching the preceding one in strata [layers]); and metamorphic—the result of heat and pressure within the Earth on either of the other two rock types. These three rock types, present before the Flood, would have been eroded in other places. (Indeed, before the Flood there would have been some sedimentary rock, formed, for example, by deposition of matter from rocks weathered by rivers.) Furthermore, as the floodwaters receded, even some of the newly formed rocks would have been eroded.

almost certainly consequences of the Flood. Although the Flood
changed some of the Earth's topography, there were still changes
yet to come. The Bible states that the Earth (that is, the part of
the surface of the Earth that is solid—dry land) became divided
during the lifetime of a descendant of Shem called Peleg, who
was born 101 years after the Flood and lived for 239 years.[1] The
Flood might have left the crust of the Earth in an unstable state,
which allowed the ensuing separation of the continents to occur.
Incidentally, Peleg's name has three meanings: division, water
channel and earthquake. He was named Peleg for the very reason
that the Earth's land was divided during his lifetime.

The Bible documents a generally steady reduction in the length
of human life from generation to generation after the Flood. In
fewer than seventeen subsequent generations from Noah practically no one lived over the age of 120 years.[2] Before the Flood,
because God was angered by events on Earth during that era, He
predicted that He would reduce the upper limit of human age,
which was at that time approximately 1,000 years, to just 120
years.[3] The 120-year maximum age became the new steady state.

---

[1] Genesis 10:25, 11:10-19, 1 Chronicles 1:19. See Timeline.

[2] Genesis 11:10-26, 11:32, 25:7, 25:26, 29:22-30:24, 35:28-29,
47:28, 50:26, Exodus 6:16-20, Deuteronomy 34:7.
See Timeline for the reduction to the 12th post-Flood generation.
This continued further: Jacob was the father of Levi (lived to 137
years), who was the father of Kohath (lived to 133 years), who was
the father of Amram (lived to 137 years), who was the father of
Moses (lived to 120 years).
A biblical exception to the 120-year-maximum-age status quo is
Jehoiada, a righteous priest who lived to 130 years (2 Chronicles
24:1-22) and died during the reign of Joash, one of the kings of
Judah, around 600 years after Moses' death.

[3] Genesis 5:1-6:3. There is a double prophecy here: a future
limitation on the maximum age of humans to 120 years; and that
God's Spirit would strive with mankind for only another 120 years

FOOTNOTE CONTINUED ON THE NEXT PAGE

The loss of the layer of water (ice) that had blocked cosmic radiation and the possible increased exposure to the Earth's own harmful forms of radioactivity due to its dramatically altered geological structure are perhaps major contributing factors in the shortening of the human lifespan (and probably other living beings). Today cosmic rays contribute approximately one third of the total harmful ionizing radiation absorbed by humans living on the surface of the Earth. The other two-thirds are from the Earth. The progressive reduction in human lifespan over many generations indicates damage at the genetic level.[1]

CONTINUED FOOTNOTE PRESENT

(hoping for humanity's repentance), after which He would destroy the Earth with the Flood (Genesis 6:3-17).

[1] A theory to potentially explain this is that the gradual reduction of length of life over the period of approximately 1,100 years after the Flood specifically indicates that the genes that determine extreme longevity were damaged. A gene is a plan or code that controls one or more traits that we express, such as eye colour. In humans genes are made up of DNA. The damage is likely to have been caused by ionizing radiation. There were perhaps many working genes that each contributed to the long lifespan. When each gene was damaged, its direct function (the role of some genes is to control how and when other genes are used) or product's function (a protein that has one or more roles and is produced according to the gene's plan—proteins have a wide range of roles, e.g., structural, digestive, reparative) was brought to an end. Damaged genes present within the cells of the gonads (ovaries in women and testes in men) are passed on to successive generations. In other words, the damaged genes would therefore be inherited (in human reproduction a baby's genes are made up of half from the mother and half from the father). During each generation additional genetic damage would have occurred, and because it was passed on to the next generation, the damaged genes would have accumulated. Therefore, the maximum obtainable age would have continued to decrease until all the critical genes that determine extreme longevity were damaged. Some genes can be damaged with little, if any, effect on their

FOOTNOTE CONTINUED ON THE NEXT PAGE

CONTINUED FOOTNOTE PRESENT

---

function. Others can be minimally damaged with complete loss of function, and the working genes that were critical to extreme longevity are likely to be within this group. The 120-year maximum age became the new steady state. The above would mean that the genes that once brought about extreme longevity are still present but no longer function as they did before.

The reason why we die of old age today is complex and not fully understood. There are both genetic and environmental determinants. One of the environmental causes is almost certainly the damaging effect of harmful radioactivity on DNA during our lives. However, today even if conditions were created in which there was respite from all harmful radioactivity, it is unlikely to result in a significant increase in the maximum age, because humans, according to the above proposed theory, would now be genetically incapable of living for much more than 120 years; the damage has been done.

In support of the above theory (first paragraph) is the fact that it became law during the lifetime of Moses that close blood relatives in addition to that of parent with offspring should not have sexual relations with one another; parent with offspring was always forbidden and always abhorrent (Genesis 19:30-38); sibling with sibling, nephew with aunt and, by inference, niece with uncle are the unions additionally declared to be forbidden (Leviticus 18:6-7, 18:9, 18:11-13). Moses was a man who lived to 120 years and represents the 16th generation from the Flood starting from Shem (see earlier in this chapter pg 94 and footnote regarding the reduction in maximum age after the Flood). In other words, genetic abnormalities were then prevalent enough to make these additional types of relationships, between people sharing many of the same genes, both dangerous and something to be abhorred, as these relationships rightly are today. Before this time, they were permitted. Specific examples are: Abraham (lived to 175 years), who married his half-sister, Sarah (lived to 127 years), who gave birth to Isaac (lived to 180 years) (Genesis 20:1-12, 21:2-3, 23:1, 25:7, 35:28); and Amram (lived to 137 years), who married his aunt Jochebed (his father's sister), who gave birth to Moses (Exodus

FOOTNOTE CONTINUED ON THE NEXT PAGE

After the Flood, because of the loss of the sunlight-attenuating yet warmth-prolonging ice shield, which would have resulted in greater temperature differences between day and night, it is likely that some of the animals would have had difficulty surviving. Moreover, the difference between summer and winter would have become more extreme. These changes and the Flood that preceded them are almost certainly the cause of wildlife's greatest extinction, because some life-forms would have failed to replenish their numbers. Animals with poor ability to regulate their temperatures would have been particularly vulnerable, for example, Diplodocus, a large dinosaur. Some kinds of dinosaurs might have died soon after leaving the Ark, whereas other kinds might have slowly faded out of existence.[1]

CONTINUED FOOTNOTE PRESENT

6:20). In the early pre-Flood era, some of the second generation would have had to have married siblings (Genesis 4:1-2, 4:17, 5:1-7).

[1] Job 40:15-24 (Behemoth), 41:1-34 (Leviathan). Two now-extinct, massive creatures, Behemoth and Leviathan, are described within the book of Job as being contemporary to the man called Job. This man lived in the post-Flood era and probably after approximately 1956 BC. The reasoning for placing him within this era and after 1956 BC is as follows. His servants were attacked by members of two post-Flood cultures: the Chaldeans and the Sabeans (Job 1:14-17). One of his friends was a Temanite (Job 4:1). The Temanites are a people descended from Teman, a great-great-grandson of Abraham through Esau. Abraham was 100 years old when Isaac was born, who was 60 years old when Esau was born, who was the father of Eliphaz, who was the father of Teman. The age of Esau when Eliphaz was born and the age of Eliphaz when Teman was born are not stated. Assuming that these unknown ages were 25 years, then Teman was born in 1956 BC—see Timeline for year of Abraham's birth. Genesis 21:5, 25:26, 36:1-4, 36:10-11, 36:15, 1 Chronicles 1:34-36, Jeremiah 49:7.

During Job's tragedies he was considered to be very old by one of his friends (Job 32:6). After God had restored Job, he lived another 140 years (Job 42:16). Therefore, Job's full age is likely to have

FOOTNOTE CONTINUED ON THE NEXT PAGE

There is physical evidence of a worldwide flood on every continent of the Earth. The memory of this event is in every race and culture; however, we humans often want to forget the time when God punished us for our sins. You might have already noticed that I am of the decided opinion that the world is only a little over 6,000 years old as the biblical account demonstrates.[1] But what of radiocarbon dating you might ask? I would reply that

CONTINUED FOOTNOTE PRESENT

---

been over 200 years, which is greater than the 175 years that Abraham lived (Genesis 25:7). This may seem to be a small inconsistency in the general reduction of the maximum age of mankind in the post-Flood era over successive generations (see Timeline), but the 140 years were considered to be a special blessing from God for Job's perseverance and faith during his tragedies (Job 42:1-17).

Behemoth was a land creature, was a herbivore, had strong muscles surrounding its abdomen, moved its tail as if this appendage was a cedar tree, had exceptionally strong bones and drank enormous quantities of water (it "drinketh up a river"). Leviathan was a creature of water; was ferocious; was exceptionally strong (it "esteemeth iron as straw"); had terrifying teeth; was able to expel fire from its mouth (clearly possessing an organ or organs that gave Leviathan this ability); had a powerful neck; created a huge, white wake as it travelled in water; had an underside with sharp barbs; was declared to be impossible to catch by mankind; had very tough scales; and was impervious to swords, arrows and spears. The description of Behemoth and Leviathan fit with that of dinosaurs: a sauropod (e.g., Brachiosaurus) and a plesiosaur (e.g., Mauisaurus) respectively.

Some dinosaurs are likely to have existed in small numbers to even later periods in exceptional environments where conditions were amenable to their survival. This would explain the memorable but rare records of human interaction with dinosaurs (dragons) in nonbiblical literature set much further into the post-Flood era. See relevant footnote further on in this chapter pg 103.

[1] See Timeline.

this method of dating material from previously living things is based on an assumption. The assumption is that the amount of radioactivity entering our atmosphere has been at the same level as it is now for many thousands of years. Carbon-14—which is radioactive and therefore also known as radiocarbon, distinguishing it from the most common stable carbon, carbon-12—is created by radiation from space (cosmic rays) bombarding the atmosphere. The radiocarbon (carbon-14) is then incorporated into living things (organisms): plants by taking up carbon dioxide; and animals and humans by eating the plants and/or eating animals that have eaten plants. When an organism dies, it no longer takes up radiocarbon; the radiocarbon then decays (decreases) over time. An observer can tell the approximate date of an organism's death by measuring the amount of radiocarbon contained within its remains: if the remains are of an organism that died a long time ago, then only a small amount of radiocarbon will be detected; and if the remains are of an organism that died more recently, then more radiocarbon will be detected. However, as described in the Bible, there was a water shield (ice shield) in space that once surrounded the Earth above the atmosphere. This would have blocked a large proportion of the cosmic radiation, thereby reducing the amount entering the atmosphere, so that there would have been only a fraction of the amount of radiocarbon in the air in the pre-Flood era in contrast to now. Therefore, the remains of any organism that died before the Flood would contain very little radiocarbon. As a result, the organism will appear to have died much longer ago than is actually the case if the assumption on which radiocarbon dating is based is applied. For example, a mammoth that died before the Flood 5,000 years ago might appear to have died 30,000 years ago if this flawed method of dating is used.

We have been measuring radioactivity only since the late 19th century, but it would be reasonable to assume that the amount of radioactivity entering the atmosphere from space has been relatively constant from the end of the Flood.[1] Therefore, radiocarbon dating the remains of organisms that died well after the end of the Flood, once sufficient time had passed for atmospheric radiocarbon levels to rise to a steady level, is more likely to give meaningful results.[2] However, this method of dating cannot be used to date organisms that died before the Flood. The Bible predicts that in the last days people would come to incorrect conclusions based on assumptions that the environmental conditions of the world in which we live today are the same as they have been since the Earth came into existence, willfully ignoring the facts stated in the Bible: that there was water above and inside the Earth, from which the world was destroyed by the Flood.[3]

---

[1] However, this is by no means certain. It may be that events in the universe have resulted in changes in the amount of emitted cosmic rays over time.

[2] It is important to realize that even organisms that died early in the post-Flood era would still appear to have died much earlier, because it would have taken a while for the cosmic rays to create a level of atmospheric radiocarbon to meet the eventual postulated steady-state level.

[3] 2 Peter 3:3-7: "Knowing this first, that there shall come in the last days scoffers, walking after their own lusts, And saying, Where is the promise of his coming? for since the fathers fell asleep, all things continue as *they were* from the beginning of the creation. For this they willingly are ignorant of, that by the word of God the heavens were of old, and the earth standing out of the water and in the water: Whereby the world that then was, being overflowed with water, perished: But the heavens and the earth, which are now, by the same word are kept in store, reserved unto fire against the day of judgement and perdition of ungodly men." Note also the indication that the universe was made old. See Chapter 1 pg 16 regarding the statement that the world and the rest of the universe were created in a mature state.

The Bible contains accurate accounts of the events before, during and after the Flood. The nonbiblical, "mythical" tales illustrate that the Flood was preceded by an age in which there were giants, gods and dragons.[1] Furthermore, and not surpris-

---

[1] The mythological accounts were all written in the post-Flood era. Being nonbiblical, they lack precise chronology, possess gaps in knowledge and are embellished, and therefore the accounts are rather muddled. Nevertheless, they describe so-called gods and giants existing before the Flood. However, superimposed on the memory of these individuals, the correct names of whom are probably mostly lost, are characters who clearly lived only in the post-Flood era, although reported to have lived in both. These characters were certainly only post-Flood because: (i) the narratives set in the post-Flood era concerning the characters are much tighter and more detailed than the narratives set in the pre-Flood era, (ii) the characters were often intimately associated with post-Flood cities, e.g., having descendants, some of whom were part of royal dynasties, within the cities, (iii) the true nature of these beings means that if existing in the pre-Flood era, then they couldn't have lived past the Flood—they would have died, i.e., they could have existed only in one era. Examples include Marduk and Zeus (Jupiter) (an ancient Mesopotamian god and a Greco-Roman god respectively and each a member of a pantheon of deities), who appear in the accounts as existing in the pre and post-Flood eras. This probably came from the lying boasts of giants and people's wishes to elevate their "god" to a higher plane of power. Marduk (described as a god of extraordinary proportions and the ruler of early Babylon, a post-Flood city) boasted that he was the initiator of the Flood. Despite this, another Mesopotamian myth reports that a different so-called god, Ellil (Enlil), was the initiator. Zeus was also ascribed the role of the initiator of the Flood. Zeus, who was prominent in the post-Flood era, will be dealt with in more detail in Creation's Mutiny. Myths from Mesopotamia *Atrahasis tablets I-III, Gilgamesh tablet XI, The Epic of Creation tablet I, Erra and Ishum tablets I and IV,* Ovid's Metamorphoses Book 1 *lines 253-347,* Apollodorus' The Library Book 1 *chapter 7:2.*
FOOTNOTE CONTINUED ON THE NEXT PAGE

Regarding pre-Flood dragons, in the following account by Apollodorus winged dragons (are pterodactyls, which were flying reptiles, being described?) are mentioned and bizarre creatures described as dragon-human combinations (Typhon and Delphyne): Apollodorus' The Library Book 1 *chapters 5:2, 6:3.*

Of accounts of the pre-Flood era to just beyond the end of the Flood found in ancient Mesopotamian, Greek and Roman sources, the following are references with brief comments. The names of the gods are deliberately omitted for the above reason of superimposition of post-Flood characters on pre-Flood individuals.

Myths from Mesopotamia *Atrahasis tablets I-III:* multiple gods, who were often in disagreement with one another, are described as existing in the pre-Flood era; and the flood related was one of widespread catastrophe—one man, his family and certain animals survived by taking refuge in a boat.

Myths from Mesopotamia *Gilgamesh tablet XI:* multiple gods are described as existing in the pre-Flood era; and the flood related was one of widespread catastrophe—one man, his family, various craftsmen and certain animals survived by taking refuge in a boat.

Apollodorus' The Library Book 1 *chapters 1:1-7:2:* multiple gods and giants are described as existing in the pre-Flood era; the supreme gods were defeated and replaced by other gods; there were both alliances and conflicts between gods and giants; and the flood related started in Greece, then overwhelmed the world—the survivors included a man and a woman who had taken refuge in a chest as well as a few people who had managed to escape the water by climbing high mountains.

Ovid's Metamorphoses Book 1 *lines 5-380:* multiple gods and giants are described as existing in the pre-Flood era; a supreme god was succeeded by another god, and this latter god killed giants; and the flood related was a worldwide catastrophe—only one man and one woman survived, having taken refuge in a small boat.

ingly, tales that are set in times well after the Flood also contain similar beings.[1] Human memory and the ability to pass on information are far better than we acknowledge. We are often overgenerous in our praise of ancient human imagination, which is more recall than independent inspiration.

In spite of the fact that fossils of massive dinosaurs have been systematically excavated and assembled to reconstruct the original skeletal forms only in the last 200 years,[2] mankind has been telling stories of these creatures—often called dragons in

---

[1] Regarding Greek and Roman mythology, the following is of interest. The number in square brackets [ ] is the number of generations before the Trojan War (the conflict was around 1200 BC) that the event(s) related to the dragon (or dragon-like monster) occurred. The sea monster that Perseus slew when it was about to kill Andromeda [4]; Hydra (the serpent that Hercules killed as one of his Labours) [1]; Ladon (the dragon that guarded the apples of the Hesperides) [1]; the dragon that protected the Golden Fleece in Colchis [1]; and the dragons used by Medea for transport on more than one occasion [1]. Apollodorus' The Library Book 1 *chapter 9:23, 9:28,* Book 2 *chapters 4:3, 5:2, 5:11,* Ovid's Metamorphoses Book 4 *lines 639-739,* Book 7 *lines 149-158, 350-353,* Book 9 *lines 64-76, 188-193,* Library of History by Diodorus Siculus Book 4 *chapters 11:5-6, 26:2-4, 48:1-3,* Hyginus' Theogony *39* and Fabulae *22, 26, 27, 30:3, 64, 151.*

Dragons were mentioned as existing during the life of Marduk, an early Babylonian king—the city of Babylon, whatever its condition, is post-Flood. Besides dragons in general, one was highlighted and referred to as the mušhuššu-dragon. A horned serpent was also referred to specifically. Myths from Mesopotamia *The Epic of Creation tablets I-VI.*

The post-Flood so-called-gods and giants have been and will continue to be dealt with in the rest of Creation's Mutiny.

[2] Before modern times, people must have stumbled across fossils of massive dinosaurs, but what they made of them is cause for speculation.

the tales—for thousands of years. This is because humans lived at the same time as these tremendous beasts. Importantly, two massive dinosaurs are described in the book of Job: Behemoth and Leviathan. The events in this book, which are reliably recounted because the book is in the Bible, took place hundreds of years after the Flood.[1]

The giants, whom some call gods, are the biblical "men of renown". They were renowned, because they were capable of feats that normal men were unable to perform. They were not gods but simply giant men. Others correctly referred to the giants as such. The memory of the giants' exploits saturates the Earth even today. As for their demon-ancestors, they are in chains in the Abyss of Hell, having been incarcerated there by God as punishment for taking human wives. The Abyss is deep within the Earth and is a location used to detain demons.[2] The fallen

---

[1] Job 40:15-41:34. Behemoth and Leviathan fit the description of a sauropod (e.g., Brachiosaurus) and a plesiosaur (e.g., Mauisaurus) respectively. For more details about Behemoth and Leviathan and for the time of the book of Job within history see previous footnote in this chapter pg 97 regarding dinosaurs slowly fading out of existence after the Flood.

[2] 2 Peter 2:4-5, Jude 1:6-7. In the New Testament of the King James Version (bar 1 Corinthians 15:55) the Greek words "Hades", "Gehenna" and "Tartarus" have all been translated as "Hell" (capitalized). In 2 Peter 2:4-5 the Greek word translated as Hell is Tartarus. It is used only once in the entire Bible and is a part of Hell for the imprisonment of demons. Tartarus should be compared to the Bottomless Pit (the Abyss) of Revelation, which is also described as a place of imprisonment for demons and is essentially the same place as Tartarus. Revelation 9:1-11, 11:7, 17:8, 20:1-7— in these instances the Greek two words together "abussos phrear" (abyss hole) and the single Greek word "abussos" (abyss) have been translated as "bottomless pit".

When Jesus encountered a group of demons calling themselves "Legion", who had possessed a man, they begged Him not to send
FOOTNOTE CONTINUED ON THE NEXT PAGE

angels who have not committed this particular crime and those not confined to the Abyss for other reasons[1] are still active on the Earth today.

CONTINUED FOOTNOTE PRESENT

them to the "deep", which is a translation of the Greek word "abussos" (abyss), i.e., they were aware that Jesus had the power to confine them to the Abyss (Luke 8:27-39).

For uniformity in Creation's Mutiny the word Abyss will be used, instead of Tartarus or the Bottomless Pit, to refer to the place of confinement for demons in the deepest part of Hell.

On reading the above biblical passages, one can understand that demons are imprisoned by God for different reasons: for taking human wives; to reserve until a certain time when they will be released to inflict punishment on humans on the Earth for a set period; to prevent from influencing events on the Earth for a set period; and possibly for possessing a human being (Jesus didn't in fact send Legion to the Abyss but into a herd of swine).

Hell is beneath us inside the Earth: Job 11:8, Psalms 55:15, Proverbs 15:24, Isaiah 14:7-9, Ezekiel 31:16-17, Matthew 11:23, Luke 10:15.

[1] See immediate previous footnote.

Chapter 5   **One Religion, Many Faces**

"I'm Captain Steven Redding. I'd like to personally welcome you on board flight BA205. We're now cruising at an altitude of thirty thousand feet. The outside air temperature is two degrees Celsius. You'll be pleased to know that we're making excellent progress and are due to land at Atatürk International Airport in three hours."

To Sam flying was a necessary evil that he had to endure in order to make rapid progress. This was now his fifth flight in only a week. He would never admit to it openly, but he was anxious when in the air. It wasn't the fear of flying but rather his lack of control. The thought of putting his life entirely into another human's hands would never sit comfortably with him. If he was the pilot, then that would be different. Of course, Sam couldn't fly an aircraft.

It was Friday morning and three days after Sam's meeting with Sol Hodaviah. The plane had left London an hour ago. Sam was sat in an aisle seat next to a Turkish man, who looked to be in his mid-sixties. On embarking, they'd exchanged greetings but in a manner that acknowledged each other's presence rather than to initiate an in-flight conversation. Sam had already flicked through the free magazine. He preferred not to take hand luggage and had no reading matter of his own. He used the time to think. The House had contacted him at an opportune time. Summer was by far the best time for a climbing expedition, because the eastern Turkish highlands could be bitterly cold in winter and accompanied by more snow on the mountains. He estimated that the first objective would take just over a fortnight. He'd realized that he would miss his preclinical graduation ceremony and had arranged for his degree to be awarded by proxy. His friends thought that he was at home with his parents, and his parents thought that he was in New York with friends.

On Sam's key-ring were two new keys. One could open a locker at a train station in Sinop, a town in North Turkey, and the other was for a safe depository box in a city called Van, 90 miles from Ararat. The keys would be needed only if the mission had become complicated. In each locked compartment were a false passport and other emergency equipment. He wondered where the House had obtained pictures suitable for the passports, as he hadn't provided them with any pictures or given them the opportunity to photograph him. Yet the passports had already been prepared and locked away in Turkey many months ago. He'd been taken aback by their presumption that he would accept the job but subsequently pleased to be part of a confident, well-organized group.

Sam travelled to Turkey under his own identity. This was a condition set by us, the House: that he entered the country as Sam March. In the UK he was well known, even famous to some sections of society. In Turkey he thought that he was unknown.

Stored in Sam's mind were seven new telephone numbers: five of which would call separate untraceable mobile phones and each of these five designated to a different location in Turkey. He'd deliberately left his own phone in the UK. No one would be triangulating his position this time. In addition, he'd memorized the location of the climbing equipment for the ascent of Ararat. The keys and a piece of paper on which the numbers, the location of the climbing equipment and other details had been printed had both been in the envelope that Sol Hodaviah had given him. The piece of paper was finely crumbled black ash in a grey polythene bag at a refuse dump outside of Cambridge.

The plan was to arrive in Istanbul on day one. On day two Sam would meet a contact. This resident of Istanbul would supply Sam with special travelling gear suitable for his mission in Turkey. Sam wasn't entirely sure what that would comprise. He knew only that the items were vital and things that he either couldn't bring into the country or might arouse suspicion if he bought whilst there. The next step would be to create a diversion by hiring a car and very slowly making his way west toward Troy. He should be able to tell after a day or two if he'd attracted any interested parties. If he was being pursued, he would actually go to Troy and pretend to explore this site. If not, he would turn around and head east for Ararat by way of North Turkey along the Black Sea coast.

The King's College Event had started disappointingly. Sam had enjoyed the events in his first and second years. This year's event probably had the same power to enthral, but for him the novelty had drastically worn off. The event wasn't a ball, although almost as expensive. It was simply a massive party set in some of the college's buildings and grounds. There were four different areas for dancing (three inside and one outside), each with its own DJ. There was a gambling hall, in which no money was staked. The "play" chips were presented at the door on admission. In one room there was a hypnotist. Sam always avoided such people. He wouldn't even watch them on television. Things started to improve once he'd caught sight of Rachel. He'd not yet had a proper conversation with her; there were over two hundred medical students in each year and their circles hadn't linked. He'd seen her in and around the medical campus. She was tall, almost as tall as him, yet well proportioned for a woman of her height. His attraction to her wasn't derived only from her beauty and intelligence. By chance he'd overheard part of a conversation that she'd had with four friends. She'd been disputing with them all on a matter of another woman's honour, which was being crushed by seemingly idle gossip. Sam had heard Rachel making her appeal on the maligned woman's behalf with such grace as he'd drifted by the female group. He'd wished that he could have heard more. On the night of the King's Event Sam watched Rachel as she stood with friends in the college courtyard. This time she was laughing and seemed at ease. He approached her, and as his introduction, he told her that he'd seen her in the medical library. She said that she'd noticed him there too. As they talked, he stared deeply into her dark-brown eyes.

Sam stood in the centre of Piccadilly Circus, gazing upward at an airship. It floated 100 metres above him in the air. To Sam the airship was a menacing sight. He could tell that neither helium nor any other gas held the craft aloft. It was broken into two unequal pieces. The front two-thirds was almost completely separated from the rear third by a large jagged tear. The two pieces were still attached at a single area at the top of the airship. It was like a cracked egg with the gaping mouth facing the ground. The surface of the airship was unadorned, grey fabric. Because of the tear, he was able to see the inner metal frame-work. The craft was otherwise hollow: stripped of the many balloons that had been inside and filled with lighter-than-air gas. The airship cast a dark shadow onto the pedestrianized streets below, on which vendors sold their wares to other Londoners and tourists.

The buildings surrounding Piccadilly Circus were dominated rather than punctuated by electric signs. Sam recognized one of the buildings situated beneath the front two-thirds of the airship. He was expecting to see the building's statue of Britannia—the female personification of Great Britain—on the roof, but instead there was a white statue of a pope. The figure wore flowing stone robes. On his head was a stone papal tiara.[1] In his right hand was a bronze shepherd's staff with a cross inside the hook. On an adjacent building, its solitary flagpole, which usually flew a Union Jack, was flying the predominantly yellow and white Vatican banner.

Sam could see a day-moon above the rear third of the airship. It was a thin crescent, which was conspicuous in the blue, cloudless sky. However, the moon wasn't appearing as one would observe if viewing from Britain but rather as one would

---

[1] A papal tiara is a bishop's mitre decked with three crowns.

observe if viewing from Arabia: the crescent's back facing the ground.

In front of Sam was an iron loop fixed to a solid concrete foundation on the ground. Secured to the loop was a rusty chain. The chain ascended skyward and was fastened to the front two-thirds of the airship. It was this apparatus that prevented the airship from drifting higher.

As Sam continued to gaze upward at the hulking, broken airship, he was approached by a middle-aged man, who stopped in order to stand next to him. The middle-aged man also looked upward. Sam turned to the middle-aged man and spoke: "This is an odd sight that I'm seeing. What does it mean?"

"What do you see?" the middle-aged man replied.

"I see an airship that appears to be broken into two unequal parts. Although the airship is broken, the two parts are still connected."

"Correct. What else do you see?"

"The balloons are missing."

"True."

"Then how does it remain afloat?"

"The airship represents the Kingdom of Satan. It's held aloft by his power. So strong is his will and ambition that the kingdom needs to be anchored or otherwise he will accomplish all that he schemes. In this way, God limits Satan's work; he doesn't have free reign."

"And what of the pope's statue and the reclining crescent moon?"

"These represent the two largest religions of the world: Catholicism and Islām. They're great in numbers but not in truth. They're the two pieces of the broken airship. Catholicism is the greater part, and Islām the lesser. They only appear to be apart when in fact they are one. This isn't the only structural defect. If you look closely at the front two-thirds, there's a subtle fissure along the entire length, yet it doesn't split this part of the airship. The larger section is Roman Catholicism, and the other is Eastern Orthodoxy, whose official title is the Orthodox Catholic Church.[1] Roman Catholicism and Eastern Orthodoxy are both forms of Catholicism, sharing a common origin."

"How about the people beneath the airship?" Sam asked.

"They live and trade in its shadow. The airship is a great attraction and the people have become dependant on it for their welfare. Their lives are linked with Satan's kingdom. In reality, they join themselves to a vain thing. The true way to live is outside of this arena and is a very narrow path."[2]

Sam opened his eyes. It had been a dream but far removed from the ordinary. There was rarely a time when he slept that he didn't dream. On waking, within the first few minutes he could usually remember a few incomprehensible particulars that then faltered and before long were lost forever. This was not one of those dreams. This dream was powerful. As he'd slept, he'd felt it absorbing every part of his mind into its fabric. It became a part of him: engraved on his consciousness, cementing his previous knowledge and preparing him for the future.

The plane landed at half-past two in the afternoon. Atatürk International Airport is in Yeşilköy, which is 15 miles from Istanbul. From the plane the passengers descended on stairways to the tarmac. A five-minute shuttle ride from the runway took Sam to passport control.

---

[1] The self-governing institutions of Eastern Orthodoxy include the Russian*, Greek*, Polish, Cypriot*, Albanian, Romanian*, Bulgarian*, American, Ukrainian*, Georgian*, Serbian* and Antiochian Orthodox Churches; and the Greek Orthodox Patriarchate of Alexandria, Ecumenical Patriarchate of Constantinople, Orthodox Patriarchate of Jerusalem and Orthodox Church of the Czech Lands and Slovakia.
*These institutions are the dominant religions in their respective regions.
[2] Matthew 7:13-29.

Sam handed his passport, which was open at the page with his picture, to a young woman sitting in a kiosk behind a thick Perspex screen with a small gap near her hands. She casually accepted the passport with her left hand. She spent two seconds looking at his picture.

"Please state the purpose of your visit, Mr March?"

"Sightseeing."

"Can you be more specific?"

"I'm planning to see some of the buildings in Istanbul: the Hagia Sophia, the Tiled Pavilion, Dolmabahçe Palace . . . After that, I'm going to tour other parts of Turkey. I may even go to Troy. Then, if there's time, I'm going to relax on a beach." Sam thought he would bore her with information excess. Anyone who knew him well would have laughed at his last sentence. Sam never sunbathed. He was already brown and found sunbathing a waste of time. To him there was always something better to do than sit around in the sun.

"How long will you be in Turkey?"

"A month."

"That's a long time," she paused to look at his passport again, "Mr March."

"I'm a student. I've got plenty of time."

"And who will you be staying with? Do you have friends or family in Turkey?"

"I know no one in Turkey. I'll be staying in hotels."

"You're travelling here alone?"

"Yes, I prefer to travel that way."

"I hope you enjoy your visit." She handed him his passport, and before he had time to put his papers together, she'd asked the next person to come forward.

Sam collected his single piece of luggage, a 20-litre-capacity backpack, and made his way to the arrivals section. The former passengers were being funnelled into a narrow corridor. At the end of this passageway there were three uniformed male customs officers, who were talking with one another. They smiled and laughed. Sam was surprised at the officers' lack of interest in the people ahead of him. At a distance of around 15 metres one of the officers looked in Sam's general direction. Sam was part of a group of at least twenty people. The inquisitive officer seemed to scan the cluster, then focus on the dark Briton. Sam thought: is there some recognition there? I suppose it's their job to single people out. He knew that he looked different from the people surrounding him. His speculation continued—recognition or job; if only the officer was closer, then I could read his eyes and discern exactly which it is. In the next few seconds Sam was near enough, but the officer in question had already averted his eyes and was again engrossed in conversation with his companions. On passing, out of the corner of his right eye Sam watched the formerly inquisitive officer. There was no momentary follow-up glance or even a halt or change in speed of this officer's dialogue. Sam was satisfied—job.

Sam entered the arrivals section. The way this area presented the new arrivals constricted his desired anonymity. The image of the waiting crowds was like a lingering photo that stood in front of him, stationary and unfamiliar, creating an unease that bit at his composure. The still faces watched, frozen in anticipation for family and friends. Then there was animated joy, sporadic and conspicuous at first but soon commonplace. The familiar emotions of desired expectations realized that characterize humanity everywhere alleviated some of Sam's anxiety, yet he remained far removed from the house of relaxation. His mind was on the mission. He searched for the coach ticket office.

Sam hadn't been to Turkey before. It was not as hot as he'd expected. He'd predicted a blast of heat as the plane doors had opened. It had never arrived. Instead, it was a bearable twenty-nine degrees Celsius. On the coach he listened to the chatter around him, even though he couldn't understand a word. This was something that he was determined to rectify while in Turkey. He'd left so quickly and had had so many other things to prepare and research that he'd had no time to even look at a phrase book.

He knew some very basic Arabic and had learnt to read and write
Latin in school but doubted that any of these limited skills would
help him in the least bit.

Turkey is both in the Middle East and a part of the Mediterranean. Sam had travelled to other similar countries and to
countries that are both in Europe and a part of the Mediterranean.
As the coach entered Istanbul, Turkey's largest city, Sam's
surroundings reminded him of a city in each of these other
countries: Beirut, Cairo, Athens and Rome—probably due to
different cultural influences over the ages on Istanbul's architecture. The many influences are also demonstrated in the city's
present and previous names. Its present name, lasting now for
hundreds of years, simply means "into the city"; although the
name has its origin in the Greek language, it was adapted by
Arabs and Turks. Istanbul was formerly named Constantinople,
"the city of Constantine", by the selfsame Roman emperor.[1] The
city carried this title for well over a thousand years. Once it was
called Byzantium (Byzantion), named, if the legends can be
believed, after the Greek leader Byzas, who founded the city in
around 1240 BC, which was before the Trojan War. Byzas was
reportedly a contemporary of the more well-known Priam, who
was Troy's king up until the day that his city fell to the Greeks.[2]

---

[1] Constantine I was emperor of the Western Roman Empire from
312 to 324 AD and, after the defeat of the emperor Licinius
(emperor of the Eastern Roman Empire), Constantine was emperor
of the entire Roman Empire (East and West) from 324 to 337 AD.
Note that Constantine was declared emperor in 306 AD after the
death of his father, the Western emperor Constantius Chlorus, but
did not possess full authority over the Western Empire until he had
defeated in 312 AD the tyrannical emperor Maxentius, who was
ruling in and over Rome. Eusebius' Life of Constantine Book
1.19:1-43:3, Eusebius' Ecclesiastical History Book 8.13:12-14,
Book 9.9:1.

[2] According to the Library of History by Diodorus Siculus Book 4
chapter 49:1-8, on their return from Colchis with the Golden Fleece
FOOTNOTE CONTINUED ON THE NEXT PAGE

Istanbul is divided into two unequal parts by the Bosporus, a strait that unites the Black Sea to the Sea of Marmara. On Istanbul's Asian side there is a single region called Üsküdar. On Istanbul's European side[1] there are two regions, which are divided by a body of water called the Golden Horn, which merges with the Bosporus. The Old City is the southern region, and Beyoğlu, which is relatively new, is the northern. These two European regions are connected by a tunnel and four large bridges, all of which cross the Golden Horn: the former beneath this body of water. The easternmost bridge, which guards the entrance to the Golden Horn against unwelcome vessels arriving from the Bosporus, is called the Galata. When the city was called Constantinople, it generally occupied the area now known as the Old City.

CONTINUED FOOTNOTE PRESENT

---

the Argonauts stopped off at Byzantium, where Byzas, the city's founder, was its king at that time. It's written that the Argonauts proceeded to Troy, where they did battle with King Laomedon (Priam's father) and his army. Laomedon was killed and Priam was made king. Priam was Troy's king during the Trojan War (around 1200 BC) up until the city was defeated (Homer's Iliad Book 1 *lines 17-21*, Apollodorus' the Library Book 3 *chapter 12:3-5*, Epitome *chapter 5:16-21*, The Fall of Troy by Quintus Smyrnaeus Book 13 *lines 212-250*).

A later account, by Hesychius of Miletus, declares Byzas to be the founder of Byzantium, but when he lived is obscure: sometime between around 11 generations before the Trojan War (based on one of his grandmothers having been Io, a daughter of Inachus) and around 400 BC. The Patria Book 1 *chapters 4-24*.

The Eastern Roman Empire with Constantinople as its capital is also known as Byzantium (the Byzantine Empire).

[1] Although the whole of Turkey is a Middle Eastern country, a section in the northwest is physically part of mainland Europe and is separated from the greater part of Turkey, which is in Asia, by the Dardanelles, the Sea of Marmara and the Bosporus.

Sam had deliberately not booked a hotel in advance and left the coach in the Old City in order to find one. After external viewings of five hotels, he secured a room in the hotel he deemed most suitable, which happened to be two blocks from the city hall. The hotel was inexpensive without being shabby. He had plenty of cash and could have afforded one of Istanbul's finer establishments; however, he wanted to a keep a low profile. He'd paid for two nights in advance with cash. The friendly woman at the desk had asked him for a credit card, but he'd told her that his had been stolen. He'd paid slightly above the asking price in case of incidentals. He didn't have his credit card with him. This was another traceable item that he'd intentionally left in the UK.

Sam deposited his backpack in his room and ensured that his passport was on his person. Inside the backpack was stowed a small Bible. He left the hotel with the purpose of seeing Istanbul and importantly to check the site of the following day's meeting in Üsküdar. He wore a pair of blue jeans and a light-grey T-shirt. He clutched a thick denim shirt in his left hand in anticipation of night.

It was then almost four o'clock, and Sam made his way toward the Hagia Sophia, a church that had been converted to a mosque. From a distance he could see the central lead-grey dome and three of the four minarets. On top of each peak, whether a tower or dome, was a golden reclining crescent moon. The moon has been a religious symbol since ancient times. It figured in the worship of the Middle Eastern lunar god Sin, whose symbol was the crescent moon.[1] Later the crescent moon became the symbol

---

[1] The worship of the moon god Sin (also known as Nanna) was prevalent in Mesopotamia—evidence below.
Within a Babylonian inscription, on a tablet found in Babylon dating from around 294–280 BC, a temple of Sin and regular offerings to this god are both mentioned: Mesopotamian Chronicles *32 Chronicle from the Time of Antiochus I, Crown Prince.*
FOOTNOTE CONTINUED ON THE NEXT PAGE

Within a Babylonian inscription, on a tablet found in Babylon dating from 312–126 BC, regarding Nabonidus, king of Babylon who reigned from 555–539 BC, it is mentioned that he dedicated his daughter as a priestess to Sin: Mesopotamian Chronicles *53 Chronographic Document concerning Nabonidus*.

In stone engravings Sin is often represented as a man in close proximity to the crescent moon (which is his symbol) or as the crescent moon on its own. The following are three examples. (i) Cylinder Seals* of Western Asia, *plate 94*. The seal is Neo-Babylonian (between 612 BC and 539 BC). The god Sin appears as a bearded man standing on a crescent moon. A man stands before Sin in worship. (ii) The Art of Mesopotamia, *plate 272*. On a stela[‡] commemorating a deed of King Nebuchadnezzar I (reigned approximately 1125–1104 BC), Sin is represented only as a crescent moon and is present together with representations of the goddess Ishtar (as a star) and the sun god Shamash (as the sun). The stela dates from the reign of the king whom it commends and was said to be discovered in 1882 in or near Sippar, which is southwest of Baghdad. (iii) Cylinder Seals* of Western Asia, *plate 96*. The seal is Neo-Babylonian (between 612 BC and 539 BC). Sin is represented only as a crescent moon, which is erected on an altar. Ishtar is represented as a star and is similarly displayed on an altar. A priest stands before both the crescent moon and the star.

*A cylinder seal is an engraved, cylindrical stone that when rolled over wet clay leaves an impression, the purpose of which was many and included securing a deal.

[‡]A stela is an engraved stone that serves as a memorial.

Worship of the moon as a god was also widespread in Arabia but under a variety of names, one of which was Sin. Other names are Wadd (Wudd) and 'Amm ('Amm-Anas and 'Ammanas). (Note that the northernmost areas of Arabia can be considered part of Mesopotamia in its broadest sense—see Chapter 3 pg 63 and footnote regarding Mesopotamian script.)

Wadd and 'Amm are identified as lunar gods from stone inscriptions in their places of worship: the former referred to as the moon

FOOTNOTE CONTINUED ON THE NEXT PAGE

of the Muslim Ottoman Turks and then the entire religion of
Islām.

The walls of the Hagia Sophia were painted in burnt orange. In
places the paint had thinned over the years to expose the well-cut
blocks of grey stone beneath. As Sam came closer, he was
surprised at how impressed he was by the Hagia Sophia's
formidable structure. He'd seen pictures, but none had captured
its strength. To him it resembled a fort more than a church or a
mosque. Inelegant buttresses supported the enormous structure.
He saw small arched windows set in circular walls and convex

CONTINUED FOOTNOTE PRESENT

---

and the latter as the crescent—Histoire Generale Des Religions,
chapter: Les religions Arabes preIslamiques (The religions of the
pre-Islāmic Arabs) page 329 by G. Ryckmans.

Wudd and 'Ammanas feature as prominent pre-Islāmic deities in
the Sīrat Rasūl Allāh (a book written about the life of
Muḥammad—born approximately 570 AD and died 632 AD) by the
author Ibn Isḥāq, who lived from around 704 to 767 AD—chapter:
Origin of idolatry among the Arabs.

Interestingly, Wadd is referred to in the Koran as a god to avoid, 71
Noah (Nūh):24.

Wadd and 'Amm-Anas are described as pre-Islāmic deities in The
Book of Idols (a formal documentation of the pre-Islāmic religious
practices of Arabia, based on the oral traditions of the Arabian
people, and written less than 200 years after the death of
Muḥammad) by Hishām ibn-al-Kalbi (lived 747 to 822 AD)—
chapters: Wadd, 'Amm-Anas, Al-Qalīs.

A major pre-Islāmic temple of Sin (in southern Arabia) was
excavated and described in detail in 1944. The temple was reported
to have evidence of different phases of construction, the earliest of
which dates from around 450 BC. Within the temple, an offering
table shaped like a bull's head and numerous stone inscriptions
dedicated to Sin were found. The Tombs and Moon Temple of
Hureidha (Hadhramaut) by G. C. Thompson. The bull was a feature
of Sin worship. Some believe that the link was because the shape of
a bull's horns is similar to the crescent moon.

semicircular walls, as if the building was designed for an all-round defence by archers. The slanted walls and the vertical walls, all sturdily built, seemed able to respectively deflect and repel cannon fire.

Sam saw a mosaic depicting four characters over the main entrance of the Hagia Sophia. The central figure was meant to represent Jesus the Christ (Messiah). To His right was an image of Mary, to His left was the angel Gabriel and at His feet was Pope Leo VI prostrate in adoration. Christ was portrayed with long, fair hair.

The Byzantine[1] emperor Justinian I was responsible for the building of the church, which was finished in 537 AD. At that time it was simply known as "Sophia" (meaning "Wisdom")[2]; only later was it known as the Hagia Sophia (meaning "Holy Wisdom"). Justinian had clearly determined that to maintain absolute power he needed to control both the secular and religious aspects of his realm. The decisions that people make on who to support reflect minds that are influenced by both a secular core and a religious core; however, how much influence each core has depends on the individual; one core often appears to have complete sway. Before the church's construction, Justinian already had secular authority, although precariously held.[3] His aim was to create a magnificent work that would make him appear to be the utmost benefactor of his religious subjects and to magnify his own name. He achieved his aims but was eventually defeated by his own death.

---

[1] Eastern Roman.

[2] Procopius' On Buildings Book 1 *chapters 1:1-78, 2:13-14*. During Justinian I's reign there was a revolt against his rule in Constantinople, during which the original church known as Sophia (built by Constantine I) was destroyed. The revolt undoubtedly influenced Justinian's future policy, one part of which was the building anew of Sophia on a much grander scale.

[3] See immediate previous footnote.

Sam entered the building and realized that as a frame is to a picture so is the exterior of the Hagia Sophia to its interior. Although outwardly impressive, the inside was clearly the architects' focus. The breathtaking span and splendour of the dome was like another sky, serene over the immense hall. The interior felt like it could be a grand public square. In 1453 AD Constantinople was defeated by the Ottomans,[1] after which the church had been converted into a mosque at the command of their leader, Sultan Mehmed II.[2] Sam saw the eight huge, circular, black medallions inscribed in gold Arabic calligraphy with names important to Islām;[3] these discs were beneath the origin of the dome. In 1935 the Turkish president ordered that the Hagia Sophia be turned into a museum to reflect the different religions that had worshipped there since its construction. The Islāmic characteristics were retained, including the minarets, which had been added by the Ottomans. Many of the Catholic features, such as the mosaics that had been plastered over, were brought to light. In like manner, the city of Istanbul has a curious blend of seemingly different religions, each represented by its own senior cleric. These clerics are: the ecumenical patriarch (the preeminent representative of Eastern Orthodoxy), a Roman Catholic archbishop and a Muslim mufti.[4]

---

[1] Laonikos Chalkokondyles' The Histories Book 8 *sections 3-30,* Doukas' Decline and fall of Byzantium to the Ottoman Turks *chapters 37:1-40:1,* Kritovoulos' History of Mehmed the Con-queror Part 1 *sections 102-252, 272-276,* Sphrantzes' Chronicon Minus *chapter 35:1-10.*

[2] Doukas' Decline and fall of Byzantium to the Ottoman Turks *chapters 40:1-2, 42:3.*

[3] Allāh, Muḥammad, Muḥammad's two grandchildren (Ḥasan and Ḥusayn), and the first four Caliphs (Abū Bakr, 'Umar, 'Uthmān and 'Alī).

[4] There is also a patriarch of the Armenian Apostolic Church, a religion that resembles Eastern Orthodoxy, although not officially part of it. The main difference is that the former adheres to the
FOOTNOTE CONTINUED ON THE NEXT PAGE

In a recess of the Hagia Sophia, Sam was surprised to find a large statue of Jesus Christ crucified on a cross. Two women were kneeling and praying before the figure of affliction. A plaque nearby declared that the statue was one of the original sculptures that had been crafted for the Church of Sophia in the 6th century. The Muslims had removed all such statues once the building was in their possession. As a result of a recent agreement between outwardly conflicting religious factions, this statue, one of the few that had been preserved rather than destroyed, had been returned. Sam had seen many similar effigies in Britain. There was a time when he'd possessed less understanding and would have questioned only the sad lack of Middle Eastern Jewish facial features[1] and the inappropriately long hair[2] of the image. Now he questioned if the individuals who'd commissioned the statue had ever read the Bible, because if that was the case, then they'd completely ignored the words within it, for Jesus would never want an idol created in His image— whether an accurate depiction or not.[3]

I've been a Christian for many more years than Sam, although the passage of time means practically nothing unless a person has earnestly sought a greater understanding of his or her maker. I've done exactly that through God's Word, the Bible, and through prayer, and God has been gracious to personally guide me throughout my Christian life. I've deduced that those responsible for such idols (or icons) have disregarded the fact that Jesus is alive, is at the right hand of God the Father and continues to

CONTINUED FOOTNOTE PRESENT

---

doctrine known as Monophysitism (see footnote in Chapter 3 pg 77 regarding the Coptic Orthodox Church).

[1] 2 Samuel 7:8-13, Isaiah 11:1-5, Micah 5:2, Matthew 1:1-2:1, Luke 2:4-7, 3:23-38, Romans 1:3.

[2] 1 Corinthians 11:14.

[3] Exodus 20:3-5, Acts 17:16, 1 Corinthians 10:19-21, 2 Corinthians 6:14-18 (Belial is a name for Satan, he being the greatest evil).

oppose idolatry.[1] The Bible clearly states that when people pray to idols, they are in fact worshipping demons.[2] Yet similar idols can be seen in churches throughout the world today. It's regrettably the rule, rather than something that is an irregularity, and is a sign of false Christianity.

In a not too dissimilar way, Islām, which makes great efforts to proclaim that it's a religion that follows only one god and has no idols, has at its centre of worship in Mecca: an ancient temple called the Kaaba, which is covered in a black shroud; and a black stone located at the temple's eastern corner. In pre-Islāmic times Arabians worshipped numerous unworked stones, including the Black Stone. They also worshipped many statues that represented

---

[1] Jesus is at the right hand of God: Matthew 22:43-46, 26:63-64, Mark 16:19, Luke 22:69-70, Acts 2:32-36, 7:48-58, Romans 8:31-39, Hebrews 7:22-8:2, 10:5-21, 12:2.
Jesus continues to opposes idolatry: 1 Corinthians 10:1-22, 1 Thessalonians 1:1-10, 1 John 5:20-21, Revelation 2:1-20, 21:1-8 (Jesus is: the Alpha and the Omega; the First and the Last; and the One who has a sword that comes out of His mouth—Revelation 1:1-20). Moreover, the entire Bible is the Word of the Living God and was inspired by Him. Jesus is God, is one with God and is the Word of God (John 1:1-18, 10:30-33, Revelation 1:1-16, 5:5-6, 17:14, 19:1-21 [the Revelation passages demonstrate that Jesus is known as the Lamb, King of kings, Lord of lords, Word of God and is the One who has a sword that comes out of His mouth]). Therefore, every passage in the Bible that criticizes idolatry is also relevant (see Exodus 20:3-5, Leviticus 26:1, Ezekiel 23:30, Acts 17:16, Galatians 5:19-21 and many more).
Although icons are two-dimensional pictures, if they are worshipped, prayed to, bowed to, revered or looked to for spiritual protection, then they meet the definition of an idol in that they have become another god before God. The Bible is opposed to the veneration and worship of pictures: Exodus 20:3-5, Leviticus 26:1, Numbers 33:51-52, Deuteronomy 16:22, Ezekiel 8:1-18.
[2] Psalms 106:36-38, 1 Corinthians 10:14-21, Revelation 9:20.

deities. Moreover, they worshipped even temples, the Kaaba being the most prominent of them. They worshipped these objects in one or more of the following three ways: by touching them (includes kissing the object); by sacrificing to them; and by repeatedly walking around them.[1] Bowing is a given in every culture as a feature of worship and can therefore be added to the collection. When the Kaaba was being rebuilt in approximately 605 AD, the Black Stone, which had been inside this edifice, was given pride of position by being incorporated into the outside wall. The 35-year-old Muḥammad had a central role in this act, as he arbitrated a dispute between various tribes regarding who would have the honour of setting the stone in place. At this point in his life he'd not yet proclaimed the religion of Islām, and at that time there were many other idols positioned within and around the Kaaba.[2] He put the stone into a cloak, the ends of which were held and lifted by a representative from each faction. As a result of Muḥammad's successful mediation, he had the privilege of performing the final setting of the stone.[3] Even after Muḥammad's public declaration of Islām (around 613 AD onward), which he stated was a monotheistic religion,[4] on a pilgrimage he worshipped the Black Stone and the Kaaba by

---

[1] The Sīrat Rasūl Allāh by Ibn Isḥāq *chapters: Origin of idolatry among the Arabs, Early monotheists, The occupation of Mecca, Khālid destroys al-'Uzzā, Destruction of al-Lāt (The envoys of Thaqīf accept Islām).* The Book of Idols by ibn-al-Kalbi *introduction (the relevant section of which is part of the original work), all chapters.*

[2] The Sīrat Rasūl Allāh by Ibn Isḥāq *chapters: Origin of idolatry among the Arabs, The digging of the well of Zamzam, 'Abdu'l-Muṭṭalib vows to sacrifice his son, Rebuilding of the Ka'ba.* The Book of Idols by ibn-al-Kalbi *chapter: Al-'Uzzā.*

[3] The Sīrat Rasūl Allāh by Ibn Isḥāq *chapter: Rebuilding of the Ka'ba.*

[4] The Sīrat Rasūl Allāh by Ibn Isḥāq *chapter: Muḥammad preaches and Quraysh reject him.*

kissing each individually and then circling the Kaaba—and therefore also the Black Stone as it is embedded in the eastern corner of this edifice—at least three times on foot.[1] When he and his army of Islāmic adherents conquered Mecca in 630 AD, his worship of these objects took the form of circling around the Kaaba seven times on his camel and touching the Black Stone with a stick that he held in his hand. The majority of other idols he treated with disdain and had destroyed.[2] Today Muslims bow down to both the Kaaba and the Black Stone. Furthermore, a major part of the hajj (pilgrimage) involves repeatedly walking around the Kaaba and touching—includes kissing—the Black Stone.

Sam left the Hagia Sophia, then walked to the ferry harbour, located in the north of the eastern projection of the Old City. From there he could cross the Bosporus to Üsküdar. As he waited for the next ferry, he watched the ships and boats pass slowly through the strait. Most of the ships were commercial vessels but one was a battleship. As he left the harbour on board the ferry, he gained a better view of the Galata Bridge to the west, which spanned the Golden Horn. To the north he could make out the Galata Tower in Beyoğlu.

---

[1] The Sīrat Rasūl Allāh by Ibn Isḥāq *chapter: The fulfilled pilgrimage*—regarding the circuits around the Kaaba, this passage essentially relays that Muḥammad performed three circuits briskly on foot, then walked at a normal pace for the rest, i.e., more was fulfilled. This pilgrimage was in 629 AD.

[2] The Book of Idols by ibn-al-Kalbi *chapter: Al-'Uzzā*. The Sīrat Rasūl Allāh by Ibn Isḥāq *chapter: The occupation of Mecca*. There is some debate about whether or not three icons (two pictures of Jesus and one of Mary) were preserved at the order of Muḥammad. See earlier in this chapter pg 121 regarding Jesus opposing idols and icons—the accompanying footnote contains a comment on icons being idols.

Before reaching Üsküdar, the ferry passed Leander's Tower, also known as the Virgin's Tower. The structure was built on a tiny island off Üsküdar. The tower and the attached building complex are separated from deep water by a narrow perimeter of stony pavement, which lacks vegetation. The island appeared to Sam as if it were the highest-point vestige of a flooded town.

Once on land again, Sam made his way to the café in the suburbs that had been chosen as the next day's rendezvous point. Having located the café, he didn't enter but instead circled the large building that the café was a part of. He then explored the surrounding area for a whole hour, specifically looking for escape routes, some of which were through public buildings. His contact had picked a busy location: a fine idea. The meeting had been arranged for half-past ten in the morning. Sam was satisfied and took a ferry back to the Old City.

Sam intended to return to the hotel via a different route from the one that had led him to the Old City ferry harbour.

It was half-past eight and growing dark. Sam was walking through the public garden in Atmeydanı. He put on his denim shirt. There were enough other people traversing the park to make him feel comfortable. He passed an obelisk, then slowed his pace as he came toward a curious monument. It was a bronze column, which had oxidized to a uniform green. The monument appeared to be made up of three snakes. They were intertwined to form the column's shaft; the tails were at the base. The serpents' heads were missing at the top. He didn't stop but turned his head to view the monument as he walked around it. He felt as if he was receiving a general anaesthetic. His legs gave way and he fell to his knees. As Sam collapsed flat against the ground, he thought of just one thing: that damned customs officer—recognition.

Chapter 6   **The Precipice**

Sam regained consciousness. He felt as if a kilogram weight was tied to each centimetre of his body, pulling him into oblivion. He fought the oppression and managed to open his eyes. There was still only blackness, which startled him. He'd been sat upright. He raised his head, the back of which struck a wall. He had the sensation that an itchy material was covering his face. He smelled dust and felt the loose weave of course fabric. He thought that the material was porous sackcloth but still couldn't see any light. His mind was working slowly, as if the connections of his brain had been drawn away from one another and insulated with cotton wool. He lifted his arms and heard the clank and rattle of chains. His wrists had been individually shackled. He pulled the sackcloth off his head, then succumbed to the chemically induced coma once more.

Sam awoke to find himself shivering with cold. Again, there was only blackness. His mind told him that it was morning. There were no sensory cues. His mental faculties were now almost back to normal. His feet were not fettered, and he managed to stand up without toppling. His back remained against the wall. He had no shoes and socks but was still wearing the jeans and T-shirt. The two wrist-shackles were connected by a 20-centimetre-long chain. The centre of this chain was linked to a thicker heavier chain. He walked forward a few steps until the thicker chain became taut. He held this chain in his hands and followed the cold links. The chain first led back to a sturdy, vertical metal hoop, through which the links passed. This hoop was positioned two metres directly above the position where he'd been sitting. The chain then led to a large metal peg (which was at a lower level than the hoop and approximately one and a half metres to its right), to which the last link was attached. The peg had been to his left when he'd previously sat facing away from the wall. The peg was embedded in the stone wall. It felt as if the peg had been hammered in like a nail, but he suspected that it had been built into the wall. When the chain was not pulled taut, there was slack between the peg and the hoop. The chain limited movement from the hoop, the extent of which was a small semicircle with a radius of two metres. He was unable to reach anything else except for an empty bucket. He returned to the spot where he'd awakened and sat down.

What could have been an hour later, Sam heard the sound of wooden furniture scraping on a stone floor. He localized the noise to his right. Soon after, a two-centimetre-high strip of faint light appeared from the same direction. He'd been in that direction to the extent of the chain's limit and knew that he couldn't reach what was probably a door, the entrance to his cell.

Sam waited and silently prayed. He was extremely thirsty. He heard voices from the other side of the door. He received them at too low a volume to individualize, but from the pauses he guessed that there were at least three people involved in the conversation. There was just enough light from beneath the door for Sam to dimly survey his cell, which was cube-shaped. The door was located in the centre of the cell's north wall. He was sat in the centre of the east wall beneath the hoop. The peg was located toward the southeast corner, embedded in the east wall.

Sam heard the characteristic sound of a sliding metal bolt being drawn across. He turned his head as the door opened to reveal a tall, gangly silhouette. The gangly man reached out with his left hand and must have flicked a switch, which was external to Sam's cell. A single light, a bare 60-watt bulb, came on in the cell. The gangly man entered the cell. The bulb provided illumination equivalent to the light in the room that the tall figure had left. Sam could see one other man in the adjoining room, who was still talking but not to the gangly man. Sam could see his own room properly now. Its walls were a mixture of stone and concrete. There were no windows or evidence of there having been any in the past. The cell had been built for its current purpose. The gangly man shut the door, which was made of metal—solidly constructed. Two seconds later Sam heard the bolt slide: the work of one of the guards in the adjoining room. Sam and the gangly man were locked inside the cell together.

The gangly man circumvented Sam, not looking at the prisoner, striding confidently beyond him, following a procedure. The gangly man was six feet four inches tall, and although thin, he had a brawny upper body. He was around forty-five years old and bald except for some hair, which was straight and black, above both ears. He reached the length of chain that was between the hoop and the peg. He pushed the chain downward, forcing Sam to stand and lift his arms above his head. Sam heard a click, then saw that in the wall near the floor was a downward facing hook, to which the chain could be secured in order to tighten it, simultaneously fixing him in his current position, with his arms raised and wrists in close proximity to the vertical hoop. He'd not registered the hook's presence before, because it was so far below the levels of both the hoop and the peg.

Small dark eyes, alive and cruel, were turned to face Sam. The gangly man hadn't shaved for two or three days, and the stale odour of nicotine and tar saturated his clothing. Sam was worried at how very singular the gangly man was in appearance: quite unlike the average street-going person. The gangly man had the look of someone who was reserved for special circumstances should they arise. He resembled a vulture, a loathsome determined carrion eater. Sam was even more concerned that the gangly man was wearing only a dark vest, combat trousers and boots in a cold room and was clearly relying on work to maintain his temperature.

"What is your name?" the Vulture asked in English, albeit with a heavy Turkish accent.

"I've forgotten. Must be the effect of the tranquilizer you shot me with." Sam knew that they would have searched through his belongings; however, he wasn't planning to cooperate. He received a punch in the stomach, which winded him. His reflex was to double up, but the chain wouldn't permit this. He tensed his abdominal muscles and pressed his back onto the wall.

The Vulture casually reached into his right back trouser pocket and pulled out Sam's crimson British passport. "Well, let's see. This says that you are Samuel Agabus March—student. I hear you are big explorer. What are you looking for in Turkey?"

"I want to be taken to a British Embassy, right now! You have no right to hold me here."

The Vulture was unfazed, taking only a derisive interest in Sam's demand. The right side of the Vulture's top lip curled, and he grinned.

Reading the Vulture's eyes, Sam didn't like what he saw. "Where am I?"

"I ask questions—you answer. What are you looking for in Turkey?"

"I'm on holiday."

The next punch was drawn slowly, then released like an explosive piston. The Vulture's fist felt as if he'd wrapped a thick sheet of lead around his clenched hand.

Sam made an involuntary gasp. It gave the Vulture no satisfaction.

"Who's paying your mission?"

This time the Vulture didn't wait for a reply. The next punch was higher, striking Sam in his chest to the left of his sternum.

"Go to Hell!" Sam shouted.

The Vulture stared into Sam's eyes. The Vulture looked as if he wanted to smash Sam across the mouth.

"Are you with anyone else?"

Sam received another punch.

"Go to Hell!" Sam exclaimed with less force than before.

From then on Sam was silent. The beating continued for a full hour. In between body blows Sam had heard the faint rumbling of a conversation on the other side of the door.

Catching his breath upright, the Vulture looked at Sam. The Vulture clenched his sinewy jaw. He didn't seem disappointed that Sam hadn't talked. The Vulture picked up the sackcloth head covering from the floor and walked to the door. The hairs on his shoulders were flattened from sweat. More sweat had collected to form a shovel-shaped patch on the back of his vest. He opened a small aperture in the door, also metal. He peered through, then said something in Turkish, "Kapıyı açın!", to an audience on the other side. The bolt slid, the Vulture closed the aperture and the door opened. He left. The door shut. The bolt slid. The light was switched off.

Sam had been left with his arms held above his head. He thought that he would have been struck in the face or other parts of his head, yet all the hits had been to his torso. He rarely bruised, even during a rugby match, but knew that his chest and abdomen would be scattered with black bruises after the pounding he'd received. He ached in many places; his right lower ribs were the worst and still acutely painful.

Some time later the light was switched on. Another man entered except with a wooden bowl of food and a plastic jug of water. He was in his mid-thirties, average height and grossly overweight. He shut the door, which was locked behind him. He didn't look at Sam. The obese man put the items on the ground near to the prisoner's feet, then unhooked the chain. Sam fell to his knees. The obese man opened the aperture and said the same phrase in Turkish that the Vulture had used, except this time the voice was slower and higher. The obese man left the cell. The light remained on for a minute. Sam had initially thought that it had been left on so that he could eat with illumination but then realized that the obese man had just initially forgotten to switch it off.

Sam remained shackled, but he'd been granted his radius of two metres. His food constituted the guards' leftovers, which had been sloppily left in the bowl. He contemplated not eating: suspicious that the food had been poisoned. On the other hand, he considered that if they wanted to kill him, then they would have done so already. He needed to maintain his strength as best as he could. The meal was a mixture of lukewarm and cold morsels. He ate with only the sliver of illumination from beneath the door. While the light had been on, he'd seen a chicken's half-eaten thigh and some rice. He'd also noticed an indeterminate vegetable, which remained so even after consumption. The wooden bowl was thin, delicate and smoothly crafted. It wasn't designed for prison or repetitive canteen use. It was the kind of domestic wooden bowel that could have been used to serve a salad—an inappropriate reminder of a better place.

Sam now properly examined his right lower ribs. The ninth was exquisitely tender. It was broken. He already had some knowledge of clinical medicine relevant to injuries. He knew that a rib fracture can, in a minority of cases, cause a collapse of the underlying lung. He was almost positive that this hadn't occurred, as he was not short of breath. Fractured ribs are splinted by the surrounding muscles and hence don't need to be bound; however, Sam recognized the need to avoid repeated injury to that area if he wanted to protect his right lung. His abdominal muscles were heavily bruised. Despite the injuries sustained, he wasn't bleeding.

Sam was awoken by the sliding bar. It was eleven o'clock at night. He was oblivious to the time. The light came on and the obese man entered. The door remained open. Sam could see the Vulture, who was standing. He smoked a thin cigar. He stared at Sam from inside the adjoining room not far from the door. The Vulture grimaced as he inhaled, destroying several millimetres of tobacco with each breath. Sam could see a sturdy wooden table and chairs positioned immediately behind the Vulture, and a desk at the far wall. Sam could partially make out an old metal filing cabinet and another door. There were no other people that he could see or hear.

The obese man turned his head to face the Vulture, trying to catch his attention. The Vulture continued to stare at Sam. The obese man then closed the cell's door, which was promptly locked behind him. He tightened the chain. As the obese man punched, Sam rotated his body to avoid the broken rib. The obese man thought that Sam was writhing from the pain. Sam had the capability of kicking his torturers, only he'd realized the futility of this action. Doing this while still restrained would merely hurt the assailant once or twice at best. The assailant would then retaliate disproportionately and probably call in another guard during the session or even restrain Sam further by shackling his feet. Sam preferred the present situation. He received the beating for an hour. The thumping had lacked the zeal of that previously received from the Vulture. There had been no exchange of words from either party. Again, Sam's head was unharmed. Before leaving the room, the obese man unhooked the chain, so that Sam could lie down and sleep. As usual, they left Sam in darkness. Instead of sleeping, he rested for a few minutes, then decided to test how securely implanted the peg was.

Sam figured that there were two men on the other side of the cell's door. It was probably night, and the guards' routine was to reduce their numbers at that time. The peg was at a height of approximately a metre and a half. As he raised his right arm to place his right hand on the peg, he felt a sharp exacerbation of pain in his broken rib. What could be felt—and vaguely seen—of the peg, which wasn't much because it was trapped in the wall, resembled a giant sewing needle, the eye of which the chain was attached to. He pushed and pulled at the peg's exposed shaft, which made him wince. He tried with his left hand; there was only enough room for one hand on the bare metal. The peg was absolutely rigid. Nevertheless, he continued pushing and pulling, regularly switching hands every few minutes. Sometimes he placed one hand over the other to increase the force applied. He tried to use the full weight of his body in addition to the strength of his arms. He was careful to keep his wrists as still as possible as he rocked his weight backward and forward. At two in the morning the light in the adjacent room, its emissions visible beneath the door of the cell, was turned off. He continued to work in total blackness.

Sam noticed the strip of light beneath the door at the precise moment of its arrival and immediately pretended that he'd been asleep by reclining on the floor. He heard the low screech of the bolt, the sound now triggering involuntary dread. The cell's door opened. The Vulture stood at the entrance. He switched on the cell's light. He seemed to be talking with someone to his left. The person with whom the Vulture was conversing was not visible to Sam, but two other men in the room were. The obese guard was not visible, and the voice talking with the Vulture was not high-pitched. Sam thought about the dungeon. This is the day shift—does the Vulture ever leave this place? These people don't care whether I live or die. They're just desperate to know what it is that I've been sent to find and who sent me. They want to know if I have an accomplice: someone who will continue in my absence. Sam knew that he needed to keep his mouth shut; he'd survive longer that way.

The Vulture talked for six minutes while he remained at the entrance to the cell. He was then passed the sackcloth head covering. He entered the cell, but this time he didn't immediately close the door behind him. He made the chain taut, thereby hoisting Sam's hands vertically toward the metal hoop. The Vulture covered Sam's eyes by tying a handkerchief tightly around his head and then placed the sackcloth. Sam heard another man enter the cell.

"Cover that bucket with a plank or something—or even better, empty it," the new man spoke English very well and with only a slight Turkish accent, commanding at conversational pace. Sam was surprised that anybody spoke to the Vulture in that manner, although it was yet another set of footsteps that removed the bucket from the room. The cell's door was shut and was locked.

Sam could tell why his head hadn't so far been struck. This was the outfit's superior, who'd probably travelled a great distance. The Vulture had tried to get ahead of what was expected, hoping to impress his chief with early results. Sam's head had been reserved.

What Sam didn't know was that the chief had berated his subordinates beforehand for capturing March too early—that is, prior to knowing which location in Turkey he was headed toward. Their argument had been that they didn't want to lose their quarry. They didn't mention that they'd lost March soon after he'd left the coach in the Old City and to their relief had spotted him at the ferry harbour on his return from Üsküdar.

"Why are you here, March?" the chief's voice came from directly in front of Sam's face. Sam and the chief were of similar height.

There was a pause, during which Sam remained silent. He was struck on the left side of the forehead; it was a hard brutal punch that made him reel. He repeatedly planted his feet as he fought to regain his balance. The Vulture was obviously standing to Sam's left and had delivered the blow with his right fist.

"I don't want you to knock him out," the chief instructed calmly.

"Why are you here, March?"

There was a longer pause. The next punch arrived—a solid strike to the head but lacking the intensity of the previous blow.

Sam thought: who are these people?

"Who sent you?"

Sam was struck again.

"Are you working with anyone in Turkey?"

Another punch landed. The left side of the handkerchief became wet.

"Are you here for treasure?" The question gave Sam some idea as to their angle.

Punch.

"Were you really headed for Troy?"

The woman at passport control must have said something, Sam thought. Damn her. He again felt the price of his silence. And what greater forfeit would he pay for his overconfidence on arrival in Turkey?

"Priam's gold has been found, March."

Punch.

"If it's gold you're after, we'll let you go with some men. They'll assist you. We'll share what you find." The offer revealed that the speaker wasn't convinced that all of Troy's treasures had been discovered.

Pause. Punch.

The offer sounded hollow. The chief was a poor actor. I know someone who can give you a few pointers, Sam thought. The chief was fishing. Sam raised his head yet remained silent.

"You know something, March, most Muslims in this country think that most of the people in your Britain are Christians. I know this isn't true—in fact, far from it. Even the majority who call themselves Christians aren't. So what are you, March?"

Sam didn't answer. He flinched beneath the sackcloth, waiting for the punch. It didn't arrive. There was no verbal exchange between his torturers. Sam imagined the speaker holding up the flat of his right hand, an order to defer the Vulture's next onslaught. The chief removed the sackcloth from Sam's head but left the handkerchief untouched. Sam still couldn't see a thing. The chief looked at Sam's face, searching for an answer within the quiet eyeless visage. Sam's left cheekbone was swollen and bruised, as was his left forehead. An area of skin above and lateral to his left eye (at the junction of his forehead and left temple) was bleeding. Below this wound, blood had soaked the handkerchief and was trickling down his cheek. The chief's last line of questioning and preceding statements were a change of tack. The statements had revealed to Sam something about this new man: the question's preamble had understanding. Sam was now deeply concerned about what the chief knew about Samuel Agabus March.

The chief continued, "Say 'There is no god but Allāh; Muḥammad is the prophet of Allāh'[1], and we'll unbind you. That's right; we'll let you go free."

Ten silent seconds passed.

Sam was surprised to hear the voice whispering in his unhurt right ear: "I don't care if you don't believe it. All you have to do is say it."

Sam stayed quiet.

Now spoken at normal volume, "Of course, you won't say it; I know what you are, March."

This time the words were followed by a series of punches to Sam's head and neck. He tasted blood in his mouth.

"Why don't you strike out? Your legs are free. I'm right here in front of you. Or are you turning the other cheek?"[2]

Sam was struck again. He wanted to lash out but held himself back.

The voice resumed with another change of tack: "Samuel, I've been to England and even Cambridge." (Sam had put his college as his address in his passport.) "I was in Trinity one evening when the college's choir sang from the rooftops into Great Court—truly magnificent. Have you heard them?"

No answer.

"Why don't you talk?"

No answer.

"I'm a civilized man, Samuel, but you're forcing me to be barbaric. Toenails!"

The Vulture walked to the door, opened the aperture and said a few words in Turkish. Another man entered, and the door was locked again. This man held down Sam's feet. The Vulture reached into his left back trouser pocket and pulled out a pair of pliers.

---

[1] This is the Muslim profession of faith.
[2] The interrogator had knowledge of Matthew 5:39 and Luke 6:29.

Five nails later from Sam's right foot and he still hadn't said one coherent word, although in agony he'd emitted suppressed groans. The last nail to be removed had been from his big toe. He'd retched from the pain but had swallowed the vomitus after it had filled his mouth. He was loath to give his captors the satisfaction of seeing him lose control.

"Mark my words: you shall eventually tell us what we want to know," the chief uttered. He left the cell.

Later that day Sam received an additional beating, which was from a solitary guard who was different from the previous assailants. This latest assailant had broken another of Sam's ribs—on the right side above the first fracture.

Sam waited until well into the night shift before attacking the metal peg again; he'd been initially afraid that there would be a night beating as before. He'd been able to tell the shift change from the reduction of voices behind the cell's metal door. He'd not yet heard movement of the door that was on the opposite side of the guards' room, even though he'd listened carefully for it. He imagined that its movements must be very quiet—perhaps muffled in some way. They hadn't fed him that day. All they'd given him were two litres of water in plastic bottles. The bucket, now empty, had been returned. The blindfold had been removed. While there had been some light in his cell he'd registered a difficulty seeing from his left eye. The toes of Sam's right foot had stopped bleeding, but he was finding it painful to weight bear. Despite injury and hunger, his efforts were nonetheless energetic. He toiled with the peg with as much vigour as he could rally whilst keeping as quiet as possible. At the same time he practised a few choice Turkish words that he'd heard the guards using.

In the early morning hours the peg loosened. A tiny sprinkling of concrete powder stuck to Sam's sweaty left hand. By six in the morning he'd almost freed the peg but was careful not to do so. It still needed to take some tension. A small heap made up of particles and chunks of concrete lay at his feet. The peg was now surrounded by a circular gap created by his efforts. He mixed the rubble with some water and pushed the mixture into the gap. Even though the peg was near to a corner of the room, it wouldn't stand much scrutiny. He ceased his activities before the emergence of light from beneath the door.

Later that morning the cell's door opened. The Vulture entered alone. The door was closed behind him. Sam had seen two more men in the adjacent room and had heard an additional two. Sam rose to his feet. He raised his arms to minimize the imminent tension on the chain.

"Where's your master today?" Sam distracted the Vulture as he hooked the chain.

"You talk today, eh? Who sent you, March? Who's your master?"

Sam didn't reply—his intention was to say nothing further.

"When we're all done here, March, I'm going to kill you, then bury you in a place where even your God will never find you."

Enraged, the Vulture started thrashing Sam. The head and body were both targets. Sam concentrated on just two things: firstly, not to look at the peg, even for a fraction of a second; and secondly, not to lose his feet, as the peg would be inadvertently pulled out of the wall at the wrong time. The session lasted the full hour, although after the first ten minutes the Vulture had given up asking Sam questions. The peg stayed in when the Vulture loosened the chain.

That morning and afternoon they didn't give Sam any food or water.

At nine o'clock in the evening four men left, one stayed and one arrived. All that Sam registered was that there were fewer people on the other side of the cell's door: at least two. He prayed that there were truly only two like the previous night shifts and that the Vulture wasn't one of them. One prayer was answered; the other wasn't. At three in the morning, as the cell's door opened, Sam saw the obese guard and the Vulture. The Vulture waited next to the door with the intention of locking his associate inside the cell. The obese man entered. Sam stood to follow the same procedure as before.

Sam was taking the beating. With a defiant battered face, he stared at the obese man. Sam knew that he needed to last the hour; he couldn't mimic the sound of one man beating another and didn't want to raise any suspicion on the other side of the door. Nonetheless, one blow to the centre of Sam's forehead was unexpected, and he was almost knocked unconscious. He managed not to fall but realized that a similar hit could ruin everything.

On the other side of the cell's door the Vulture was sat at the table, eating some bread and cheese. He used a large sheath knife to slice the bread. Both of his booted feet were on the table. As he ate, he looked at Sam's belongings, which had been placed on the table that afternoon. They'd already been searched on the day that Sam had arrived, and one of the other guards had decided to re-examine the items again during the previous shift. There was a wallet with a few million Turkish liras amounting to several hundred pounds sterling. It was otherwise empty. Sam's only identifier was his passport, which had been in the left pocket of his denim shirt. His set of keys lay on top of his cheap map of Istanbul, which rested on the table. One of the keys was to the hotel room, but he'd shrewdly removed the tell-tale fob. The Vulture picked up Sam's thick denim shirt and closely examined it. The Vulture threw the shirt back down onto the table. He looked at the passport again. There were numerous stamps, which marked journeys to different countries. The chief had talked with the Vulture about the destinations, some of which were confirmed as trips made by March on previous missions. Eventually, the group would "discuss" the missions with March. The Vulture placed the passport onto the table and took another bite of his meal. He glanced at the shirt. The right hem leading up from the tail was distorted. He thought that it could be a factory-mistake, as the stitches seemed to be uninterrupted and of the same colour along their combined length.

Sam's inner clock sensed that the duration of the beating was perhaps only forty-five minutes or at most fifty minutes, but he needed to act. With every ounce of force that he could muster, he kicked his assailant firmly in the genitals. The obese man dropped to the floor. Sam pulled his arms downward with a sharp, vigorous thrust. His broken ribs cried out. He ignored the pain while turning quickly to catch the freed peg before it could clang against the stony floor. With continued haste, he pulled the loose chain away from the hook and fed the peg through the vertical hoop. The torturer was on his knees, clutching his groin—voiceless and struggling to breathe. Sam struck the obese man soundly on the back of the head with the peg.

In the adjacent room the Vulture noticed a reduction in the sound of violence, then looked at his watch. He rolled his eyes in contempt for his associate. The Vulture lifted the denim shirt and felt something hard within the distorted hem. He took hold of the knife and started to cut the stitches with his habitual excess. He folded back the cloth to expose a small, shapeless fragment of wood. For a second he almost dismissed it as a splinter. He turned it over to reveal a black underside. His facial expression was one of recognition. He quickly rose to his feet to make a phone call. The aperture opened, and the wide-eyed face of Osman called out to the Vulture, "Kapıyı açın!", which means "Open the door!"

"Osman, you fatso. Can't you even last an hour?" the Vulture said in Turkish. Sam didn't understand a word. He thought about repeating the mimicked "Kapıyı açın!" of Osman except more impatiently. Sam decided to say nothing. He wasn't sure if the Vulture had asked a question or had made a statement. Sam continued propping Osman up, so that his mouth was just below the aperture. Sam's legs started to tremble from the sheer effort required to keep the obese man in position. The bolt slid and the door opened.

The Vulture saw the body of Osman fall away to reveal Sam. The Vulture raised his left arm as the peg descended in an arc toward his head. He couldn't deflect the heavy metal rod. It hit his left temple and smashed his cheekbone. He let out a deep grunt and staggered backward. Barely steady on his feet, he came forward, and with his right fist he threw a punch at Sam. Sam dodged the attempt and landed his next blow with the peg in the centre of the Vulture's forehead. Both attacks to the Vulture had been struck with maximum force, unlike the blow to the back of Osman's head. Having been intimidated by the strength and brutality of the Vulture, Sam had felt that anything less than his utmost would have been ineffectual. Sam felt his second strike crack thick bone and sink deeply. This time there were no backward steps to stop the Vulture's fall. He didn't get up. He didn't even twitch. He lay flat with his eyes open, staring blankly at the ceiling.

There was no more opposition in the room. Sam searched the two men for their keys and found a bunch on each. He immediately released his shackles, then started to rummage around for his belongings. The first thing that he saw was his denim shirt on the table and the fragment of wood, which he'd broken from the amulet and then concealed. He'd done this, so that he could make comparisons with any other wood fragments that he found. "Damn!" Sam said. His famished mind was frantically cogitating. How long has that been there for? Do they know what it is? It's just a piece of wood to them, surely? Then again it's a piece of wood that's important enough for me to hide. They haven't asked me anything about it or the Ark. He put on the shirt. Neither of the guards was uniformed, and no advantage lay in wearing their clothes. He retrieved his socks, shoes, passport, keys, map and wallet. To his surprise none of the money was missing. He picked up the fragment of wood and placed it into the left front pocket of his jeans. He put on his shoes and socks.

There were no windows in the guards' room. Sam had no clue as to what locks and doors he was yet to face beyond this room. The guards didn't have cards with magnetic strips, nor had they any identification documents in their wallets, which Sam left unplundered. Sam started scouring the room. He was desperate to discover the origin of his torturers. In the middle drawer of the three-drawer filing cabinet he found a loaded semiautomatic pistol with a round already in the chamber. He made sure that the safety was off and held the pistol firmly in his right hand. In the bottom drawer he found a tarnished metal potato peeler, which he shuddered to think had probably never been used as such, and the Vulture's pliers. His overall impression was that the room was intentionally clear of ownership-revealing items. Although rushing, he finished the rest of the Vulture's meal. There was a black phone hanging on the wall next to the filing cabinet. He rendered the phone useless with the pliers. He noticed that they were still stained with his blood. He felt his right toes being constricted by the shoe. He tried his best to disregard the pain.

Sam walked softly to the door that was his only apparent exit. He gently put his ear against this door to fathom what lay on the other side. He listened for a full impatient five minutes. There had been only silence and not even a draft from beneath the door. The key that fit the lock of the door was on the Vulture's set. Sam slowly turned the key. It smoothly unlocked the door. The pistol was aimed forward. The door opened toward him to reveal a vertical, cylindrical shaft, which rose upward into the darkness. The ascent was by means of a metal ladder. He peered upward and could see no conclusion. He started climbing. The shaft and the lack of windows in both rooms made him suspect that he was underground in some kind of bunker. After an ascent of 20 metres, he met an abrupt ending, which lacked a handle or any other graspable thing. He slowly pushed upward. What he was lifting had a woody texture. The wooden board rose easily, and its grounded edge emitted a scraping sound as it shifted laterally. He rose from the shaft to be met by a large stone chamber. He was in an alcove at one end of the chamber. He replaced the board, which his exit had displaced, and realized that he'd also displaced a set of thin stone tiles, which had covered the board and had served as camouflage. The base of the chamber minus the alcove was an almost perfect square. The chamber reminded him of one within a pyramid that he'd visited in Giza. At the far end there was a flight of stone stairs rising toward a rectangular, horizontal opening. The stairway was illuminated by soft moonlight. He cautiously ascended into the cool Turkish night.

Sam was in an ancient, ruined temple on a high point relative to its surroundings. The temple itself was roofless, and the tallest of the broken pillars that still stood was below his eye line. There were other ruins round about. The area had evidently been excavated a long time ago and not frequented by tourists. There were no signs explaining what each building was or guiding paths. He could see the moon reflected in the windscreens of two cars parked in the distance; the distorted lunar images shifted warily as he moved his head. The area was remote. Even from his present vantage point, he couldn't see a single artificial light or sign of an unlit dwelling.

The two vehicles were parked in parallel. One was an old, battered, khaki-coloured Isuzu Trooper (a large, boxy Japanese four-wheel drive for those not acquainted with the vehicle), and the other was a maroon Ford saloon. Sam tried both. Each started and sounded healthy, but the Ford had only a quarter of a tank of fuel. He crippled the Ford and took the Vulture's Trooper. Sam was accustomed to operating vehicles with the steering wheel on the right-hand side. The Trooper's left-hand-side steering wheel was a convenient reminder that he would need to drive on the right-hand side of the road. He followed the only track that left the site. The track led to a rough, unlit single-lane road. He didn't drive as carefully as he should. He was frantic to put as much distance between him and the dungeon. As he drove, he thought that he should have replaced the stone tiles to camouflage the wooden board. This could have bought him more time, even if just a few minutes. The day shift would know that something was wrong immediately. He cast the thought from his mind and concentrated on finding a main road. He had no inkling of where he was but knew that he was no longer in Istanbul. He stuck firmly to the principle of sequentially following roads of greater size and with more recently laid tarmac. He finally met a lit highway and soon saw a sign to a place called Afyon. Moments later he was no longer a solitary driver.

When Sam was five miles from the city of Afyon, the day dawned. As a reflex, he turned his right wrist, but no watch was there. He'd been too preoccupied in the dungeon to look for the watch specifically and hadn't noticed it in his general rummaging. He estimated that it was between five and six o'clock. From his reading of a newly noticed compass built into the dashboard, he knew that he was travelling southward. Dawn's diffuse radiance was the first natural light that he'd seen in four days, and it wasn't entirely welcome. The light brought a new fear. He was gravely concerned that his torturers may live in Afyon and that the day shift may spot him as they headed in the opposite direction, toward the dungeon. He didn't know when the morning changeover was, and this made him more anxious. He had no idea who his torturers were; the lack of identifiers suggested independence, but if not police, military or another government group, he wondered if the outfit in question was connected in some way to these official groups. He suspected that he'd been recognized by the customs officer. He also suspected the woman at passport control or maybe both were involved he considered. Sam had to assume that the mysterious group had police in its service. When he'd taken the Isuzu Trooper, he knew that it would have only a few hours of use. He also knew that Afyon was probably the first place where his captors would expect him to go.

Sam looked at himself in the rearview mirror. His entire face was swollen—worse on the left. He looked like a boxer who'd reluctantly lost the fight and whom even the most blood-thirsty of punters had cringed to see rise from the canvass again and again. Superimposed on the swelling were spots of dried blood (some of which clung to his stubble), black bruises and cuts. He gritted his teeth, and he pressed each bruise, all of which were tender. The large cut above and lateral to his left eye would become a yawning scar; it was too late for stitches. He placed his right hand over his right eye in order to test the left eye's sight. He could see normally despite the fact that the left eyelid and the skin of the ridge above the left socket were so swollen that they'd merged into one mass, the lower part of which occupied most of the socket. He dug deeply into the left front pocket of his jeans and grasped the wood fragment. As he drove, he wound down the window to his left. He thrust his left arm out and crumbled the fragment in his hand, letting the bits fall to the tarmac.

Sam had realized that he was inland; however, he didn't know that Afyon was 175 miles southeast of Istanbul. The daylight had revealed the rocky highland terrain of his surroundings. He could see a mountain in the far distance to the east. On mounting the summit of a foothill, he saw the city of Afyon. By British standards it was more the size of a town than a city. In distinctiveness it did not have its equal in the world. He saw a citadel, which had been built on a massive, isolated outcrop of black stone in the middle of the city. It looked as if a mountain had erupted beneath the citadel elevating it to the haughty position. He was determined not to enter Afyon, yet he was driving on a main road, which was the only one he'd seen so far, that was headed directly to the city. He needed a plan. He stopped at a fuel station. He'd been careful to park the Trooper so that it wouldn't be visible from the station's shop. He bought a map. Having read it, he figured that the closest House contact was in Alaşehir, which is 100 miles west of Afyon. He made a call from a phone booth outside of the shop.

"Hello," a man's voice said with a Turkish accent.

"Hello, it's . . ." Sam was interrupted.

"No names. Tell me, which king's pride was punished with leprosy?"

"Uzziah,"[1] Sam answered immediately.

---

[1] 2 Chronicles 26:1-23.

"What's the trouble?" the Turkish man replied, without acknowledging Sam's correct answer.

"Don't you know? I never met my contact in Istanbul."

"I know nothing about this contact. I don't even know why you're in Turkey. Tell me your situation, and I'll try to help you."

"From your question you know who I am?"

"That's right."

"I was captured in Istanbul, then transported to some kind of dungeon. They broke me up badly and were just getting started. I escaped and am heading south toward Afyon. It's maybe two or three miles away. It seems to be the only major settlement near me, but it's too close to where I was imprisoned. I had to take a car from my captors—which is rapidly outliving its usefulness. For all I know, they may be searching for me right now."

"We'll need to confuse them. Just before you reach the city, there's another main road, which bisects the one that you're currently on. Instead of heading south to Afyon or west directly to me, go east for thirty miles and dump the car outside of a town called Çay. Walk into the town and take the first method of public transport southwest to Dinar. Don't take a taxi. I'll meet you there, then drive us west to Alaşehir."

"Where exactly will we meet?"

"Phone me again when it's safe, and we'll decide then."

"Fine," Sam agreed, and the Turkish man hung up.

It was a good plan. My associate Sol Kadmiel had hand-picked the Turkish contacts, who were all brave and clever people. Sam followed the contact's advice precisely. Before dumping the vehicle, Sam searched the glove compartment and boot for any further information on his torturers—a fruitless investigation. Sam met the contact in the town of Dinar later that morning.

Chapter 7   **The Philadelphians**

The contact looked tense as he turned his head to greet Sam. "I'm Mustafa. We'll leave right away." Mustafa remained sat in the front seat of his car as Sam got into the back. Through the rearview mirror, Mustafa inspected Sam's swollen, bruised and cut face. Sam noticed that he was being stared at. Mustafa tried his best to avert his eyes but didn't quite manage.

"That suits me just fine—the quicker we get out of this place the better," Sam replied.

Mustafa started the engine and pulled out of the parking spot, which was three blocks from the Dinar coach station. "When we pass a quieter area and you think that nobody can see, lie down on the back seat. You can put that blanket over you. Don't you have any other possessions?"

"All I have is what you see. While I waited for the coach in Çay, I went and cleaned up. I hope that I don't smell too bad."

Mustafa made no comment.

When they drove through an empty, narrow street, Sam lay down on the back seat. Sam thought that Mustafa was a very unlikely-looking contact for the House. Sam's notion that a contact should look a certain way demonstrated some youthful inexperience. What was more important was the condition of Mustafa's mind.

Mustafa was middle-aged. He was very thin to the extent that he looked fragile. He wore large plastic-frame spectacles, which sat on his small nose. He had a thick moustache and a deep T-shaped cleft in his chin. There was a steadiness to his driving that engendered confidence. This together with the sympathetic expression that he'd exhibited when he'd seen such a battered face increased Sam's trust. Sam began to relax, and the adrenaline in his blood melted away. He was soon overwhelmed with tiredness and fell asleep.

Two hours later Sam awoke as the car's engine halted. They were in a well-lit underground parking lot beneath a block of flats in Alaşehir. There were only a few cars and no other people; it was a regular Tuesday afternoon.

"The plan was that if you needed refuge, then you'd stay with a family who lives in this block of flats. I was the backup. It's very sad. My friend Ismet died only two days ago. His wife, Adalet, is very upset. One of his sons is at home at the moment from university. He's the man of the house now. He's about your age. I'd have you stay with me and my family, but Adalet is a nurse, and you need some attention—at least for the first few days. The phone that you called had been given to Ismet. His wife handed it on to me only yesterday. She agreed to still have you stay with them. She's being very strong. I'll take you up to their flat and introduce you."

Adalet answered the door and beckoned the two men to enter. She managed a smile, which was followed by a look of pity for Sam's appearance. Sam entered and took off his grubby shoes. She led the guests to the lounge and introduced Sam to her son Irgal.

Sam estimated that Adalet was around fifty years old. She had dark hair, which was already greying in places, and a kind, round face. Sam thought that Irgal had a very different appearance from her and so probably more resembled his late father. Irgal was thin-faced. He was older than Sam by two years. Irgal greeted Sam professionally. Adalet and Irgal both looked crushed by their recent tragedy.

After a brief conversation, Mustafa left Sam with Adalet and Irgal. Mustafa had mentioned that he would return in a few days. Adalet cooked Sam some food, which he quickly ate, tended to his wounds and then guided him to the spare room.

Sam slept for eighteen solid hours and awoke the following day in the late morning. There was a mirror in his room. Bright sunlight streamed through the eighth floor window, and he examined his distorted face unemotionally. Near his left eye, Adalet had brought together the edges of the large cut with four adhesive strips. He ran his right index finger over them both to admire her work and to unwisely test their resilience. His nose was tender but, to his surprise, hadn't been broken. The grazes and scrapes to his torso Adalet had washed with antiseptic. The toes of his right foot were still raw. On waking, the slightest pressure from any direction had made them squirm, but once up and walking, this eased somewhat. Adalet had given him a pair of sandals to wear, so that his toes could remain dry and unabraded. Now he needed to heal.

Sam was conscious of the fact that he couldn't leave the flat looking the way he did. The stares that he'd received on the coach trip to Dinar had told him that. He also thought that the police would be hunting him for a murder. Sam was positive that the Vulture was dead. Sam didn't think that the obese guard would have died but wasn't sure of that. The first few days went by slowly. Sam's helpers appeared to know who he was and a little about his former exploits yet seemed to be entirely unaware as to what his mission was in Turkey. He decided that he wouldn't tell them a thing, and this didn't seem to be a problem, as they weren't inquisitive. Or was it that they'd been told not to ask? Even so, he needed information on what was going on outside the confines of the flat, and he thought that he would try to gain this whilst revealing as little as possible about his own situation.

Sam got to know Irgal very well. Irgal was revising for his university engineering exams at home, and in his breaks he would talk with Sam. Irgal spoke English well but insisted that Sam learn some basic Turkish during his stay in Alaşehir. Sam was in complete agreement with this plan. He was not naturally gifted at languages and tried his best. Adalet had a full-time job at the Alaşehir General Hospital. Because of a severe staff-shortage, she'd taken only four days off, after which she'd returned to work, yet her inward mourning continued. She was out of the flat for the best part of the days.

Sam learnt a great deal about the town Alaşehir and the two families. Alaşehir is located in the same place where the city of Philadelphia was founded. This was the same Philadelphia mentioned in the book of Revelation. The early church in this city was praised by Jesus the Messiah, because they obeyed His command to persevere and didn't deny Him.[1] I should mention at this opportune moment in my narrative that the word "church" used today commonly signifies a building in which people congregate to worship. In the Bible church mostly has a different meaning, which is simply a group of people who are unified in the worship of Jesus the Messiah, or to put it another way, the church is a body of Christians with Jesus at the head.[2]

The Christians within the families of Mustafa and Adalet represented the church of Alaşehir at the time of Sam's refuge. These Turkish Christians knew of no other true Christians who lived in the town. There was no specific building where the Christians within the two families congregated that anyone could call a church. Instead, the church, the people, met secretly in one of the two homes. Mustafa, his wife, Ismet and Adalet had all become Christians as teenagers, each having been brought up to believe that he or she belonged to another religion. It's important to understand that nobody is born a true Christian nor can a person be forced. To follow Christ is a decision that an individual makes at some point in his or her life. For example, Ismet and Adalet had brought up their two children to know the truth about Jesus, yet these same parents had accepted their sons' rights to decide which way they would take their own futures. Irgal, the younger son, had become a Christian at the age of sixteen, whereas his brother had declared himself an atheist and now lived in Istanbul with his own wife and family.

---

[1] Revelation 3:7-11.

[2] Ephesians 5:23, Colossians 1:24. See also the entire New Testament, although the following are exceptions, which indicate the additional definition of church as a physical place where believers congregate (i.e., similar to today's common use of the word): 1 Corinthians 11:18, 14:19, 14:28, 14:34-35, Colossians 4:16.

Today the word church also means an institution that calls itself Christian.

In the religious climate of that time the church of Alaşehir lived in fear. Irgal told Sam about the recent murder of a mostly Turkish Christian group in a town on the west coast. One of the men amongst the dead was a foreign missionary. The church of Alaşehir always had difficulty maintaining a balance between evangelism and keeping their faith to themselves. On the one hand, they felt a burden of responsibility to share the good news with their fellow Turks, and on the other hand, the church also wished to live in peace and stay alive. The pivot of the balance moved to favour one or the other according to the mood of the society, which depended on which political party was in power and the prevailing public religious opinion. Some years they, the church, were more outgoing. At other times, no matter how reserved they were, they suffered persecution.

This is a convenient place for me to fully explain what this "good news" is, as so far I have mentioned it only in passing and not by this name, besides above. It's not surprising that God gave the Earth a similar appearance to Heaven, because our planet could have been our never-ending utopia. We had a chance to live for a sinless eternity.[1] As I've explained, the consequence of the first sin committed by humankind was death. Adam and Eve's immediate deaths were replaced with the sacrifice of animals, but humans were prevented from living eternally and therefore eventually died. However, the human condition is that death is not the end. Although our earthly bodies die, our spirits are eternal.[2] It is God's judgement as to whether an individual's spirit goes to Heaven or Hell after death. Ideally, God would prefer it if all humans made the right choice in life, so that He

---

[1] See Dispensations (1).

[2] Earthly human bodies that die will one day be resurrected, made eternal and reunited with their respective spirits to either endure everlasting punishment or experience eternal bliss with God. See Soul and Spirit for a detailed explanation on this; particular note should be paid to the times of the resurrections and to the difference between soul and spirit.

was able to grant everyone a place in Heaven. Once sin was in the world, the original way that a person's sins could be atoned for was by asking God for forgiveness and sacrificing an animal or animals.[1] This went on for thousands of years, and those who died and then went eventually to Heaven[2] were people who'd put

---

[1] Leviticus 4:1-35, 5:1-13 (regarding the poor, offerings of crops were acceptable at certain times), Job 1:1-5. See Dispensations (2, 4).

[2] KJV means King James Version. Before Jesus' ascension into Heaven, the spirits of righteous people, those who were faithful to God, went to a place called Paradise (also known as Abraham's bosom), which was the good section of Hades (Hades is also known as Sheol). Hades is located beneath us inside the Earth (see footnote in Chapter 4 pg 104 regarding the Abyss). The other part of Hades is Hell, which is a place of fiery torment. Jesus' Spirit visited the righteous in Paradise for three days when He died. When He ascended to Heaven, which was on the 40th day after His resurrection, He took the people in Paradise with Him to Heaven. Thus, Hades is now only a place of fiery torment, in other words, it is now only Hell. Therefore, currently, at death believers' spirits go directly to Heaven and non-believers' spirits go directly to Hell.

Paradise: Genesis 37:35 (note that the righteous went to Sheol, Jacob being one of them—Sheol incorrectly translated as "grave" in the KJV in this instance), Luke 16:19-31, 23:42-43.

Hell: Deuteronomy 32:22 (note that the unrighteous go to Sheol but are punished with fire—Sheol precisely translated as "Hell"* in the KJV in this instance), Job 24:19 (Sheol incorrectly translated as "grave" in the KJV in this instance), Luke 16:19-31. *Capitalized (also see below).

Jesus' visit to Paradise: Psalms 16:8-10 (Sheol incorrectly translated as "Hell"* in the KJV in this instance), Matthew 12:40 (denotes the 3-day period of time), Luke 23:42-43, Acts 2:22-27 (Hades incorrectly translated as "Hell"* in the KJV in this instance), Ephesians 4:8.

The Ascension: Acts 1:1-10, Ephesians 4:8-10.

Confirmation that Paradise is now in Heaven: 2 Corinthians 12:2-4.
FOOTNOTE CONTINUED ON THE NEXT PAGE

The fiery torment section of Sheol in the Old Testament is also known in specific instances as the pit (a translation of the Hebrew word "shachat"): Job 33:14-18, Psalms 55:12-23, Isaiah 38:16-18. See Soul and Spirit.

This is a convenient time to state that there is no such place as purgatory. According to Roman Catholicism, purgatory is a place of the dead (but neither Heaven nor Hell) in which individuals are imprisoned and from which they can receive salvation and go to Heaven. The passage of the Bible that is often cited as the basis for this doctrine is 1 Peter 3:18-20: "For Christ also hath once suffered for sins, the just for the unjust, that he might bring us to God, being put to death in the flesh, but quickened by the Spirit: By which also he went and preached unto the spirits in prison; Which sometime were disobedient, when once the longsuffering of God waited in the days of Noah, while the ark was a preparing, wherein few, that is, eight souls were saved by water." However, this passage does not reveal purgatory but rather the patience and mercy of God (the entire Trinity: Father, Messiah and Spirit) in trying to save humans while they are still alive, for our life on Earth is the only chance we have to receive salvation from God. This is in keeping with the rest of the Bible, which demonstrates that once dead and in Hell, there is no chance to see Heaven. Below is an interpretation of the above passage in the context of the entire Bible, which is the method of interpretation that should be applied to all passages of Scripture. The passage doesn't mean that during the three days that Jesus was dead His Spirit went to Hell (the place of fiery torment)—or to a type of purgatory—in order to preach to those disobedient people who had lived in the pre-Flood era while the Ark was being built. Some also assume that the preaching resulted in salvation; however, this is not stated. Throughout history many people have heard correct biblical preaching but weren't interested in letting it change their lives, and as a result they didn't receive salvation. This also happens today. The Bible reveals that during the three days Jesus' Spirit went in fact to Paradise (Luke 23:42-43 and above supporting references). Genesis 6:3-17 demonstrates that many people who

FOOTNOTE CONTINUED ON THE NEXT PAGE

their faith in God. They strove to do what would be pleasing to Him. These people still did wrong things, sometimes tragically, but they had a relationship with God and looked to Him as their leader and source of forgiveness. Understandably, God later became tired of animal sacrifice, especially as it had become a ritual without genuine regret for wrong actions.[1] So instead, God gave us the ultimate gift. He sent His own Son to Earth. This individual, the Messiah, had been in existence with God since the beginning and is one of the three characters who make up the one

CONTINUED FOOTNOTE PRESENT

---

died by the Flood had had 120 years to repent of their sinful ways, and it was the Spirit of God who had struggled with them during that time. He was the same Spirit whom Jesus has inside of Him and simultaneously works throughout the Earth (Matthew 3:11-17, Luke 4:1, Acts 2:4-47 [in verses 27 and 31 Hades is incorrectly translated as "Hell"* in the KJV], 1 Corinthians 6:17-19, 1 Thessalonians 4:7-8, 1 Peter 1:11-12, 1 John 5:7). The Spirit struggled with them in the same way that He does today, that is, by pricking the consciences of people to turn away from sin to God (Hebrews 9:14-15). Noah played an active role as well in that he too preached righteousness at that time (2 Peter 2:5). The reason why the 1 Peter passage states "spirits in prison; Which sometime were disobedient" rather than "people on Earth; Which were disobedient" is because at the time of the writing of this passage that was their condition: spirits in the prison of Hell, having previously each been a spirit united with his or her body on Earth before the Flood. This is the same manner as some people might converse about a prisoner's earlier life while he was free; because he is now in jail, they refer to him as "the prisoner", even if they are relating an event that he was involved in before his imprisonment. The passage continues with "when once the longsuffering of God waited in the days of Noah, while the ark was a preparing", demonstrating when Jesus' Spirit struggled with the disobedient people, which was before the Flood (over 2,500 years before Jesus' death).

[1] 1 Samuel 15:22, Hosea 6:6, 8:13. See Dispensations (1-4).

God.[1] On Earth the Son felt the things we've felt and understood what it was to be human, yet unlike us He did nothing wrong for His entire life. This fact was vital, because only a perfect human could be offered as the final sacrifice for the entire world. Every human is responsible for that one great sacrifice, whether living at that time or at a time future to that event.[2] The good news is that if you turn away from sin, believe in the Son, Jesus the Messiah, who died for the things you've done wrong, and ask for forgiveness from Him, then God will allow you to spend your eternity in Heaven.[3]

---

[1] Micah 5:2, John 1:1-18, 1 John 5:7.

[2] God on the Earth in the form of a man (God the Son): Isaiah 7:14, 9:6, Micah 5:2, Matthew 1:23, John 1:1-18, John 10:24-30, 1 Timothy 3:16, 1 John 5:1-7.

While on Earth, Jesus experienced the following: birth, loss of a friend, despair, joy, physical pain, compassion, friendship, righteous anger, betrayal, life-threatening danger, death and more. Matthew 1:25-2:1, 9:35-38, 11:19-20, 15:30-38, 21:11-19, 26:1-27:50, Mark 14:1-15:37, Luke 2:4-7, 22:1-23:46, John 2:1-11, 10:31-39, 11:1-44, 15:9-17, 17:1-19:30.

Jesus was directly tempted by Satan: Matthew 4:1-11, Mark 1:13, Luke 4:1-13.

Jesus was the perfect sacrifice: 2 Corinthians 5:18-21, Hebrews 7:22-28, 9:24-28, 1 Peter 2:21-25, 1 John 3:4-5.

[3] John 3:13-21, 14:1-11, Acts 3:1-26, 4:10-12, 5:29-31, 13:33-38, 26:15-18, Ephesians 1:2-14, Colossians 1:12-14, 1 Peter 1:3-4. Currently Heaven, the home of God, then the New Heaven-New Earth when the old are replaced. From the New Heaven will descend the New Jerusalem, which will rest on the New Earth. The New Jerusalem is referred to as "the holy city" and "the tabernacle of God", His sanctuary. In other words, the most important part of Heaven will come to Earth. From this vast city, the New Jerusalem, God the Father and God the Son will reign for all eternity. People will literally reside in the New Heaven-New Earth. Matthew 6:20, 8:11, 22:30, Revelation 4:1-5:5, 7:7-17, 21:1-22:18. See Timeline and Dispensations (8).

For Sam the belief that he'd killed a man was weighing more and more heavily on his conscience with each passing day. Even though Sam had done what was necessary to escape his imprisonment and the Vulture had been planning murder, Sam felt terrible about what he'd had to do. Probing for an indication as to his impending doom at the hands of the authorities, every day Sam would watch the television and ask Irgal if there was anything interesting in the newspaper. Turkey was not Sam's country, and he imagined that his captors could make up just about any story for their own end. The reality was that he didn't yet understand who his captors were.

On the seventh day since Sam's arrival in Alaşehir, Mustafa returned. Sam had still not left the flat, even though his injuries were healing well and much of his strength had been regained.

Mustafa and Sam talked together alone in the lounge.

"How are you, Sam?"

"Much better, thanks to you all."

"I've contacted Sol Hodaviah. He wants to talk to you."

"I'd like to talk to him as well!"

"I can tell that you're angry. You've clearly suffered since being here. Whatever you've endured, it's not his fault."

"Maybe not."

"Are you thinking of giving up?"

"I'm not sure."

"Sam, I don't know why you're here in Turkey. We were informed that you were coming and that we might receive a call if you needed help. If the House has gone to all this trouble, then it must be important."

"It is."

"The world is a dark place." Mustafa paused as if to change tack but then continued, "To push back the darkness is the most worthwhile of endeavours. Surely the completion of your task is worth the risk?"

"So few words, yet a compelling argument. Did Sol Hodaviah put you up to that?" Sam smiled. Mustafa watched Sam earnestly. "I'm just kidding, Mustafa. I know that what you're saying comes from the heart. I know, because I agree with you. It's just the thought of being captured by them again. If I hadn't escaped, it would have been over for me. I'm positive of that. And perhaps next time they won't bother with the capture-to-interrogate routine. To imagine what it would be like to face death is one thing, but its imminence . . . When its nearness is palpable—that's another thing altogether."

Mustafa appeared to not quite understand the last sentence; however, he could tell that Sam was fearful of the future. "Our Lord has suffered much for us. He bore our sins, so that we can have eternal life. We must try to do what we can. I haven't been given the tools that the Lord has given you. And I know that whatever it is that you're here to do, I couldn't accomplish it. Yet I struggle on in my own way, using what He has given me. You've been given a great opportunity to make a difference. Don't waste it."

"You're a good man, Mustafa."

"I'm not so sure about that; I try though. Maybe I should try harder with my own community, even when times are at their worst—and take a few more risks myself." Mustafa cleared his throat. "We arranged a time tomorrow: 2300 hours. The public phone box is a few miles away from here. Irgal should drive you. Sol Hodaviah will be in Paris especially to make the call, so don't miss it. He won't ring again for at least a week."

"Why Paris?"

"Your enemy probably suspects that you're in the general area of Afyon or not far from it. If they have people in their employ at the telephone exchange, they may be looking out for calls to and from the UK."

"I understand."

After Mustafa had left, Adalet joined Sam in the lounge. "How are you, Sam?"

"I'm fine, thank you. I have a lot of things to think about. And how are you? I can't thank you enough for all that you've done for me."

"It's been a pleasure. In a way it's been good having you here to give us something else to think about. Irgal needed someone like you around the place. His brother came to the funeral but went back to Istanbul straight after."

"How are you coping?"

"I'm managing, Sam." The brave face slipped. "It's just so hard. I don't think that I'll ever get used to Ismet not being here. I keep on expecting to see him: when I wake up; when I walk into the lounge. In the evening I imagine him walking through the front door. He was so young. Ismet was only fifty-three years old when he died."

"Can I ask . . . how did he die?"

"He died of a pulmonary embolism. He was at work, then became short of breath. There was no pain. I met him at the hospital. He was so ill. I thought that it might have been a silent heart attack. The tests showed that it was a clot in his lungs. They thinned his blood, but he still died—just two hours after being admitted. We buried him the next day."

"You know that that's not the end, don't you? From what I've heard he was a strong Christian, who loved the Lord."

"I know where he is. He's with God in Heaven. I just miss him so much."

"People were never meant to feel what you're feeling. I'm so sorry that you have to go through this pain." Adalet was in tears and reaching for a box of tissues.

"I'm sorry, Sam."

"Sorry for what? Everything you're feeling is completely understandable. I'll pray that God gives you the strength to get through this."

They were joined by Irgal. They all talked and prayed till late in the evening.

By the eighth night there had still been no news related to Sam's escape. He wondered if the enemy had covered up any deaths, as they weren't a legitimate organization. His other idea, which he felt was less likely, was that the police weren't advertising the investigation, because they'd referred it to the secret service, who were now handling it as a case of death connected with espionage.

Sam didn't see anyone notice him and Irgal leave the basement car park. Sam was wearing a baseball cap that Irgal had given him. The town was still relatively busy, though it was after ten o'clock. The phone itself was exposed, lacking its own booth, but was positioned in an area sheltered by trees. At eleven o'clock the phone rang into the night. Sam quickly terminated its song.

"Hello," Sam said.

"How are you?" Sol Hodaviah answered.

"How am I? Where have you sent me? I've been captured and tortured."

"Our friend mentioned. I did say that you'd have some opposition . . . I didn't think that they'd be onto you so quickly though."

"Who are they?"

"I'm not entirely sure. However, let's just say that you're on course for both objectives."

"Both objectives! I like how you assume that I'm going to carry on. Do you know how many times I've thought about healing, then heading home?"

"How would you get back?"

"With one of the other identities and overland through eastern Europe."

"You're on the path to an incredible discovery—perhaps discoveries. I truly don't know anybody else who has even the faintest chance of completing this mission."

"Don't you get it? I failed to get past day one."

"You must trust me. Things happen for a reason. And you've escaped. Tell me, how did they capture you?"

"Tranquilizer dart—I think. I never found an entry point though."

"Who interrogated you?"

"Two men."

"Did one of them appear to be in charge or more important than the other?"

"Yes."

"What did he look like?"

"I don't know. They covered my face when he interrogated me."

"That's a shame."

"I'll tell you what I can about him based on his voice and what he said to me. He was Turkish . . . clearly educated for a while in the UK. He's visited Cambridge University or maybe even studied there . . ." Sam continued to give Sol Hodaviah as full an account as possible.

"And the other?"

"I got a really good look at him. He was rancid. Not as clever as the other man, but he knew the plot all right."

"Tell me more about him."

"The first thing I should say is that he's now in another place."

"Another place . . . Ah, I understand. Describe him anyway."

Sam gave Sol Hodaviah a detailed description of the Vulture.

"Oh, and before you ask, I didn't talk, but I should say that they found a piece of the amulet in my shirt."

"Did they ask you about it?"

"No, they didn't."

"Well, do you want to continue?"

There was a pause.

"Yes."

"I'm glad you've made that decision. We'll speak another time. Goodbye."

"Goodbye." Sam hung up the phone.

Two days later Mustafa made an unexpected visit. He entered the flat, wringing his hands with a deeply concerned expression on his face. He was desperate to talk to Sam.

"Sam, it's my daughter; she's in the hospital."

Before Mustafa had spoken, Sam had thought that he himself was in trouble. He now felt rather selfish.

"What's wrong?"

"She has meningitis."

"Which one?" Sam was having difficulty coming to terms with the fact that his hosts, the church of modern Philadelphia, could be suffering so much in such a short space of time.

"I don't know, but she's confused and has a purple rash. Oh, the doctor said something about her condition being caused by bacteria."

"Is she ventilated?"

"No, not yet. The doctor said that if she becomes drowsy or has difficulty breathing, then they may have to."

Bacterial meningitis is an infection of the lining of the brain, which is often fatal. Sam knew that the rash meant that Mustafa's daughter had meningococcal meningitis, which is a particularly aggressive form. Sam also knew that the need for ventilation carries a poorer prognosis. Although clinical medicine, these facts were important basics that he'd picked up in preclinical pathology. Mustafa had only one child. He and his wife, Ceyda, had had difficulty conceiving, and their daughter arrived many years after their marriage; when she was born, they were both well in their forties. They looked upon their nine-year-old daughter, Nadiye, as a great blessing from God.

"How can I help?" Sam offered.

"I'd like you to come to the hospital with me and pray for her. You could also help me understand better what's going on . . . what treatment she's having . . . I feel so helpless."

Mustafa was distraught. Sam was glad that he could be of service and accepted Mustafa's request immediately. Sam forgot about his own concerns of being noticed outside the flat.

"Adalet would have finished work about fifteen minutes ago and is probably on her way home. She's usually here by now. Do you want to wait for her?"

"She already knows. We contacted her from the hospital while she was still on duty, although I think she's been through enough recently."

Sam quickly told Irgal the situation. Sam asked if he could have some olive oil to take with him.

When Mustafa and Sam arrived in Nadiye's room in the Alaşehir General Hospital, they were met by Ceyda and Adalet. Nadiye was awake, although still confused. She could recognize her parents and Adalet but was disorientated. Sam took the liberty of looking at the charts. Nadiye had a high temperature despite the use of a pain reliever for her headache. She was on large doses of an intravenous antibiotic, which had been started from the moment that a diagnosis of bacterial meningitis had been considered. Sam saw a drip attached to her left arm. The drip had been carefully bandaged to stop it from being accidentally removed. He noticed the characteristic rash of a meningococcal infection on her skin above the bandage and also a few spots on the whites of her eyes. Ceyda told him that the doctors were treating Nadiye for exactly that condition.

Ceyda stayed with Nadiye. The others went to the relatives' room, where they prayed. This was Sam's prayer:

"My God and my master, there is none greater than You.
We long for Your kingdom to come soon but ultimately want only Your will.
You know our present trouble; there's nothing that You can't see.
You came to Earth in the form of a man.
You've felt our suffering and pain.
You Yourself know how it feels to lose a loved one.
Nadiye is the only child of Mustafa and Ceyda.
Watching our children grow up—this is one of the simple pleasures of humanity.
What parents want to outlive their own children?
Please don't let her go. Heal her. Prolong her life. Let this be part of Your plan.
These people have been good to me.
They risk their very lives to help me.
They've recently suffered so much. Let their suffering end.
My Lord, forgive us for all the things that we've done wrong.
Help us to also forgive those who've done us wrong.

Have Your hand on us. Guide and protect us.
Amen."

After praying, Mustafa, Adalet and Sam went back into
Nadiye's room. At Sam's suggestion, Mustafa put some of the oil
onto Nadiye's forehead and prayed over her. This was done in
accordance with the passage in James in the situation of there
being sick members in the church seeking healing—Mustafa
being the only elder present.[1] Sam stayed for a while, then was
driven home by Adalet. Mustafa and Ceyda stayed in the hospital
overnight.

The following morning Mustafa phoned the flat. Adalet was
delighted to tell Sam that Nadiye was improving. It was the first
time that Sam had seen Adalet smile fully. Nadiye stayed in the
hospital, receiving treatment, for three more days and was then
discharged. (The plan was for her to continue receiving
intravenous antibiotics for another week but as an outpatient.)
Sam was both pleased and relieved; he knew the pit of despair
that Mustafa and Ceyda would have plunged into if the outcome
had been different.

Sam had almost healed. His two fractured ribs still ached
occasionally, but he felt the need to continue his mission.
Mustafa implored Sam to stay for a further two days, which he
agreed to do.

The next day Mustafa arrived at the block of flats. Instead of
going directly to the eighth floor, he insisted that Sam come to
the basement. Sam did so and was met by Mustafa leaning
against an old, blue Toyota hatchback.

"This is for you," Mustafa said. He smiled. "I bought it with
cash at a car auction yesterday in İzmir. It's good for a few
thousand miles. On a police computer it will appear as if it has a
Turkish owner from Ankara. That person doesn't exist. This
means that it can't be traced back to anyone. On the other hand,

---

[1] James 5:14-15.

this also means that you shouldn't attract too much attention to yourself."

Sam could see that the vehicle was ideal for the task—a perfectly ordinary car. Mustafa gave Sam the keys. They went to the flat, where Mustafa also gave Sam an envelope of money.

"Thank you," Sam said.

"Don't thank me. When this is all over, the House will cover me for that and the car. No money will be changing hands for now, especially electronically."

"Thank you anyway, to all of you—for everything. I'm heavily in your debt."

"Don't worry about that, Sam. We look forward to eventually finding out what this is all about."

"You'll know if I make it. Trust me."

That evening Mustafa, Ceyda, Nadiye, Adalet, Irgal and Sam ate together in the flat. After the meal, Adalet and Irgal presented Sam with a new set of clothes, a map, a watch and a compass. Sam left the following afternoon at four o'clock. As he drove from Alaşehir, he reflected on the church of modern Philadelphia. They loved their fellow Turks who didn't yet know Jesus and were eager to tell them about Him. Sam was uplifted by the fact that the families were managing to endure despite the inherent danger from the community in which they lived. His thoughts then turned to Britain and the freedom that most Christians have to tell others about Christ—a once hard-fought-for liberty, which was now often unexploited.

An expensively suited man arrived on the intensive care ward of a hospital in Afyon. He was the same man who'd interrogated the blindfolded Sam. He approached the nurses' station. "I'm here to see Mr Basalan." That wasn't the patient's real name. "I was told an hour ago that he'd regained consciousness."

"You must be his uncle; I spoke with you earlier," the nurse answered.

"That's me," he lied. The nurse had in fact called someone else, who had informed the man who now stood in front of her.

"Mr Basalan said that he needed to speak with you urgently. He should really rest!"

The Guardian of Turkey walked into one of the ward's rooms and closed the door. The room was large, clean and designed for a single patient. The Guardian sat next to the bed on a chair, the seat and back of which were green plastic and the legs metal tubes. The ventilator was by the bedside, although the patient no longer had a need for this instrument.

"I left you in charge, and he escaped," the Guardian said.

The Vulture tried to talk. Two weeks of a breathing tube positioned inside him from his lips to beyond his larynx meant that his vocal cords weren't yet functioning properly.

The Guardian was impatient. "Where do you think he is now? I've had men searching the entire area. They've found nothing."

The Vulture started to speak; his voice was strained and quiet: "I don't know . . ."

The Guardian was annoyed that he needed to put his head forward so that his ear was closer to the Vulture's mouth.

The Vulture continued, "But I know where he's headed . . . Ararat."

"How do you know?"

"I saw a piece of wood . . . It was sewn into his shirt. I blew up the remains of the Ark twenty years ago. Your predecessor ordered it. The wood is the same."

"Are you sure?"

"I'm sure."

"So all he'll find are splinters."

"I blew up what we found," the Vulture's voice was improving. "It was a section that was thirty-five metres long. We couldn't find any other parts. The Ark was meant to have been four times that size."

The Guardian rubbed his left temple. "He must know something. We need to stop him. I'll send a crew to the mountain. They'll find and destroy what's left."

Chapter 8   **The Scouts of Cotton Castle**

The Toyota's fuel tank was full. The boot was loaded with provisions. Sam had placed the pistol in the glove compartment. He'd removed the round from the chamber. This round and seven others were in the clip. Even though Alaşehir is 100 miles west of Afyon, he still felt uneasy about being that close. His plan was to first gain as much distance as he could from Afyon. He would head south to the Mediterranean Sea and then travel eastward along the coast. Prior to reaching the Syrian border, he aimed to drive inland and take a more direct route to Ararat. He anticipated that on his journey to the coast the largest town that he'd pass through would be Denizli, which is 60 miles by road from Alaşehir. He had more than enough fuel to reach the coast without stopping—a distance of 200 miles.

Sam had left Alaşehir uneventfully. He now travelled along an evenly laid tarmac road. There were two lanes in each direction. Instead of a central physical barrier, there was just a thin white line, which designated the central partition. The two southbound lanes were separated by a broken, faded white line, as were the two northbound lanes. The signs marked the speed limit in kilometres and miles per hour. He stuck to the 55 mph limit. He was desperate not to attract any unwanted attention. He was accustomed to the 70 mph limit of British motorways and found the driving slow. This combined with his urge to flee Alaşehir made him impatient. Mustafa and Sam had talked generally about driving in Turkey. Sam had found out that the coastal highways were, for the most part, proper motorways with an 80 mph speed limit, and he was looking forward to using them to his advantage.

After 25 miles, Sam started to settle into the slow pace. The road became uneven. He dodged a few potholes. It was a clear, hot day, and he could see two cars slightly ahead of him and five more in the far distance. Approximately every half a minute, a car or truck would pass in the opposite direction. He silently praised Mustafa for finding a car with air-conditioning. It was being put to good use. Sam had a bottle of water on the passenger seat, which he occasionally drank from. For no particular reason he remembered the numerous agricultural fields that he'd passed while driving the Vulture's Trooper from near Afyon to Çay. That was a stark contrast to the semi-arid area through which he now travelled. The ground appeared to be hard and uneven. To his right he saw some scattered brown bushes and a single deeply rooted cypress tree with green leaves. He passed some indeterminate stone ruins that were by the roadside. He thought that some of them could be toppled by a mere push yet had probably been standing for well over a thousand years. In the far distance were rocky hills. Their dark-grey slopes seemed to beg for climbers.

When Sam was 30 miles from Denizli, he saw the wreckage of an accident a mile ahead of his position. Black smoke was rising from the locality, and there were two queues of cars, each queue facing the smash. He looked about him for alternative routes, but there were no immediate exits. The terrain on either side of the road was rough, and the Toyota wasn't four-wheel drive. The last thing that he needed was to break down.

As Sam came closer, he saw two police cars parked near the wreckage. A policeman had kept the blue light of one of the police cars flashing. Sam hadn't noticed this visual alarm earlier because of the brilliant sunlight. He immediately thought about performing a U-turn. He'd passed the exit to the village of Buldan two miles back. He wondered if Buldan possessed a road that led south. He continued to advance, only more slowly. He looked at the map. A car passed him on his left in the inner (fast) lane. The map illustrated two small roads that left Buldan (that is, roads additional to the one that connected the village to the road that Sam was presently on): one to the east and the other to the west. They led to Alandız and Yenicekent respectively, each of which was an even smaller village when compared with Buldan. Neither of these tiny settlements had a clear exit southward.

Sam placed the baseball cap on his head and drove on. The car that had passed him slowed, and he did likewise. As he approached the smash, he could see the situation more clearly.

Sam saw three cars involved in the crash. They together with the vehicles giving assistance had occluded both of the lanes in his direction of travel and the nearest of the opposite lanes. Regarding the two southbound lanes, before one would reach the wreckage, traffic cones had been placed so that over a stretch of 20 metres the traffic in the outer lane merged into the inner lane. He estimated that the accident had happened within the last hour. He recognized that within the wreckage the car furthest from him was a Mercedes Benz. He could tell that it was one of the larger models. This was the vehicle that was most badly damaged and in flames. Although the Toyota's windows were closed, he could already smell the acrid synthetic tang of burning rubber and plastic.

The traffic slowed to a crawl. Sam had been filtered into the inner southbound lane. There was no fire truck yet, but an ambulance sped away in the direction of Denizli. The car behind the Mercedes was a Skoda saloon. Its bonnet was crumpled and the wheels beneath the bonnet were distorted, yet the passenger compartment was intact. The Skoda had hit the Mercedes from behind and was similarly hit, although to a lesser extent, by the damaged car nearest to Sam. This last car, which had only a crumpled bonnet, was a small Renault hatchback.

The traffic in Sam's lane stopped. He thought that the Mercedes had probably been hit by an oncoming vehicle that had already been towed, because all three cars were facing the same direction, southward, albeit each somewhat askew. Off to the side of the wreckage, in the outer southbound lane, there was a breakdown tow-truck with the words "Yol Yardımı" (Roadside Assistance) written boldly on its flanks. Sam could only see the left flank, on which there were no police markings, and he assumed that the vehicle was used by a civilian-run business. The breakdown man was occupied with attaching the front of the central car to the hook of his vehicle.

There were three policemen in total. One of them was taking statements from four people on the roadside near to the tow-truck. Sam presumed that the four had been the occupants of the two cars with the least damage. The other two policemen were acting as temporary traffic lights to control the flow of vehicles around the wreckage. The nearest policeman to Sam had halted his Toyota and the four cars queuing ahead of him, and the furthest policeman was letting the opposing traffic pass smoothly in the only free lane, which was the northbound outer lane. Neither policeman was paying particular attention to the occupants of any of the vehicles. Both looked to be engrossed in the job at hand. Sam relaxed and waited his queue's turn.

After a few minutes, the policeman closest to Sam started to signal his group through. They had to pull out into the single free lane and drive by the smash. They could have passed more quickly, but the drivers of the two leading cars drove slowly to gaze at the wreckage. Sam passed the Renault, which he suspected could still be driven. He then drove by the Skoda, whose front end was now being slowly hoisted upward by the tow-truck's whirring winch. The breakdown man held a remote control in his hand. Sam was close enough to see the man's thumb firmly pressed on the green button. Sam heard metal crunch as the Skoda's own weight pulled at its damage. He then passed the Mercedes. The black tyre marks on the tarmac indicated that this car had been spun around a full three hundred and sixty degrees to face its original direction of travel and had simultaneously been displaced partly into the oncoming inner lane. The stench of burning synthetic material became intense. The heavy smoke that partially surrounded the vehicle obscured the windows, and hence Sam couldn't tell whether the occupants had been freed or not. The smoke was rising in the still air, first thick and black and then thinning to a dirty grey before fading 50 feet above the wreckage. He turned his head to see the heavily distorted front end of the Mercedes and realized that no cars had been towed yet. There was a fourth car, which had been so compressed by the collision that it hadn't been visible before. It was embedded in a pocket, created by the impact, in the central front of the Mercedes. Crushed beyond recognition and ablaze, this now metal pellet was inescapable death incarnate. The last policeman had his back to the wreckage. He was holding up his right hand to stop two northbound cars and was beckoning Sam's group forward with his left. Once past the debris, the southbound cars were able to return to their own two lanes. Sam drove into the outer (slow) lane and resumed his journey at 55 mph.

The breakdown man lifted his thumb from the green button, then pressed the red. The Skoda jolted as the hoisting action came to an abrupt halt. He walked to the tow-truck's cabin and calmly sent a message on his radio.

The road led to a bridge that spanned the Büyük Menderes Nehri, a river that descended from a plateau located west of the receding Afyon. On reaching the town of Sarayköy, Sam was met by an oasis sustained by the river. He saw a large valley, which was broad and flat, with an abundance of olive groves and vineyards. The shade beneath the olive trees looked to be the perfect place to unwind and rest. Maybe another time, he thought—as he drove past Sarayköy's southern limit. He was 15 miles from Denizli.

The southbound traffic was light, even though some cars had filtered in from Sarayköy. Sam observed that the traffic headed toward Alaşehir was busier. He remained in the outer (slow) lane, travelling at a controlled 55 mph. It was at this time that something unusual caught his attention. In his rearview mirror he'd noticed a brown saloon car half a mile behind. It had been in the inner (fast) lane, then had moved into the outer lane, yet once there it had still travelled at a velocity well exceeding the speed limit. This on its own wouldn't have troubled him. However, having caught up with Sam from half a mile away in a mere minute, once the brown car had reached a distance of 100 metres behind him, it had slowed to his own pace.

Sam continued to watch the car in his rearview mirror. It was a large Volvo with a single occupant. The car came closer, then hung back at a distance of 50 metres. Sam could see that the Volvo's driver was wearing large black sunglasses. This was all that Sam could discern owing to the reflection from the Volvo's windscreen, which obscured the face of its driver. The Volvo remained behind the Toyota for a period of two minutes before Sam decided to determine whether the brown car was truly following him. Sam slowed the Toyota to a sluggish 40 mph, a speed that would have caused irritation to even the most carefree of trailing drivers. The Volvo slowed, revealing its driver's intent.

Sam thought: how on Earth could they have found me so quickly? He continued at the slower pace for a minute before returning to 55 mph. He contemplated stopping to see if the Volvo would continue on. Sam disregarded that plan. Its driver had such scant regard for concealing his purpose, that he would probably stop as well: a situation that would not benefit Sam.

Sam was thinking about his next move as he passed the exit for the village of Aşağısamlı. From this small road came another car, a dark-blue Audi, which he was both surprised and dismayed to see join the Volvo in pursuit. The Audi settled in the inner lane in parallel with the Volvo. The Audi let a single speeding car pass by getting into file behind the Volvo in the outer lane, then returned to the parallel formation. The speeding car passed Sam and was soon a waning object in the distance.

Together the Volvo and the Audi advanced forward. Sam marked two men in the Audi. The passenger, sitting to the right of the driver, appeared to be leaning forward, reaching for something. Sam accelerated to 65 mph, yet he was still mindful of his desire not to be stopped by the police. Almost immediately the Audi took a more aggressive stance by surging forward—still in the inner lane. The Volvo lingered. In a matter of seconds the Audi was in Sam's blind spot, aiming to get alongside. Sam turned his head to the left to see the situation more clearly. The Audi's passenger held a pistol in his right hand in clear view. This vehicle's two men both had the appearance of being in their late twenties. Its driver, who was the further of the two from Sam, was looking at the Toyota, preparing to flank it. The passenger's window of the Audi descended in one smooth movement. The armed man, his teeth bared in readiness, was staring directly at Sam. This foe had thick, black hair and grey, murderous eyes.

Sam swerved to close off the Audi's lane, then accelerated to 75 mph. After that, he positioned the Toyota so that one half was in one southbound lane and the other half was in the other southbound lane. He drew his pistol from the glove compartment with his right hand. He briefly let go of the steering wheel to cock the pistol. With a round now chambered, he placed the pistol on the passenger seat to his right. He flicked the baseball cap off his head. The cap tumbled behind his seat. The Volvo rapidly advanced to further pressure Sam's position. Again, the Audi attempted to flank the Toyota. Sam swung over to shut the inner lane, but this time the Audi was propelled by its superior engine into the nearest oncoming lane to return ahead of Sam.

The three cars were now lined up, each selfishly obstructing both southbound lanes. Sam felt the mounting threat from being sandwiched between his foes. He knew that in an instant they would exploit their advantage. He slammed on his brakes. The Volvo was still accelerating at the time, and the driver had difficulty avoiding the front of his car colliding with the rear of Sam's car. While slowing, the Volvo veered with poor control to the right of the Toyota and eventually passed the object of its pursuit. The Audi slowed to maintain its tight position in front of Sam, and it was this cue that he'd waited for. He immediately returned his foot to the gas pedal and pressed deeply. The Toyota leapt forward, passed the Volvo and then swerved to the left to overtake the Audi via part of the inner lane as well as part of the nearest oncoming lane, narrowly missing a motorcycle. Passing to the left of the Audi had also removed the imminent danger of Sam being shot by the pistoleer sitting on the right side. Sam was in front again. He then put caution to the wind and accelerated the Toyota to its maximum speed.

This just can't be happening, Sam thought—as he shook his head and continued to press his full weight onto the gas pedal. The Audi soon caught up. Sam was travelling at an unsafe 115 mph. As the Toyota hit a pothole, he heard and felt the impact of the front right wheel rim, because the ability of the tyre's cushion had been exceeded. The shock altered the direction of both front wheels, and he struggled to regain control. The car shook as its course straightened.

The rear window of the Toyota was pierced by a bullet from the Audi. Another penetrated, so that the entire rear window was shattered and fell away from its frame. Sam had barely heard the gunshots. Neither bullet had struck him, but he noticed that the second was embedded in the upholstery of the left front pillar, not far from his head. He started to swing the Toyota between the two southbound lanes in an attempt to evade any further projectiles. He heard another gunshot—now louder on account of the Toyota being minus a rear window. He didn't perceive that his vehicle was hit by the matching bullet. Sam's brain was ticking over wildly. The frustration of having just left Alaşehir with a slow, small family car that was now recognizable was combined with a sense of life-threatening danger, a mental image of Mount Ararat and the need to remain uninvolved with the authorities. From this medley came the overriding aim to survive. He could tell that this meant only one thing. He had to devastate his pursuers. Every brain cell was activated to that end.

Five seconds later Sam commenced his plan. He electronically wound down the window to his left and firmly applied the brakes, although with less force than previously. The Audi had been directly behind him at the time and somehow managed to dodge the rear of the Toyota by way of the inner lane without braking—probably because the driver had anticipated Sam's latter action. As the Audi attempted to pass, Sam turned the slowing Toyota left. The Audi was forced to move out further and into the nearest oncoming lane, on which there was traffic. The nearest oncoming car was far enough away not to cause an immediate collision but was an imminent danger to the Audi. Both the Audi's driver and passenger were concerned enough to momentarily lose their concentration. Sam fired his pistol at their vehicle. The first bullet penetrated their right rear tyre. The second entered the cabin. It missed both men. The third struck a section of metal below the fuel cap without the desired result. The Toyota was still decelerating. The Audi passed the Toyota, then braked heavily and was pulled back into the southbound inner lane directly in front of the Toyota. Sam lifted his foot slightly off the brake and narrowly avoided the Audi by turning right into the outer lane. Sam floored the gas pedal again and passed the Audi, as did the Volvo.

Sam's car was deliberately hit from behind by the Volvo. Although the impact was a crunching jolt, the pistol was still firmly in Sam's hand. The hit had also been placed off-centre in order to spin the Toyota. Sam successfully countered the ensuing rotation, but the Toyota almost stalled. He changed to a lower gear and slammed the gas pedal. He half-turned his upper body, then discharged three bullets through the windowless rear of the Toyota at the driver of the Volvo. Even before the first shot, the Volvo's driver had started to duck down behind the dashboard, giving up control of the steering wheel and the pedals. The first and second shots had penetrated the windscreen above the steering wheel. The third had struck the bonnet as Sam had tried to track the movement of the man's head. The Volvo faltered. It appeared driverless as it came to a halt in Sam's rearview mirror. The Volvo was diagonally positioned in the outer lane, facing the wilderness. The driver got out and fired a single controlled shot, which struck the damaged rear of the Toyota without consequence.

The Audi slowly pulled up behind the Volvo. The Audi's right rear tyre was completely deflated, and the vehicle was limping. Both cars were clearly visible in Sam's rearview mirror. Stay put, stay put, Sam thought—willing them to give up. The Audi's pistoleer switched cars to become the passenger of the Volvo, which resumed the pursuit. The Audi attempted to follow.

Then there was another vehicle: this time a four-wheel drive Nissan, which had arrived from behind the first two cars. At first Sam had thought that it was simply part of the normal traffic, but this vehicle had come alongside the hobbling Audi and the drivers had communicated with one another. The Nissan had then sped ahead with the same resolve as the Volvo. Sam discerned two dark figures in the front seats of the Nissan. He was now being tailed by five men in three vehicles and knew that there were only two rounds left in his pistol.

Sam saw a coach full of people pass by in the oncoming outer lane. A few seconds later he saw a road sign that was a yellow shield. He knew that this meant that a site of historical (and possibly archaeological) interest was ahead. On the shield was written the word "Pamukkale". He presumed that the coach had come from that location. He saw the exit for Pamukkale and decisively took it. He was now on a road that was still tarmac but had only two lanes for bidirectional traffic. His direction of travel was eastward. The three vehicles continued their chase, although he could no longer see the Audi. The road wound its way toward his destination. Because of the twists and turns, Sam slowed his speed to stay on the road. The surrounding vegetation increased, and soon trees filled the adjacent land. He passed another coach, which was again travelling in the opposite direction. He looked at his watch. It was five o'clock, and he hoped that there would still be people at the site—whatever that could be. He drove the Toyota hard through the bends, and after three miles there were instances when he couldn't see his pursuers owing to the twists in the road. On a long straight stretch they would reappear as two relentless shapes in his rearview mirror. He estimated that he'd put the nearest pursuing car a minute behind him. A few minutes later the road crossed a bridge, beneath which was a railway track, and then took him northward. He pressed his advantage further. The trees started to thin out before the road came to an end at the ancient Phrygian city of Hierapolis.

In the car park there were five coaches and many cars. A young couple were returning to their vehicle as Sam's car skidded to a halt. Surprised by his haste, they looked at him, then toward the damaged rear of the Toyota and then back at him. He cast them a stern glance, and they looked away. He stuffed the pistol into the right front pocket of his beige chinos. He completed the weapon's concealment by ensuring that his T-shirt covered the handle. He grabbed the now half-full bottle of water, exited the Toyota and headed north for the crowds.

Sam was soon in the midst of the ancient ruined city. He saw blocks of stone strewn about the area and an array of partially intact architectural structures. He walked on hard stony ground, which in areas somehow managed to support clumps of dry, yellow grass. He briskly passed the relic of a less old Byzantine[1] church, which had been erected hundreds of years after the city had been founded. He passed a few small groups of people while listening closely for what languages were being spoken. As he continued north toward some of the bigger tourist groups, he noticed a large semicircular theatre to the east. He'd seen many of this type of theatre on his travels and paid it no mind. If he wasn't so preoccupied, he might have noticed how incredibly well preserved the theatre was. It owed this to recurrent repair and subsequent use through the ages and the fact that the structure itself was entirely supported by a hillside.

Sam tried to focus on the people rather than his surroundings yet became awestruck by an enormous, white terraced hill to the

---

[1] Eastern Roman.

west. He tried not to look at it and refocused on the crowds. He watched faces and their expressions, and when close enough, he read eyes. He thought: why is the hill so white? It was broad and enveloped almost the entire western face of the ancient city. There were no people on its slopes, but he felt as if the city was a stage and the white terraces were the seats of an auditorium. Together the city and the terraces made up a vast theatre dwindling the one within its confines.

The first act of Sam's play started as he heard voices speaking English with American accents within a group of approximately thirty people standing next to the temple of Apollo. As Sam approached them, their guide began to speak. Sam quickly glanced behind him. The car park was now 400 metres away. He saw the Volvo and the Nissan draw to a halt and their four occupants disembark.

The remains of the temple were no more than two feet above ground level; however, what was left was remarkably well preserved. The stones were precisely cut, and their edges barely eroded after thousands of years. The stones were blackened in places, yet the sheer whiteness of the untarnished areas hinted to the former splendour and expense of the temple's construction.

The guide was standing with her back to the southern side of the temple. In front of her the group had formed a haphazard semicircle, which was two and in places three persons deep. Sam entered the group and started reading eyes, watching for the various people's reaction to him. They were a collection of mostly late middle-aged persons, and, judging from the accents that he'd heard, he'd worked out that many different parts of the United States were being represented. As the guide addressed her audience, some of them talked with one another in low volumes. Their whispers were lost in the open air and didn't disturb her.

". . . *alongside the street. This is the temple of Apollo. His mother was Leto, and his father was Zeus—all three of them*

Greek deities.[1] Apollo was said to be a god of prophecy and would occasionally share his knowledge of the future with mortal men by means of oracles.[2] Although this suggests that he was a distant god, he sometimes had direct contact with humans, even fighting in the field of battle to assist men with their conflicts. Indeed, he was the slayer of mighty Achilles during the Trojan War.[3] One of the other major deities to be worshipped in Hierapolis was Cybele . . ."

Sam selected his target and walked with purpose in the direction of a man in his early sixties with brown hair. Every step had to be trustworthy in order for Sam to achieve his goal. The brown-haired man was positioned away from the guide's immediate focus. He was already in conversation with a lady who, Sam thought, was probably the brown-haired man's wife. Sam, by his own admission, wasn't fantastic at placing American accents and thought that the couple were from somewhere in the Northeast. In Sam's best British accent he calmly introduced himself: "Excuse me, I'm Paul Roberts. I wonder if you could help me?"

The brown-haired man disengaged from his conversation. "That depends on what the problem is, young man."

---

[1] That is what is reported regarding Apollo's lineage: Hesiod's Theogony *lines 918-920,* Homer's Iliad Book 1 *lines 8-52,* Apollodorus' The Library Book 1 *chapter 4:1.*

[2] Homeric Hymns *3 To Apollo lines 127-546,* Livy's History of Rome Book 29 *chapters 10:6-11:6.*

[3] During the protracted siege of Troy (approximately 1200 BC) Apollo reportedly aided the Trojans, and he and Paris together killed the greatest Greek warrior, Achilles: Apollodorus' The Library Epitome *chapter 5:3-5,* Greek Epic Fragments Aethiopis *argument 3.*

It has also been reported that Apollo was the sole slayer of Achilles: The Fall of Troy by Quintus Smyrnaeus Book 3 *lines 1-185,* Hyginus' Fabulae *107.*

Sam now spoke in a manner that reflected his predicament: "My car's broken down, and I could really do with a lift to the nearest town or city."

"I'm Simon Scott, and this is my wife Katherine." Simon and Sam shook hands. "Does it drive at all?"

"The worship of Cybele, the great mother goddess, seems to have arisen from Phrygia, an area now in Turkey, and probably well before 600 BC. In fact, this ancient city—in which we're now standing—was once part of Phrygia. From Phrygia her cult spread first to Greece and then to Rome. She was also known as the 'Idaean Mother'. In addition, she was known as the 'Mother of the gods', because she was considered to not just be a goddess herself but also the mother of other deities."[1]

"What's Idaean mean?" a member of the crowd asked the guide.

"Ida is a mountain near Troy. The forests at the crest of the mountain were sacred to Cybele."[2] The guide then continued with her presentation: "Cybele was another of Zeus' many children. She gave birth to a son, the god Attis, who grew up to be a tremendously handsome man. Cybele fell in love with him, but he planned to marry a different woman, the daughter of a Phrygian king. Cybele interrupted the marriage ceremony and Attis, driven mad by the sight of his mother, castrated himself.

---

[1] Dio Cassius' Roman History Book 46 *chapter 33:2-4*, Livy's History of Rome Book 29 *chapters 10:4-11:8,* Pausanias' Description of Greece Book 1 *chapter 3:5* (the Mother of the gods image in her sanctuary in Cerameicus, a district of Athens, in Greece, was made by the sculptor Pheidias, who was prominent some time between 500 BC and 400 BC), Book 2 *chapter 4:6-7,* Book 3 *chapter 22:3-5,* Book 4 *chapter 31:6,* Book 5 *chapter 14:9,* Book 8 *chapter 30:4.*

[2] Ovid's Metamorphoses Book 14 *lines 530-541.*

This is why her priests castrated themselves: to mimic her own son. "[1]

Sam used his peripheral vision to observe his four pursuers while he talked with Simon. They'd obviously spotted Sam within the group of Americans and were walking in his direction.

"I just about managed to get it here. It won't survive another mile, and it'll be slow and dangerous on the main road." Sam's concern was growing.

"Why don't you call for roadside assistance?"

---

[1] Pausanias' Description of Greece Book 7 *chapter 17:9-13* reports that Agdistis (Cybele) was an offspring of Zeus and that Attis was an offspring of Agdistis. This passage also mentions an alternative origin for Attis: that he was the son of a Phrygian (and was born as a eunuch). Regarding the origin of Cybele, Pausanias' account conflicts with the Library of History by Diodorus Siculus Book 3 *chapters 58:1-59:8,* which reports that Cybele was the daughter of Meïon, king of both Phrygia and Lydia, and only later was she raised to the rank of goddess. The same book by Diodorus reports that the Corybantes were sons of the Mother of the gods (Cybele) (*chapter 55:7-9*) and that Attis was a local Phrygian youth (*chapter 58:4*).

Attis was worshipped as a god: Pausanias' Description of Greece Book 7 *chapter 20:3.*

Agdistis, Cybele, Idaean Mother and the Mother of the gods are different names for the same individual: Library of History by Diodorus Siculus Book 3 *chapters 58:1-59:8,* Strabo's Geography Book 12 *chapter 5:3,* Livy's History of Rome Book 29 *chapters 10:4-11:8.*

The Romans identified Cybele with Rhea, one of the Titan goddesses, thus making Cybele the mother of Zeus (Jupiter, Jove) and five other Olympian deities: Ovid's Fasti Book 4 *lines 179-214.* These six Olympians were reportedly the goddesses Hestia, Demeter and Hera, and the gods Hades, Poseidon and Zeus: Hesiod's Theogony *lines 453-458.*

"That'll cost me a fortune. I'm still a student. I know what's wrong with it. It just needs a new part for the radiator. I can fit it easily. All I need are the part and a couple of tools."

"What are you studying?"

"Medicine."

"That's great," Katherine remarked.

"Toward the end of Hannibal's Carthaginian invasion of Italy, from 218–203 BC, the Romans followed a prediction in the books of a prophetess called Sibylla[1]—not to be confused with the goddess Cybele herself[2]—that a foreign enemy could be defeated if the 'Idaean Mother' was brought to Rome. So the idol of Cybele was transported from the Phrygian city of Pessinus to Rome, arriving in 204 BC.[3]

"Hannibal was recalled to Carthage, in North Africa, the following year, and then in 202 BC he was defeated at the Battle

---

[1] The original prophetess called Sibylla (also known as Sibyl), who lived and prophesied before the Trojan War (the conflict was around 1200 BC), was an oracle of Apollo. Other female oracles of Apollo, who lived later in history, were also given the name Sibyl. One of these oracles—she lived in Cumae, in Italy—sold Sibylline books to Tarquinius Superbus, the last Roman king before the republic (reigned until 509 BC). Until destroyed by a fire in 83 BC, these books were consulted when Rome faced a crisis such as a war. Pausanias' Description of Greece Book 10 *chapter 12:1-11,* Dio Cassius' Roman History Book 2 *epitome by Zonaras 7.11, supplement by Tzetzes in Lycophron's Alexandra 1279,* Dionysius of Halicarnassus' Roman Antiquities Book 4 *chapter 62:1-6.*

[2] The C in Cybele is properly pronounced as a K, although often articulated as an S. Either way, the rhythms of the names Sibylla and Cybele are similar.

[3] Livy's History of Rome Book 29 *chapters 10:1-11:8* (the idol was a sacred stone), *14:5-14,* Dio Cassius' Roman History Fragments of Book 17 *chapter 57:61,* Strabo's Geography Book 12 *chapter 5:3.*

of Zama, near Carthage, by the Roman general Scipio.[1]
Incredible, isn't it? As for Cybele, her worship grew and grew.
She became one of the most important deities in the Roman
Republic and then the Empire."[2]

"I just need a lift to the nearest town. I'll stay there overnight,
buy the part and tools in the morning and come back here."

"I'll ask the tour organizer. She's with us now. I'm sure it
won't be a problem. Tonight we're staying in Denizli. It's only
ten miles down the road. Will that do?" Simon looked in the
direction of the organizer, who was listening to the guide speak.

"Sounds good to me," Sam replied.

---

[1] The recall: Livy's History of Rome Book 30 *chapters 7:1-9:12*,
Polybius' The Histories Book 14 *chapters 8:1-10:1*.
The defeat: Livy's History of Rome Book 30 *chapters 32:1-36:11*,
Polybius' The Histories Book 15 *chapters 10:1-16:6*.
[2] Once brought to Rome, the idol of Cybele was temporarily placed
in the temple of Victory on the Palatine. 11 years after Hannibal's
defeat Cybele had her own temple dedicated to her (191 BC), which
had been recently built on the Palatine. Livy's History of Rome
Book 29 *chapters 14:5-14, 37:1-3*, Book 36 *chapter 36:1-5*, Dio
Cassius' Roman History Book 46 *chapter 33:2-4*, Ovid's Fasti
Book 4 *lines 179-372* (describes Cybele's yearly festival, the
customs around her worship and Rome's devotion to her).
Note that the end of the Roman Republic and the beginning of the
Roman Empire is arguably marked by the acceptance of the
elevating title "Augustus" by Caesar (Octavian) in 27 BC. Augustus
Caesar is considered to have been the first emperor. There is no
uniformly accepted year in which he became emperor, but the
conferment of the title Augustus in 27 BC coincided with his
preeminence in military leadership and recent securing of his
widespread civil authority. Livy's History of Rome Summaries
Book 133, Book 134, Dio Cassius' Roman History Book 53
chapters 3:1-22:5.

At a distance of 30 metres Sam's pursuers stopped and talked amongst themselves. Sam had rendered them virtually powerless while he stayed within the crowd; however, he imagined that they were devising a plan to separate him from the mass.

"The Romans were so devoted to Cybele that I can scarcely imagine how Christianity could have eclipsed such a goddess. Anyhow, I like to think that her spirit lives on in the Virgin Mary. At the Council of Ephesus in 431 AD the holy Virgin was officially given the title 'Mother of God'. And not long after this, the pope ordered a wonderful basilica to be built in her honour."

"What's a basilica?" a man within the group inquired.

"Basilicas are the most important of Catholic churches," the guide replied. "Senior clerics often perform the services. They're constructed to give a saint the highest praise and are usually the largest and most ornately decorated."

"Which basilica was it?" a female voice asked.

*"The Basilica of Saint Mary Major[1] in Rome. It **is** one of the most beautiful churches I've ever been to. I had the privilege of attending mass there a few years ago."*

Sam couldn't help but register what the guide had just related. He'd long since established that Mary should not have been given the title "Mother of God".[2] It's uniform within the Catholic

---

[1] The Basilica di Santa Maria Maggiore. Built by Pope Sixtus III (pope [bishop of Rome] from 432–440 AD), the basilica was initially called the Basilica of the blessed Virgin Mary, then the Basilica of Mary at the Manger, and ultimately the Basilica of St Mary Major: Bartolomeo Platina's Lives of the Popes Volume 1, *46:4.*

[2] The Third Ecumenical Council, the Council of Ephesus held in 431 AD, was convened to oppose the doctrine of Nestorius, the bishop of Constantinople. Part of Nestorius' doctrine resisted the title "Mother of God" being given to Mary. The opposing faction

FOOTNOTE CONTINUED ON THE NEXT PAGE

was headed by Cyril, the bishop of Alexandria, who was firmly supported by Celestine, the pope (bishop of Rome), who was represented by legates. Cyril threatened to excommunicate (denounce and expel) Nestorius from the Catholic Church. Cyril wrote that the majority of bishops wished that Mary (whom he referred to as the "holy Virgin") be called the Mother of God but recognized that the nature of the Word of God (the Messiah God, who was one with God from the beginning [John 1:1-18]) and His divinity did not originate from Mary. Cyril stated that to call her Mother of God had also been the wish of the "holy Fathers", meaning the early church leaders who were prominent after the time of those who wrote the New Testament; in other words, this was not the opinion of those who were inspired by God to write the New Testament. Cyril wrote that the wish for her to have the title Mother of God was because through her the Word was born of flesh. Put plainly, he contradicted himself, because by correctly recognizing the favourable use of Mary for the Messiah God to take on flesh he did not provide reasonable grounds for her to then warrant the title Mother of God.

Nestorius is not exonerated by the above, as he had erroneous beliefs contrary to the Bible that were correctly highlighted by the council. It is beyond the scope of Creation's Mutiny to comment further on this matter except to say that both opposing parties had erroneous doctrine, but the side supporting Cyril won.

Instead of making up new doctrines and new laws, they should have just stuck with the Bible, which is the Word of the Living God, as their guide and exerted their energies to make the Bible accessible to anyone who wanted to know what was inside by: transcribing more Bibles and giving them away as gifts or if this was prohibited by cost, allowing people to purchase Bibles or giving access to Bibles at the churches; and teaching people to read the Bible and if not possible, then reading it to them in a language that they could understand. Therefore, all the people could have direct access to the truth if they desired.

FOOTNOTE CONTINUED ON THE NEXT PAGE

churches (Roman Catholicism and Eastern Orthodoxy) to call her so rather than restricting her title to the "mother of Jesus", which is how the Bible refers to her.[1] Some biblical passages also explain that she is the mother of Jesus the Messiah.[2] Although Jesus was simultaneously one hundred percent God and one hundred percent man on Earth,[3] Mary was only necessary for the latter characteristic. Mary was selected so that God could be born into this world as mortal flesh, in order that He could die and be a true sacrifice for our sins.[4] She was not necessary for God to visit mankind on Earth, which He'd previously done on many occasions.[5] In effect, the title "Mother of God" elevated Mary beyond her station, from having been a mortal woman to being a virtual goddess, for once her new title became a dogma (an officially recognized essential belief for members of the church), it was then later decided that she must be sinless to give birth to

CONTINUED FOOTNOTE PRESENT

References for original documents—The Third Ecumenical Council: *The Epistle of Cyril to Nestorius; The Epistle of Cyril to Nestorius with the XII Anathematisms; The XII Anathematisms of St. Cyril against Nestorius; Extracts from the Acts, Session III; Canons II to V.* English translations of these original epistles (letters), acts, and canons (decreed regulations and doctrines) of the Council of Ephesus can be found in The Seven Ecumenical Councils of the Undivided Church.

[1] Mary is not given the specific title "Mother of God" anywhere in the Bible. She is referred to as the "mother of Jesus" in John 2:1-3 and Acts 1:14.

[2] Matthew 1:18-25, Luke 2:1-11.

[3] Thereby being Immanuel, meaning God with us: Isaiah 7:14, 8:8, Matthew 1:23.

[4] Romans 1:3-6, 2 Corinthians 4:5-14, Hebrews 2:6-18, 1 Peter 3:18.

[5] See Chapter 1 pg 21 and footnote regarding the appearances of "the Angel of the LORD".

God, a perpetual virgin, capable of receiving prayers[1] and deathless.[2]

Sam and Simon walked over to the organizer, who was happy to be disturbed. She'd heard the guide's speech over twenty times. There were two vacant seats on their coach, and she was glad to help Sam.

---

[1] In 553 AD Mary is officially referred to as "ever Virgin Mary" and "Holy Mother of God" and is described as "Mary, Mother of God and always a Virgin" in the documents of the Fifth Ecumenical Council [α]. In 680 AD Mary is officially referred to as "our Lady, the holy, immaculate, ever-Virgin and glorious Mary" and "immaculate Virgin Mary" in the documents of the Sixth Ecumenical Council [β]. In 787 AD Mary is appealed to for intercession, is said to be "exalted above all the heavenly powers" and is officially referred to as "spotless Lady", "immaculate Mother of God" and "Ever-Virgin Mary", all evident in the documents of the Seventh Ecumenical Council [γ]. Immaculate and spotless both mean without sin.

References are from The Seven Ecumenical Councils of the Undivided Church. [α] The Fifth Ecumenical Council: *The Sentence of the Synod; The Capitula of the Council II, VI, XIV.* [β] The Sixth Ecumenical Council: *The letter of Agatho and of the Roman Synod of 125 Bishops which was to serve as an instruction to the legates sent to attend the sixth synod; The Prosphoneticus to the Emperor.* [γ] The Seventh Ecumenical Council: *Extracts from the Acts Sessions I, IV; The Decree of the Holy, Great, Ecumenical Synod, the second of Nice.*

Specifically in Roman Catholicism, in 1854 Pope Pius IX additionally declared the dogma of the Immaculate Conception, which is that Mary was free from the moment of her own conception of the sinfulness of mankind brought into the world at the time of the fall in the Garden of Eden.

See also Chapter 20 pg 399 and footnote regarding Mary worship.

[2] See Chapter 9 pgs 210-211 and footnotes regarding the same topic.

"So, Paul, have you ever been to Pamukkale before?" she asked.

"No, I haven't," Sam said.

"Then I'm sure you won't mind joining us for the rest of our tour. We're going to see the limestone terraces and then the necropolis before we head off."

"I'd be delighted."

"Now hear an interesting fact. That walled up area next to the temple of Apollo is preventing us from reaching an opening that descends into a cavern, known as the Plutonium. The cavern was called the Plutonium, because it was believed to be one of the entrances to 'the Underworld'. A thick, visible, deadly gas was once constantly seeping from somewhere inside the cavern. The gas hugged the floor but sometimes rose higher to spill over outside. To demonstrate their power as favoured servants of the great goddess, during rituals the priests of Cybele would descend into the cavern with livestock in front of crowds of people. The animals, some even as large as bulls, were immediately killed by the poisonous gas and needed to be carried or dragged out, yet the priests survived unharmed.[1] The ancients said that their castration gave them immunity.[2] Now some say that the priests held their breaths, whilst others say that they descended only when the height of the gas was below their own mouths. Anyway, it must have been a convincing spectacle. Next we'll walk over to the limestone terraces. They and the hot

---

[1] Dio Cassius' Roman History Epitome of Book 68 *chapter 27:1-3*, Strabo's Geography Book 13 *chapter 4:14.*

[2] Strabo suggested this as well as other possible explanations for the priests' protection from the poisonous gas, including their fanatical devotion to their deity and some special power that counteracted the gas' effect. He also observed the priests holding their breaths but gave no further comment on this (see Strabo reference in immediate previous footnote).

springs are the big attractions of Hierapolis and are probably why this location was picked as the place to lay the foundations of the city."

The group walked west approximately 500 metres to the limestone terraces. All the while Sam kept a close eye on his four pursuers, who were still together and hanging back—now at a distance of 20 metres. The guide again stood with her back to the object of interest with the intention of turning to point out various significant features as she described them. The group once more stood in a semicircle in front of her, but the members were more widely spaced. Simon had taken a central position in front of the guide. Sam stood to Simon's left.

"I think that it looks like a delicious white-chocolate fondue. Isn't it just beautiful? The limestone deposits were formed over thousands of years and have attracted visitors since antiquity. Within the hill are hot water springs that contain dissolved chalk. On reaching the surface, the chalk becomes solid. As the water trickles down from one ledge to another, it forms stalactites. The deposits have built up over time to eventually look like fluffy, white cotton wool. And that's how it got its name. Pamukkale literally means Cotton Castle. Oh, the castle part of the name is because the terraces resemble a castle. Pamukkale was then later used to refer to both the terraces and the ruins of Hierapolis."

Sam saw his pursuers approaching the crowd. The four split up. Two of them rapidly acquired positions on the flanks of the assembly and pretended to view the natural phenomenon. These two shiftily watched the central two, who slowly advanced toward Sam.

This is a bold move, Sam thought. The central two entered the group, one on either side of him and each at a distance of approximately five metres from him, thereby splitting his vision. Each of these two was separated from him by at least four persons. Sam tried desperately to see what was in his closest pursuers' hands and around their waists. He was concerned about being tranquilized again. Because of the crowd, he knew that the dart would have to be fired at close range. He spied nothing in the hands of the pursuer to his right but was having difficulty seeing the hands of the one to his left. This man's hands were obscured by bodies, backpacks and other hands. While looking left, Sam simultaneously moved his head backward and forward to obtain a better view. Even a fleeting glimpse may suffice, he thought. Simon turned to look at Sam. Simon had been distracted from the guide's presentation by Sam's erratic head movements. Sam turned, looked at Simon and smiled reassuringly. Simon re-engaged with the guide's presentation without investigating what was diverting Sam.

"I'm sure that many of you have seen old pictures of people walking on the hill and even bathing in the shallow pools."

From the angle and position that the group was observing the terraces, no one was able to see the pools. What they were able to see was a combination of gentle and moderately-steep slopes separated in places by natural steps, which are themselves the terraces. These steps were irregular both in height and width and each possessed white stalactite beards.

"This was the past. You'll have noticed that there's not a soul on the hill now. The terraces are extremely fragile. Like many other natural phenomena, the terraces had been spoilt by man. Countless people—mostly tourists—had walked on the terraces, which had become damaged and discoloured. To compound this further the water in the hot springs had been diverted in order to supply nearby hotels. This meant that at one time there were no new deposits forming at all."

The two nearest pursuers were closing in on Sam's position. Sam continued to look at their hands. In moments these pursuers were next to him, one on each side. Both were visibly unarmed. Simon was then aware of the two new presences, especially as one of them now stood between Simon and Sam. Simon turned again to Sam. Simon looked at Sam's unflinching face, then at the two irregulars. They were both tall, and Simon had to look upward. Both of the irregulars' faces were expressionless as they tried to appear nonchalant whilst listening to the guide. Sam's continued lack of apparent acknowledgement of the new company made Simon ask Sam if he was all right. "I'm fine," Sam replied.

Sam took a small barely noticeable step backward in order to better observe his nearest two foes with his peripheral vision. What were they planning? He thought that they were trying to put pressure on his position in order to scare him to leave the group. He held his ground. He was convinced that his enemies wouldn't try anything in broad daylight in front of everyone.

"Over twenty years ago a decision was made to preserve this unique wonder. All hotels and other businesses were removed from around the terraces."

Sam overheard two ladies speaking. "Who are they? They're not part of our group."

"Shhh . . . I think they're locals."

"But what are they doing in our party?"

Sam thought that his two pursuers inside the group would have heard the women. Whether the irregulars understood the women was another thing. Either way, these two men would ignore what had been said, which was exactly what they did.

At the outer lower corner of Sam's left visual field he noticed a glint of steel. He immediately turned his head to see more clearly. The foe to Sam's immediate left had drawn a stiletto knife. This pursuer held it against his own right thigh and began to side shuffle ever closer toward Sam. This irregular could have drawn the knife later, but it was a deliberate ploy for Sam to see the blade. Sam thought: would they stick me right here in the open? A precisely executed strike could kill me with a small entry site and minimal, if any, visible blood. It could even look like I'd simply fainted. Would they dare? Are they that desperate? Sam had mere seconds to make a decision: whether to stand his ground or move.

"After all, what would be the attraction of the place if the terraces were destroyed? So today we see them in their original splendour. And long may it cont . . ."

Sam couldn't enter the minds of his pursuers. The immediate threat to his survival took precedence. And with that he bolted up the white hill.

"Stop, you can't do that!"

Sam sprinted at his fastest pace. The hill was hard and dry, which gave his training shoes excellent grip. From below the hill had had the appearance of melted wax rather than cotton wool, and Sam was both surprised and thankful that its surface wasn't slippery for him. He avoided the green pools within the step-like terraces by running up the slopes in between these terraces. With their jagged yet curved edges, the terraces were like massive clam halves filled with sparkling water, resting on a white sandy beach. Sam's legs were at full stretch, and he made short work of the first 100 metres. From behind him he could hear the clatter of hard shoes on the stony hill. While running, he looked back and saw the two men who'd infiltrated the crowd following him. The closest was just 40 metres away and also wearing training shoes. Sam hadn't heard that man's footfalls. However, the other was clumsily making his way up the slopes in black shoes more suited to an office. He took short inefficient steps in order to prevent himself from slipping. The two who'd flanked the Americans' party were moving laterally. One headed north toward the necropolis, whilst the other headed south toward the car park. Sam had to assume that they knew the area and were somehow manoeuvring to intercept him on his present trajectory. Although the car park was at least 800 metres away, from the hill's superior position Sam was positive that he saw the Audi arrive. He briefly looked for Simon's face in the crowd but couldn't make him out.

Sam looked forward and upward. He could see that at the summit of the white hill was a dense grove of small trees. He wanted a situation in which by the time his immediate pursuers were no longer visible to the crowd, he would be out of the effective range of handguns. He put his head down, and with each stride he thrust his toes and the balls of his feet into the gradient, propelling himself toward his first goal, the grove. The screen that this would provide could dissolve another fear. Neither of the two men running up the slopes could possibly possess a rifle, but Sam was concerned about the others: specifically, the man who moments ago had been returning to the car park and the Audi driver. Sam had no idea what kinds of weapons they had in their cars and wanted to be completely out of their sights.

As Sam reached the grove, the hill levelling off, he again turned his head whilst still running. Sam saw only a single bobbing head, which belonged to his closest pursuer, who, Sam estimated, was 80 metres away. This chaser was the man who'd wielded the stiletto knife. Sam had estimated this pursuer's age to be twenty-seven or twenty-eight. He was slim, although that didn't necessarily mean that he was physically fit. Sam judged that by the way this chaser was already trailing, he would be half-spent by the time he reached the summit. Sam pressed his advantage further now that he was running on the flat but switched to a three-quarter pace. He looked to his left and then right as the trees thinned. Once past the grove, he could properly view the overall landscape. He planned to stay well away from any roads and to run over terrain that would be impossible for normal cars to traverse and hopefully four-wheel drives.

As Sam ran, he thought about what Simon would be thinking. Would Simon call the police? Sam hoped that Simon and his wife would be safe. Sam lamented the loss of the Toyota, which was laden with at least two weeks of provisions.

The man who possessed the stiletto knife reached the grove and within seconds he was through it. He could now see Sam almost 250 metres in the distance. This pursuer ran on, clutching his sides, for another 50 metres and then stopped, gasping for air. Sam was soon 400 metres away. The breathless man pulled a slim walkie-talkie from his back pocket and spoke in broken sentences into the microphone.

It wasn't until five minutes later that Sam was sure that the two men who'd chased him up the white hill were no longer following him on his selected route. He'd covered just over a mile in that time. By sticking to his plan, he now found himself in a remote and desolate location west of Pamukkale. Around him were hills of different heights. Some of their edges were sheer enough to resemble cliffs. The ground was rocky and dotted with boulders. There were no trees—only the occasional course bush. On his person were the compass, the pistol and the map. In his left hand he held the half-full bottle of water. He stopped. He drank some of the lukewarm water, then examined the map. Although charting the roads well, the map had only sparse details of the natural topography. The nearest town was Denizli; however, the enemy would also be aware of this. Nevertheless, his plan was still to head south to the coast but now to circumvent Denizli along the way. South of Denizli he would follow the main road from a distance and then catch a coach on its route to one of the towns or cities that lie on the shore of the Mediterranean Sea.

For a time Sam continued west. As expected, after a mile and a half, he reached the Aksu Çayi River. This river wasn't as broad as the Büyük Menderes Nehri, to which the Aksu Çayi was connected further to the northwest, yet still possessed a strong current. It took Sam ten minutes to cross from bank to bank. He'd swam inefficiently, one-armed, because he'd held the pistol and the folded map above the water for the entire width of the passage. After his swim, he rested amongst some tall bushes that lined the bank. He spent over an hour there, using the time to refer to the map, attempt to dry off and gather his strength for the next push.

Still sodden, from there Sam continued his flight, now southward. He knew that before covering a mile he would meet a small road, which he would have to traverse. On arrival, he spied the road and the surrounding area until he was satisfied that they were completely empty of human life. He crossed the road with great caution. As he ran on, he heard a gunshot. He immediately changed his step to an irregular zigzag and headed for cover. While running, he frantically looked around him. There was no one visible. Now alert to bullet strikes, he saw a puff of dirt flick up to his left, and a split second later the corresponding shot rang out. From the lag between the strike and the gunshot he knew that he was being shot at from a distance by an opponent with a high-velocity rifle. Sam thought that the shot had come from the west but didn't entirely trust his ability to localize the sound. He knew that it hadn't come from directly ahead, from the south. He dove behind a boulder, which was simultaneously struck by a bullet, and then the third shot sounded. He was hunched down with his back to the boulder and his legs tucked up into his chest. Quickly looking to his left (north) and right (south), he quickly established that there was no one in either of these fields of view. This was confirmed by the silence that followed. He drew the pistol and held it firmly in his right hand.

Sam realized that whoever was shooting at him must have driven to the current position, hidden the vehicle and then waited to ambush him. Sam slowly rotated his body through a hundred and eighty degrees. He used the power in his legs to rapidly and repetitively straighten his knees in order to repeatedly pop his head over the boulder. He did this several more times, during which there had been only a single unsuccessful shot. He worked out that there were three possible origins of the gunfire. All were hills: two were to the northwest and one to the west. By then the sun was low in the sky, and the west position was almost a silhouette. Before he could look more closely or devise a plan for the shooter to reveal his position, a man came running from over a mound on the western hill, which was 500 metres away. Sam raised his head for a longer period of time than before to more closely observe the running man. Sam felt a bullet whistle past his right ear. While ducking down, he then understood their plan. He'd observed that the running man wasn't carrying a rifle. This man was probably armed with a handgun. His objective would be to intercept Sam or flush him out from behind the boulder while the static rifleman continued to fire.

The risk of executing a controlled shot on the running man as he approached was too high, and anyway he was out of the effective range of Sam's pistol. Therefore, Sam left his position under a spattering of bullets from the rifleman. Sam thought that an additional 400 metres would put him out of the effective range of the rifleman's weapon. Sam swiftly achieved this whilst dodging the gunfire. The running man had pressed on. Sam's compulsory zigzagging had given this pursuer an advantage. He was 300 metres behind Sam.

After three-quarters of a mile, the pursuer was just 250 metres behind Sam. This foe's running strength surprised Sam. For this reason, Sam knew that this opponent couldn't be either of the men who'd ascended the white hill. He also didn't look to be either of the men who'd flanked the group of Americans. Perhaps he's the Audi driver, who'd possibly switched to the Nissan, or maybe he's somebody new, Sam thought.

Sam put on a spurt and in doing so he spent his energy reserve. The sun was setting. He crossed a railway track. His clothes had dried, but his feet were still damp. His own sweat and the river water had mixed and remained in his shoes. There was no cover in the locality. He cast a glance behind him. The pursuer was still there. His tread was strong and unfaltering. Sam knew that if he continued directly southward, he would after a short time meet the main road to Denizli. He'd planned to cross this road under cover of darkness, after which he would attempt to bypass Denizli west of this town.

Yet still without surrounding cover, Sam dove to the ground. In another movement, almost as swift, he swivelled to face the opposite direction with the pistol drawn. He presented himself as a flat target to his pursuer and waited for the runner to get into effective range. Instead, Sam's opponent also dove to the ground with his pistol drawn. They were 200 metres apart, both well out of effective range. Nevertheless, Sam's pursuer elevated the tip of his pistol and fired. The shot landed two metres short of Sam's head. Sam rolled to his right in order that his opponent would learn less from his shot. Sam's two rounds were precious and he consciously decided not to waste them on a difficult target. He got up and ran southward again. At least he knows that I'm still armed and ready to use my weapon, Sam thought.

The sun had disappeared from view, but it was twilight and furthermore the clouds reflected light from the fallen orange globe. Sam anticipated that he would imminently meet the road to Denizli. He delayed this by heading southeast. He would cross the road only when the night had truly defeated the day. His pursuer knew what the growing darkness meant and tried to sprint to Sam's position as if finishing a long-distance race. Sam heard his pursuer's footfalls become louder and louder. Sam's mind spurred his body to quicken his pace, but there was a worrying lack of augment. As the darkness finally conquered the Anatolian landscape, the pursuing footfalls stopped, and Sam could hear no one except himself.

Chapter 9   **Out of the Strong came forth Sweetness**

It was a little after six in the morning, and Sam was on the coach to Antalya, a seaport city on the Mediterranean coast. Overnight he'd run 35 miles to reach the town of Serinhisar. The last 10 miles had been a grinding uphill struggle and running further off road would have necessitated climbing the Gölgeli Mountains. Therefore, he'd risked catching the coach from Serinhisar. He hadn't slept overnight and had prepared himself to stay awake for the entire 115-mile journey to Antalya. The coach had been almost completely filled from its point of departure in Denizli. This suited him. An external viewer would have more to scan. In addition, there had been only aisle seats available; thus, he was shielded from the windows. He was sitting next to a woman in her early thirties. He'd embarked covered in sweat from the night's exertion, and the woman had avoided establishing even the briefest eye contact to acknowledge his presence. Her attitude suited him as well. He'd pushed himself as far back into the seat as possible. He made a point of not peering laterally through the windows at the passing cars but looked straight ahead whilst using his peripheral vision to its fullest possible effect. He was particularly alert when the coach stopped at the various stations on the schedule or slowed because of heavy traffic. He still thought that there may be an ongoing murder investigation; however, this impression was fading.

The coach arrived in Antalya: the end of a four-hour trip. It didn't take long for Sam to find accommodation. This time he didn't go for a standard hotel but a much cheaper affair, the Neredeyse. It was bordering on being a hostel. Critically for Sam it possessed private rooms with no shared amenities. He checked in with a similar arrangement as in Istanbul: he used a false name; he claimed that he'd lost both his passport and credit card; and he paid for two days in advance with cash. He accepted the key, then left to buy some new clothes and a backpack in the first suitable store that he would come across. With this small task accomplished, he returned to the hotel and slept till mid-afternoon. Next he went to the nearest supermarket to buy food and water. He ate the massive cold meal in his room and slept till the afternoon of the following day.

After a shave and shower, Sam left the hotel to find a place to buy a hot meal. He initially thought about going to one of the backstreet eateries nearby. However, on walking through this quarter, he realized that the restaurants were frequented mostly by locals, and so he would be more conspicuous there than in the touristy locations on the coast.

Sam got onto a colourful tram. A single landscape picture had been skilfully painted on its sides around the entire vehicle. The picture was dominated by its sky, and as a result the tram was mostly light blue. To onlookers within the city the tram was a vivid attraction in the foreground against the buildings behind, but on reaching the coast, the vehicle was embarrassed by the background that was Mediterranean Sea.

The city of Antalya combined the modern and the old: antique mosques and traditional white houses with orange slated roofs stood amongst high-rise flats; and the harbour retained its timeworn stone walls, but elegant contemporary yachts floated within its protective arms. As Sam was walking along a coastal street that followed the line of the beach, he observed the sweeping scape of the Bey Mountains to the west.

The pebbly beach was 80 metres to Sam's left. The sea was calm and had an inviting light-blue hue. All was peaceful and he began to relax, although only a little. He noticed a busy restaurant. From the outside he observed a tourist to local ratio that he felt comfortable with. A few people were eating al fresco. He entered with the intention to sit at one of the small tables to the rear and did exactly that. To reach his table he'd passed a dark wooden bar ornamented with polished brass. If viewed from the main entrance, the bar was situated on the right-hand side of the restaurant. From the time that he'd entered the restaurant to the end of the second minute, he'd registered the opposition potential of each and every person.

A waiter came to ask Sam if he would like a drink. Sam hadn't looked at the menu and therefore started to do so as he requested a bottle of water. He chose a dish before the waiter left. The waiter returned a few minutes later with an unopened bottle of mineral water and a glass. Sam had deliberately not mentioned that he wanted the water served that way to avoid appearing out of the ordinary. However, if the bottle had been presented open, he would have insisted on another with the seal intact. While he waited, he watched the other customers in the restaurant. He noticed that customers had the option of either paying their bills at the dining tables or at a till near the bar. The moussaka that he'd ordered arrived ten minutes later. Interestingly, when one considers Sam's distrust of the water being presented unsealed, he appeared to have no comparable concern over the food.

Half of the way through the moussaka, Sam noticed two slim young women enter the restaurant. One was a tall blonde and the other was of medium height with black hair. He fixed his eyes on the flaxen-haired beauty. The women were approached by a waiter. Sam saw the blonde point to the back of the restaurant in his general direction. He dropped his eyes as they drew near. The waiter sat the women at a small square table close to Sam's. The women were sat opposite one another, so that Sam could see both their profiles. He could hear them talking in a language that wasn't English. It was one of the romance languages, but the women's voices weren't loud enough for him to pick out any words that would allow him to determine exactly which language was being spoken. After a few minutes they ordered their meals, and before long two salads arrived.

From a distance the blonde had caught Sam's eye. Up close, he saw that she had rounded facial features and a button nose—a beauty for sure but not his taste at all. In his opinion her face seemed to lack character. The raven-haired woman now captured his attention. Her hair, straight and thick, was worn off her face and fell past her shoulders. She had black eyebrows, and as she talked they moved in concert above a pair of intelligent, bright-green eyes. Her long, slender, majestically hooked nose had a minute cleft beneath the tip. She had full lips, which hadn't yet shaped a smile. Her chin had a dimple in the centre. Sam followed her neck down to a camel-coloured V-neck top. Her lightly tanned skin glowed, even in the low illumination of the restaurant. Around her neck were two gold necklaces, each suspending a different object. Sam recognized that one object was a crucifix, but the other he couldn't identify. He guessed that it was a type of figurine.

Sam slowed the consumption of his meal and ordered another bottle of water. He tried his utmost to look as if he gave to the two women's table no more attention than he gave to the rest of the restaurant. An onlooker would have thought otherwise. As the women talked, the blonde occasionally laughed. The woman with dark hair neither laughed nor smiled; she merely spoke. While Sam was watching the dark-haired woman's lips move, he was surprised to see her turn and look directly at him. He held the gaze and unintentionally started to count the duration in seconds in his mind. Her profile had been enchanting, but eye contact was captivation itself. A friend from university had joked with Sam about the laws of attraction. It was these that Sam remembered at that moment. One second of eye contact means that the woman has a fleeting interest. Two seconds means "It's a shame that there's nobody to introduce us—oh well, have a nice life." Three seconds means "Make your move, boy!" Sam counted all three, then the dark-haired woman turned back to her friend. Sam returned to his meal. Although he was still hungry, it no longer had appeal. He could feel the effect of the dark-haired woman's stare. It had created an overwhelmingly hollow feeling in the pit of his stomach that couldn't be slaked by caloric nutrition. He played with what was left on his plate. He ate two tasteless forkfuls. The women finished their salads.

Without looking toward the women's table, Sam pondered the situation. The mission, the mission, stay on course for the mission, he thought. But life is unpredictable, he argued to himself; opportunities come and go, sometimes at the most inconvenient times, and it's those individuals who grasp these chances who are truly alive and live without regret. The dark-haired woman looked like no one he'd ever seen—singularly beautiful and utterly alluring. Now I should tell you a little more about Sam before you get any wrong ideas. He'd not slept with anyone yet. It was his passionate intention to refrain until married. He'd dated many women (not at the same time) and had come to realize that the majority of them had been fazed by his confidence and all that came with it. None of them had realized that his confidence, that ability after reasoned thought to act without delay and with utter conviction, was a gift from God. The Lord had endowed Sam with the gift at birth, knowing that one day he would give his life to Him and the gift would be put to good use. Anyhow, the resultant feelings communicated between those women and Sam had always thwarted the foundation needed for a working relationship. Sam's desire burnt for a woman who could be a true partner to him. The dark-haired woman got up and started to walk toward the bar. Sam thought that the women were leaving and that he'd missed his chance. The blonde didn't rise.

As the dark-haired woman walked, Sam noticed her shapely figure accentuated by her small thin woollen pullover and tight jeans. The hollow in his stomach became a void. At the bar she ordered two coffees. Sam saw a wealthy-looking man to her immediate left watching her. He was the type whom Sam had seen hanging around yachting marinas yet had little interest in sailing. Not the old sleazy kind, but . . . Young, handsome and lazy, Sam thought. The rich man was sat on a bar stool, which he'd swivelled forty-five degrees in the dark-haired woman's direction. He stared at her as she talked to the barman and while she waited patiently for her order. Sam saw her turn her head to meet the rich man's stare. She shot the "yachtsman" with an arrow of cold contempt, a disqualifying glance, and then turned to receive the two coffees. The rich man slowly swivelled his bar stool back to the forward position. So that's how she looks when she doesn't like you, Sam thought. She returned to her table and said something to the blonde before sitting back down. As the dark-haired woman adjusted her chair to sit comfortably again, she gave Sam a half-second glance.

For a fragment of time Sam had felt the pain of regret as he'd watched the dark-haired beauty rise and walk to the bar, believing that she was going to pay her and her friend's bill and then leave with her friend. He'd felt the consequence of inaction and was now determined to make his move. He got up and walked over to the women's table.

"Hello, how are you both?" Not the best opening, Sam thought, but it'll have to do. There was no angle in the question, only an obvious interest.

"You assume that we both speak English. Do you speak Italian or Swedish?" the dark-haired woman answered.

"I can read Latin," Sam replied, smiling. Ease up, girl, he was thinking. He was relieved to at least see the Swede smile.

"Then it'll be easier if we all speak English," the dark-haired woman asserted. "I'm Prasseda." Sam estimated her age to be between twenty-three and twenty-five.

"I'm Liv. It's short for Livonia," the blonde said.

"I'm Mark. Well, you've already told me where you're both from. So what are you doing here in Turkey?"

"Why don't you have a seat?" Prasseda suggested. Sam sat down in the nearest chair, so that Prasseda was to his right and Liv to his left. "Backpacking—we're doing a six-month round-the-world trip." Prasseda seemed to have assumed the role of the women's principal speaker.

"Wow, that sounds great. But where are the backpacks?"

"At the hotel. And they're not really backpacks—light cases in fact. It's easier if we tell everyone that we're backpacking, except our journey is a little smoother. We aren't students anymore. We've both managed to get a break from our jobs for a while."

"So you're not penniless?"

Prasseda paused to understand the last word.

"We have some money, although we're not earning right now. What we've saved has to last the whole six months."

"Where have you been so far?" Sam could see that the second necklace within the V of Prasseda's pullover was suspending a small gold figurine of the Virgin Mary.

"We're only three weeks in. We began our journey from Italy. We've been to North Africa. Our first stop was Morocco. We then went to Algeria and on to Egypt—and now we're here."

"You missed out Libya!" Sam commented.

"Funny that." The outer edges of Prasseda's lips drifted upward at their shared joke.

Sam thought: was that a smile? Almost, but not quite.

"How about you? What are you doing here in Turkey?" Prasseda asked.

"I'm here with a group from university. We're visiting the ancient church sites in Asia Minor and Greece that were written about in the New Testament."

"Oh, and where's the group?" Prasseda inquired while glancing to Sam's left and right, pretending to look for people.

"I have a Turkish friend from university, a law student. He lives in Dalaman. I broke off from the group—just for a couple of days to visit him and his family." Sam had remembered the map and had chosen a coastal town 100 miles west of Antalya. "I'll catch up with the group tomorrow—I hope."

"Which university do you go to?"

"Edinburgh."

"What are you studying?"

"History."

"Isn't the university term finished for summer?"

"It is. This type of trip is optional—organized for the long summers that we have free. It's expensive, but I'm going to do a module on this subject next year." Sam was so far giving most of his attention to Prasseda. He watched every flicker of her eyes and also noticed a tiny scar on the right side of her lower lip. Rather than being a negative feature, the flaw, combined with her innate arresting features, intensified her beauty. He made occasional momentary glances to Liv, mostly out of politeness. "So what do you both do when you're not seeing the world?"

Prasseda answered first, "I work in advertising."

"Any area in particular?" Sam asked.

"Yes . . . I work for a small innovative company. We have short-term contracts, mostly with different fashion houses in Milan and Rome."

"How did you get into that?"

"I did an arts degree. Some of what I learnt was in textiles and design. After that, I sort of fell into this."

"How about you, Liv?"

"I work in Rome as an events organizer for a hotel chain."

Sam's eyes redirected the conversation back to Prasseda. "Have you been to any interesting places in Turkey?"

"Yesterday we went to the ruins of the city of Olympos[1]," Prasseda said. "It's around eighty kilometres from here. Do you know of it—or the surrounding area?"

"No."

"We hiked up a mountain to an ancient temple to Hephaestus.[2] We camped nearby overnight in a truly unique place. There, from holes in a region of the rocky slopes flammable gas has been escaping, burning constantly for thousands of years. It doesn't look like much in the day, but at night you can see an expanse of living flame—blue and yellow—a vision of something everlasting. Fire, yes, but it looked so serene—so soft that it made me want to reach out and touch it."

"That's incredible . . . and how beautifully you've described it."

"Where have you been, Mark?"

"Nowhere quite like that—Ephesus was good though." He could tell that Ephesus hadn't sparked either of their interests.

---

[1] Nothing to do with the Mount Olympus in Greece that was related to Zeus' kingship.

[2] A Greek god described as an expert blacksmith, and he was reportedly a son of Zeus: Homer's Iliad Book 1 *lines 568-583*, Book 14 *lines 329-340*, Book 18 *lines 368-617*.

"To some I suppose it might seem like a typical ruin, but I have a very active imagination. That combined with a bit of historical knowledge can go a long way."

"Go on, show us!" Prasseda requested.

". . . In 57 AD there was a dispute there against Paul's teachings.[1] A silversmith who represented the craftsmen realized that if the people turned to Christ, then he and his kind would lose their trade selling statues of the goddess Diana[2] and shrines to place them in. In fact, the entire city was in an uproar. Some of the crowd made hostages of two of Paul's companions by dragging them into the theatre. As I stood outside of that very theatre, I could imagine Paul's distress as he arrived there to meet a riot—his distress was mostly because he knew that his friends had been seized and their captors were probably preparing to harm or kill them inside the theatre. He desperately wanted to enter but was persuaded against this by some other friends, who feared for his life. The mob grew louder and they started shouting, 'Great *is* Diana of the Ephesians.' I could go on."

Prasseda neither encouraged Sam to continue nor commented on what he had said about the ancient dispute. "I've heard that Ephesus was the last home of the Virgin," she said.

"You mean Mary?" Sam asked.

"That's right," Prasseda replied.

"Do you believe that?" Sam inquired.

"That she was a virgin when she gave birth to Christ or that Ephesus was the last place where she lived?" Prasseda expanded.

---

[1] Acts 19:22-41.

[2] Throughout Acts 19:22-41 in the Greek she is called Artemis. Her name has been translated in the King James Version as Diana, because this goddess is Artemis' Roman equivalent.
Artemis was reportedly a daughter of Zeus (Jupiter) and the full sister of Apollo: Hesiod's Theogony *lines 918-920,* Apollodorus' The Library Book 1 *chapter 4:1,* Ovid's Metamorphoses Book 1 *lines 689-698.*

Sam noted that the questions that she'd posed herself had been expertly worded. "How about that she was a virgin when she died and that she died there?" Sam altered the questions, so that the alleged lack of death of Mary and her alleged lifelong virginity would be specifically addressed.

Sam knew that Jesus was conceived not through sexual inter-course but by the overshadowing of the Spirit of God.[1] Mary was therefore truly a virgin when she became pregnant with Jesus. Note well that Jesus' conception should never be confused with that of the first-generation Nephilim, who were the result of demonic-human sexual intercourse. Jesus' physical appearance on Earth was neither gigantic nor handsome. Gigantic size and handsomeness are attributes that, if present, would make us regard Him beyond His acts and words.[2] In contrast, the Nephilim were not just renowned for their awe-inspiring statures, but some of the men were reportedly uncommonly handsome and the women of unsurpassed beauty, and thus believed to be deities or descended from them or both, no matter how atrocious their behaviour, being a people given over to violence and licentious-ness.[3] Sam knew that Mary was also a virgin when she gave birth

---

[1] Matthew 1:18-25, Luke 1:26-35.

[2] Isaiah 53:1-12. In fact, in his mid- to late thirties Jesus had the appearance of a man much older than His actual years, for a group of people who observed Him said to Him, "Thou art not yet fifty", when estimating His age: John 8:53-57.

[3] Genesis 6:1-6. The following have been reported and represent only a fraction of possible examples.

Regarding beauty:

Persephone, an arresting beauty and the daughter of Zeus and Demeter, was abducted by Hades (the Greek god of the Under-world): Homeric Hymns *2 To Demeter lines 347-433*, Hyginus' Fabulae *146*, Hesiod's Theogony *lines 886-914* (in this reference, although Persephone was abducted by Hades, Zeus had consented to the union; and in the preceding Homeric Hymns and Hyginus references Zeus also assisted in planning the abduction), Apollo-

FOOTNOTE CONTINUED ON THE NEXT PAGE

dorus' The Library Book 1 *chapter 5:1,* Library of History by Diodorus Siculus Book 5 *chapter 68:2* (this reference reports that Persephone was ravished by Hades, also called Pluto and Pluton).

Aphrodite, a daughter of Zeus, was a radiant beauty and known as a goddess of love: Homeric Hymns 5 *To Aphrodite lines 45-201, 6 To Aphrodite lines 1-21.* Another reported origin is that she was an offspring of Uranus (Sky), but she was still a goddess of love: Hesiod's Theogony *lines 173-206, 956-962, 979-983.*

Adonis, a great-grandson of Poseidon, was so handsome that Aphrodite and Persephone competed for his love: Hesiod's Catalogue of Women *fragments 106, 107,* Apollodorus' The Library Book 2 *chapter 1:4,* Book 3 *chapters 1:1, 14:3-4* (alternative lineages for Adonis are also proposed).

Narcissus, the son of the river god Cephisus (a son of the Titans Ocean and Tethys), was so handsome that he spurned the love of others and became besotted with his own reflection: Ovid's Metamorphoses Book 3 *lines 342-510,* Hyginus' Theogony *6* and Fabulae *271,* Apollodorus' The Library Book 1 *chapter 1:1-3,* Hesiod's Theogony *lines 126-138, 337-370.* Pausanias, although aware of the most popular story (above), preferred a different rendition, in which after Narcissus' twin sister died, who looked exactly like him and with whom he had fallen in love, he sought solace in looking at his own reflection: Description of Greece Book 9 *chapter 31:7-9.*

Conversely, one Nephil in the Bible (a relative of Goliath) was malformed, possessing six digits on each limb: 1 Chronicles 20:5-8. Consider the Cyclopes of Greek mythology (see footnote in Chapter 3 pg 73 regarding offspring of Neptune [Poseidon]).

Regarding violence and licentiousness:

Apollo and Artemis—respectively a god and a goddess, and twins—slaughtered the six sons and six daughters of Niobe for Niobe's boast that she had more offspring than the deities' mother, Leto, of whom were born only the twins. Leto, a Titan goddess and a daughter of the Titans Coeus and Phoebe, was one of the wives of Zeus, to whom she bore the twins. Hesiod's Theogony *lines 404-*

FOOTNOTE CONTINUED ON THE NEXT PAGE

428, 886-920, Homer's Iliad Book 24 *lines 596-620* (text states that Niobe had 6 sons and 6 daughters), Ovid's Metamorphoses Book 6 *lines 146-316* (text states that Niobe had 7 sons and 7 daughters). Hyginus' Fabulae *9-11* mentions the same numbers of sons and daughters as Ovid but that one daughter survived. Other numbers of sons and daughters are also reported and that two might have survived the massacre: Apollodorus' The Library Book 3 *chapter 5:6*.

Medea, a granddaughter of the sun god Helios (the son of the Titans Hyperion and Theia), murdered her own brother and all of her own children (two sons) by her husband Jason (of Argonaut and Golden Fleece fame): Hesiod's Theogony *lines 126-138, 371-374, 956-962*, Apollodorus' The Library Book 1 *chapters 1:1-2:5, 9:24-28*, Euripides' Medea *lines 1236-1404*, Argonautica by Apollonius Rhodius Book 3 *lines 235-259*, 4 *lines 395-491*, Hyginus' Fabulae *239, 255*. Three different murders of Medea's brother are described in the above references: before Medea left Colchis (the land that had possessed the Golden Fleece), he was killed at a hearth by her (Euripides); as a child he was killed by Medea, who cut off his limbs whilst she was escaping from Colchis on the ship called the Argo (Apollodorus); and as an adult he caught up with the fleeing Argonauts, who were accompanied by Medea, and being drawn into an ambush by her, he was killed by Jason (Apollonius). An alternative story relates that Medea's brother, while pursuing her, came across Jason and was killed by him (Hyginus' Fabulae *23*). Medea murdered her two sons because of Jason's marriage to another woman, a Corinthian princess. In addition to this best-known story of the murder of the children by Medea, which Apollodorus did relate (above reference), he also mentioned an alternative account of their death, which was that Medea abandoned her children in Corinth, and because she had murdered the Corinthian princess, Medea's two sons were murdered by the Corinthians. A variant of the best-known story relates that there were three sons, two of whom were murdered by Medea but one escaped: Library of History by Diodorus Siculus Book 4 *chapters 54:1-55:3*.

FOOTNOTE CONTINUED ON THE NEXT PAGE

to Jesus but didn't remain that way. She slept with her husband, Joseph, after Jesus was born. Jesus (whom the book of Luke calls Mary's firstborn son, which means that she later had at least one other son) had brothers and sisters, and no mother other than Mary is identified in the Bible.[1] Furthermore, Sam was

CONTINUED FOOTNOTE PRESENT

Hercules (Heracles), a son of Zeus (Hesiod's Theogony *lines 943-952*), murdered his own children whom he had with Megara by throwing them into a fire (Apollodorus' The Library Book 2 *chapter 4:11-12*) or by the use of his weapons (Library of History by Diodorus Siculus Book 4 *chapter 11:1-2,* Euripides' Heracles *lines 621-1038*).

Zeus ravished Aegina, who gave birth to Aeacus: Apollodorus' The Library Book 3 *chapter 12:6,* Library of History by Diodorus Siculus Book 4 *chapter 72:4-6,* Pausanias' Description of Greece Book 2 *chapter 5:1,* Book 5 *chapter 22:5-6,* Hyginus' Fabulae *52*.

Hercules ravished Auge, who gave birth to Telephus: Hyginus' Fabulae *99-100,* Hesiod's Catalogue of Women *fragment 117,* Strabo's Geography Book 13 *chapter 1:69,* Library of History by Diodorus Siculus Book 4 *chapter 33:5-12,* Pausanias' Description of Greece Book 8 *chapter 47:4,* Apollodorus' The Library Book 2 *chapter 7:4,* Book 3 *chapter 9:1,* Pausanias' Description of Greece Book 8 *chapters 4:8-9, 47:4, 48:7*.

Note the variant nature of many of the above nonbiblical accounts. For more information on the gigantic Titans see Chapter 3 pg 73 and footnote regarding Titan.

[1] Mary was a virgin when she gave birth to Jesus: Matthew 1:18-25, Luke 1:34-35.

Mary had sexual relations with her husband, Joseph, after the birth of Jesus: Matthew 1:25.

Matthew 1:20-25 and Luke 2:5-7 state that Jesus was Mary's firstborn son.

Jesus had four brothers and an unknown number of sisters (but must be two or over); no mother other than Mary is identified as their mother. Therefore, Mary was the mother of at least seven children. Matthew 13:55-56, Mark 6:3.

convinced that Mary died like other human beings, for to him there was no reason to think otherwise. Sam wanted to know what Prasseda believed.

"First of all, I don't believe that she died but was taken directly up to Heaven," Prasseda stated. "I also believe that she remained a virgin throughout her life on Earth. I'm Roman Catholic."

There are many events in the Bible that mention Mary. If the events are arranged chronologically, then the last took place on the 50th day after Jesus' resurrection. She was gathered with the disciples and other followers of Christ in Jerusalem. At that point the resurrected Jesus had already ascended to Heaven.[1] The biblical absence of a further account of Mary's life demonstrates that it's not something that God deems important to impart to the world, and so death would be expected. In addition, there is no reliable historical account outside of the Bible beyond the 50th day after Jesus' resurrection that tells of Mary's subsequent life.

---

[1] Acts 1:1-2:1. Before reading the following footnote, it is important to understand that according to the Bible, a new day starts in the evening after the sun goes down and lasts until after the sun next goes down (Genesis 1:5, Deuteronomy 24:15). The Pentecost (also known as the Feast of Weeks) is celebrated on the 50th day after the Sheaf Offering (this being the 1st day). The Sheaf Offering occurs on the second day of the seven days of the Festival of Unleavened Bread. The day of Passover is the day before the seven-day Festival of Unleavened Bread, even though unleavened bread is also eaten at the Passover meal (Exodus 12:8), which occurs on the evening that starts the day of Passover. Therefore, unleavened bread is eaten for eight days. Exodus 12:1-20, Leviticus 23:1-21, Deuteronomy 16:1-10. Jesus was crucified during the daylight hours [Friday daytime] that followed the evening Passover meal [Thursday nighttime], i.e., both the meal and crucifixion happened on the same biblical day, which was Passover. Jesus rose on the day of the Sheaf Offering [Sunday daytime], i.e., on the third day from the day of his death as predicted. Matthew 16:21, 17:23, 20:19, 26:18-28:11, Mark 9:31, 10:34, 14:1-16:9, Luke 9:22, 18:33, 22:8-24:10, John 13:1-20:21.

Despite this, in the mid-19th century Roman Catholics started to petition the pope to declare officially that she hadn't died, but having reached the end of her natural life, she had been taken directly to Heaven. This belief that Mary was assumed into Heaven is known as "the Assumption". Almost 100 years later and after millions of petitions, in 1950 the pope at that time, Pius XII (Eugenio Pacelli), made the belief official and essential for Roman Catholics to believe. In other words, the belief had become a dogma, yet the belief ignores the basic fact that a person taken directly to Heaven is an extraordinary event that would certainly be recorded in the Bible, as it is for Jesus (the Son of God), Elijah and Enoch.[1] The absence of the assumption of Mary in the Bible indicates that it didn't happen.[2]

"And how about you?" Sam said to Liv.

"I'm an atheist," Liv declared.

Sam was surprised that the conversation had reached such a depth so quickly. It was mostly his fault. He'd discussed deep topics with strangers before. It hadn't been a problem on those occasions; however, his circumstances were different now, and he was eager to bring the conversation back to shallower water. He thought: and who are these two women anyway? He wanted to ask Prasseda where exactly in the Bible is it written about what she believed. He wanted to tell her: that the New Testament makes it clear that at the conception of Jesus, throughout the

---

[1] Jesus: Mark 16:19-20, Luke 24:50-53, Acts 1:1-11.

Elijah: 2 Kings 2:10-12.

Enoch: Genesis 5:23-24, Hebrews 11:5.

Consider also the future Rapture of the church, which is predicted in the Bible (see Timeline for definition of the Rapture and time of the event): Matthew 24:31-51, 1 Corinthians 15:50-54, 1 Thessalonians 1:10, 4:13-18, 5:1-11, 2 Peter 3:10, Revelation 3:10.

[2] Furthermore, to be assumed does not make a person into a deity. Elijah and Enoch were both assumed, but neither is a god nor should they be worshipped in any way.

pregnancy and at the birth, Mary was indeed a virgin, but after the birth of Jesus she later slept with her husband, Joseph, and had other children;[1] and that Mary, although favoured by God, was a sinner like everyone else (except Jesus) and also needed to accept her son Jesus as her saviour.[2] Sam felt compelled to tell Prasseda that salvation can never come through Mary but from Jesus alone.[3] Instead, Sam held his tongue. It wasn't his style, yet maybe this approach was tailored to this particular moment. He tried to relax. Maybe I'll see her again, he thought, and have the opportunity to discuss these subjects privately when she won't feel so affronted in her friend's presence.

Who are these two women? That question was lingering in Sam's mind. There was also something else about them. His deep train of thought was interrupted.

Without prompting, Prasseda said proudly: "I pray to the Virgin for guidance every day."

"Do you get an answer?" Although that question wouldn't necessarily bring the conversation to trivial territory, Sam was satisfied that it would permit the exchange to carry on until he had a better opportunity.

"Yes, I do. She always hears me. She's so . . . How do you say . . . within reach."

"Accessible?" Sam ventured. He knew that Mary was dead and her spirit was certainly in Heaven, but she was incapable of either listening to or answering prayers. So he wondered who was answering Prasseda's prayers!

"That's not quite the word I was looking for. Maybe I'll think of it in a minute. The Virgin is the greatest of mothers who are tender and kind and always listen."

---

[1] See earlier in this chapter pg 206 and footnote regarding the same topic.

[2] Luke 1:28-35, 1:42-48, John 14:6, Acts 1:11-14, Romans 3:22-24.

[3] John 14:6, Acts 4:8-12, Romans 3:22-26.

Sam would have liked to have told Prasseda about Cybele and the fact that the early Catholic Church[1] had turned the cult of this goddess, as well as others, into the worship of Mary. Praying to Mary is as useless as praying to a rock, even if perfectly sculpted and covered in gold. The New Testament is clear on these facts. Salvation is through Christ alone, and it is He who acts on our behalf as our great and only intercessor.[2] Praying to Mary or any other saint is wrong, as it shows a lack of faith in Jesus and is an obstacle that prevents a person from having a relationship with God. This obstacle is a form of idolatry.[3]

"Do you pray to Jesus?" Sam asked Prasseda.

"I do sometimes. Inside my church in Rome there's a beautiful statue there."

---

[1] The early Catholic Church, from which Roman Catholicism and Eastern Orthodoxy (the Orthodox Catholic Church) originated.

[2] John 14:6, Acts 4:10-12, Romans 8:34, Colossians 1:13-20, 1 Thessalonians 5:9-10, Hebrews 2:9-10, 7:22-28.

Furthermore, the Spirit of God (who is Jesus' Spirit—Jesus being God), even when a Christian doesn't know what to pray for, He understands that person's needs and makes intercession for him or her (key passage: Romans 8:26-27).

The Spirit of God is Jesus' Spirit and God the Father's Spirit: Matthew 3:16, Luke 4:1, 11:13, John 15:23-27, Acts 1:1-8, Romans 1:1-4, 8:1-11, 1 Corinthians 12:3-13, Galatians 4:4-6, Philippians 1:19, 1 John 5:1-11.

[3] See Chapter 20 pg 399 and footnote regarding promotion of idolatry.

It is a falsehood that human beings can bestow sainthood on one another. The Bible demonstrates that everyone who accepts Jesus as his or her personal saviour is a saint. And before Jesus died for the sins of the world all the righteous people, those who sought to do God's will, were also saints. Psalms 30:4, 31:23-24, 34:9, 50:3-6, Daniel 7:18-27, Acts 9:13-32, Romans 1:1-8, 15:31, 1 Corinthians 6:1-11, Ephesians 5:1-3, Philippians 4:20-23, Philemon 1:3-5, Revelation 14:12.

Wrong answer, Sam thought.

Almost as if Prasseda had read his mind she said, "Now and then I pray to Him when I'm not in my church."

How sad for you, Sam thought. Even if you truly pray to Jesus without the use of a statue, it won't do you any good until you've given up praying to Mary and your other idols. God has another name and it's "Jealous".[1] The first two commandments are "Thou shalt have no other gods before me. Thou shalt not make unto thee any graven image, or any likeness *of any thing* that *is* in heaven above, or that *is* in the earth beneath, or that *is* in the water under the earth: Thou shalt not bow down thyself to them, nor serve them: for I the LORD thy God *am* a jealous God, visiting the iniquity of the fathers upon the children unto the third and fourth *generation* of them that hate me; And shewing mercy unto thousands of them that love me, and keep my commandments."[2] Jesus the Messiah (God the Son) is at the right hand of His Father ready to hear your prayers and act as your advocate between you and God the Father. The Messiah is your advocate,[3] because He lived on the Earth as a man, so that He could suffer

---

[1] Exodus 34:14. This is a righteous jealousy, not a jealousy that desires what belongs to another. If a man and woman enter into a marriage contract and one of them has an affair, the response of the other will be a righteous jealousy, because together they'd made a binding agreement to be faithful to one another. Think about how God feels, who is our creator and sustainer, deeds that bind us contractually to Him, when we run after other gods. Jesus, God the Son, is the aspect of God who both created and sustains us: John 1:1-18, Colossians 1:12-17, Hebrews 1:1-3.

[2] Exodus 20:3-6. Regarding verse 5, the iniquity (sin) of the fathers affects the third and fourth generations if the offspring do not resist the negative influence of their ancestors through righteous behaviour. Every person will be judged individually. Ezekiel 18:1-32.

[3] Matthew 22:43-46, 26:63-64, Mark 16:19, Luke 22:69-70, Acts 2:32-36, 7:52-60, Romans 8:31-39, Hebrews 7:22-8:2, 9:24-28, 10:5-21, 12:2, 1 John 2:1-2, Revelation 5:1-14.

the things that you suffer, yet He remained sinless. Furthermore, He died for you.[1] All this turned over in Sam's mind as he faced Prasseda.

"I rarely get an answer from Him. It's the Virgin who I have a link with. Just today I woke up and knew that I'd meet someone interesting, and here you are."

"Is that so?" Sam said. "That's a rather non-specific premonition, and anyhow some people find me quite dull." No one ever found Sam dull: perhaps a little straight-laced but definitely never dull. Although inherently wilder, whilst growing up in Britain he'd experienced a general lack of forbearance for his kind, and this combined with his desire to succeed had suppressed much of his unruliness. Yet that ungovernable core was often tapped, so that Sam could abound for Christ, not fettered by the contrary opinion of men.

"Do they?" she said. "Somehow I find that surprising. I find you very interesting."

"Why?"

"I don't think that you're a very modest man to ask me that; you're quite striking, you know," her sentence ended in a way that indicated that she had more to add but was thinking about how best to say it.

"So are you," Sam replied.

Prasseda seemed to take no notice of his compliment. "It's not just that. When I talk with you, your eyes talk to me as well. And they tell me another story."

"And what story is that?" Sam started to get worried.

---

[1] See Chapter 7 pg 155 and footnote regarding the same collection of topics. The footnote includes the following four headings: God on the Earth in the form of a man (God the Son); While on Earth, Jesus experienced the following: birth, loss of a friend, despair, joy, physical pain, compassion, friendship, betrayal, righteous anger, life-threatening danger, death and more; Jesus was directly tempted by Satan; and Jesus was the perfect sacrifice.

"You like me, yet you disapprove of me."

Sam's anxiety lessened. "You've no problem expressing yourself." He didn't deny her statement, although he was tempted to do so. He felt that their connection was floundering. He'd heard similar statements from women he'd dated, only this stage wouldn't normally arrive so quickly. Those relationships fizzled away after that.

"We Italians are more open than you English." She was displaying more assuredness and tenacity than he was used to. She smiled her first smile to show him that she wasn't hurt by his lack of denial and that she was still interested. Her smile radiated warmth that he didn't think possible from her. "In some ways I can tell that we're opposites."

That was an extra piece of encouragement for Sam. He couldn't fail to recognize the age-old adage, which Prasseda completed with her eyes. Although silently excited to have her leap the hurdle where other women fail, he began to subconsciously calculate the probability of this particular meeting happening.

"Excuse me," Liv said. Sam had practically forgotten that she was there. She got up and walked to the ladies' room.

"Where did you meet each other?" Sam asked Prasseda.

"We met at Heathrow airport about four years ago."

"Really?"

"Yes, we were both on the same flight to Miami. We met in the departure lounge."

"Which airline was that?"

"Virgin, of course."

"Yes, of course, I should have guessed." They gently laughed together. To Sam her face was stunning in any movement or expression.

"Did you also sit together?"

"No, our seats were separate, but we met and talked on board the flight, then met again in Miami. It's incredible to think that we've known each other for that long."

"She seems nice." Nice was an adjective that Sam didn't generally use and hoped that Prasseda's grasp of English didn't extend to recognizing inadequate words.

"Where are you catching up with your group?" Prasseda asked.

"Tarsus, the birthplace of Paul," Sam replied.

"What a coincidence. We're also following the coastline."

"Yes, what a coincidence."

"How are you getting there, Mark?"

"By coach. And where are you and Liv travelling to after Turkey?"

"We're heading to Syria—to Damascus. The plan is to then skip the rest of the Middle East by flying to India. Maybe we can travel with you tomorrow to Tarsus on the coach?"

"I'd like that," Sam replied. "We can get to know each other better." His subconscious mind's computation was complete. The probability of him meeting Prasseda at this time and place was exceptionally low, but not so low as to be impossible. Although unable to control his growing doubt as to the women's genuineness, he managed to hide the resulting emotion so that his conversation could remain natural. "I don't know the exact times. I was simply planning on turning up at the main station at nine. How would that suit you both?"

"That sounds fine. At least it's not too early in the morning."

Liv returned. Sam thought that that was an opportune moment to take his leave, and before she sat back down he said, "It's been a pleasure meeting you both."

"You too," Prasseda replied.

"Yes," Liv joined in, watching Prasseda's eyes as she looked at Sam. "We might as well leave too."

The three of them paid their respective bills at the table, during which Prasseda briefly talked with Liv about the planned journey to Tarsus. Sam and Prasseda rose simultaneously. Prasseda headed for the door of the restaurant ahead of both Liv and Sam. Liv followed, and Sam caught up with her in three hurried steps.

"So, Liv, we haven't had much of a chance to talk. Tell me, how did you and Prasseda meet?" Sam pitched his voice at just the right level: to blend with the ambient noise created by the restaurant's voices and music in order that Prasseda wouldn't hear; and to not give the impression that he was whispering.

"We met at Heathrow airport four years ago."

"Oh, where were you flying to?"

"We were both flying to Miami. We met in the departure lounge."

"I bet Terminal 4 is a cool place to meet someone." Sam knew that Virgin's flights to the USA were only from Terminal 3.

"Yes, I suppose."

Sam wondered if she'd registered how he apparently knew which terminal the two women had departed from. Maybe she'd just thought that he'd supposed that all transatlantic flights left from Terminal 4. "It's a shame that Terminal 4 doesn't have a Harvey Nichols. I love strolling around there to pass the time . . . sometimes I even buy something." He'd assumed that Liv was familiar with the world-famous flagship store in London and the company's many other branches. He also knew that Terminal 3's departure lounge had long had a Harvey Nichols that was in conspicuous view.

"I can't say that I noticed." Liv had answered after a definite two seconds of thought.

They walked out of the restaurant and into the bright afternoon. Sam immediately stopped talking with Liv and directed a question to Prasseda: "Which way are you headed?"

The coastal street gave only two immediate options, west or east, unless one wanted to go to the beach, which meant leaving the street by heading south.

"We're going that way." Prasseda pointed in the direction that led away from Sam's hotel.

"My hotel's that way," Sam replied truthfully, pointing east.

"I bet your hotel's better than ours," Liv said. "We're staying at the Destek. It's not much to look at, and that's just the outside. It's about half a kilometre away."

"That's what happens when you need to budget for a whole six months!" Prasseda added. "Where are you staying?"

"At the Gerçek." This was one of four hotels that Sam had seen on the way. It was the largest, and he hoped that it was full with guests.

"How's that?"

"Not bad." His answer was too generic. He thought about the hotel briefly. "After your description of the Destek, I'm embarrassed to say that it's really first-rate. I'm sorry." The two women smiled. "Anyhow, till tomorrow."

"Yes, see you at nine," Prasseda replied. And they parted: Prasseda and Livonia to the west and Sam to the east.

Sam walked. He turned back twice before leaving the coastal street to head inland. Each time he'd seen the women's backs heading away from him. They'd been merely talking with one another. He entered the Gerçek, asked the concierge about the hotel's restaurant's opening times and then left by means of a service entrance at the back of the building.

The recent encounter was the only thing that now occupied Sam's mind. A part of him, namely his heart, wanted to believe that the meeting was a random event, but his mind wouldn't let him. The women's replies of how they'd met one another were too similar, although not quite at the point of being rehearsed. Liv had then fallen when responding to both of his false statements. This could have simply represented errors of her memory. Conversely, she'd countered neither of them positively in order to dispel doubt. In truth, the questions that Sam had asked Prasseda when they were alone should have reflected a more personal aspect of her and Liv's friendship; however, the ones that he'd asked were all he could think of at the time. A lumbering effort, he thought.

Sam arrived back at his room. He looked at his comfortable bed and realized that he wouldn't be sleeping in it. He packed his things and left, without checking out, via a fire exit.

Later that night, at two o'clock in the morning, Sam stood in the dark behind an olive tree. He could see the window of his room on the second floor. The room was unlit. He was in the rear garden of the hotel. He'd stood there for over four hours, silently watching and waiting. The night was still and undisturbed except for the irritating background hum of crickets. He'd closed the curtains of his room before he'd left and could see the cream fabric despite the reflection from the glass.

Sam saw four flashes of light in quick succession, then a solitary fifth. They'd lit the parts of his room's window frame that the curtains hadn't sufficiently covered. The flashes were the sign that he'd waited for. Not a sound had been emitted, and neither did the hotel stir. With assassination as their sole intent, his enemies hadn't even checked to see who was lying in the bed before shooting. As a consequence, they'd hastily shot the two pillows concealed beneath the sheets.

Sam's next destination wouldn't be Tarsus, and he'd be travelling alone.

Chapter 10   **A Man from Cappadocia**

Sam slipped away from the grounds of the hotel and made his way under the cover of darkness to Northeast Antalya's main road, by which he left the city. He walked overnight, a total distance of 18 miles, to the small town of Köseler. He found a telephone booth and made a short call to the House's Cappadocian contact. Cappadocia is a region in eastern central Turkey and is 200 miles from Köseler. Sam spent the rest of the night watching the Köseler coach station from a distance of 100 metres whilst hidden behind a small parked van in an alley.

The first coach heading northward arrived at twenty to six in the morning. The sun was rising in a cloudless sky. Sam watched the stark white light search its way across the streets, slicing night's residue into wedge-shaped shadows. He saw that the coach was three-quarters full. He left his hiding spot and started to walk toward this vehicle. He tried his best to make out each passenger as he approached the coach's left side. As he crossed the road, he also scanned the coach's surroundings that he'd been unable to observe from the confines of the alley. He held the pistol's handle tightly; both the weapon and his right hand were concealed by the right front pocket of his navy-blue chinos and his untucked T-shirt. The passengers on the coach's right side were more difficult to see than those on the left. From his viewpoint he could barely see the top halves of the heads of the shorter individuals, and this worsened as the distance narrowed. He watched for purposeful movements of heads and white flashes of fixating eyes. The interior of the coach was dimly lit by three fluorescent tube lamps. He strained his eyes to distinguish the face of a passenger who stood up and then rummaged in the overhead storage space. Sam noticed two glances in his direction, one from a man. Sam read apathy in the man's eyes and the simple need to observe human diversity in the woman's. Sam proceeded to confidently walk around the coach and board it. He found a seat at the back in the penultimate row.

The people behind him were a family of five, who occupied the entire last row, which was one long bench seat.

Sam was determined to remain alert throughout the convoluted seven-hour journey to a place called Konya. He thought about the two women in Antalya. He wondered what their real names were. He wasn't entirely surprised that the enemy had such beautiful female members. He started putting together a picture of his adversaries: a highly educated graduate, a monster (deceased), brutish guards, dauntless assassins and now two scheming temptresses. The addition of the two women had added an international dimension.

The coach passed through Isparta and Akşehir, the latter of which is only 50 miles southeast of Afyon. Progress! Sam thought—as he looked at his map. He arrived uneventfully at Konya. The coach could have taken him further east, which would have brought him closer to Cappadocia, but the contact's instructions were to disembark at Konya—it would be harder to trace Sam's subsequent movements this way.

At the rendezvous point the slowing car and the contact's description of himself was as he'd described over the phone. His facial expression was unexpected. Sam could see extreme anxiety in the driver's eyes. Sam quickly glanced around him, after which he was positive that it was himself who was provoking the response. The contact had sounded so composed on the phone, yet this man was even more nervous than Mustafa had been when he and Sam had met. The driver's tension made Sam uncomfortable. Sam thought: is this really the same man whom I'd spoken to earlier? Sam slowly placed his hand into his right front pocket. He was holding the handle of the pistol as the car pulled to a stop. He looked around the general vicinity again except this time with less-hurried and more-inquiring eyes. A stuttering electronic movement brought the window to the left of the driver to a quarter-open position. Sam didn't smile. He approached the window.

"What was the second plague before the Exodus?" Sam asked the driver, without leaning forward.

The driver didn't need to think about the reply, but his anxiety and the resultant need to swallow before speaking delayed the response. "Frogs."[1]

"And the seventh?"

"Fiery Hail."[2]

"Emin, then?" This contact is a seriously jittery one, Sam thought.

"That's me, and I won't mention your name, even now. From now on I'll call you Charles."

"Charles . . . Why Charles?"

"The actor Charles Clarke . . . I've seen some of his films." Clearly a fan but not in the right frame of mind to admit it.

Sam pictured the actor in his mind. He briefly thought about some of the Charles Clarke movies broadcast on television as midweek matinees that he'd seen as a child. The films had an innocent charm about them. Sam reflected on the West's broader influence on Turkey. "Fine, I shouldn't have a problem answering to that."

Sam got into the front passenger seat of the vehicle. Emin started the car and pulled out into Konya's afternoon traffic. As Emin drove, out of the corner of his right eye he watched Sam, who pretended not to notice.

After several miles, Sam observed that Emin's tension was lessening. Emin started talking: "Since Sol Kadmiel's visit there's been some trouble in our community—in Cappadocia."

"Oh?" Sam replied, awaiting details.

"We have around two hundred members. Most of us are Christians. Our present difficulty means that there won't be a general introduction."

"That's what I would have suggested anyway given my present situation. However, can I ask you: what's the nature of the problem?"

---

[1] Exodus 8:1-14.
[2] Exodus 9:18-34.

"It's very difficult to explain. Maybe it'd be better if I tell you when we arrive, and perhaps you can see for yourself." Emin turned to look directly at Sam. He returned the gaze, waiting for Emin to continue talking. Emin returned his attention to the road.

"No. It's definitely better that you explain now. My mission is in a mess. I need to make an assessment now as to whether it's appropriate for me to stay with you and if it's safe for you all to receive me," Sam's answer was firm.

"I'll carry on driving in the direction of Cappadocia, and if you decide against, then I'll take you somewhere else and drop you off."

"All right, go ahead."

"It wasn't exactly at the time of Sol Kadmiel's visit that the current problem arose, but it happened two days after he left. Whether they're connected or not, I don't know."

Emin was overweight and bald. His chubby hands gripped the steering wheel tightly. Even though Emin was seated, Sam estimated his contact's height to be around five feet six inches. Emin was in his mid-fifties. Beneath both eyes were large bags, each hatched by two groups of wrinkles running in opposing directions. Each horizontal group ran laterally to join with deep crow's-feet, which radiated over his temples.

"Am I correct in assuming that you're the leader of the community?" Sam asked.

"Yes, you're right, although recently . . . Well, it's better if I just explain what the problem is. Have you got an open mind?"

"Like a field," Sam answered. It took a moment for Emin to understand the metaphor. "Please carry on," Sam said.

"First, I need to tell you about our home. Because I've lived there for most of my life, I assume that people know Cappadocia, but it's different from anywhere you'll have ever been. They say that it was formed by a combination of volcanic action and some type of heavy erosion that followed. Cappadocia is what you would call a natural phenomenon. What you can see on the surface are lots of rocky prominences, some of which have entrances."

Sam knew practically nothing about Cappadocia except that it was one of the many places where some of the earliest believers in Jesus had lived,[1] almost 2,000 years ago.

"Beneath the surface are underground villages and towns. You see, the rock is soft enough to dig yet strong enough to support. Some of the towns are as much as ten levels deep. We don't live in anything nearly as large and as deep as that, but most of our own community exists beneath the surface. We're made up of fifty-six families. Not all of them live in our village. Some come from other areas to hear the preaching at our church. A friend of mine called Teoman has a home on the fifth lower level, which is the deepest in our community. His home is beneath the largest communal storage hall, where we mostly keep grain. His bedroom is directly under one of the sealed storerooms, which is an offshoot of the hall. This side room is used to store oil, kerosene and petrol . . . flammable things, and so it's kept closed by a boulder that can be rolled across the entrance."

Sam started to wonder where Emin's story was heading.

"One night when Teoman was asleep he heard the sound of something above him. He told me what it sounded like later. I'm not sure if there's an English word for it. I want to say scratching. I know that this isn't correct, and it maybe makes you think of a rat. There's at least five feet of solid rock between his bedroom and the storeroom, and the only thing he can usually hear from the storeroom is the sound of the boulder when it's being rolled."

"And did he hear the boulder move," Sam asked.

"No, he didn't," Emin answered, again turning briefly toward Sam.

Emin continued, "Have you ever had a noise disturb your sleep and you think that it's part of your dream?"

"Yes, I have—a few times," Sam replied.

"Well, I think that this is what happened to Teoman, and so instead of waking, he called out into the night the words 'Be bound!'"

---

[1] 1 Peter 1:1-2.

"Just 'Be bound!'—that's it? That's all he said?"

"That's all he could remember . . . 'Be bound!' Maybe he said more. Who knows? Anyway, the sound must have stopped, and he continued to sleep for the rest of the night."

"Was he sleeping alone?" Sam asked.

"That's right. His wife was away, looking after her sick mother in Sardis. The following day he remembered what he'd heard, only he wasn't convinced that it had actually happened. He went to the storeroom to see what had made the noise. He took one of the other men with him just in case. He's called Hersek. They went inside with a torch—or should I say flashlight."

"I think they say flashlight in the United States. I understand torch very well."

"That particular room is deliberately not lit by our electrical system for obvious reasons."

"And what about the torch?" Sam asked.

"It's one of those that don't generate sparks. We keep it by the entrance, so that nobody uses a dangerous one of their own. At first Teoman and Hersek couldn't see anything out of the ordinary. Then they noticed the torchlight reflecting strangely off of something further inside the storeroom. They could see what looked like glass chains floating in the air. They walked toward the chains and had the scare of their lives."

"What did they see?"

"As they walked closer, they saw that the floating chains weren't the only oddity. Within the chains was a vague figure, who was slowly becoming more and more visible, and the two men soon realized that the chains were binding a supernatural being."

"A supernatural being? I can see why you wanted me to have an open mind."

"Yes, and I think that he is a demon."

Sam noted the present tense and realized that the supernatural being was still in the storeroom. Emin's English was good, and he wouldn't have confused tenses. Furthermore, from the way the matter was being described, Sam could tell that Emin believed that he was delivering an accurate report. Sam felt his heart beating at full strength. This sensation in the absence of exertion, which elicited a disconcerting emotion, he'd had once before while discussing the dangers of the occult with friends. "A demon . . . Why do you think he's a demon?"

"That's not an opinion shared by everyone who's seen him."

"What? How many people have seen him?"

"Six of the men in our community that I know of. That number includes myself. The spirit has been there for months. He can't escape. I think that the words that Teoman called out in the night have imprisoned the spirit in the storeroom."

"What do the other men think he is?"

"Some say he's an angel."

"And if you think he's a demon, then why haven't you cast him out?" Sam inquired.

"I haven't got the power to do it." Emin looked frustrated.

"Nor does any human being, including myself, but he can be banished in the name of Jesus: in the way that you've read in the New Testament."

"I've tried . . . I've been down there once with that intention, but . . . But he talked to me. It felt as if I was there for only twenty minutes, but I was there for over four hours. He confused me and I left powerless. The demon does that to everyone who goes down there except for Yurtsev. He leaves there with more power."

"And what happens if you try to banish the spirit when out of his sight, for instance, from Teoman's bedroom. After all, aren't you assuming that what Teoman said from there chained the spirit to his present location?"

"I've tried. He's still there. What's more, Yurtsev is now dividing our community. I'll tell you more about him if you choose to come with me to Cappadocia."

Sam noticed that he'd unconsciously sat bolt upright in his seat. He sat back, pressing himself into the cushioned fabric. He took a deep breath. "And what about Teoman?"

"He's in a state. Ever since meeting the demon face to face Teoman hasn't been the same. I think he blames himself for all this." Emin paused. "I know that it's a lot to take in. To tell you the truth, for months I've been in anguish over the whole situation, and it's got a lot worse in the last two weeks. I've been asking God to give me the strength to deal with things. Last night I got down on my knees in despair and prayed to God, and then this morning I got your call."

Sam was thinking deeply. He silently prayed. His eyes remained open.

"I'll come to Cappadocia—but there's a real danger that I could bring even more trouble your way."

"I'm sure that the timing of your call is no coincidence," Emin said.

"Perhaps."

"Try and get some sleep; you look tired," Emin suggested.

"I feel tired. I won't sleep just yet though. It's important that I know the surroundings of where I'm going to stay. I'll sleep when I get to your home."

"As you like."

"Emin, there's something that I need to ask you. When you first met me, you looked so anxious?" Sam was probing for other problems not yet mentioned, especially for any that could be directly related to his mission.

"There's just been one thing after another. I was so worried that something would go wrong at the pick-up. I suppose that I'm just not used to all this. Don't mistake me, I've had a tough life, and I've had to deal with troubles before. Only since Sol Kadmiel's visit the nature of my troubles have changed. I've never dealt with things like this before . . . the demon . . . the discord. And there's so much at stake."

The sun was near to setting as Sam and Emin reached the border of Cappadocia. Sam had been awake for over thirty hours.

"Good timing," Emin said. "When we reach my home, it'll be dark."

Sam replied silently with a smile.

Turkey revealed another unique landscape to Sam's inquisitive yet tired eyes. The car was first driven through a land of huge serrated ridges; the entire scape resembled the magnified surface of an elephant's molar tooth.

As the two men travelled further into this seemingly other world, the white ridges gradually morphed into colossal, sharp canine teeth. Soon these teeth looked to be brushed with pink and mauve pastel shades. As the sun fell, it accentuated the stark jagged landscape but restrained the wealth of colour trying to emerge.

Before long the two men were advancing through a strange dark planet. There were no street lights, and all that Emin and Sam were able to see was that which was illuminated by the car's headlights. Emin slowed the vehicle's speed to 25 mph to negotiate the winding road, whose course was dictated by the rock formations. Fleeting views of cones, boulders and natural stone ramparts fluttered past the men like a flicked deck of cards on a loop. The soporific repetition reduced Sam's interest, and his fatigue started to gnaw.

The two men approached a group of seven approximately 40-foot-tall, mushroom-shaped, rocky outcrops. The stalks were elongated and white, and the heads small and grey. As the car came closer, Sam saw small windows irregularly spaced in the naturally white walls.

"Here we are," Emin said as he pulled up to the troglodyte dwellings.

"This place is incredible!" Sam exclaimed. He was so exhausted that his statement lacked the intended vibrancy.

"Wait till you get inside," Emin replied.

"This is your home?"

"Not all of them: just those two over there." Emin pointed to two of the mushroom-shaped outcrops. He kept the car's headlights on, so that Sam could see. The two outcrops appeared to be fused at the base. The one closest to the two men was much wider than the other. The outcrops would have looked like homes even before people lived in them, Sam thought. Moreover, to not take advantage of the natural phenomenon would have been course neglect. He could tell that even the roofs (the heads of the mushrooms) were natural, although in the low light they appeared as if tiled. He saw a door that he presumed was the entrance to Emin's home.

Emin left the car first and beckoned Sam to the larger of the two outcrops. As Sam disembarked, he saw that Emin was indeed a short stout man. Emin walked with small paces, appearing to almost shuffle.

"Before we go inside, I need to ask you: how many in your family live with you?" Sam inquired.

"There are just the three of us now: my wife and me, and our daughter. Our other children are all grown up and have left."

"Is there any way that you alone can see me? I'm thinking of them—the less they know the better."

"I see. They already know that someone is going to stay . . . they don't know who yet. I believe we can work it so that they never meet you—but it will take some explaining."

"Do you want to go in and do that? I'll wait out here. Oh, and they can't tell anyone that you have a guest staying."

"Give me a moment," Emin replied, and he entered his home.

A few minutes later Emin returned. "Everything's fine. Come in. You won't meet my family, and they'll be the soul of discretion."

"That's a very English turn of phrase."

"I picked it up from one of the Charles Clarke movies."

"And how well you've placed it," Sam observed.

The following day Sam saw a land with myriad rocky prominences decorated with the colours brilliant-white, pink, mauve, and yellow. The scenery was different from the landscape that he'd first met on entering Cappadocia. The bizarre rock formations had persisted, but in his current locale they appeared to be more independent from one another, at least on the surface. There was also more greenery, both unplanned and agricultural, between the rocky outcrops. Each protuberance was uniquely weathered and had its own character. He noticed that some of them had doors, perhaps to access homes like the one in which he was now staying, or maybe these penetrated protuberances were communal entrances to a subterranean village or town. He wondered if the doors were linked to the community that he was now connected with. He was looking out from a small glassless window, which was like a porthole. It was too small even for a small child to slip through yet provided his little room with just enough light to read without artificial assistance. He was careful not to put his face too close to the window, although he felt that this was overcautious. Emin's home had three floors: one at ground level, one above this and one subterranean. Sam's room was on the top level of this troglodyte dwelling.

The room itself was full of character. The interior walls revealed how it had first been hollowed and then smoothed. There were no straight lines. Nor was there the addition of plaster, although the walls had that appearance. They'd been whitewashed in order to contain as much light as possible by reflection. The bed had a thin wooden frame. Stretched both longitudinally and horizontally across the frame was rope, which supported a slim mattress. Sam had slept comfortably between fresh cotton sheets and beneath a beautifully patterned woollen blanket from Siirt. He'd awakened to a soft, cool breeze over his face. There was a single chair standing in front of an antique foldable desk, on which Emin had placed a pile of books, one of which was a well-used Bible, printed in English.

Emin and Sam hadn't talked much after they'd arrived. A meal had been prepared for them, which together they'd eaten in another small room on the same level as Sam's bedroom. During the meal Emin had told Sam that where they were eating wasn't the main dining room but would be a place where they could meet and talk without disturbance. Sam had then slept through to eleven in the morning, and instead of breakfast, an early lunch had been kindly prepared by one of his hosts.

Again, Sam and Emin sat and ate together. This time Sam had the energy to seek deep answers. After the customary pleasantries of the morning, the two men talked seriously.

"So one of the House was here with you: Sol Kadmiel," Sam stated.

"That's right," Emin replied.

"Known for giving good advice to those in battle," Sam added.

"True, although they're all meant to be good at giving general advice."

"Is there any point in asking you what he looked like?" Sam ventured.

"No, Charles, there's no point in asking what he looked like. In the same way that if anyone questioned me about you, I wouldn't tell them either."

"But he met a few of you?"

"Yes; however, they didn't know that he was a member of the House. They thought that he was a visiting missionary. Just a bit of encouragement for you though: he was much younger than I'd expected he'd be."

"Is that so?" Sam said, thinking about his own experience with Sol Hodaviah.

Emin reflected. "I guess I shouldn't have been that surprised; Solomon himself was at his wisest as a young man. It was only in his later years that he fell away from the truth."[1]

---

[1] The wisdom of Solomon in his early years: 1 Kings 2:1-4:34.
In his later years Solomon became a worshipper of idols, and as a result the Kingdom of the Hebrews was split into Judah and Israel: 1 Kings 11:1-12:24.

"That's true," Sam agreed. "You mentioned previously about the possibility of some sort of link between Sol Kadmiel's visit and the demon. Did Sol Kadmiel stay at Teoman's home?"

"Sol Kadmiel was in our village for only five days. He stayed here with us. He did visit Teoman at his home on one occasion though."

"And what did they talk about?"

"I don't exactly know. I wasn't there. I dropped him off, and Teoman brought him back a few hours later. Until now I've not had a need to question what they discussed, but Teoman mentioned a few things in passing. It seems to me that it was a discussion personal to Teoman. Sol Kadmiel gave Teoman some advice on his life, especially family life—probably similar to what Kadmiel passed on to me while he was in my home. He really is an excellent adviser."

"Yes, yes, that's their reputation," Sam remarked with blunted praise. He was keen to hear more pertinent facts.

Emin appeared to have not noticed Sam's eagerness to progress. "The way he provided solutions to my problems . . . such practical depth of thought . . ." Emin was clearly thinking about Sol Kadmiel's advice as he talked.

"Hmm . . . It doesn't seem that Sol Kadmiel's visit has anything to do with the occurrence of the demon."

"Perhaps not, although the House's presence in our community is a general reflection of our Christian work, which Satan will always oppose."

Sam thought carefully about Emin's last statement. "Yes, you're right . . . You're of much more interest to sinister forces than any random community."

"The attention that they pay to corrupting mankind . . ." Emin then changed what he was planning to say. "Well, I imagine that we're like a magnet to them."

"This is obviously something that you've felt as the head of your community. It's something that I've experienced on a personal level. It must be much harder to deal with when you're trying to guide a group of people."

"Yes, it is."

Emin reached into his pocket and pulled out a small brown bottle with a childproof lid. He removed the lid with a single proficient twist. Without waiting to be asked, he spoke, "It's my heart, Charles. I have a condition . . . What do you call it in English?"

"Angina?"

"Oh, is that what you still call it? Actually, I knew that but thought you used another term." Emin shook out a single white pill and popped it into his mouth. He washed it down with half a glass of water.

"What's that you're taking?"

"My lunchtime beta-blocker. I take some others when I get up and before I go to bed."

"Have you had any operations?"

"No, not yet, although my doctor says that I'm heading that way."

"Have you had a heart attack?"

"No."

"It's better to have the work done before you get one of those."

"So I've heard," Emin said wryly. Sam could tell that Emin had been offered some kind of operation but was delaying it.

Sam changed the subject: "Can I ask you: what happened when you went to confront the demon?"

"I was afraid when I went there."

"As anyone would be."

"Yes, except not in a good way . . . in a way that prepares you. Instead, it was the type of fear that disarms you," there was disappointment in Emin's voice. "As I entered the room, all I could think of was what I'd read in the Bible about Sceva's seven sons, who together confronted a man possessed by a demon in Ephesus."

"The passage doesn't leap to mind. Tell me about it." Sam had read the relevant passage in the New Testament but had forgotten the name Sceva.

"It's in the book of Acts.[1] They tried to cast out the demon by saying, 'We adjure[2] you by Jesus whom Paul preacheth.' The demon replied, 'Jesus I know, and Paul I know; but who are ye?' And the demon-possessed man beat them up, and they ran from the house naked and wounded."

"I remember the passage that you're talking about. The reason why they couldn't cast out the demon was because they themselves didn't believe in Jesus and were seeking fame for themselves. It's not our power that casts out the demon; it's the power of Jesus."

"I'm aware of that, Charles. However, it's still me who faces him. And it's my body that will be broken if he attacks me."

"That's true, but you're a believer."

"Yes, I am."

"And so if you pray to Christ, then He'll protect you and give you the courage to face anything. Be afraid of God, who can destroy both body and soul, rather than those things that can destroy only your body."[3]

"The demon started talking to me the instant I entered the storeroom. My fear was my first mistake. The second was that I engaged him in conversation. He just wasn't what I was expecting. Terrible, yes . . . but not hideous at all . . . quite the opposite in fact. Human features, only not like any man I've seen in my life. And there was something about his voice . . . I left hypnotized."

Sam started to feel uncomfortable. His aim was to encourage Emin, not to dishearten him. Sam often found it difficult to empower people. It usually meant that he would have to relay some constructive criticism, which resulted in a number of different reactions, some of which were negative and irrevocable.

---

[1] Acts 19:11-20. Sceva was the chief priest at that time.

[2] Adjure, a word not commonly used today, means command.

[3] Matthew 10:28. See Soul and Spirit pg 590 for an in-depth interpretation of this passage.

He thought that the difficulty occurred more because of his
method than because of the character of the individual with
whom he was communicating. I personally think that every
individual is different from another, and each can take encouragement and advice from some people but not from others.

"At least you tried, Emin. Who else in your community has
gone there with that intention?"

"Just me—and I'm positive that I would have heard about any
other attempts."

Sam continued, "And there's another man who's done the
opposite. He's gone there to profit from his meetings with the
demon."

"I suppose you're right."

"There's no supposing in it. I'm sure I'm right. Life is difficult
for you here in a country where your faith is persecuted . . . with
only a few true Christians to turn to for advice."

"Yes, there are Christians I can talk to but hardly any with
understanding beyond my own."

"Don't worry; God knows your predicament. However, He
also wants you to tell Him about it. Put your trust in Him! Ask
Him for guidance in the form of more wisdom to deal with
situations such as this—wisdom to find and understand those
passages in the Bible that are relevant to your circumstances."
Sam was now feeling positively awkward talking to a man more
than twice his age that way.

"You're young, yet your advice is good," Emin said, forgetting
his own earlier comment about the wisdom of Solomon.

Sam deflected the compliment: "I've had to pray similar
prayers to Him as well on more occasions than I can remember. I
think that they've been answered. And I know that I'll spend the
rest of my life depending on Him in this way. Anyway, I'm sure
that you'd give me excellent advice about other things: perhaps
things that I've not yet experienced."

Emin appeared to be thinking very deeply.

"The food is superb," Sam said. "Please thank the cook for
me."

"I'm glad you like it. My daughter cooked it for us. She has a real gift. She's engaged to one of the young men in our community."

"Good for him," Sam replied. "How old is she?"

"Eighteen. Her fiancé is not much older than you. And how about you, Charles—are you married?" Emin had said Sam's most recently assumed name in such a natural way that Sam was almost convinced himself.

"Not yet. One day I'd like to be."

"All in good time—there are a few things that you need to do first, yes?" Emin underestimated.

"Just a few," Sam replied.

"I know that you've just arrived, but I need to ask you: how do you propose to leave us? It's important that we make plans now . . . you never know, you may need to leave earlier than you intend."

"I've been thinking about that. I'm planning to head east from here," Sam said.

"I know nothing about your mission, so please tell me if I'm way off the mark with any of my suggestions. How about public transport?"

"No . . . I'd prefer not to use buses, trains, and the like, especially in this area. I've noticed a steady decline in tourists as I've travelled further inland . . . well . . . I'm going to stand out like a sore thumb."

"You don't look like a Westerner."

"True, but I also don't look ethnically Turkish. And then when I open my mouth—my Turkish is limited at best."

"How about a car?"

"That sounds better. At least I'd have my independence. The last car I had didn't last long though. They're watching the roads. Is there any other way that I can avoid the roads?"

"Let me have a think about that," Emin replied. "Charles, I need to go now; duty calls. I won't be able to have dinner with you tonight. If you enter this room at seven o'clock, there'll be food set out for you."

"No problem. Will we catch up tomorrow?"

"Yes, a little later: one o'clock."

Sam returned to his room and performed some upper-body exercises. Afterward, he opened some of the books on the desk. There was a basic Turkish-language book for beginners. There was also a guide book, which was of particular interest. It was written by a Turkish author for an English-speaking market. In preparation for the trip Sam had read the greater part of two guide books on Turkey; however, neither had been written by Turks.

Sam flicked through the guide book to the section on Mount Ararat. Directly below the heading the mountain was declared to be the highest in Turkey. The article then stated that "Some regard Mount Ararat as two mountains, Great Ararat and Little Ararat, but most as one with two peaks." The article continued to refer to Mount Ararat as one mountain with two peaks: "Both peaks are the result of volcanic eruptions, Great Ararat being the highest peak at 5,137 metres (16,854 feet). The mountain has other names. We Turks call it 'Ağrı Dağı', which means 'Mountain of Pain': a name derived from the hardship of its ascent. Many with Kurdish ancestry call it 'Çîyayê Agirî', which means 'Fiery Mountain', because of its history of volcanism. Over the centuries the mountain has been controlled by many different peoples, which in chronological order include the: Urartians, Persians, Greeks, Armenians, Romans and Seljuk Turks. More recently it was conquered by the Ottoman Empire in 1517. Subsequently, for three centuries this empire fought with Persia for control of the mountain. In 1855 the Ottoman Empire shared possession with Russia, which later became a major part of the Soviet Union. At one time the mountain became the only point at which Turkey,[1] Persia and the Soviet Union all met,

---

[1] The massive Ottoman Empire (controlled by Turkish rulers), which encompassed many racial and religious groups spanning parts of Europe, western Asia and the Middle East, although

FOOTNOTE CONTINUED ON THE NEXT PAGE

serving as a natural barrier to the three countries." The author proudly stated that "In 1920, following a peace treaty signed with Armenia, Ararat became the sole possession of Turkey." A few lines further down Sam read that "Many people have climbed the mountain in order to find the legendary Noah's Ark, yet none have discovered any conclusive evidence." The article ended with the final statement, "Not surprising, since the Koran states that the Ark came to rest on a different mountain, called Mount Judi, which we Turks call Cudi Dağı,[1] which is in southeast Turkey near the border with Iraq."

Unlike this article, for the rest of my account when Mount Ararat is mentioned, then it will be only Great Ararat that is being referred to.

The following day Emin and Sam picked up where they'd left off.

"Tell me about Yurtsev?" Sam asked.

"Yurtsev . . . Yurtsev is a greedy manipulator. Over half of the community have been utterly beguiled by him, and the other half are just confused. I don't care that someone else becomes the leader . . . I mean it's inevitable, and maybe sooner than I expect with this heart of mine. Only I want the right person to take over: someone who serves the people and not himself: someone who's trying his best to guide others onto the right path, not take them off it."

"It appears that you're in trouble with this man. I want to help you, but I need to know more about him."

"Help us get rid of the demon, and this will all settle down," Emin was becoming wound up.

"I'm not sure if it's that simple, Emin."

CONTINUED FOOTNOTE PRESENT

breaking apart for many years, came to an end in 1922. In 1923 the Republic of Turkey was declared and contains the area that had been central to the Ottoman Empire.
[1] The Koran 11 Hud (Hūd):44.

"This all started with the demon's presence. Before that, Yurtsev was fine. Well, not completely . . . I had a couple of disagreements with him but no earthquakes."

"Earth-shattering?" Sam should have resisted correcting Emin's phrase.

"That's right—nothing earth-shattering."

"The demon may be the trigger. However, even in his absence, Yurtsev could still pursue his present course. In fact, there's no reason why the problem won't intensify."

"He's a self-serving . . ."

"I understand that, but tell me more about the man."

"Well, he's rich: by far the richest of us all."

"Not a crime in itself—rich from what?" Sam asked.

"He owns a small supermarket in the nearest aboveground town."

"How old is he?"

"Forty years old. He's also very intelligent."

"What does he look like?"

"Aren't you more interested in his character?"

"I am, which is why I need to know what he looks like. I'll ask you more about your assessment of his character afterward."

Emin broke off from his series of answers. "I tell you who you remind me of."

"Who?"

"Sol Kadmiel."

"Really? Why?" Sam inquired.

"When I asked him for advice, he also wanted to know what the people involved look like."

Sam answered, "Because what a person looks like has some measure of an effect on the formation of his or her character. The world is a mirror to the human soul, allowing us to constantly make adjustments as we interact with people throughout our lives. How this man looks will influence how people respond to him, and so this knowledge will help me understand him better and predict how he'll behave in the future."

"That's pretty much what Sol Kadmiel said," Emin replied.

"It's the truth."

"Yurtsev is tall: easily six feet. He's thin—not bony."

"Has he still got hair on his head?"

"Yes, a full head—it's white though."

"Has he a beard or moustache?"

"No, he's always clean-shaven."

"How do people regard him?"

"He's a friendly sort—gets on with most. Women generally like the look of him. I first got to know him properly when he was a teenager. I was in my late twenties then. He's one of those people who are determined to achieve the goals they set themselves. That can sometimes cause friction, yet he always managed to not stir up any resentment."

"Has he got a family?"

"Yes, a wife, a son and a daughter."

"So far he sounds all right. I'm just joking. Go on." Sam realized that his joke was misplaced. He'd tried to alleviate Emin's tension but had failed.

"You see, that's the thing. If you'd asked me a year ago whether I thought him likely to do any of this . . . even with the intervention of this evil spirit . . . I would have said no, absolutely not. I guess there are dormant ambitions inside some people that need the right conditions to surface."

"Maybe there are hidden ambitions inside us all," Sam proposed.

"Yes, maybe—but some people's deep desires are good."

"True." Sam then changed tack: "Of the two hundred members in your community, how many were converts from Islām?"

"Around a third of us. I'm sure that you're aware that there's a great deal of hostility directed toward Muslims who find Christ—and toward those who told them about Him. We face much: death threats, actual death—sometimes even from members of our own families."

"I'm aware of this—and more than ever since entering Turkey."

"This is our life."

"Do you ever think about leaving Turkey?"

"Yes, I have, especially when things get really bad. But these are my people. Without us, who else have they got to tell them about Christ? Some of us have left though, spreading the good news wherever we go. I suppose that all peoples are our brothers and sisters."

"And how about the others—the two-thirds? What are their backgrounds?"

"A few have Roman Catholic and Eastern Orthodox origins, who then became Christians and later joined us. As for the rest, they're second-, third- or more generation Christians, who were born in the community. Of course, nobody is born a Christian. You know how it is—personal choice—the children grow up—some choose Christianity—others don't."

"Yes, true Christianity can never be imposed, otherwise it isn't Christianity. And do you baptize?"

"Certainly, once an individual has become a Christian. In keeping with what's written in the Bible, we baptize by fully immersing him or her under water."[1]

"So there must be some amongst you who aren't Christians?"

"Yes, there are some who haven't chosen this path. They're welcome to stay as long as they want."

"And how about Yurtsev? Where does he fit into all of this?"

"Yurtsev is kind of second generation. He was brought up in the community. His father, Ahmet, was formerly Muslim, like me. Ahmet had lived on the west coast and had become a Christian there. He suffered so much persecution that he moved inland to us. He was a strong man. I remember him well. In Cappadocia he met his wife, whose family is one of the oldest here."

---

[1] Matthew 3:16, 28:18-20, Mark 16:15-16, Acts 2:37-42, 8:12-38, 9:17-18—the Greek word for baptize (baptizo) in the New Testament literally means to make fully wet, i.e., to cover completely with water.

"Is Yurtsev a Christian?"

"That's a good question. He goes to the church services, he sings the songs and to a certain extent he used to talk the talk, but a true believer . . . I really don't think so. And now that this has happened."

"Has he been baptized? Not that this means he's definitely a Christian, but usually before people are baptized in the UK they make a public declaration of their belief; they openly tell people what's led them to the decision to follow Christ."

"We do that here as well. And no, he hasn't been baptized."

"So what did the demon say?" Sam asked.

"Do you want to hear what he said to me or what he said to all of us as a community?"

"I'd like to hear both, except it's important that in our conversation you separate what he said to you from what he said to others. I'm inclined to put more weight on your firsthand evidence."

"As I said, I've been there only once, unlike Yurtsev, who's been there many times. Much of what the demon has proclaimed has been relayed to the community by Yurtsev. I'm not just talking about a few statements but an entire way to behave based on a set of beliefs. You might call it a 'teaching' or put more strongly, an 'instruction'."

"Actually, I might call it a 'doctrine'."[1]

Emin paused and thought. "That would be the correct way to put it. By the way, what's the difference between doctrine and dogma?"

"Practically nothing. A dogma is a doctrine that's essential for members of a faith to follow. However, a doctrine works in exactly the same way: once accepted by people, it too becomes essential to their faith."

---

[1] Doctrine means teaching or instruction (the latter is more precise). Doctrine can also mean a collection of all the doctrines encompassed by a religion.

"I understand. Which would you like to hear first: what the demon said to me or what he said to others?"

"Firstly, what Yurtsev and the others have declared that the demon said."

"The demon says that his name is Shezeren or something very similar to that. He claims that his first post was as an angel in Heaven—a soldier in one of God's armies.[1] After the Flood, he was made a Sumerian captain and was later elevated to the position of deputy of Lagash, one of Sumer's most prominent ancient cities." There was a mutual understanding between Emin and Sam that the posts occupied by Shezeren on Earth were supernatural positions.

"After the Flood! Haven't you missed out a whole chunk of time: over one and a half thousand years?"[2]

"I presume that when Lucifer fell, Shezeren joined the rebellion," Emin suggested.

"Has he told anyone this?"

"No. And he also didn't mention who gave him these positions on Earth."

"Has anybody asked him directly if he's a demon?"

"Not that I've heard. And that's not because some, including myself, haven't wanted to. You see, when a person enters that storeroom, it's as if Shezeren has complete control over what happens there. He somehow takes charge over what's said—in both directions. Questions are asked of him, only never the right ones."

---

[1] God has armies—the "LORD of hosts" literally means "Yahweh of armies", Yahweh being God's personal name: 1 Samuel 1:3, 1 Kings 18:15, 1 Chronicles 17:7 and many more.

Before Lucifer's fall, the entire Heavenly hosts were at God's command. God ultimately has control over all His creation, but it is His will that Lucifer now commands those angels who chose to reject Him and who are not already confined to the Abyss. See Chapter 4 pg 104 and footnote regarding the Abyss.

[2] See Timeline.

"Please carry on."

"He then worked with, or 'on' you might say, the Assyrians in the city of Ashur—again as a deputy. He was later raised to what was his highest position as the general of Nineveh, north of Ashur, and was the force behind the statue of Nergal. That last bit came from only one of the men—Çelebi. So far all of the post-Flood positions that I've told you about were within the borders of what is now Iraq. I imagine that the higher Shezeren's rank, the more demons he had beneath him to command and so the more influence he had over the affairs of men."

"Who or what is Nergal?"

"He was known as the god of the Underworld, amongst other things."[1]

"The god of the Underworld, no less." Sam's eyebrows rose.

"Shezeren was later transferred from Nineveh to Babylon, still in Iraq, although he seems to have deliberately not mentioned what his role was there. He claims to have flown to ancient Albion after Babylon fell to the Medes and the Persians."

"What? Britain!"

"I thought you'd get a start when I mentioned that."

"And what did he do there?"

---

[1] Myths from Mesopotamia *Nergal and Ereshkigal (Amarna version)*—reports on how the god Nergal descended to the Underworld, where he became its ruler.

Nergal was reportedly a brother of the god Sin: Myths from Mesopotamia *Atrahasis tablet II (Old and Standard Babylonian inscriptions)*.

Nergal was also a prominent god in the cities of Babylon and Cuthah: see above reference, *Atrahasis tablet II* (Nergal mentioned in a Standard Babylonian inscription); Mesopotamian Chronicles *19 From the end of Aššur-nādin-šumi to the revolt of Šamaš-šuma-ukīn (694-652) and a few earlier reigns; 52 Chronographic Document concerning Nabû-šuma-iškun.*

"He hasn't said; however, he was in your country for about two thousand years. He says that he's now a wandering instrument of his master."

"And aren't you fortunate that he wandered to you," Sam said. "I think that his roving is more purposeful than he wants us to believe."

"Now I'll tell you what he's been spreading, that is, the doctrine through Yurtsev."

"His high priest."

Emin thought about the mediatory priest-like role of Yurtsev. "Yes, that's right." He then continued, "As Shezeren is a demon, I'd have thought that the last thing that he would want to talk about was God and Christ, yet they're the main focus of his conversations. He says that there is only one God. Of course, you and I agree with that, but the Bible makes it clear in the New Testament that God has three aspects: the Father, the Son and the Holy Spirit.[1] Shezeren absolutely denies this Trinity."

"You know, Emin, the Old Testament also tells us about these three aspects."

"Really?"

"Yes, for example, in the first three verses of Genesis there are both God[2] and the Spirit of God. And the Hebrew name used in these verses for God is Elohim, which is plural, therefore literally meaning Gods, yet the Hebrew verb in the first verse (to create) and the Hebrew verb in the third verse (to say), which both relate to what He did, are singular, demonstrating that He is one."[3]

---

[1] Matthew 3:16, John 1:1-34, 4:23-24, 5:5-27, Acts 2:17-18, 20:27-28, Romans 15:6, 1 Corinthians 6:11, 2 Corinthians 1:3, Galatians 1:1, Colossians 2:8-11, 1 Timothy 3:16, Hebrews 1:1-14, 1 John 4:14-16, 5:7, 2 John 1:19.

[2] Note that the New Testament demonstrates that the creator aspect of God is the Messiah God: John 1:1-18, Ephesians 3:9, Colossians 1:12-19, Hebrews 1:1-2.

[3] Genesis 1:1-3. In verse 2, the verb (to move) related to either Spirit of God or Spirit of Gods would naturally be singular.

"And how about the Son of God?" Emin asked.

"Hundreds of years before Jesus was born the Jewish prophets wrote about the Messiah (the Christ) as a being who would come into the world as a baby but whose existence would be from everlasting. There is no being who fits this description other than God.[1] More directly, it was also written that this Messiah, who would be born from among the Jewish people, would be known as mighty God and everlasting Father. This makes it absolutely clear that the Messiah is one with God the Father."[2]

"It'd be great to look at those passages with you some time." Emin had in fact read them many times except hadn't appreciated their significance.

"Definitely."

"Shezeren says that Jesus is just a man, and not both man and God. In this way, he brings Jesus down."

"And therefore downgrades the work that Jesus did on the Earth for the benefit of mankind,"[3] Sam added.

"It's worse than that. Shezeren says that Jesus didn't even die on the cross. Moreover, he says that Jesus never died at any time! Shezeren says that Jesus' would-be executioners were tricked, and another man died in His place. Then, he says, at a later time Jesus ascended to Heaven. The last bit about the Ascension is the only true part."

Sam placed his palms onto his forehead and thought very carefully. "So by appearing to loyally set God above and apart

---

[1] Micah 5:2.

[2] Isaiah 9:6-7.

[3] Sam was referring to the fact that Jesus' life on Earth as the incarnation of God (Jesus being fully man and fully God) is replete with instances of miracles that directly benefited mankind and that confirmed His divinity. Furthermore, although Jesus could command a myriad of angels to take Him off the cross, He remained there, again for our benefit. Matthew 4:5-7, 11:2-27, 13:41-43, 26:47-57, Luke 4:9-12, John 5:19-36, 10:23-38, 14:10-13, 15:23-24, Acts 2:22.

from others, the situation becomes the opposite of what God
Himself intended. Moreover, the sacrifice of God's own Son is
ignored." He then posed a question to Emin: "In Shezeren's
world how can people's sins be forgiven if Jesus didn't die for
them?"

"He does away with that entirely. Shezeren says that the first
thing you have to do is believe in God. After that, God designates
to you a pair of scales, onto which He places your good deeds on
one side and your bad deeds on the other. At your death, if the
good outweighs the bad, then you get into Heaven."

"Therefore, what he's saying is in direct opposition to what's
in the Bible. The Bible says that if you turn to God, ask Jesus'
forgiveness for your sins and accept Him as your personal
saviour, then you will get into Heaven;[1] the second and third
parts are required, because Jesus is the one who sacrificed His
life for you. We Christians have the Heavenly assurance while on
Earth.[2] But according to Shezeren, there are no assurances in this
life. You have to wait until your day of judgement before you
know what God decides. What a desperate situation: people
living their lives trying to please God yet not doing what He truly
requires. They're counting deeds and hoping. And the Bible tells
you what happens when you follow this uncertain path: your
destination is Hell.[3] There are no individual acts or series of good

---

[1] John 3:13-21, 14:1-11, Acts 3:1-26, 4:10-12, 5:29-32, 26:15-18, 1
Peter 1:3-4. Salvation is a gift from God through Christ's sacrifice.
Good deeds are commendable but cannot in themselves grant you a
place in Heaven. The Bible encourages us to both put our faith in
Christ and do good works, but only the former can access Heaven.
Matthew 5:14-16, Ephesians 2:1-10, 2 Timothy 3:17, Titus 2:11-14,
3:4-8.

[2] John 14:1-3, Acts 4:10-12, Romans 1:16, Ephesians 1:1-14, 2
Timothy 3:14-15, 1 Peter 1:1-9.

[3] Matthew 25:31-46, Mark 9:47-48, John 3:13-21, 3:36, 2 Thessalonians 1:7-9, Revelation 20:13-15.

deeds that can get you into Heaven. Heaven is a gift from God, granted through His Son."[1]

"That's about it in a nutshell," Emin said.

"And what about your meeting with him?" Sam asked.

"He told me some of what I've said. In addition, he told me things about myself that I and only I know. He told me secrets about people in our community and even told me about the future."

"The future?"

"What he thinks is the future. As you'd expect, he said it as if it's the absolute truth that time would bring to pass. Don't worry; I know that demons can't tell the future. They might be able to predict events better than us humans. After all, they've more information at their disposal and have the experience of seeing earthly events played out for thousands of years. What he told me is only a possible future. Only God knows the future. And me— I'm just going to live my life to the best of my ability with God as my guide."

Sam puffed out his cheeks, and his brow furrowed deeply. "Shezeren's scam is quite something. I've read some of the literature published by the Jehovah's Witnesses, and their stance on Jesus sounds like Shezeren's. The obvious difference is that they accept that Jesus did die, but they still believe that He's less than God and shouldn't be worshipped.[2] Therefore, the purpose

---

[1] John 3:13-21, Acts 4:10-12, Romans 5:1-21, 2 Timothy 1:9, Titus 3:5-7, 1 Peter 1:3-4. See Dispensations (5).

[2] The official stance of Jehovah's Witnesses is that they believe that Jesus is the Son of God, that Jesus was human on the Earth and that Jesus' perfect life and sacrifice allows us to have our sins forgiven BUT that: Jesus is not Almighty God; Jesus is only godlike or at best a type of lesser god being able to be called "a god" only because He represents God; Jesus is a created being; Jesus is the archangel Michael; Jesus should not be worshipped; and salvation is through (i) "faith in the value of the sacrifice of Jesus' human life"—an uncertain term, (ii) applying to one's life what Jesus said

FOOTNOTE CONTINUED ON THE NEXT PAGE

of His life, although important, doesn't have its true significance: that God walked with us on Earth in the form of a man and felt the things we've felt, including temptation, but, unlike us, He did no wrong and could therefore be the perfect sacrifice for our sins.[1] Jesus is our God, who we should pray to and worship."[1]

CONTINUED FOOTNOTE PRESENT

---

regarding the type of people His disciples should be, and (iii) doing the work that Jesus ordered His followers to do. The source for the above is Reasoning from the Scriptures published by Watch Tower Bible and Tract Society *chapters: Jesus Christ, Salvation, Trinity.* This is a book used to instruct Jehovah's Witnesses in delivering the message of their doctrine and answering questions asked by those they address. The book contradicts itself by stating that Jesus is an angel and yet also had a human life on Earth. Jesus cannot be Michael. The Bible states that: angels are separate from Jesus; angels are to worship Jesus; and God the Father has only one Son, whom the Father claimed as His own and calls God along with Himself (Hebrews 1:1-14). Furthermore, Michael, when contending with the Devil (Satan), deferred to the Lord to rebuke the Devil (Jude 1:9), whereas Jesus rebuked the Devil (Matthew 4:1-11, Luke 4:1-14). These facts demonstrate that Jesus is both a different individual from and is superior to Michael. Moreover, Jesus is Lord. To believe in Jesus Christ is to believe that He is God (John 20:24-29), the Almighty God (Revelation 15:3—Jesus, the Lamb [John 1:29], is referred to as Lord God Almighty). The reason why Jesus said (John 14:28), "Ye have heard how I said unto you, I go away, and come *again* unto you. If ye loved me, ye would rejoice, because I said, I go unto the Father: for my Father is greater than I", is because God putting on flesh was humbling; Almighty God made Himself lower than the angels for us, so that He could be sacrificed (Hebrews 2:7-9).

The other objections to the doctrine of the Jehovah's Witnesses are within this chapter.

[1] See Chapter 7 pg 155 and footnote regarding the same collection of topics. The footnote includes the following four headings: God on the Earth in the form of a man (God the Son); While on Earth,
FOOTNOTE CONTINUED ON THE NEXT PAGE

"It's interesting what you say about the Jehovah's Witnesses, because this is similar to what the Koran says about Jesus. The Koran says that He was only a prophet, and that He was a man and not also God[2]—of course, I'm translating the word Allāh as God, which is commonly done; however, I'm not convinced is the right thing to do." Emin stopped to think for a few seconds, then continued with their main topic of discussion: "The main difference is that the Koran says that Jesus didn't die[3] . . . what Shezeren says."

"I've read only a few passages from the Koran," Sam said. He stored what Emin had mentioned concerning the uncertain translation of Allāh.

CONTINUED FOOTNOTE PRESENT

Jesus experienced the following: birth, loss of a friend, despair, joy, physical pain, compassion, friendship, righteous anger, betrayal, life-threatening danger, death and more; Jesus was directly tempted by Satan; and Jesus was the perfect sacrifice.

[1] Zechariah 14:1-21 (this chapter is about the Messiah's return—see Chapter 20 pg 406 regarding the Messiah arriving at the Mount of Olives), Matthew 2:1-2, Romans 8:34, Philippians 2:9-11, Colossians 1:13-20, Hebrews 1:1-10, 7:22-28, 1 John 2:1, Revelation 5:1-14 (the Lamb is Jesus the Messiah, the Word of God, the King of kings and Lord of lords—John 1:1-18, Revelation 5:6-7:17, 17:14, 19:1-21).

[2] The Koran 3 The Family of 'Imran (Āl 'Imrān):59-62, 4 Women (An-Nisā'):170-173, 5 The Feast (Al-Mā'idah):15-17, 70-77, 116-118, 9 Repentance (At-Tawba):30.

[3] The Koran reports that although it was declared that Jesus the Messiah had been killed, this was not in fact the case, for He had not been crucified, but it was made to appear that way. It then essentially states that He was raised up to Heaven, therefore not experiencing death at any time. This is odd, as it contradicts another part of the Koran that states that the infant Jesus predicted that He would die and be raised to life again. The Koran 4 Women (An-Nisā'):155-159, 19 Mary (Maryam):27-34.

"I've read it many times. The Koran indicates that there have
been five great prophets on the Earth. Many others are mentioned, but the Koran emphasizes five. Jesus is one of them."[1]

"And the others?"

"In chronological order: Noah, Abraham, Moses, (then Jesus)
and Muḥammad.[2] The Koran affirms that although the five great
prophets received special messages that set them apart from
others, they were still merely men.[3] Muḥammad is believed to be
the greatest prophet in the Koran, even though Jesus is the only
one born of a virgin."

"The Koran actually says that Jesus was born of a virgin?"

---

[1] The Koran 2 The Cow (Al-Baqarah):252-253, 3 The Family of
'Imran (Āl 'Imrān):45-54, 4 Women (An-Nisā'):171, 5 The Feast
(Al-Mā'idah):46-47, 73-77, 109-111, 19 Mary (Maryam):27-34,
43 Ornaments of God (Az-Zukhruf):57-59, 61 Solid Lines (As-
Saff):5-6.

[2] The Koran 2 The Cow (Al-Baqarah):87, 33 The Joint Forces (Al-
Ahzāb):7, 36 Ya Sin (Yā-Sīn):2-6, 42 Consultation (Ash-Shūra):13,
57 Iron (Al-Hadīd):26-27.

[3] Regarding the prophets being merely men according to the Koran:
Noah sought for forgiveness—71 Noah (Nūh):21-28; Abraham was
concerned about being disgraced on the Day of Resurrection and
wanted forgiveness for his sins on the Day of Judgement—16 The
Bee (An-Nahl):120-121, 26 The Poets (Ash-Shu'arā'):69-89; Moses
needed forgiveness for slaying another man—28 The Story (Al-
Qasas):14-17; Muḥammad needed past and future sins forgiven—
48 Triumph (Al-Fath):1-9; and references for statements that Jesus
was only a prophet, a man and not God are in the relevant previous
footnote (pg 251). Interestingly, nowhere in the Koran does it
mention that Jesus sinned or needed forgiveness. The Koran's only
attempt to deny His divinity by logic rather than blind statement is
by reporting that He ate food—5 The Feast (Al-Mā'idah):75.
However, this completely misses the point regarding Jesus' nature:
that He is God made flesh and therefore ate food whilst with us on
Earth.

"Yes, it does very clearly."[1]

"Then how can Jesus be a lesser prophet than Muḥammad?!"

"Indeed, it doesn't make sense. Also, Muḥammad didn't perform any miracles during his lifetime."[2]

"Whereas Jesus performed many great miracles: He gave sight to the blind, made the lame walk, cast out demons, walked on water and raised the dead to life."[3]

Emin produced a folded up piece of paper. He opened up the single sheet. "This is something that I looked up before you arrived. It's about a man called Arius, who lived in Alexandria, in Egypt, in the third and fourth centuries AD. I'll read it to you.

"The doctrine of Arius is as follows. There was a time when the Son of God did not exist, but God the Father has always existed. The Father created the Son from nothing in a similar way to His other creations. As a created being, the Son is changeable, whereas the Father is unchangeable. The Father is not divisible, and as the Son is a created being, He cannot be part of the Father and therefore cannot truly know or understand the Father. For these reasons the Father is the only true God and He alone should be worshipped. At most the Son should be venerated."[4]

---

[1] The Koran 3 The Family of 'Imran (Āl 'Imrān): 45-48, 19 Mary (Maryam):16-34, 21 The Prophets (Al-Anbiyā'):91.

[2] The Koran 17 The Night Journey (Al-Isrā'):89-96.

[3] Jesus performed these miracles and more: Matthew 4:23-24, 9:20-35, 14:14-21, 14:24-33, Mark 2:1-12, 7:25-30, 8:22-25, John 2:1-11, 11:14-45.

[4] The above articulation of the doctrine of Arius, a presbyter (a minister)*, is formulated from Arius' own statements, those of his supporters and those of his opponents. Variations of the above doctrine are also evident, which include: that the Son is a superior creation to the rest of creation in that He is perfect; and that the Son is unchangeable. Documents of the Early Arian Controversy: documents by Arius—1 and 15; documents by Arius' supporters—4, 9, 10, 11, 12, 13(a), 16 and 24; documents by Arius' opponents—

FOOTNOTE CONTINUED ON THE NEXT PAGE

Emin continued, "Arius' doctrine completely ignores the passages of the New Testament that clearly show that Jesus Christ (the Messiah) is God and was with God the Father before coming to us in the form of a man. And that Christ is in fact the creator of all things and not something that was created.[1] Also, that He is unchangeable and one with God the Father."[2] Emin folded the piece of paper.

Sam added, "His doctrine also ignores those passages I mentioned in the Old Testament that show that the Messiah predicted to come to Earth as a man was in existence already and had been

CONTINUED FOOTNOTE PRESENT

2.2, 17, 20, 25 and 26. For referencing of documents see Bibliography.

*With regard to the church, in the New Testament the Greek word "presbuteros" (presbyter) means "an elder", but in many churches after the period of the apostles presbyter wrongly came to denote a minister.

[1] John 1:1-18, 8:23-59, 17:1-5, Ephesians 3:9, Colossians 1:12-19, Hebrews 1:1-2.
Arius and his followers were willfully in error over the biblical passages related to the Son being begotten. The eternal God Messiah put on flesh, so that He could be a sacrifice for our sins. The putting on of flesh, that is, being born on Earth in the form of a man, did happen at a discrete point in time, but the Messiah coexisted, coexists and will coexist with God the Father and the Holy Spirit eternally (from eternity to eternity). It is the Messiah's birth on Earth that the biblical passages refer to when stating that He was begotten of the Father (John 1:14-18, 3:16-18, 16:28, Hebrews 1:3-9, 1 John 4:9-10). Jesus the Messiah was begotten by the Father through the overshadowing of Mary by the Holy Spirit (see Chapter 9 pg 206 and footnote regarding the same topic).
[2] John 10:30-38 (in this passage Jesus states that He is one with the Father, that He is the Son of God, and that He is in the Father and the Father is in Him), 14:9-11, Hebrews 13:8.

from everlasting, and furthermore is God.[1] The Old and New Testaments are in perfect harmony about the divinity of Christ."

"Arius was one of many men to take up the false doctrine that now carries his name and disseminate it. The doctrine was named after him and not the others, who also espoused it, because he was the most famous of its promoters. He died in 336 AD, over two hundred years before Muḥammad was even born."[2]

"Shezeren's obviously trying to rehash some of the old lies in order to deceive," Sam observed.

"It's incredible that none of these false doctrines break away entirely from the Bible to make something completely new."

"That's the way of things: the most convincing lie is a mixture of truth and lie," Sam accurately commented. "Whatever web of deceit Shezeren's spun, he's chosen one that could entangle your community more than any other he could have devised."

"So it seems."

"I can see just how easy these doctrines are to believe as well. Their followers could genuinely think that they're pleasing God yet at the same time be rejecting their only way to Heaven— Jesus. And if they stay on these deceptive paths, then Hell will be their destination."

"That's what Satan wants," Emin said.

---

[1] Isaiah 9:6, Micah 5:2.

[2] Islām and the religion of the Jehovah's Witnesses (started by Charles Russell in around 1880) contain doctrines that resemble the erroneous doctrine of Arius.

Chapter 12   **Shezeren**

500 miles east of the Cappadocian caverns stood Mount Ararat, a majestic snow-capped monument to God's judgement. Its southwestern face towered over a plain that was 10 miles distant, on which lay the town of Doğubayazıt. To the southeast of the town the land rose to a small peak. On this hilltop was the İshak Paşa Sarayı, once a working fortress from the 14th to 18th centuries and named after one of its last owners, a Kurdish governor. The fortress's position had allowed its occupants to control the local region through which a segment of the Silk Road had passed. At the time of Sam's mission, the Iranian border was located 8 miles south of the fortress. To some individuals this border was not any less significant than the Silk Road had been, yet a crumbling fortress was all that the tourists met. Unlike many older Anatolian ruins, the İshak Paşa Sarayı was still roofed in places, and the different buildings that made up the whole were easily identifiable. There were halls for entertaining, a mosque with a standing minaret, a library, courtyards, bedrooms, soldiers' quarters, a harem containing over twenty rooms, kitchens and other rooms besides. In the day visitors came to see the fortress's remains—an eclectic fusion of architectural styles reflecting the varied ethnic origins of those who'd had possession over the centuries—and the imposing view of the plain of Doğubayazıt along with other lands south of Mount Ararat. The visitors would walk around the fortress's skeleton, oblivious to the fact that it was still alive. Three areas were still roofed: the mosque, the school and the baths. In the latter and less-visited site was a secret entrance, which led downward to the Guardian of Turkey's eastern base of operations.

50 metres underground—beneath layers of steel and concrete, which made the installation impregnable to bunker-penetrating missiles—the Guardian was at his desk in his large well-illuminated office. He was sitting too far forward, taking scant

advantage of his comfortable black leather chair, as one of three standing men reported to him. The Guardian's body was tense, and his elbows dug into the desk. His left hand was rolled into a fist, and his right hand enveloped the left. The organization to which he belonged had expectations of him. His role as their chief Turkish tactician carried great responsibility. He glared at the three men. One of them had already nervously delivered his report.

The middle subordinate was speaking—the end of a lengthy exchange. "I assure you, emir; he's no longer in Antalya. We've scoured the entire area and left a patrol . . . nothing."

"And how about you?" the Guardian referred to the last of the three, who stood to the left of the one who'd just completed his report. This last man had connections within the Turkish police as well as other government agencies.

"There are only three Samuel A. Marches in the world of his approximate age with credit cards. Cards belonging to two of these men have been used in the USA within the last two days. We have limited information on these men, but their profiles suggest that they aren't . . ."

"Neither of them is him," the Guardian interrupted. "He's still here in Turkey, hiding yet moving toward us."

The subordinate continued, "We have the relevant highways covered: there's a man for every fifty miles. Every Mount Ararat climbing permit for this year and all future years has been reviewed and cross-checked."

"He won't have a permit." The Guardian then addressed all the men, "I know something of this man. I want you to change your approach. I think he's being harboured. Go back to Antalya. Use your teams efficiently. Make a systematic search of all the known Christian communities. Spread out in an ever-increasing semicircle. Stop after one hundred miles in the westward direction. Continue eastward in a quarter circle toward the mountain. Make inquiries. Infiltrate—pretend to be a Christian if you have to. Don't go in heavy—all you'll do is alert him and he'll run. Contact our spies already in the groups." The Guardian was also aware that anyone could have taken March in. The harbourer didn't need to be a Christian to do this. March wouldn't need to tell the harbourer anything. The Guardian was simply looking for maximum return: both time and manpower were limited. If the Christian enclaves failed to deliver a result, he would command his men to survey the expatriate communities. "Continue to cover the highways. Check every mountaineering shop. I want a man in the minaret watching day and night. You have your orders."

On Sam's fourth day in Cappadocia he ate lunch with Emin as usual. Their conversation persisted after the meal.

"Would a flight to Batman be helpful? Do you know where it is?" Emin looked pleased that he could offer this to Sam. Batman, located in Southeast Turkey, is a province that contains a town that's called by the same name. Emin was referring to the province, which is approximately 300 miles east of Cappadocia.

"Yes, I know where it is," Sam replied. "But I need to avoid commercial and chartered flights. The airports are likely to be watched. I know nothing about the airport in Batman. Is it quiet?"

"That doesn't matter. You would land in Batman but not at the airport. One of the men in our community has a small plane, which he uses to spray crops." Emin saw Sam's face light up as he realized the significance of the offer.

"Why Batman in particular? It suits me well enough." The location addressed a concern of Sam: that if detected, an anonymous plane may attract unwanted attention. Batman would progress his journey by a few hundred miles, and if the plane was spotted by the enemy, he could possibly lose them again far from his own intended goal. Flying further east into regions near either the town of Doğubayazıt or the city of Van could draw the enemy's interest to where he didn't want it to be.

"There's a particular group of fields in Batman. One field has been left fallow, and it's long enough for the pilot to land. He can identify it at night, because it's bordered by a well-lit freeway. It could all be done after dark. It's the furthest east that he can carry you and put you down safely."

"And the pilot?"

"Kenan—he's fine with everything. Owes me a dozen favors, and he's very trustworthy. He hasn't even asked me any questions about you—although I did tell him that you're a missionary."

"Of sorts," Sam added.

"And in this country that's dangerous work. So don't worry about Kenan."

"Well, Emin, Batman works for me."

"Once he sets you down . . . that's it . . . you'll have no transportation."

"Let me worry about that, except, if you could, I'll need you to get me a few things." Sam handed Emin a piece of paper.

"What's this?" Emin looked closely at the single white A6-sized sheet. "A shopping list?"

"Kind of."

"Do you want to see the tunnels tonight? If we go in the early morning hours, nobody will be in the communal section."

"I do want to see them—not tonight though. I can risk only a single outing. On that night I'll go to the storeroom as well."

"And face the demon?"

"That's right."

"So soon?"

"I would go tonight, but there's some preparation that I need to do. Emin, don't look so worried. I've gathered the facts, and now . . . Now I need to act."

"What preparation do you need to do? Is there anything I can help with?"

"In addition to praying, I'm going to fast tomorrow before I confront the demon."

"Why are you going to do that?"

"Because of what's written in the book of Mark. There was a time when the disciples failed to cast out a demon. They asked Jesus why, and He replied that they needed to pray and fast before the demon could be cast out. The demon lacked the ability to both hear and speak, and this was why the disciples needed to pray and fast before facing him."[1]

"But Shezeren listens and talks. How does what you've just said apply to him?"

"It doesn't specifically. Listen, Emin, I've never cast out a demon before, and I'm not taking any chances. And who knows what else might down there? Demons are well known to inhabit a person or place as a group.[2] I'm planning to go into the store-room only once, and I want to be ready for anything. The Bible tells us that the best way to be prepared is to have God on your side. Before the Hebrews went into battle, they consulted God to ensure that He would deliver the enemy into their hands. They didn't win the battle; God won it for them.[3] When they didn't consult God, then they lost.[4] In the same way, when I confront Shezeren, it'll be the power of God that banishes him, not me. My prayer will be my communication with God and my fast a way of showing Him just how much I need his help."[5]

---

[1] Mark 9:17-29.

[2] Matthew 12:43-45, Mark 5:1-19, 16:9, Luke 8:2, Revelation 18:2.

[3] Examples:

God spoke with Moses about the impending battle against King Og and the people of Bashan: Deuteronomy 3:1-7.

Joshua received instructions from God regarding the approaching war with King Adonizedek and four other kings, plus all these kings' armies: Joshua 10:1-28.

[4] Examples:

Without consulting with God and against His will, the Hebrews went into battle against the Amalekites and lost: Numbers 14:27-45. Saul sought a witch's guidance when God, who had already anointed David to be the future king because of Saul's disobedi-ence, did not answer his inquiry about the forthcoming battle with the Philistines. The dead Samuel was brought forth and told Saul that the LORD would allow the Philistines to defeat Israel. Saul and his army still fought with the Philistines and were defeated. Saul and three of his sons were killed. 1 Samuel 28:5-25, 31:1-13.

[5] Daniel 9:3-23, Joel 2:12, Acts 14:22-23.

"You've obviously thought about this. I prayed before I confronted Shezeren as well. I didn't fast, but then I also didn't tackle him properly."

"Try not to dwell on it, Emin. I'll stay in my room tomorrow. It would be good if you could join me in the evening to pray—perhaps at eight."

"I'd be happy to do that."

Day five in Cappadocia had been consumed by hunger and prayer. The first two hours after midnight had passed slowly. Emin held a torch in his right hand. It was already switched on, even though he and Sam were still in the well-lit home.

Emin was commenting on the caverns below them. "I wish you could see the place at full light. It's artificial lighting, but you'd be able to fully appreciate what those before us have achieved in digging out this village. The lighting system for the entire communal complex is turned off at midnight. Anyhow, you'll get the general idea by torchlight." He was mostly making conversation to lighten the mood.

Emin and Sam were in the subterranean level of the domicile. This level occupied a much broader area than each of the two above. Together they walked to the hall that was used to receive guests from the subterranean communal section of the village. Once inside, Emin guided Sam through a small, doorless opening (a black, square hole), which on traversing a person had to stoop, even the owner. The torchlight revealed narrow steps (all hewn out of the Cappadocian rock), which descended steeply. Emin led the way down the tight stairwell with his left hand on the wall as a stabilizer and the torch in his right. Sam was surprised at how steadily Emin was able to fix the light beam to the front. Emin had used the steps thousands of times and was familiar with their uneven disposition. Sam took the narrow steps more cautiously and soon trailed by ten paces. In the receding light he silently cursed one of the steps as he felt his left ankle twist.

"Hold on a second, Emin!"

The reply was a beam of light, first directed at Sam's face and then at his feet. He'd anticipated such an injury and therefore hadn't been placing his entire weight onto the foot in front until sure of a supportive platform. He'd quickly pulled the ankle back and had prevented a sprain.

"Is everything all right?" Emin asked.

"It's fine now. I just twisted my ankle a little."

"Are you hurt?"

"Not at all, only could you shine the light onto the stairs ahead of me until I get to you?"

"By all means, Charles." And Emin fulfilled Sam's request. "There's not far to go now." And there wasn't. They continued a little slower this time and soon met a door. "This is our entrance. On the other side of this door the entire area is communal— except of course for other entrances such as this to other private homes. Beyond this door you should walk softly. We don't want to wake anybody."

"No problem. Are you sure that there'll be nobody else about?"

"There shouldn't be. In times of rampant persecution the men patrol overnight in pairs. We haven't had that kind of trouble for a year. And because of Shezeren, I doubt that anyone would go for a casual stroll down here in the dark."

"What about Yurtsev? Does he ever visit the demon at night?"

"I really don't know, Charles. But we should keep a careful eye out."

"And a careful ear as well."

Emin produced a steel key and inserted it into the wooden door. Sam saw that the door was set in a timber frame that reminded him of the supports of an old mine. As the door opened, the air changed, and Sam felt a cooling wind. He was expecting it to rapidly dissipate, as if it had been caused by the release of gas from a nearly empty pressurized container, yet it persisted quite uniformly. They both stepped out.

They were no longer constricted in a tight stairwell but were in a wide, high-walled passageway, which presented them with choices in the form of more passageways. These choices were unevenly spaced, and the directions in which they led were all different. Emin quickly scattered the torch beam, so that Sam could better view their new location. Sam could see five new passageways: one heading upward, two horizontally and the rest downward.

"How deep are we, Emin?" Sam whispered.

"About fifteen metres."

"Then what's that cool wind that I can feel on my face?" Sam whispered again.

"You don't need to talk so quietly. Just talk normally . . . don't shout though."

"I get it," Sam said calmly. "And the wind?"

"It's the effect of the ventilation shafts. There are seven in all, which feed air into the caverns and allow it to circulate."

"They're doing a pretty good job. Emin, if the rest of this place is like what I'm seeing, then I hope we don't get split up."

Emin handed a tiny pen torch, which had been in the right pocket of his jacket, to Sam. "Come, Charles, let's go this way. That little torch is our backup. You can carry it just in case."

As they walked, Sam tried to make a mental note of the route. They mostly travelled in silence, occasionally exchanging a few short sentences. After fifteen minutes, three chambers, numerous passageways and several stairwells, Sam felt that he wouldn't get back alone with ease.

"How far is the storeroom?" Sam asked.

"About this distance again."

"And how deep are we now?"

"Maybe around thirty metres."

They'd passed regions that in better circumstances Sam was sure that Emin would have commented on. Instead, the torchlight had merely flickered over writings on walls, carved rock utilities and peculiar doorways, which Sam would never enter. The fleeting illumination of all these things had allowed him only enough time to partially delineate them. These denials of completion heightened the unease that he already felt over the endeavour. He didn't share his growing anxiety with Emin. It was better that his disquiet remained deep and silent—a personal concern.

The current passageway opened out into another chamber. "This is where we worship together," Emin said. He stopped and shone the torch around the chamber. It was the largest that Sam had entered so far. There were long stone seats, created when the chamber was excavated, and short wooden pews, added at a later date to increase the seating capacity. "We weren't the first to use it as a church." Emin focused the light onto one of the walls. The wall was blank, although not without a story. "I was told that a hundred and ten years ago this wall had a large fresco. In fact, there were frescos on all the walls in here. Most were of biblical subjects: mainly solitary well-known characters, but also groups of figures together with fitting landscapes. The frescos were painted around a thousand years ago. Our community started much more recently: almost two hundred years ago, when ten Christian families moved into this village. It was deserted at that time. They left the frescos. I guess they thought that the images were harmless, yet would you believe that after eighty years a few of the people started to bow to them and pray toward them."

"I'm afraid that I can believe it."

"Not so harmless after all, even to a true Christian community. They eventually had the frescos scrubbed, and what was left painted over."[1]

Although hardly a relaxing subject, the distraction was a comfort to Sam. Perhaps Emin had detected Sam's mounting tension.

---

[1] From the Bible we can tell that the earliest Christians in Cappadocia at the time of the writing of the New Testament were genuine and lived amongst non-Christians from whom they received persecution (1 Peter 1:1-5:14). However, much later, from the evidence of the frescos still visible in Cappadocia, there were clearly different Christians living there, who did not adhere to biblical truth. Amongst these Christians it's possible that genuine Christians still existed, who resisted the iconography.

Sam spoke, "I've been thinking about Shezeren. I'm not at all convinced that he can't just leave by his own will. I believe that he's deliberately manifested himself to your community to destroy it. By masquerading as your prisoner, he's made you all think that you hold some power over him."

"You're describing one of the ways of the jinn," Emin remarked.

"Jinn?" Sam was unsure of the word.

"You call them genies. We call them jinn."

"I wouldn't have put it quite that way myself . . ." Sam considered Emin's suggestion. "Yet the more I think about it, the more I agree with you."

"In our culture the jinn are demons. There are many stories about the jinn—most of them wrong.[1] The truth is that the jinn create an illusion of servitude to men—Satan is one of the jinn, and the rest of them serve only him."[2]

---

[1] Wrong in that even when the truth is combined with a lie, a lie is still the overall result.

[2] The jinn are mentioned in the Koran. In this book Satan (also known as Iblis) is both referred to as an angel and as one of the jinn in a similar way that the Bible reveals that he is in fact both an angel (was created as such) and a demon (a fallen angel) owing to his rebellion (see Chapter 1 pgs 22 and 25 with relevant footnotes). In the Koran the jinn are portrayed as beings created out of a different substance from man: fire rather than clay. The above combined with a reported former ability to visit Heaven and listen to meetings clearly demonstrates a belief that the jinn are demons (fallen angels). Indeed, the Arabic word "jinn" could be translated into the English word "demons". Contradictory attributes are ascribed to the jinn in the Koran: the jinn misguide men, especially lying sinners, yet some jinn are believed to be righteous; and the jinn are sometimes worshipped, yet some jinn were commanded by a man (Solomon!), some of these jinn being in fetters. The truth is that the jinn are all deceiving demonic spirits. The Koran 2 The Cow (Al-Baqarah):34-36, 7 The Heights (Al-A′rāf):10-25, 15 Al-Hijr (Al-Hijr):26-42, 18 The Cave (Al-Kahf):50, 26 The Poets

FOOTNOTE CONTINUED ON THE NEXT PAGE

"If that's the case, then Shezeren's tailored himself masterfully to your community: in his masquerade and in the content of his false teaching. He's damaged faiths and even turned some away from Christ."

"Let's move on," Emin recommended.

"Yes, none of this changes what we need to do," Sam replied.

They now walked in complete silence. Deeper into the catacombs they descended. Sam felt that the torchlight had become less effectual. Indeed, it had: the stone walls were darker and reflected less light. The blackness encroached, but there was something more. A cold shiver went from the base of Sam's neck to the middle of his spine.

"We're close, aren't we?" Sam said quietly, breaking their silence.

"Yes, you can sense it, can't you? Even during the day, on this level everyone can feel his presence."

They walked into a chamber that was much larger than the place of communal worship. The current chamber was full of wooden crates stacked to a maximum height of 20 feet, which in some places left little space between the top crates and the ceiling. The chamber had a smell that was a mixture of synthetic substances and cereals, the latter dominating.

"I can't believe that anyone lives this deep," Sam remarked whilst thinking about Teoman, whose home was even deeper still; Sam's voice was barely an audible whisper.

The crates were stacked to form a broad central passageway. At both sides were intervals every roughly 12 feet, which were offshoots of the central passageway. Emin walked a few paces ahead of Sam along the central passageway. "You really don't need to whisper. Shezeren will already know that we're here. He'll even know who we are. As to what you said, only a few

CONTINUED FOOTNOTE PRESENT

(Ash-Shu´arā´):221-224, 34 Sheba (Saba´):12-14, 40-41, 37 Ranged in Rows (As-Sāffāt):1-10, 38 Sad (Sād):34-40, 76-85, 55 The Lord of Mercy (Ar-Rahmān):14-16, 72 The Jinn (Al-Jinn):1-15.

families lack homes that are partly over ground. Since Shezeren's arrival, Teoman and his family have moved to other quarters. There's no one living near this area now. Only the men have been coming to get supplies from this chamber."

Emin turned to their right down one of the offshoots. It was a narrow passageway, the crates of which at its end opened out to form a semicircle. The line that could unite the two ends of the semicircle was a crateless wall. As they neared the wall, the torchlight revealed a round seven-foot-wide hewn rock, which Emin called a boulder. It had a depth of less than a foot. Sam thought that it resembled a millstone.

Emin stopped. "Here it is." He picked up a torch, whose resting place was on the floor next to the round stone, and switched it on. "This is the one that doesn't give off sparks." He handed it to Sam. Emin switched off his own torch.

"Isn't this storeroom locked?" Sam asked.

"No, it isn't. There's never been a need. There's just the boulder. It can be opened by one man." Sam's expression made Emin expand his explanation: "Don't worry; it can be rolled from the inside as well: there are two brass handles built into a recess of the boulder." Emin paused and looked directly at Sam. "Are you ready?"

"As I'll ever be. I'm going in alone, Emin."

"I thought you'd say that. Anyway, one person should be on the outside—just in case."

Sam took a deep laboured breath and handed the tiny pen torch back to Emin. Sam held the special storeroom torch in his right hand. "May the Lord give us victory!"

Together they pushed the stone to the right. It rolled, moving slowly with a deep grinding sound, within a gutter that guided its path. Sam realized that the storeroom's stone had been clearly hewn from a low-density rock and therefore couldn't be an adapted millstone. The storeroom's stone was heavy only because of its size. The smell of fuel struck his nostrils.

Sam stood in the round opening. The safety torch wasn't nearly as powerful as the torch that Emin had used to guide them through the caverns. Sam shined the safety torch's feeble light into the blackness. Emin reached out and touched Sam's shoulder. "Keep your eyes forward. I'll roll the boulder back behind you." And with that Sam stepped inside.

As the stone rolled into place, the air in the storeroom became motionless. The oily smell intensified, as did the feeling of the powerful other presence. Sam shone the torchlight in the forward direction and then from side to side, searching for Shezeren. The storeroom was small in comparison with the main chamber but of equal height. Off to the sides, to Sam's right and left, were large canisters containing petroleum for the village's emergency generator, which were neatly stacked on the floor, and above them were other fuels in smaller metal containers positioned on stone shelves, whose many layers extended upward to three feet shy of the ceiling. There was also a sturdy, tall, wooden ladder resting against a high shelf to his right.

Sam's search ended quickly when he heard the rattle of chains. He'd already glimpsed the empty rear wall; however, that was where the noise had come from. He shone his torch toward the sound.

Shezeren was kneeling with his back against the wall. He was bound hand and foot with shackles, which were connected to chains, which were wound tightly around the length of his torso. His bonds glimmered like a cut diamond. They were so transparent that if it wasn't for the sparkle of the facets, then the restraints would have been invisible. The demon was of enormous stature. Even kneeling, his height was almost 14 and a half feet, and his breadth filled over half of the room's width, which was most of the room's width not occupied by the shelves. He appeared to be not entirely solid, yet his presence was a formidable reality. His hulking body was fully clothed, and he wore metal armour over his garments. The backs of his giant uncovered hands were extraordinarily muscular. His unblinking eyes watched the newcomer. Sam felt as if the intense gaze had been directed at him since the moment he'd entered. Shezeren's face was handsome and reminiscent of humanity—similar to a man's face: two eyes, a nose and a mouth, except not like any man whom Sam had ever seen. Sam recalled what Emin had said. Furthermore, there was something that Emin had only alluded to that was more powerful than the demon's physicality. Shezeren's character radiated from his face, creating a sense a dread in the onlooker. It was a feeling that told you that this being standing before you was unbeatable and that you would be defeated. Beyond form to function, Sam thought.

"And who are you?" the demon asked. There was not only Shezeren's speech but something else that seemed to drift on the air—another voice, which was whispering a hypnotic incantation.

Sam said a brief prayer in his mind. He then opened his dry lips. "In the name of . . ."

"Stop! Stop!" The demon's visage had immediately changed since Sam had said his first four words. Shezeren's countenance was now a mixture of anxiety and rage.

". . . Jesus, the Son of the Most . . ."

"You're from England." Shezeren had recognized Sam's accent. "Tell me your name, and I'll tell you your future!"

". . . High God . . ."

The demon rose from his knees and broke his diamond-like chains. He was no longer kneeling but crouched, coiling himself for action. His solidity increased. His right fist, now free, clenched. The muscles bulged above his knuckles. As Shezeren started to lunge forward, he spoke again, "Rimoth, help me! Quickly—who is this?"

Now at over 20 feet Shezeren was barely contained in the storeroom. Sam's first thought was to step back. He raised his right leg but then restored it to its first position and dug the ball of his right foot into the stone floor. All the while Sam kept the torchlight shining on his enemy. ". . . I order you . . ."

Shezeren's forward charge gained velocity. The shimmering chains and shackles lay uselessly on the floor behind him. "He hid you, you wretch. How dare you?"

". . . to leave this place and never return!"

Shezeren shouted an incomprehensible word, then was gone. For a brief moment a subtle wind rushed past Sam's ears toward the empty wall. The floor at the rear of the storeroom was bare. The bonds had gone.

Sam's entire body was tense, as if every muscle was contracted. He slowly rubbed his left hand on the back of his neck. He exhaled deeply, then took a few restrained shallow breaths. He still held the torch in his right hand. The sensation of Shezeren's presence had left, as had the hypnotic whisper, yet Sam shone the torch around the room anyway. A stone chamber with an abundant stock of fuel was all that he could see.

Moments later Emin heard the scrape of the round stone as he waited in complete darkness. Emin added to the stone's momentum and greeted Sam as he stepped out of the storeroom. Together they rolled the stone back. Emin gently took the safety torch out of Sam's right hand. Emin switched this torch off, placed it on the ground and then switched on the torch that he'd used to light the way through the caverns.

Together they slowly walked back to Emin's home while Sam conveyed to his host what had happened.

For Emin the following day was a new start. He was overjoyed that the demon had been expelled and spent much of the day propagating the news. His story was cautiously confirmed. He'd deliberately left out Sam's role in casting out Shezeren and had also taken no personal credit for the expulsion. Instead, Emin had given all the glory to Jesus, because, after all, it was He who had performed the feat and none other.

The day after that, Emin drove 200 miles north of Cappadocia to gather the items on Sam's list.

On the eighth day Emin and Sam talked as they had lunch together.

"He could see me . . . I mean he was looking directly at me . . . so I'm not sure why he said the words 'He hid you'. 'He'—do you think that Shezeren was referring to God?" Sam said in earnest.

"You mentioned that Shezeren didn't know who you were. That's never happened to anyone else. He always addressed us by name as we entered."

"Yes, and he was trying to figure out who I was. He picked up on where I was from."

"Maybe there's someone who's protecting you from demonic scrutiny. Someone who's thwarting their steps to find you . . ."

"Unless I walk directly into their paths?" Sam proposed.

"Yes."

"Who knows? Maybe one day I'll understand all of this. Right now I thank God for His protection, and I put my trust in Him for the rest of the mission."

"Speaking of which—I have the things that you asked me to buy. I've packed them into this backpack. I won't ask what the snorkel is for."

"You're right, don't ask!" Sam replied. "And the camera?"

"Exactly as you requested and with four rolls of film. There were much better digital ones that I could have bought for you though."

"The old-fashioned kind is what I need."

"And I have something else for you." Emin reached into a cloth bag. He pulled out an old revolver and a small box of ammunition. He handed them to Sam. "I bought this gun many years back. It used to be used for the night patrols. It's never been fired. We replaced it two years ago. I have a feeling that where you're going you may need it."

Sam felt the weight of the revolver. He released the cylinder and examined the six empty chambers. "For self-defence, of course."

"Naturally," Emin replied.

Chapter 13   **Burial**

Sam had a problem. He was certain that if he found the Ark on Mount Ararat, remaining in Turkey directly after the event would result in his death. His demise would mean that any evidence retrieved from the Ark would most likely be intercepted and the as yet unknown second objective would stay a mystery. The only thing that he knew about the second objective was that the task needed to be completed in Turkey. He figured that the best thing to do, for himself and the mission, was to leave Turkey after Ararat by descending into Armenia. He would then re-enter Turkey at a place that was far from Ararat. His other exit from Ararat was Iran, but he gave that option little consideration save for the fact that the enemy would think it unlikely for him to escape to there. He knew that he needed a new identity to re-enter Turkey. It would also be sensible to have a new identity to cross from one Transcaucasian country[1] to another and even more so if he needed to enter Russia. He couldn't assume that his enemies in Turkey weren't collaborating with individuals in these other countries, although he hoped that this was so. The nearest of the two false passports was in the city of Van, 160 miles from where he was planning to land in the province of Batman. Similarly to Batman, Van is also a province that contains an urban centre that shares its name. He wondered if the House had predicted that he would be in such trouble by the time he'd reached this point of the mission. Anyway, this was his predicament, and he set his sights on the city of Van. He lamented the need to enter a city. He would have liked to have travelled far from civilization all the way from Batman to Ararat.

Sam was sat in the cockpit behind Kenan. The small plane had only a single seat, so Kenan had brought his seat forward as much as possible and had created a shelf behind him, on which Sam could sit with his baggage on his lap. They'd exchanged

---

[1] Armenia, Azerbaijan and Georgia.

only a few words since take off: Sam's large backpack obstructed his forward view and the noise of the engine would drown out all but a shouting match between the men. Furthermore, the pilot needed to focus on the job at hand. They'd been flying for half an hour, and Sam had observed that they hadn't ascended over 200 feet from the ground. It was Kenan's intention to fly as low as possible for the entire two-hour flight in order to be beneath any potential radar surveillance. He was used to flying at low altitude on account of his work; however, he wasn't used to doing such manoeuvres over extended periods or at night.

Emin had driven Sam 60 miles eastward to a small aboveground town—still in Cappadocia—called Zincidere. There, Kenan kept his plane on his farm, not at the local airport. He'd bought the plane second-hand ten years previously in order to dust his own crops but also to provide a paid service to other farmers in the region. Emin had introduced Sam and Kenan to one another, then had quickly left. Sam and Emin had parted properly earlier that night as one would expect of two close friends who'd experienced a trial together. The crop duster resembled a fighter from World War II (one of the single-propeller low-winged monoplanes) except with unaggressive civilian styling and a smaller engine. The crop duster had also seen better days.

"Is it safe?" Sam had asked with a smile, which was probably the only way that one could get away with such a question said to the man who was both the pilot and mechanic.

"Sure, sure—no problem. I never crash—not one time," Kenan had cheerfully answered.

There's always a first time; for me flying truly is a necessary evil, Sam had thought.

"It have short range, because carry fuel and pesticide." Kenan had stressed the word "and". His English wasn't a fraction as good as Emin's but better than Sam's Turkish. "Now no pesticide on board, so less weight. We fly farther."

Below each wing of the plane was a large straight metal artery, which fed twelve nozzles, which would spray the pesticide. The wings and body were brightly painted in red and white. The wings extended from the body of the plane with a five-degree upward slope instead of horizontally. Each wing was strengthened at that angle by a single metal rod. These two rods also originated from the body of the plane, above the wings' origins but below the cockpit's windows, and were inserted halfway along the wings.

Sam was impressed by Kenan's flying skills. There was only a sliver of moon to illuminate the night. When Kenan wasn't keenly watching the dark terrain ahead, he was referring to the altimeter and the artificial horizon. What he was attempting was dangerous, and a single error of judgement could be paid for with both their lives. As they flew, Sam thought about the Christian Cappadocian community and especially about Emin. The community needed to pick itself up and renew its faith. Sam wondered what needed to be done about Yurtsev. Dealing with him would be critical to the community's recovery. Anyhow, there was nothing more that Sam could do other than pray for them. His thoughts led him to what Emin had said about the Koran. The Koran claims that Allāh is the Almighty God,[1] yet this book contradicts the Bible. Sam discerned that Allāh of the Koran and the God of the Bible are clearly not the same being.

"We about to land now," was the belated warning shouted by Kenan as they touched down. With Sam's thoughts elsewhere, the jolt had surprised him: they'd been flying so low just before then that the descent had taken only a few seconds. They came to a halt in the intended field, which was in West Batman (that is, Batman the province) (620 metres in altitude). Kenan had to disembark first in order to let Sam out.

---

[1] The Koran 42 Consultation (Ash-Shūra):3-6, 57 Iron (Al-Hadīd):1-6, 64 Mutual Neglect (At-Taghābun):1-18. Together these passages declare that Allāh: is the Almighty; is the creator, controller and possessor of the universe; and has knowledge about everything.

Sam gave Kenan a grateful handshake and congratulated him for his prodigious skill. Each of them expressed the wish that God would bless the other on his journey, and then they parted.

It was eleven o'clock. Except for the empty lit road, the area had no landmarks. It appeared desolate. Everything was just as Sam had intended, although the reality of the area's isolation was more daunting than he'd anticipated. Batman's chief activities are cultivation of cereals, raising livestock and oil production. This region shared these characteristics with the province of Siirt (east of Batman), which Sam would also need to traverse. His aim was to keep to the wilderness as much as possible and away from agriculture and industry. Between his location and the city of Van was rough country: many rivers, mountainous areas and a large body of water, called Lake Van (Van Gölü). Emin had provided Sam with a detailed map to negotiate the terrain.

Sam was wearing one of only two outfits now in his possession: a thin black cotton T-shirt, which had long sleeves, together with a thick pair of black cotton trousers. In Cappadocia he'd disposed of anything that he'd deemed unnecessary for this phase of his mission. The T-shirt could be washed easily in a river and if needed, would dry rapidly on his back. The dark colours of the T-shirt and trousers would help keep him hidden at night.

Although the crow could fly to the city of Van by covering 160 miles, a man would have to trek double that distance because of the terrain. Sam was hoping to complete the journey in less than two weeks. He confirmed his bearings and set out in an easterly direction. He wore a pair of hiking boots that Emin had provided. Sam's 40-litre-capacity brown backpack was crammed with items and weighed around twenty-five kilograms. Despite the weight, he ran through most of what was left of the night. The farmlands that he'd first met had petered out after five miles. He'd circumvented the town of Batman and had then slogged over parched grasslands and hills for another nine miles.

At four o'clock in the morning the alarm on Sam's digital watch had sounded, and he'd stopped running. The sun hadn't risen yet, and neither had the day dawned. After a brief rest, he removed a small collapsible spade from his backpack and started digging in a well-selected area near a dried-up bush.

It took Sam fifteen minutes to dig what looked like a two-foot-deep grave. From his backpack he removed: the snorkel, which was black and had been adapted in Cappadocia for the task ahead by tilting the mouthpiece; a bivvy bag, which resembled a sleeping bag; a two-by-two-foot, smooth, synthetic mat; a large, empty cotton bag; and one of two two-litre water bladders. The bladders reminded him of the bags of saline[1] used in hospitals for intravenous fluid rehydration. The bladders were made of clear plastic, so that any dirt or fungal growth could be noticed and effectively cleaned away. Each bladder had a clear, flexible, long feeder pipe with a bite valve at the tip. He placed the bivvy bag and the backpack inside the hole.

The bivvy bag was made out of a lightweight, breathable synthetic fibre—not that these attributes mattered too much for Sam's intended use. What was essential in his choice was that at the head end there were two rigid arches built into the bivvy bag that made it appear tent-like. The arches created a small bulging area at the head end of the bag for its intended occupant's movement and to reduce the chance of claustrophobia. The arches raised the bivvy bag's height to a foot and a half, which meant extra digging. He positioned the backpack next to the head end of the bag. He started to shovel the displaced earth back into the hole to cover the bivvy bag and the backpack. He left a small area at the head of the bivvy bag, which was also the entrance, free of earth. He tidied up the earth that he'd put back into the hole, so that this earth merged with the surrounding dirt.

Sam held twigs and long strands of wild grass around the straight length of the snorkel. He secured these pieces of flora just above the bend of the snorkel with a tight elastic band. He unzipped the entrance of the bivvy bag and placed the water bladder and the snorkel inside. He raised the snorkel and zipped

---

[1] Sterile salt water commonly used as a fluid for intravenous drips.

the bivvy bag closed so that the snorkel was caught half inside such that the mouthpiece and lower section of the shaft, part of which was surrounded by the elastic band, was in the bag and the rest of the shaft was outside tickling the air. He placed the mat at an easily reachable distance from the uncovered gap. On top of this mat he placed some very fine dry earth—resembling sand in behaviour—that wouldn't clump on movement and would hopefully slide easily into the gap. There was plenty of earth left over, and he filled the cotton bag, using the spade, and carefully emptied the contents beneath a different bush, which was 100 metres away. He did this repeatedly. It took him four trips to dispose of all the earth.

Sam tapped his right hip to ensure that the revolver was present and performed a quick three hundred and sixty-degree scan of his environment. He unzipped the bivvy bag, while holding the snorkel in position, and carefully entered, with the spade, still holding the snorkel in position and making every attempt not to disrupt his handiwork above. Once inside, he raised his arms and pulled in the mat while continuing to keep the snorkel in as fixed a position as possible. The fine earth poured into the gap. Some of it fell into the bag, but he knew that this was inevitable. From inside he zipped the bivvy bag closed, dusted off the snorkel's mouthpiece and inserted it into his mouth. He soon drifted into a tired sleep.

The day dawned on Batman. Sam could only imagine what his hiding place looked like from the outside. It blended beautifully with the surroundings. The only sign of his subterfuge was the snorkel; however, this resembled an old, discarded pipe with vegetation growing around it. Despite altitudes reaching over 1,000 metres in the province of Batman, the summer temperatures are similar to Turkey's Mediterranean coast. By midday it was hot, reaching twenty-eight degrees Celsius. A small number of well-defined clouds hung in the blue sky. A gentle wind stroked patches of wild grass and the hum of crickets was all that could be heard.

Sam slept silently beneath the ground, insulated from the heat.
The earth that surrounded the bivvy bag was cool and dry.
During the first few hours he turned infrequently. When he did,
his mouth pulled on the snorkel, which returned him to position.
Once, the snorkel had slipped out of his mouth, and he'd half-
awakened gasping for air. He'd reattached the snorkel and had
become fully immersed in sleep again.

At four o'clock in the afternoon Sam half-awoke for a second
time. His mouth was parched and sore. He reached up and tried
to remove the snorkel from his mouth. The mouthpiece was
stuck to his top lip. He pulled the snorkel more slowly, and it
came free without skin. He took a sip of water mostly to
moisten his mouth but also to quench his thirst. He was careful
not to drink too much, as he'd made no provision for an
underground convenience. He went back into a deep sleep.

Sam was awoken at quarter-past eight that night by his wrist-
watch's alarm. For three minutes he listened very carefully for
sounds above him. He wished that he had a periscope. He'd
realized that his emergence would be the most dangerous part of
sleeping beneath the ground. He heard nothing. He unzipped the
bag. Soil fell onto his face. He blinked repeatedly to shift
particles from his eyeballs. He paused. Still nothing. He raised
his hands, pushed the earth aside and wriggled his way to the
surface. He was met by Batman's chilly night air. The surface
was how he'd left it: dark and empty of human life.

And this is how Sam travelled: trekking at night and sleeping
during the day in his cocoon beneath the ground. Under the cover
of night he managed to travel between 14 and 15 miles; each
night had approximately eight hours of darkness, but time was
also needed to prepare and dismantle the cocoon. He'd crossed
into Siirt on the third night. Despite hiking up and down hills, the
overall effort was upward. He witnessed neither dawn, sunrise,
sunset nor nightfall. He always ate at night and sometimes while
running. He'd packed a mixture of three foods: sun-dried beef,
milk chocolate and high fibre crispbread. Each night he also took

a single combinational tablet of multivitamins and minerals. He'd worked out that a thin layer of petroleum jelly rubbed onto the snorkel's mouthpiece would prevent it from sticking, yet he hadn't found a way to not feel dehydrated by the time night fell. He drank lots of water overnight while travelling, at least three litres, but this never seemed enough for his prolonged daytime confinement (approximately 16 hours). He would collect water from the many rivers that he crossed and make it drinkable with the use of a small purifying pump. He had some chlorine tablets as a backup if the pump ever failed. He always remembered to void before entering his subterranean bed, although at a distance of over a mile from it. He was worried about being tracked.

Four days after landing in the field, despite the exhaustion from each preceding night's effort, Sam started to fully awaken in the day and sometimes wouldn't get back to sleep for two or three hours. At these times, in order to avoid the inherent boredom and irritation of being attached to the snorkel, he either forced himself to imagine solutions to possible future conflict scenarios or prayed. One day a beetle crawled into the snorkel. He woke with a start as it entered his mouth. He spat out the insect, then crushed it in the bivvy bag. For the rest of that day he didn't sleep particularly well, and his thoughts focused on his weapons. That night at a river he wiped his fingerprints off the semiautomatic pistol and the two rounds, and threw them all into deep water. He preferred the revolver, which Emin had given him. Unlike the pistol, the revolver was a weapon that he knew would fire one hundred percent of the time. With a pistol, there was always the chance of a jam. He'd also been thinking of the freezing mountain conditions that lay ahead. The pistol could have been a backup weapon; however, with an incriminating history, a weight of one and a half kilograms and only two remaining rounds, it found itself drowned at the bottom of a river.

It was now the seventh night since the landing. The moon was two-thirds full yet miserly with its beams. Although Sam hadn't seen daylight since Cappadocia, he yearned more for his GPS receiver. He'd lost his way amongst the many hills. He pressed on as best as he could in a direction that was approximately correct. He wasn't worried that he wouldn't eventually re-establish his location on the map but felt frustrated that he was wasting time. He'd run with that emotion for two hours. It was quarter-past three, and he was scrambling up the slope of a hill. The slope became steeper, and his pace slowed. He reached the summit and stopped. From there he could see a single large orange flame licking the darkness. The flame illuminated the upper section of its origin, which was a metal frame. He estimated that the flame was three miles distant and guessed incorrectly that it was being emitted by an oil refinery. The flame was in fact emanating from an oil drilling station, one of many in the region. He should have looked at the map but didn't.

Sam decided to circumvent the flame under the cover of what was left of night's dark cloak. His attempt was initially a speedy downhill journey and then a run on the flat; however, after thirty minutes he realized that he'd misjudged the flame. When he'd been at the hill's summit, the flame had in fact been much further than three miles away, being in actuality larger than he'd thought.

Sam was in a huge valley and could see the flame soaring above the centre of many sprawling metal structures, which were also in the valley. He could now easily determine the flame's true size, because some of structures had windows. He opened the map and chided himself for not consulting it earlier. With his back to the structures, he illuminated the unfolded sheet and the compass by shining his pen torch through the flesh of his right hand. At least he now knew where he was. He continued his journey, attempting to circumvent the drilling station to the south of it. The ground underfoot was uneven, and he had to slow his pace to mind his footing. He was aware of the time, and his miscalculation was worrying him. He had only forty-five more minutes before dawn, and over half of that time would be needed to prepare his subterranean cocoon. If he'd known the true distance to the station, he would have made his bed on the hill. He ran as far as he could for the next fifteen minutes. He was only two miles clear of the station and still in the valley when his alarm sounded. He turned to look at the flame before he started digging. It was still bigger than when he'd first seen it and now a menacing herald of the day ruled by people. He was hidden before daybreak and fell asleep as the first light of the sun touched the valley.

Sam climbed twenty polished marble steps and then walked between two immense columns to enter the Temple of Persuasion. The temple, which was white, was vast. In many ways it resembled the Parthenon in Athens but was much larger: easily able to fit four football pitches. Like the Parthenon, the Temple of Persuasion was ancient, yet it was so well maintained that it appeared as if it were a new construction. Its rectangular perimeter was lined with fifty columns, each of which had a breadth of 20 feet at the base. The temple had not a single wall: there were the columns, the floor and the stone roof with its triangular faces, front and back. The temple was accessible from all directions. Its immense height reflected its floor area, and birds flew silently beneath its remote ceiling. The temple was on a mountain for the world to see and for humanity to be drawn to its resplendent yet hollow heart. From a distance Sam had noticed the temple gleaming, reflecting sunlight into the valleys roundabout. He hadn't been personally attracted to the temple but nevertheless appreciated why mankind was so captivated. He was there on an assignment.

There were thousands of people already present. Sam's face looked older, and he perceived this. He stood alone on the temple's marble floor near to a column. He planned to meet his apprentice there. The young man was late. The marble floor was the perimeter of a rectangular courtyard. The courtyard was where the majority of people were located, and those on the marble floor were headed to the courtyard. Sam imagined the courtyard as a manicured green lawn if it had been as well tended as the rest of the temple. There would be plenty of sunlight for growth as the roof above was so distant. Instead, the courtyard was a sand-filled desert with seemingly incompatible rosebushes in bloom randomly dotting the surface. In the centre of the desert was a circular stone island, the focal point of the temple. Fully occupying this island was a large stone hemisphere, which resembled an imposing domed roof. Numerous alcoves dimpled the dome's exterior, and within each of these niches was an idol. The alcoves were present at every level around the entire structure. From Sam's position he could see at least thirty.

There were stone, metal and wooden idols of: men and women; winged angels and demons; creatures such as oxen, cats, dogs and fish; different kinds of trees; and celestial bodies, including the sun and the moon. Other idols were geometric shapes and still others were simply formless rocks.

Six idols particularly caught Sam's attention. The first was cut from marble in the image of a woman holding a small male infant. The next was cast from silver and resembled a man but with four arms. To the left of this idol was a gold statue of a male warrior, and to the right was a wooden figure of a seated, content man. The fifth, carved from marble, was of a bearded man with a scroll representing a book of Scripture held in his left hand, but the sculpture of the man minus the scroll was reminiscent of statues of Olympian deities. The last was of a bearded man who stood above a crescent moon; both were part of the same wooden statue.

Thousands more people were joining those already present in the temple. Sam saw them flooding in, each on a path of his or her choosing. Many paths were similar to others, and hence there was coalescence into several well-populated routes. However, within these large crowded groups, despite proximity's inevitable harmonizing influence, each person had his or her own subtle variation in the manner in which he or she walked. Different ways yet all headed toward the same destination, the desert.

Sam's apprentice finally arrived. He and Sam stood together on the marble floor, the bank of the desert, and watched the multitude. Everyone had their eyes open. Those in the desert slowly milled about; each person was trying to find a comfortable position. Suddenly the desert became quicksand. The people started to be sucked downward. Even near to the rosebushes, the desert lost its firmness and began to ingest. Some of the people called out, but their cries were smothered by the rustling chorus of sifting sand. Others said nothing as the desert engulfed them along with their last breaths. Despite witnessing these events, those on the marble shore continued to march onto the sand. Their advancement was relentless. They walked in fear yet neither turned around nor slowed their step. Their numbers were being replenished by people entering the temple. Some of those already on the sand didn't even wait to be engulfed but thrust themselves beneath the yellow grainy mass, burying themselves into its gruesome embrace. This continued for hours until the number of people who were entering the temple fell to nil, and soon there was not a soul on the desert. The previously animated sand lay motionless and silent. The rosebushes had not been disturbed. Sam and his apprentice were now the only people in the temple. They'd not moved from the hard marble floor. They remained there together for a little while longer.

Without a word, the apprentice left the marble floor and entered the desert. Sam called out a warning, but the young man continued. After a few well-supported steps, the apprentice turned to face Sam. The young man raised his hands in the air as if to say "Look, no problem." Sam continued to watch from the edge.

Now the apprentice looked unsteady. His body jolted backward to maintain his balance, and he quickly dropped his arms. His feet and ankles were covered by sand. He lifted his right leg in order to step out. Instead, his left leg sank deeper still and he slipped forward. He was then buried up to his knees. He called out to Sam. It took only two more seconds for the apprentice to be submerged up to his waist. His legs were immobilized, and he frantically twisted his torso to get loose. His thrashing accelerated the increasing depth of his internment.

Sam ran into the desert and soon reached an area in front of his apprentice. Still standing on seemingly solid desert, Sam stooped forward and reached out with his right hand. He grabbed hold of the apprentice's right forearm and the young man gripped Sam's right forearm. Sam had stopped his friend's descent. Sam pulled, and inch by inch the apprentice started to rise. Then Sam started to sink. Immersed up to his knees, he maintained his grip on his apprentice. Sam simultaneously searched for solid ground with his left hand. He felt his apprentice start to sink again. Sam's left hand found only soft sand that flowed upward through his fingers. Before long Sam was submerged up to his waist and the apprentice up to his neck.

In desperation Sam shouted out the words, "In the name of Jesus, Son of the Most High God, be still!"

A cold blanket of blue flame covered the entire courtyard. Neither man was burnt, and the sand congealed. Sam pulled himself out of his snare, then assisted his apprentice. Together they staggered to the safety of solid marble.

Once again, they stood on the hard temple floor and looked toward the sandy courtyard. To the apprentice's astonishment the rosebushes now went under. Finally, the island and the dome together with its idols disintegrated. All were consumed by the desert. There was not a petal, crumb of stone, splinter of wood or glint of metal to be seen.

"What does it mean?" the apprentice asked.

"The false religions of the world have the same origin, the angelic rebellion, and therefore the temple housed them under one roof," Sam replied.

"What part do the idols play?" the apprentice said.

Sam answered, "First of all, I should say that idols aren't just things made of stone, metal and wood. In many cases idols are also those things—alive or dead—that the inanimate materials represent. Moreover, some things are worshipped without being represented in lifeless material forms.

"Mankind will worship practically anything that God has created rather than Him. We saw idols of: demons and angels (whether fallen or not, angels should never be worshipped[1]); giants and giantesses; ordinary men and women; and other beings. The beings have led mankind astray or been used to that end or both. As for the things that have never been forms of life, they too have been used to mislead mankind. Idolatry pervades the Earth. Sometimes it's obvious as in Hinduism and Buddhism owing to their conspicuous idols. In these religions gods are relatives of giants known as Asuras. I hope that you noticed the four-armed god Vishnu between two of his believed incarnations: the giants Krishna and the Buddha—although these two were reportedly giants, they are not classified as Asuras.[2] In other

---

[1] Leviticus 17:1-7, Deuteronomy 32:15-20, 1 Corinthians 10:19-21, Colossians 2:18, Revelation 9:20, 22:8-9.

[2] There are similar as well as conflicting accounts of the origins and natures of the gods and Asuras and of the relationships between the gods and Asuras in the many Hindu and Buddhist religious texts. For clarity the Mahābhārata is mostly cited.

In the Mahābhārata the beings called Asuras are also called Dānavas, Daityas and Rākṣasas; the designatory words are used interchangeably. These beings are often described erroneously in English as demons owing to their frequently displayed cruelty and sometimes monstrous appearances in the non-English literature, but in the strict sense the Asuras are not demons, as they are mortal and have parents. The Asuras are portrayed as gigantic and direct competitors with the gods with whom the Asuras did battle in a similar way to Titan gods, who together fought against united Olympian gods in Greek mythology (the Titanomachy—see footnote in chapter 3 pg 73 regarding Titan). These and other clues (see further on) support the opinion that many of the characters in the Mahābhārata were Nephilim. Interestingly, the traditional date of the war between the Pāṇḍavas and their cousins the Kauravas in the Mahābhārata is around 1300 BC; compare with the Hebrews' conquest of Canaan (1406–970 BC), which had combatant giants and took place at a similar time but in a different place. The five
FOOTNOTE CONTINUED ON THE NEXT PAGE

Pāṇḍava brothers (Yudhiṣṭhira, Bhīma, Arjuna, Nakula and Sahadeva) as well as their ally Krishna are each believed to be an offspring of a god. That Krishna (also known as Vāsudeva and Keśava) was reportedly an offspring of the god Vishnu should be especially noted. At least two of the Pāṇḍavas and Krishna have been portrayed in the Mahābhārata as gigantic (tall as mature śāla trees and bulky as elephants)—although they were reportedly giants, they are not classified as Asuras—and wielded weapons to match (Arjuna strung and fired a bow that was 15 feet tall and that others couldn't wield; Bhīma, a renowned Asura killer, used uprooted trees as missiles and clubs; and Krishna used a bow that fired arrows so large that they could completely sever the limbs from the bodies of his foes, even other giants [Dānavas]). Śāla trees are prevalent in India. Size depends on many factors, including age. The trees can grow beyond 100 feet in height. The śāla tree's use as a comparison is a possible hyperbole. Even if so, the comparison illustrates that these men were enormous. References for this paragraph are found in [α], below.

Vishnu is also known as Hari and Nārāyana. He is one of the principal Hindu gods. One of his proposed origins in the Mahābhārata is as follows. Brahmā, the so-called self-created god, had offspring. Two of his sons were Marīci and Dakṣa. Marīci was the father of Kaśyapa. Dakṣa was the father of 50 daughters, 13 of whom were consorts of Kaśyapa. These 13 daughters included Aditi, Diti and Anāyus. From Aditi were born gods, including Vishnu, Varuṇa and Indra, and from both Diti and Anāyus were born Asuras, therefore making these gods and Asuras both brothers and cousins. Many other gods and other Asuras were also related in some way or another to the above family. Gods, like the Asuras, were portrayed as mortal, yet still called gods. References for this paragraph are found in [β], below.

Vishnu is believed to incarnate himself on the Earth at different times. Two such incarnations are believed to have been Krishna and the Buddha (also known as Gotama and Gautama); the latter incarnation is found in the Bhāgavata Purāṇa. Thus, Krishna is believed to have been both an incarnation and an offspring of

FOOTNOTE CONTINUED ON THE NEXT PAGE

Vishnu. Some passages in the Mahābhārata present Vishnu as the creator god. References for this paragraph are found in [γ], below.

The Rig Veda, written earlier than both the Mahābhārata and Bhāgavata Purāṇa, has some interesting differences to the above, two of which are as follows. Although Aditi is still regarded as a mother of gods, her son Varuṇa is believed to be both a god and an Asura: a strong indication that there was barely, if any, difference between gods and Asuras. Dakṣa, although still believed to be the father of Aditi, is also believed to be one of her sons. References for this paragraph are found in [δ], below.

Although Buddhism's origins are in Hinduism, Buddhism has distanced itself from the Hindu gods and Asuras to a greater or lesser extent depending on which branch of Buddhism is followed. Indeed, an alternative origin of the Buddha—called fully the Buddha Gotama to distinguish him from other buddhas—is also proposed: he having been an ancient Brahman (a member of the priest caste) in a former life, eons ago. According to the Chronicle of Buddhas (Buddhavaṃsa), this Brahman, called Sumedha, met a buddha of that time called Dīpaṅkara, who told Sumedha that in a future life he would become a buddha. Dīpaṅkara was reportedly a colossal giant (80 cubits, 120 feet, 36.6 metres—possibly an exaggeration) and was additionally known as the Conqueror, believed to be the leader of the world. Gotama reportedly had 23 lives in between Sumedha and the Buddha Gotama (25 lives in total, including the first and the last). In his last life as the Buddha Gotama he was reputedly aware of all his previous lives. He was also reportedly a giant (18 cubits tall, 27 feet, 8.2 metres—again possibly an exaggeration but indicating giant proportions compared with normal men). Chronicle of Buddhas (Buddhavaṃsa) *chapters 1-28,* Old Burma-Early Pagán *chapter 19.* The Buddha Gotama's height was obtained from writings in the hall of a Burmese temple (Wetkyi-in Kubyauk-gyi) dating from between 1174 AD and 1211 AD: found in the second reference above. (Burma is now known as Myanmar.) He and 24 additional buddhas, including Dīpaṅkara, are named and described in detail within the chapters of the chronicle; 4 more are mentioned (3 past and 1 future) but only in passing.

FOOTNOTE CONTINUED ON THE NEXT PAGE

CONTINUED FOOTNOTE PRESENT

Regarding the 25 buddhas who are all described in detail in the chronicle, they are in series in the chronicle, and in addition to Gotama, the other 24 buddhas' names were also found written in the Burmese temple. In the chapters of the chronicle all their heights are listed except the Buddha Gotama; one measurement is missing from the temple writings: the Buddha Nārāda. Where present, the heights of each buddha in the chapters of the chronicle and from the writings in the temple are the same except for one (the Buddha Paduma: chronicle vs. temple, 58 vs. 88 cubits). The reported heights of these 25 buddhas range from 18 to 90 cubits: the Buddha Gotama being the shortest and the Buddha Sumana the tallest. Note that none of these 25 buddhas, who were gigantic based on their reported heights, are classified as Asuras. There are differing opinions on when the Buddha Gotama lived. Many say around 500 BC, his lifespan having been approximately 80 years. Others place his life in a time hundreds of years before then. The Buddha Gotama was and is worshipped.

Regarding reincarnation, whether believed to be the rebirth of the soul or part of it in another body, the spiritual awareness of former lives is clearly a form of demonic possession resulting from idolatrous practices. The demons deliver false sensations of other lives either fabricated or real that they have witnessed.

[α] The Mahābhārata: The Book of the Beginning—Āstīka *17:1-18:1*, Yayāti *71:5-14, 73:15-25, 75:10-15*, The Origins *113:20-116:1*, The Slaying of Hidimba *139:10-15, 140:5-10, 141:15-142:1*, The Slaying of Baka *147:20-152:15*, Draupadī's Bridegroom Choice *179:1-181:1, 181:25-30*, The Five Indras *189:30-35*, The Coming of Vidura *198:1-25*, The Burning of the Khāṇḍava Forest *218:25-30;* The Book of the Assembly Hall—The Building of the Assembly Hall *1:5-2:1, 3:25-30*, The Killing of Jarāsaṁdha *19:20-30;* The Book of the Forest—The Slaying of Kirmīra *12:25-75*, The Razing of Saubha *21:1-34*, Agastya *99:1-10*, The War of the Yakṣas *157:35-158:15, 170:40-65*, The Session with Mārkaṇḍeya *180:30-181:5*.

[β] The Mahābhārata: The Book of the Beginning—The Origins, *59:7-60:55*, The Partial Incarnations *61:1-35*, Yayāti *71:5-15*,

FOOTNOTE CONTINUED ON THE NEXT PAGE

religions the idolatry is more subtle, as with Catholicism[1], in which the erroneous worship of Mary has been superimposed on the fading worship of the mother goddess Cybele. In addition, the Romans had worshipped two other relevant goddesses: a goddess of childbirth called Juno, a wife of Jupiter (Zeus);[2] and a virgin goddess called Diana, a daughter of Jupiter.[3] The combined

CONTINUED FOOTNOTE PRESENT

Sunda and Upasunda *201:1-203:1;* The Book of the Forest—The Mountain Man *13:15-24*, The Tour of the Sacred Fords *82:105-114*, Dhundhumāra *192:5-19*, Rāma *260:4-7*.

[γ] The Mahābhārata: The Book of the Forest—The Mountain Man, *13:1-25,* The Session with Mārkaṇḍeya *187:1-55;* The Book of the Bhagavadgītā *26:5-11, 32:1-33:35.* Bhāgavata Purāṇa Part 1 *Skandha 1 chapter 3 verses 1-26.*

[δ] The Rig Veda: Creation, Aditi and the Birth of the Gods (10.72) *verses 1-9*; Varuṇa, The Deeds of Varuṇa (5.85) *verses 1-8;* Varuṇa, Varuṇa (2.28) *verses 1-11.*

[1] Catholicism used in the broadest sense of the definition, i.e., the universal religion of Catholic Christianity, not restricted to Roman Catholicism.

[2] The Roman goddess Juno is identified with the Greek goddess Hera, who was reportedly a sister and a wife of Zeus (Jupiter).
Goddess of childbirth: Ovid's Metamorphoses Book 9 *lines 300-315.*
Relation to Zeus: Ovid's Metamorphoses Book 1 *lines 601-621,* Hesiod's Theogony *lines 453-458, 886-923.*
Roman worship and temples: Livy's History of Rome Book 34 *chapter 53:3-4,* Book 37 *chapter 3:1-2,* Book 40 *chapter 52:1-4,* Dio Cassius' Roman History Book 39 *chapter 20:1-2,* Dionysius of Halicarnassus' Roman Antiquities Book 3 *chapter 69:1-6,* Book 7 *chapter 72:13-14.*

[3] The Roman goddess Diana is identified with the Greek goddess Artemis, the reported daughter of Zeus (Jupiter) and Leto (Latona), and the full sister of Apollo.
Virgin goddess: Ovid's Metamorphoses Book 12 *lines 24-38.*

FOOTNOTE CONTINUED ON THE NEXT PAGE

characteristics of these two eclipsed goddesses would have undoubtedly also stimulated the rise of Mary worship. Similarly, the worship of the apostles[1] filled a spiritual gap left by the former Roman gods such as Jupiter, king of the gods,[2] and

CONTINUED FOOTNOTE PRESENT

Perpetual virginity: Apollodorus' The Library Book 1 *chapter 4:1*, Ovid's Metamorphoses Book 1 *lines 478-487*, Book 5 *lines 373-377*.

Lineage: Ovid's Metamorphoses Book 1 *lines 689-698*, Book 5 *lines 329-331*, Book 15 *lines 547-551*, Hesiod's Theogony *lines 918-920*.

Roman worship and temples: Livy's History of Rome Book 1 *chapters 45:1-7*, 48:6-7*, Book 5 *chapter 13:4-8**, Book 40 *chapter 52:1-4*, Dio Cassius' Roman History Book 2 *epitome by Zonaras 7.9**. *Animal sacrifice mentioned.

[1] The 12 disciples (apostles) chosen by Jesus the Messiah were initially: Peter, Andrew, James son of Zebedee, John, Philip, Bartholomew, Thomas, Matthew, James son of Alphaeus, Judas (who was undoubtedly also known as Thaddaeus to avoid being confused with the betrayer), Simon and Judas Iscariot. Judas Iscariot was replaced by Matthias after prayer and the use of lots. There is then no further mention of Matthias in the Bible. Jesus later chose Paul. Matthew 10:2-4, Mark 3:14-19, Luke 6:13-16, John 14:22, Acts 1:13-26, 9:1-20, Galatians 1:1, 1 Timothy 1:1, 2 Timothy 1:1, Revelation 21:14.

[2] The Roman god Jupiter (also known as Jove) is identified with the Greek king of the gods, Zeus.

King of the gods: Livy's History of Rome Book 3 *chapter 39:1-5*, Ovid's Metamorphoses Book 1 *lines 177-198*, Homer's Iliad Book 2 *lines 667-670*.

Roman worship and temples: Livy's History of Rome Book 1 *chapters 38:5-7, 55:1-56:3*, Book 2 *chapter 8:6-9*, Book 22 *chapter 10:1-10**, Book 35 *chapter 41:8-10*, Book 38 *chapter 51:1-14*, Dio Cassius' Roman History Book 37 *chapter 44:1-2*, Book 43 *chapter 14:1-7*, Dionysius of Halicarnassus' Roman Antiquities Book 3 *chapter 69:1-6*.

*Animal sacrifice mentioned.

Mercury, the messenger.[1] The Bible makes it clear that neither Mary nor the apostles should be worshipped.[2] They're worshipped with and without the use of physical idols, but even without, if worshipped, they're idols all the same. Islām attempts to mask its truthful origin. Nevertheless, the signs are there. The ancient Arabian god Allāh was part of a pantheon of deities that preceded Islām. He was known as the Lord of Bakka (Bakka is an ancient name for Mecca).[3] The pantheon included Allāh's daughters, the three goddesses al-Lāt, al-'Uzzā and Manāt, who were believed to plead with Allāh on behalf of mankind.[4] Allāh

---

[1] The Roman god Mercury is identified with the Greek messenger god Hermes, the reported son of Zeus and Maia.

Lineage and messenger of the gods: Ovid's Metamorphoses Book 1 *lines 668-681*, Book 2 *lines 676-707*, Hesiod's Theogony *lines 938-939*, Homeric Hymns *4 To Hermes lines 1-9*.

Roman worship and temples: Livy's History of Rome Book 2 *chapters 21:7, 27:4-7*, Book 5 *chapter 13:4-8**, Book 22 *chapter 10:1-10*.

*Animal sacrifice mentioned.

[2] Luke 11:27-28, Acts 14:6-23.

[3] The Sīrat Rasūl Allāh by Ibn Isḥāq *chapter: Rebuilding of the Ka'ba*. The Koran 3 The Family of 'Imran (Āl 'Imrān):96.

[4] Al-Lāt is also known as Allāt and Alilat.

According to The Book of Idols by ibn-al-Kalbi, the three daughters of Allāh were advocates for humans in their dealings with Allāh. The three daughters were represented by idols. *Chapters: Manāh (Manāt), Allāt, Al-'Uzzā*.

The Sīrat Rasūl Allāh by Ibn Isḥāq refers to many idols of deities, including al-Lāt, al-'Uzzā and Manāt—*chapters: Origin of idolatry among the Arabs; 'Ali the first male Muslim, then Abū Bakr and his converts; Active opposition to Muḥammad; 'Amr's idol; Khalid destroys al-'Uzzā; Capture of al-Ṭa'if; Destruction of al-Lāt (The envoys of Thaqīf accept Islām)*.

The Greek goddess Aphrodite's Arabian counterpart was Alilat: Herodotus' The Persian Wars Book 1 *chapter 131*.

FOOTNOTE CONTINUED ON THE NEXT PAGE

is not the true God but simply a regional figure raised to prominence by Muḥammad, who selected some of Allāh's distinct characteristics[1] and combined them with some characteristics of the true God[2], which doesn't make Allāh and God the same. Within Islām, there is also the worship of the Black Stone and the Kaaba. Furthermore, there is the veiled worship of the Middle Eastern moon god Sin, whose crescent symbol is on practically

CONTINUED FOOTNOTE PRESENT

In the Koran—53 The Star (An-Najm):19-32—Muḥammad tries to distance Allāh from al-Lāt and the other two goddesses, al-'Uzzā and Manāt. In summary, the passage denies that Allāh has daughters and that they have power. However, whilst promoting Islām, Muḥammad declared to his tribe that he approved of the intercessory role of al-Lāt, al-'Uzzā and Manāt, which pleased the tribe. He later rejected the three goddesses hence the above passage in the Koran. Sīrat Rasūl Allāh by Ibn Isḥāq *chapter: Active Opposition to Muḥammad.*

[1] Such as being an individual who commands humans to perform the Meccan pilgrimage, which preceded Islām, and being the individual who established the Kaaba itself as a rallying point for humans: The Koran 5 The Feast (Al-Mā'idah):94-97, 22 The Pilgrimage (Al-Hajj):25-30.

[2] See earlier in this chapter pg 274 and footnote regarding the Koran claiming that Allāh is the Almighty God.

Note that Allāh's characteristic of being a creator god preceded Muḥammad's public declaration of Islām (around 613 AD): when the Kaaba was being rebuilt (approximately 605 AD), a writing was found that stated that the Lord of Bakka, Allāh, had created Bakka (Mecca), the Earth and Heaven. The Sīrat Rasūl Allāh by Ibn Isḥāq *chapter: Rebuilding of the Ka'ba.* The Koran 3 The Family of 'Imran (Āl 'Imrān):96.

It was not unusual for people to ascribe to their gods a creator role, as has been done for Brahmā, Vishnu, Prometheus and others. See footnote earlier in this chapter pg 285 regarding Hinduism and footnote in Chapter 14 pg 325 regarding Prometheus leading people to Hell.

every mosque.[1] Sin was also a member of a pantheon of deities.[2] Make no mistake, although to many people all these idols seem harmless, behind them are living demons.[3] Demons inspire false religions and receive the worship.[4] This is the terrible truth of idolatry. Idolatry survives till today, and its hold over the people has not diminished."

"Why were the people consumed by the desert?"

"The people were attracted to the temple and the idols. They worshipped the idols, and they knew what they were doing. The people being swallowed by the sand represents their spirits descending to Hell. This is where idolatry leads."[5]

"But the rosebushes gave the impression that the sand would support the people," the apprentice uttered.

"The rosebushes signify the leaders of the false religions. The leaders declare that their religions will give people a sure footing in the afterlife. The flowers represent the leaders' ceremonial

---

[1] See Chapter 5 and relevant footnotes regarding: the Black Stone (pgs 122-124), the Kaaba (pgs 122-124) and the moon god Sin (pg 116).

[2] The moon god Sin was believed to be a member of a four-generation pantheon of gods and goddesses. The deities of his line were reported to include Enlil (Ellil), Sin, Ishtar and Shara. Enlil was the father of Sin, who was the father of Ishtar, who was the mother of Shara: Myths from Mesopotamia *Atrahasis tablet II, The Descent of Ishtar to the Underworld, Anzu (old Babylonian version) tablet II.*

See previous footnote in Chapter 5 pg 116 for the extent of Sin worship in Mesopotamia and Arabia.

[3] Psalms 106:36-38, 1 Corinthians 10:14-21, Revelation 9:20.

[4] Deuteronomy 32:16-17, Psalms 106:36-38, Matthew 4:7-10, Luke 4:4-8, 1 Corinthians 10:19-21, 2 Corinthians 11:13-15, Ephesians 2:1-5, 1 Timothy 4:1-6, Revelation 9:20, 12:9, 13:1-15, 20:2-3.

[5] Galatians 5:20-21, Revelation 20:12-21:8, 21:10-22:15 (after the Millennium, the residents of Hell will be judged by God, then cast into the Lake of Fire—see Timeline, Soul and Spirit and footnote in Chapter 20 pg 398 regarding the Lake of Fire).

garments and/or head coverings, which deceive people into believing that these leaders are pious and their instructions worthy to heed."

"And the thorns?"

"They're symbolic of the true danger of these religious leaders to mankind."

"You called on the name of Jesus; without that action, neither of us would have been saved from the sandy mire," the apprentice remarked.

"That's right. God the Father has given Jesus authority over all things in Heaven and Earth."[1]

"I can understand why I started to sink; after all, I've just recently put my trust in Christ and hadn't yet understood the temple's deception. But why did you start to sink?"

"Because even experienced Christians can be trapped by the deception," Sam answered. "Although Christ has already saved us from Hell, we can still be tangled in the snare of idolatry.[2] Only remember, we resisted and turned to Jesus. And here we are standing on the edge—safe and sound. We looked to Jesus, and it is He who freed us. What's more, He can save anybody willing to turn from idolatry to Him. Salvation is through Christ alone."[3]

"And it is He who will eventually bring these false religions to an end,"[4] the apprentice added.

"Indeed," Sam replied.

Sam was awoken by the repetitive thud of beating blades. The characteristic sound of a helicopter at low altitude was unmistakable, even from his subterranean cocoon. He could even tell the helicopter's bearing. It had come from a southeasterly direction

---

[1] Matthew 28:18, John 3:35-36, 13:3, Colossians 1:13-20, Hebrews 1:1-3, 2:9-10.

[2] John 6:27-28, John 10:27-30, Hebrews 6:1-19, 10:10-39.

[3] John 3:35-36, 14:6, Acts 4:10-12, 1 Thessalonians 5:9-10, Hebrews 2:9-10.

[4] Revelation 19:7-20:10, 21:1-22:16.

and was heading toward the drilling station. He looked at his watch while simultaneously illuminating its face. It was eleven o'clock in the morning. After a minute, the sound had gone, and he thought very little of it before falling to sleep.

A few hours later Sam was awoken again except this time by the faint sound of men's voices. He was immediately worried, because to hear voices from the cocoon meant that these men had to be close. His arms were by his sides. He was about to tilt his head forward to look at his watch, but, realizing that this would cause snorkel movement on the surface, he stopped himself. He also decided not to move his right wrist (to which his watch was attached) to his face to avoid shifting the soil above him. He estimated the time to be around two o'clock in the afternoon.

Thoughts rushed through Sam's mind. How do they know that I'm here? What have I left outside? I've been so careful. Who are they? How many are they? Did they come from the helicopter? How quickly can I surface from the ground? Why did I have an apprentice in my dream? Please don't have a dog!

Sam felt extremely vulnerable. He was lying face up with a tube inserted in his mouth. The head end of the bivvy bag was beneath only eight inches of soft soil. He thought about the two rigid arches. Although metal, they were thin and definitely not designed to take a heavy load. If one of the men on the surface stepped onto the area above the head end of the bivvy bag, the arches would collapse and he would fall onto Sam.

The voices sounded as if they belonged to a group whispering at the opposite end of a large hall. Since leaving Cappadocia, Sam had had neither the time nor adequate light to shave and already had a short beard. His face itched enormously, and at that very moment the prickly sensation seemed to be magnified a hundred-fold. He strained his ears in an attempt to determine the number of men on the surface from their voices and when they walked from their footsteps. He could also sense their steps as a palpable vibration from the nerve endings in the skin of his back. He heard and felt the men getting closer. The revolver was next to his right hand. He gently flicked the safety to the off position and enclosed the grip in his right hand. The revolver was fully loaded, as it had been every night. He thought about how clumsy surfacing would be. It would take at least three movements before he was in a position to effectively defend himself: plenty of time for them to shoot him dead. Although, would the strangeness of seeing a figure rise from the ground covered in soil buy him some time?

Two of the voices became distinct, and Sam imagined them being almost directly above him. He could even pick out a few Turkish words. The other voices, which were rumbling and belonged to at least four men, were not far from the two. The two closest voices seemed to pass by Sam, then grow fainter. He didn't relax. Sure enough, three minutes later they came back, except this time the voices were louder than before. Sam placed his index finger on the trigger. I hope that there are fewer than seven, he thought. The owners of the two voices stopped walking. Sam made a conscious decision. If he felt any new direct pressure on any part of him or if the snorkel was tugged, he would come out blasting. He was ready for battle.

The two voice's dialogue decreased in intensity and soon merged with the rumbling voices. Then all the voices drifted away. They moved in the direction that would lead them to where they'd come from. Before long Sam couldn't hear them at all. He thought that they'd walked to a distant location but subsequently heard a vehicle's engine start, which was followed by the rolling tread of tires. The vehicle had obviously not wakened him when the men had arrived. After that, there was only silence. Nonetheless, Sam didn't sleep for the rest of the day, and instead of emerging five minutes after nightfall, as was his habit, he waited for a further two hours.

On the eleventh night since landing in Batman, Sam reached the borderlands of the city of Van (1,750 metres in altitude). It was two o'clock in the morning. He was south of the city, having made his way eastward through the province of Van. For the preceding 60 miles to his north had been Lake Van. He'd deliberately kept a safe distance from this vast body of water: its perimeter possessed many old ruins that attracted tourists. His only knowledge of the lake's position had been his map readings in the dark.

Sam could see the city's streetlights in the distance. He spent the following hour running six miles to a hilltop east of the city. He dug a small hole, which would receive nothing larger than his backpack. After that, he dressed himself in his only other outfit: a getup that a typical Kurdish farmer would wear, which Sam had reserved. He'd washed himself in a river during the night and was pleased to wear fresh garments. The disguise had been bought by Emin, and therefore Sam was completely dependant on his former host's familiarity with Kurdish apparel for its validity. Sam lay in the open beneath the stars. His last thought before he fell asleep was concerning the Kurdish name that he'd given himself.

Sam's alarm woke him before dawn. He removed a few items from his backpack, then sat, facing the city, waiting for sunrise. After dawn, the sun's direct rays soon struck the land, brightly illuminating the small metropolis, which was just two miles away.

Sam held a pair of binoculars to his eyes. At the top of his field of view he could see Lake Van. Beneath the lake he saw the ruins of Van Fortress and the Old Town. Below these and hence nearest to him was the New Town, the modern city, his destination. He removed the guide book that he'd read in Cappadocia—another donation from Emin—from his backpack. It contained a detailed map of the city. While continually referring to the view provided by his pair of binoculars, he memorized the map. He spent an hour doing this and an additional thirty minutes learning a few new words and sentences from his Turkish phrase book. He planned to not view the guide book's map, even once, while in the city because of the curiosity that might be aroused. Nevertheless, he neatly tore out the map, folded it and placed it into one of his pockets.

Whilst in Cappadocia, Sam had read in the guide book that Van is a half-Turkish-half-Kurdish city, whereas the town of Doğubayazıt is predominantly Kurdish (actually written as "Half of the population of the city of Van have Kurdish ancestry, while farther to the north most of the residents of the town of Doğubayazıt have this ancestry."). He'd also read that, according to the Turkish Constitution, the word Turk includes all citizens of the republic without distinction of race or religion, and that ethnic minorities have no official status. The Kurds represented twenty percent of the overall population of Turkey, and as in the other countries (mainly Iran and Iraq) where the unratified Kurdistan existed (Kurdistan being the region inhabited by the Kurds for many centuries), there were troubles.

After burying the backpack, Sam waited to see Van become busy. An hour and a half later he strolled toward the city. As he walked, he was reminded of the men who'd come close to discovering him near the oil drilling station. He was still unsure as to whether it had been a random event or if the men had actually been searching for him. He wondered if they worked at the complex and had had some related task near to where he'd buried himself. No matter how many times he played it over in his mind, no further angles arose to reveal their intent.

Sam was wary on seeing the first people near the city's border. He started to feel very conscious of his clothes, which were unfamiliar to him. None of the first five individuals were wearing anything similar, yet at the same time they paid him little interest. It was then around nine o'clock. Before long he was part of lively East Van. He moved easily, looking like a man who'd walked the streets of the city a million times. Each step had casual purpose.

Without turning to look left or right, he read the names of the shops and tried to determine what each sold.

Sam noticed a few people dressed similarly to him. On its own this might have alleviated some of his tension; however, he also heard some people talking in a language that wasn't Turkish: clearly Kurds using their own tongue, some of whom were wearing garments that reflected their ethnicity and others typical European garb now customary to Turks. He rapidly became convinced that his disguise wouldn't support what he'd planned. He imagined it working well from a distance, which Emin had envisioned, and even in silent proximity, but in the city it invited failure.

Sam could smell the aroma of cooked breakfasts from the shops of food vendors. What he would have given to have bitten into some hot food, I can only speculate. He walked on. To risk the mission for his stomach was foolish, and he maintained his plan to keep human interaction to an absolute minimum. He remembered his costly lunch in Antalya. After walking for a further ten minutes, he spotted a hardware store. On the way he'd noticed a large expensive-looking hotel and had noted its location.

The shop was larger inside than its outward appearance had suggested. The first thing that Sam wanted to know was from whom he would have to buy his intended purchases. His success depended on that interaction and less on the goods that the store had available. Positioned at the entrance, he looked toward the cashiers' counter. This was positioned on the left side of the store (Sam's right) near to the entrance. The rest of the shop was spread to the right (Sam's left). There were two tills manned by a middle-aged man and a young woman. Her features suggested to Sam that she was the man's daughter. Not the ideal set-up, Sam thought, but it could be worse. He thought further. Are they Turks or Kurds? If Kurds, will they initiate speech with me in Kurdish or Turkish? He picked up a metal basket.

The merchandise was positioned alongside three parallel aisles, which were perpendicular to the cashiers' counter in such a way that together the man and the woman could comfortably observe most of the store.

Sam had a mental picture of exactly the items he needed. The objects were distributed throughout the store, and he strolled in a relaxed fashion placing them into his basket. There were six other customers present. Sam was careful not to catch any of their eyes or accidentally bump into them. He collected a hard hat, protective plastic goggles, a grey one-piece protective work smock, a small tin of paint remover, protective gloves and a disposable face mask that would cover his nose and mouth. The penultimate item was a blue metal toolbox, which he held by its handle in his right hand.

Sam walked over to the section of the middle aisle that was nearest to the cashiers' counter. He pretended to ponder over his last purchase as he waited for the moment when a customer with many intended purchases occupied the male cashier's position while at the same time the female cashier was free. When these conditions were met, Sam picked up a screwdriver, walked over to the female cashier's position and placed all of his items onto the scratched wooden counter in front of her. He'd made sure that every product displayed its price and that he had the exact money ready for the exchange. He also ensured that she wouldn't have the opportunity to initiate their communication; he quickly said, "Günaydın," which means "Good morning" in Turkish.

The young woman returned the greeting and started to scan the objects' barcodes. After half a minute, she quoted the correct price to Sam. He handed her the money. As she counted, he quickly packed everything except the tool box into a light-blue plastic bag while out of the corner of his left eye he watched the male cashier. This middle-aged man was busy with his customer and had barely noticed Sam.

The woman placed the money in the till. "Teşekkürler," she said, thanking Sam for his purchase. This was followed by something else that Sam didn't understand, not even slightly. It was an entire sentence, but fortunately for him her intonation had ended as one would expect of a statement rather a question.

Sam thanked her in Turkish, which, judging by the expression on her face, appeared to satisfactorily conclude their dealings. He removed the empty toolbox from the counter using his left hand, and with the plastic bag in his right, he turned and left the store. He was pleased that he hadn't yet needed to use any of the more complicated phrases that he'd memorized on the hill. He made his way to the hotel. On the way he scooped up some black dirt, which he'd seen wedged in a curb, and placed this muck into the plastic bag.

Even a swanky hotel has guts. That's what Sam's first ever job, which was as a porter, had told him. He walked to the back of the hotel to find the service entrance. He found two. The first was a door at ground level, outside of which a housekeeper smoked a cigarette while she punched the buttons of her phone. The second and more-promising alternative was a ramp, which started at ground level and descended to the lower ground. There was no one present on the ramp, and he immediately ventured down. The double door at the bottom of the ramp was fixed open by a bolt on each door, which had been slid and secured an inch into the concrete floor. Just after the threshold there were two heavy, clear plastic sheets that hung from the top of the door-frame. He passed through them and was now in a long corridor. He progressed, vigilant for a suitable opportunity. To his left he heard the clanking of a large kitchen. A junior chef passed Sam in the corridor, taking not the slightest notice of him. Sam tried an unlabelled door to his right. It was locked. The next door to his right, also without designation, opened, and he peered inside. He saw a large room containing spare hotel furniture and quickly entered.

On the floor to Sam's left were several full-length mirrors standing one behind the other at an angle that ensured that they wouldn't fall. He looked at his reflection. His beard was thick, black and naturally sculpted. The hair was straight—not yet long enough to curl as the hair on his head. He'd never grown a beard before and was surprised at how much it changed his appearance. His eyes seemed to stand out more, and overall the beard aged him by at least five years. The most striking thing was that it seemed to alter the way he perceived himself. Maybe his thinned face from the intense exercise over the previous two weeks contributed to the effect. He felt gravely serious as he stared at himself. In college his unshaven face had never been far from a smile, but the beard buried all signs of levity. He looked at his Kurdish farmer's apparel. He then inspected the outfit directly, rolling the trousers' fabric between his right thumb and index finger while still holding the bag. He returned his gaze to his reflection. No wonder no one took any notice, he thought; I look like part of the scenery. Indeed, Emin had picked an excellent disguise except more for the wide open spaces of the eastern Turkish highlands. Perhaps Sam would have call to use it again in more appropriate circumstances. Since entering the room, he could hear a faint mechanical pounding from deeper inside. He noted a door at the far wall. Desiring not to be caught during his transformation, he made his way to this door to investigate. He passed chairs, chests of drawers, mattresses, bathroom accessories and other items. The rhythmic noise became louder. He cautiously opened the door to reveal a large, dark boiler room.

"Perfect," Sam said to himself and entered. He secreted himself behind the boiler, so that he wouldn't immediately be seen by anyone entering the room. He placed the metal toolbox and plastic bag onto the floor. He first strategically smeared the grey overalls with some of the dirt from the road, then put them on over the Kurdish clothes. He donned the protective gloves, and before dressing further, he opened the tin of paint remover and poured some of the contents onto selected areas of the empty metal toolbox. The warmth of the room magnified the stench of solvent. He poured a tiny amount of paint remover onto two areas of the smock, in order that he could not only look authentic but also smell the part. He carefully returned the lid of the tin into position, pressing heavily on the lid so that the container was tightly closed. He placed the tin inside the toolbox.

Sam removed the hard hat from the bag. The hat was white and clean. He decided that it was better not to age that particular item and placed it on his head. He aged the goggles by scratching the lenses slightly with the screwdriver. To make it look as if he'd already been working that morning, he pressed some of the dirt onto the front of the left lens. He shook off the particles that hadn't stuck and used water from a gently leaking pipe to create two streams of fake sweat, each partially clearing a path through the dirt. They would dry to produce the final effect. He placed the goggles onto the hard hat. They were secured by an elastic strap, which rested on the back of his neck. As for the disposable face mask, he merely crushed it in one hand, then attempted to regain its structure with his fingertips. This too had an elastic strap. He placed the mask so that it sat loosely beneath his chin as if temporarily placed there in between use.

The tang of solvent had lessened. Sam looked down at the toolbox. The blue paint had bubbled in the places that he'd selected. He used the screwdriver to flake the paint and scratch the toolbox. With that small job complete, he removed the gloves and put them into the right hip pocket of the smock, and the revolver followed. He placed the screwdriver into the smock's top pocket (with part of the handle visible) and put the plastic bag inside the toolbox.

Sam left the boiler room and returned to the front mirror to admire his handiwork. "Not bad, March," he said to himself. No fine-tuning was required. He left the hotel and headed toward the safe depository, which was in the centre of the city. He was clearly more confident in this disguise. Entering the city centre as a manual worker in appropriate garb, that is, conspicuously rather than discreetly, was now the plan. The occupation would become the man, thus deflecting the observer from truly noticing the person beneath the disguise: Turk, Kurd, foreign worker—it wouldn't matter. At least that's what he thought.

The city centre wasn't especially built-up. This zone possessed two parallel main streets around which the principal shopping area resided. Sam moved deftly through the city with more haste than before. After all, he had "work" to get on with; industrial electrical generators didn't maintain themselves. He was aware that the disguise would fit a number of different occupations, including that of an electrician, but he felt that his performance would be more convincing if he imagined only one.

The time was nearly half-past eleven and the city was bustling. Sam was walking down one of the main streets. Near to the end of this street, at a distance of 400 metres, there was a tall building. It was far enough away that, despite the building's height, he barely needed to lift his head to observe its summit. On the rooftop a lean man stood next to a water tower. His hands held a large pair of binoculars to his eyes. Sam was walking westward and the lean man facing southward. Although the vigilant figure was distant, Sam was able to determine that the lean man wasn't wearing a uniform—just standard European attire. Sam had already registered the building as one of the city's tallest (fourteen storeys) when he'd scoped the city with his pair of binoculars from the hill. The tallest was to his immediate left. He looked upward by craning his neck to view the summit of this building. He quickly looked down. His heart began to race. There was a stocky man standing on the edge of that rooftop. He was also wearing civilian clothing and possessed a pair of binoculars. This man's unused pair of binoculars rested against his chest, hanging loosely from a strap that looped around his neck. On top of sixteen storeys, the stocky man was almost straight above Sam. Sam had registered that he wasn't currently the direct object of the stocky man's gaze but was in this stalker's general field of vision. As tempting as it was to look up again in order to see if the stocky man had noticed the nimble manual worker, Sam felt that a second upward glance would significantly increase the likelihood of calling this stalker's attention. Instead, Sam took advantage of the white safety helmet, the brim of which, although small, was large enough to conceal his face from the view of the man directly above him.

Sam continued to walk westward except now more slowly: at a pace that matched the general crowd. The safe depository was only a few hundred metres away—near the train station. On the hill, ever cautious of the enemy staking-out the hearts and major arteries of public transport in large towns and cities, Sam had planned a route that would avoid the train station. The depository had been built on a street that met the station's street. However, his goal could be reached via a side street without a person being visible from the train station. He kept his head forward aiming for this side street, which was near to the building that held aloft the first identified stalker.

Now well beyond and with his back to the tallest lookout tower, Sam noticed movement from the first stalker. Being careful not to look upward, utilising the limits of his upper field of vision, Sam observed the lean man rotating his body in an unwelcome direction. With his pair of binoculars, the lean man was now searching the street on which Sam walked. Sam was determined to hold his course. He silently repeated the words "Keep going".

Before coming to within 100 metres of the first stalker, Sam's daring slipped, and he turned into the market of the New Town, where the streets were narrower and more densely populated. Sam was now out of view of both rooftop stalkers; however, there were so many people milling about the market that he found this almost as nerve-racking. He started to meet the gaze of those around him, trying to determine their intentions. He wondered how many of the enemy were employed at ground level to survey the streets. His tension increased, as did the speed of his steps and his own fidgety surveillance. He perceived his own heightened anxiety and realized that it was counterproductive. He took a large veiled breath and forced himself to stop staring into people's eyes. He slowed his steps and re-entered his role as an electrician.

Now if the two rooftop stalkers were his enemies, then Sam was absolutely sure that others would be staking-out the train station. It was a hub that could deliver a large return for a small investment. The two men on the rooftops had brought Sam closer to the station than he'd planned. He was now on the station's street, walking on the opposite side to the transport complex. Before long he could see the main entrance itself and the alfresco

cafés outside. The bisecting street that led to the safe depository
was just a few steps away. The "Van Tren Garı" (Van Train
Station) sign above the station's main entrance became clear. The
nearest café was just 15 metres away. There were several people
sitting on wooden chairs. One of the customers sat alone,
smoking a cigarette. A newspaper lay on the table in front of him
along with a glass ashtray full of cigarette butts.

Another one, Sam thought. The stalker's vigil was poor. He
half-heartedly watched the crowds as he smoked. Sam saw the
smoker's eyes follow a young lady as she walked by. Sam
ducked into the safe depository's street.

Three suspicious men already, all in one small city, and they
were just the ones whom Sam had seen. He thought about his
predicament. He tried to estimate how many men the enemy
would have to have at its disposal to watch every town and city
in Turkey in such numbers. He wondered if his assessment of the
situation was simply paranoia and the men were there for a
reason unrelated to him. He decided that they had to be there for
him. However, he found it impossible to conceive that the enemy
could mobilize a ground force so massive as to cover even a
modest fraction of the towns and cities in Turkey. It was then that
he grasped that the enemy was aware of his plan. The city of Van
is near Ararat, and that's why they're concentrated here, he
thought. But how do they know that the mountain is my
destination? He took off his work helmet and entered the safe
depository.

The lobby was quiet and besides Sam there were only two
others present: an armed guard and a desk clerk. It was a relief
compared with the stir outside and the suffocating presence of the
enemy. The air was cool, and Sam presumed that the depository
was air-conditioned, although he couldn't hear the characteristic
hum. The guard had scrutinized the depository's newest customer
as Sam had entered. The guard continued his observation. In spite
of this, Sam could tell from the guard's eyes that his observation
was mostly to ease the boredom of standing in the bare reception
area rather than because he perceived the manual worker as a

threat. The lobby fit the appearance of belonging to a safe depository that held very valuable items and thus would attract fittingly wealthy customers. So much for my electrician disguise, Sam thought. There was a large window on either side of the entrance's double door. Both of these windows had thick, black solid-steel bars, which prevented much of the natural light outside from entering. For this reason the lobby was well lit artificially. The bright lights reflected off the highly polished marble floor. Sam felt uncomfortably underdressed and approached the counter. The clerk sat behind two-inch-thick reinforced glass. There was a thin microphone in front of him. Sam could see two robust-looking doors behind the clerk's right shoulder.

Sam greeted the clerk politely in Turkish and smiled. The guard stopped watching Sam. The clerk returned the smile. He was a slight, old man who wore thin wire-frame spectacles. Behind them were judicious eyes.

Sam continued to speak to the clerk in Turkish. Sam reasoned that the clerk would almost certainly speak English, but Sam preferred that his own Turkish was heard by the old man. If the clerk was questioned about a foreigner at a later date, perhaps the old man would find it more difficult to state precisely where Sam was from. "I wish to see Box 97, please."

"What name would that be, sir?"

"Suleiman Yousefi."

"You'll see some paper in front of you together with a pen. Please write down your password and hold it up to the glass."

Sam wrote the word Parsa, which is the Old Persian name for the ancient city of Persepolis. He pressed the paper firmly against the glass.

"And your key."

Sam held his key up in plain view for the clerk to see.

"Thank you, sir," the clerk replied. "Would you like to step this way." He motioned with his right hand toward a door that was to Sam's left. "If you go through that door, I'll meet you on the other side in a minute or two." The door clicked.

Sam wondered if the clerk was aware that his current client had never been there before. The clerk's instructions had been clear and complete: a communication that a new customer would expect to receive. Maybe that's just his routine with everyone, Sam thought. Sam pushed the door and walked into a hallway, which had another guard. This guard got up from his seat but paid little attention to Sam. Four minutes later the clerk appeared from a different door, another entrance to the same hallway. This door shut and automatically locked behind the clerk. In his right hand he held a black metal box with scrape marks on its upper and lower surfaces, indicative of its years of use.

"Your box," the clerk said. "Follow me to the private room."

All three of them walked to the private room, which was, like the lobby, sparse yet richly constructed. There was a single sturdy table with four chairs. The clerk placed the box onto the table.

"We'll leave you here. Take as long as you need. When you're finished, press the buzzer. You won't hear it ring. Someone will be along shortly after you've pressed it." The clerk and the guard left Sam alone in the room.

Sam quickly scanned the room. There were no video cameras visible. He opened the box with his key. Occupying a fraction of the space inside were a Canadian passport and five small gold ingots. Starting from the picture-page with his new identity, he quickly flicked through the passport. He noted some of his previous trips (invented), which were mostly to European countries. According to the Turkish entry stamp, he'd been in the country for just three days. His name was Anthony Burrows. He looked at the photograph again. It was him dressed very smartly. He wondered how the House had managed to obtain that particular photograph of him. He then realized that it had been acquired from his matriculation (enrolment) picture, which was a group shot of all the undergraduates in his Cambridge college taken within a few days of their arrival—each person presented as a tiny figure. He recognized the tie that he'd worn that day. The picture was sharp. He thought: how did they manage that?

The truth is that instead of buying a copy of the photograph, I persuaded the photographer to sell me the original data file. The picture had been taken with a high definition camera and had the capability of being significantly enlarged. No facial hair though, Sam thought; they didn't predict the beard.

Sam still hadn't fathomed how the enemy knew his plan. Furthermore, another question arose as he closed the now empty box: whether he should abandon the mission or not. Because the city was under heavy surveillance, he decided that his ultimate decision would be best made outside of Van, where he'd feel less intimidated. His mind focused on his exit. He'd already presumed that the enemy would have a picture of him, copied from his British passport. He was now also worried that some of his guards during his confinement north of Afyon and some of his would-be assassins at Cotton Castle might be in the city. Sam locked the box, then pressed the buzzer.

On leaving the safe depository, Sam put the helmet back on. He decided to make maximum use of his disguise. He didn't return the way he came. He was well aware that human recognition worked best with repetition and wanted to avoid giving the same enemies another visual cue. Instead of turning right out of the shop, he turned left, which led deeper into the city and westward, further from the hill.

He remembered with clarity a series of small side streets on the map. The first didn't have what he was looking for. The second did, but the street was too busy to risk what he was planning. The third was just right.

At that time of day the third street had no access to cars. There was a tarmac road, but this was used only in the early morning for the vendors to receive merchandise for their market stalls. The stalls were positioned on either side of the street, chiefly on the pavements but also spilling onto the road itself. The resulting path between the stalls was full of pedestrians. In the road near to the pavement to Sam's left, there was a visible manhole cover. It was next to a stand that sold sandals. The vendor was a young man, about the age of sixteen, who, Sam presumed, was looking after the stall till the owner returned. Sam confidently strode over to the manhole cover. He deliberately opened the map of Van, and by looking at this and around him, he continued in a manner that suggested that he was confirming the exact location. He didn't verify his location. Instead, he observed the surrounding merchants and customers, looking carefully at their eyes to see if any were paying him any undeserved attention. He removed the screwdriver and prised the manhole cover. The iron disc was heavy and shifted laterally with a yawning scrape. He'd revealed a dark, cylindrical, vertical shaft. There were metal bars embedded in the concrete wall. They formed a ladder that disappeared into the blackness below. He climbed inside, making a point of not looking around him while his head was still exposed. He wedged the toolbox between his chest and the metal steps. With his right hand, he quickly returned the manhole cover to its original position.

Sam's nostrils told him that he was where he needed to be: the Van sewer. It was pitch-black. He could have illuminated his surroundings with his pen torch but decided to save the batteries and allow his eyes to adapt to the darkness. He reached the bottom of the ladder and felt a concrete platform beneath him. He paused to discern any subsequent movement of the manhole cover. After two minutes, he'd desensitized to the majority of the smell; however, it was too dark for his adapted vision to see properly. Although weak, the pen torch's beam illuminated the sewer well. He started to walk along the platform. It bordered a channel of effluent.

Sam used his compass to head eastward. The sewer was surprisingly capacious for one servicing such a small city, albeit there were some cramped passages. Afraid of the batteries expiring, he turned the torch on intermittently: he shone the light onto his path ahead, then switched the torch off until he reached the point that it had not previously illuminated. He spent two hours trying to find the easternmost extremity of the sewer. Having satisfied himself that he'd achieved his aim, he climbed up to a manhole cover in order to gauge what type of area was above him. He held his right ear to the iron cover and listened. He could hear the drone and rumble of vehicles. He tried another cover nearby. He heard similar sounds to before—but louder this time. He climbed down to the platform below and rested. While he waited, he reflected on how the events of his life had brought him to a sewer in Van.

At two in the morning Sam tilted the first of the two manhole covers that he'd examined earlier and peered out. The manhole was in the centre of a small road in East Van. He checked the road for traffic. The road was void of vehicles and he couldn't see any pedestrians. He exited the sewer. He quickly found the street that he'd used to enter the city. He made his way back to the hill. As he walked up its steep slope, he wondered if the enemy had seized any of his main contacts, namely Mustafa, Adalet and Emin. Sam had told none of these three of his intended destination. Could it be determined where he was headed from the conversations that he'd had with them? Thoughts of them and their relatives under forceful interrogation rushed through his mind. He felt nauseas at the thought of his friends being brutalized. While still on the move, he prayed to God to protect all three families and begged Him to bless them.

The enemy clearly knew about some of Sam's previous missions. How many places could Sam March, finder of artefacts and revealer of secrets, go to in Turkey to discover something of significance? They also knew that he was a Christian. The more deeply he thought, the more ideas about places came to mind, besides that of the Ark on Ararat.

The seven churches of Revelation were all situated in Turkey: Ephesus, Smyrna, Pergamos, Thyatira, Sardis, Philadelphia and Laodicea.[1] What secrets do those locations hide? Perhaps ancient scrolls of Scripture used by some of the earliest Christians (almost 2,000 years ago)—documents that would add to the

---

[1] Revelation 1:4-3:22.

already overwhelming evidence that the Bible has been preserved unchanged.[1]

Sam wondered if the enemy thought that he was searching for evidence of the popularly termed "Ten Lost Tribes of Israel": a title derived from the fact that after the Kingdom of the Hebrews spilt into Judah and Israel, essentially containing two and ten tribes respectively,[2] Israel was defeated by Assyria in 723 BC and many Israelites exiled to the conqueror's empire.[3] The title is misleading, as it implies that there are ten tribes currently not accounted for amongst the Jewish people. The split of the Kingdom of the Hebrews occurred in 930 BC, and many members of the ten tribes of Israel migrated to Judah before the defeat of Israel by Assyria. Therefore, all the twelve tribes are still represented in the Jewish people today.[4] The Assyrian

---

[1] Of course, when these proofs emerge, genuine Christians with faith are never surprised.

[2] The twelve tribes are as follows: Judah, Benjamin, Joseph (represented by the tribes of Ephraim and Manasseh, both being the descendents of Joseph's two sons), Gad, Levi, Dan, Zebulun, Reuben, Simeon, Asher, Issachar and Naphtali (Genesis 29:32-30:24, 35:15-18, 41:50-52, 49:1-28, Numbers 1:33-35, 32:33, Joshua 13:1-7, 18:7). At the time of the split, although the name Judah suggests that this kingdom was represented by only one tribe, the tribe of Benjamin stayed with Judah. At that time there were even some members of the ten tribes of Israel who remained in the cities of Judah. Of these, some of the tribe of Levi would have also stayed to fulfil their roles as maintainers and priests of the Temple in Jerusalem. 1 Kings 11:1-13, 11:28-43, 12:1-33 ("the remnant of the people" means those not of the tribes of Judah and Benjamin), 2 Chronicles 11:5-12.

[3] See Timeline.

[4] After the division of the Kingdom of the Hebrews into Judah and Israel (930 BC), some of the members of the ten tribes in Israel relocated to Judah, as this region contained the city of Jerusalem, which was the centre of Hebrew worship (2 Chronicles 11:16-17). Of special note is the fact that the Levites migrated en masse to
FOOTNOTE CONTINUED ON THE NEXT PAGE

Empire was partly located in what is now southeastern Turkey. So what could be there? Were the exiles assimilated? Did they form their own enclaves? Or did they have another fate?

Sam's thoughts drifted next to Troy in Northwest Turkey. Most of his previous jobs weren't related to his religious beliefs,

CONTINUED FOOTNOTE PRESENT

Jerusalem and other parts of Judah, because they were prevented from performing their priestly role in Israel (2 Chronicles 11:13-15). Therefore, despite the later exile of many of the occupants of Israel by the Assyrians, today within the Jewish people of the world all of the tribes of the Hebrews are represented (see Timeline). There is further evidence for this from the Bible:

(i) In the time of Ezra (a priest who served God some time between 500 BC and 400 BC) sacrifices were performed for all the twelve tribes: Ezra 6:14-22, 7:1-6.

(ii) In the time of Paul's preaching (which was after 33 AD) he explained to King Agrippa that Jesus is the promised Messiah, whom the twelve tribes of Israel hope for intently: Acts 26:1-32.

(iii) In the future seven-year Tribulation period there will be 144,000 Jewish men selected from all twelve tribes (12,000 from each) by God the Father to serve Jesus the Messiah: Revelation 7:1-8, 14:1-5, see Timeline. In Revelation 7:1-8 the tribe of Dan is replaced by the tribe of Manasseh. The tribe of Joseph (most likely representing the other half of the tribe of Joseph, Ephraim) is included. As verse 4 states that all tribes are represented, it is probable that Dan will somehow be combined with Manasseh. Verses 1-8 do not mean that Dan won't exist at this time, because according to Ezekiel 48:1-35, which relates to the 1,000-year reign of the God Messiah (which is after the Tribulation), the twelve tribes will include Dan in the allotted space for the Hebrews (Ezekiel 40:1-48:35 is all the same prophetic vision, and within this the passages 41:1-43:17 and 45:1-6 demonstrate that in the allotted space for the Hebrews will be a future temple, where the LORD God will reign forever; note that His 1,000-year reign will continue into the eternal New Heaven-New Earth—see also Timeline, Chapter 20 pg 397 and Chapter 24 pgs 534-536 with their relevant footnotes).

so there was no reason why the enemy wouldn't deduce that his mission was there. They'd even questioned him about Troy. Sam's thoughts ran deeper. Although Troy is a seemingly secular destination, the "heroes" of the Trojan War (the conflict was around 1200 BC) could be linked to the "men of renown" in the Bible: specifically, the giants who were born after the Flood. According to mythographers, Achilles' mother, Thetis, was meant to be an "immortal" goddess.[1] Moreover, through his father, Peleus, Achilles was a great-grandson of the believed immortal Zeus,[2] king of the gods of Mount Olympus.[3] Assuming that there is some measure of truth within the Greek legends, Sam inferred that Achilles was almost certainly a Nephil, similar to the warrior-giants described in the Bible. Sam recalled that the Trojans Priam, Hector and Aeneas[4] as well as Achilles' fellow

---

[1] Hesiod's Theogony *lines 240-264, 1003-1007*, Homer's Iliad Book 1 *lines 493-559*, Hyginus' Fabulae *96*, Apollodorus' The Library Book 3 *chapter 13:4-6*.

[2] Reportedly, Zeus was the father of Aeacus, who was the father of Peleus, who was the father of Achilles: Homer's Iliad Book 2 *lines 858-861*, Book 21 *lines 184-199*, Homer's Odyssey Book 11 *lines 465-472*, Book 24 *lines 35-40*, Hesiod's Theogony *lines 1003-1007*, Euripides' Iphigenia at Aulis *lines 691-708*, Hyginus' Fabulae *14:8, 52, 96*, Apollodorus' The Library Book 3 *chapters 12:6-13:6*.

[3] Hesiod's Theogony *lines 35-52* and see Chapter 13 pg 290 and footnote regarding Jupiter, king of the gods.

[4] Reportedly, Zeus was the father of Dardanus, who was the father of Erichthonius, who was the father of Tros, who was the father of Ilus, who was the father of Laomedon, who was the father of Priam, who was the father of Hector; Tros was also the father of Assaracus, who was the father of Capys, who was the father of Anchises, who was the father of Aeneas. Homer's Iliad Book 20 *lines 199-241*, Apollodorus' The Library Book 3 *chapter 12:1-5*, Dionysius of Halicarnassus' Roman Antiquities Book 1 *chapter 62:1-2*.
Reportedly, Zeus was the father of Aphrodite (Venus), who was the mother of Aeneas: Homer's Iliad Book 20 *lines 86-109*. Alterna-
FOOTNOTE CONTINUED ON THE NEXT PAGE

Greeks Odysseus, Agamemnon and Ajax[1] were all reportedly descendants of Zeus and therefore likely to have been Nephilim as well. Furthermore, Poseidon, Ares and other believed immortals were also meant to have had offspring who fought in the war. Sam remembered how many of the so-called heroes, descendents of the immortals, would slaughter with ease normal men, and the battles would only become a true contest when one of these heroes faced a like adversary.[2] Neither did Sam forget incomparably

CONTINUED FOOTNOTE PRESENT

---

tively, it has been reported that Aphrodite was an offspring of Uranus rather than Zeus: Hesiod's Theogony *lines 173-206.*

[1] Odysseus (Ulysses): reportedly, Zeus was the father of Arceisius, who was the father of Laertes, who was the father of Odysseus—Ovid's Metamorphoses Book 13 *lines 123-147,* Homer's Odyssey Book 16 *lines 112-125,* Apollodorus' The Library Book 1 *chapter 9:16,* Book 3 *chapter 10:8.* Alternatively, it has been reported that Odysseus was a son of Sisyphus rather than Laertes. However, through Odysseus' mother, Anticlia, Odysseus was still a descendant of Zeus: reportedly, Zeus was the father of Hermes (Mercury), who was the father of Autolycus, who was the father of Anticlia, who was the mother of Odysseus—Ovid's Metamorphoses Book 1 *lines 668-681,* Book 2 *lines 676-707,* Hesiod's Theogony *lines 938-939,* Hyginus' Fabulae *201.*

Agamemnon: reportedly, Zeus was the father of Tantalus, who was the father of Pelops, who was the father of Atreus, who was the father of Agamemnon—Homer's Iliad Book 5 *lines 550-553,* Book 7 *lines 365-374,* Euripides' Orestes *lines 1-28,* Euripides' Iphigenia Among the Taurians *lines 1-9,* Euripides' Iphigenia at Aulis *lines 473-505,* Library of History by Diodorus Siculus Book 4 *chapter 74:1-4,* Hyginus' Fabulae *78, 82, 84.*

Ajax (a cousin of Achilles): reportedly, Zeus was the father of Aeacus, who was the father of Telamon, who was the father of Ajax—Apollodorus' The Library Book 3 *chapter 12:6-7,* Homer's Iliad Book 6 *lines 5-8,* Hyginus' Fabulae *14:8, 52, 107.*

[2] The brothers Ascalaphus and Ialmenus were reportedly sons of Ares by the same mother, Astyoche. Ascalaphus was killed by Deïphobus, a son of Priam. Homer's Iliad Book 2 *lines 511-516,*

FOOTNOTE CONTINUED ON THE NEXT PAGE

beautiful Helen (the focus of the war), who was reportedly no less than a daughter of Zeus.[1] Sam knew that the 10-year Trojan

CONTINUED FOOTNOTE PRESENT

Book 12 *lines 88-97,* Book 13 *lines 468-539,* Book 15 *lines 100-112.*

Cycnus, reportedly a son of Poseidon, was killed by Achilles: Ovid's Metamorphoses Book 12 *lines 64-145,* Greek Epic Fragments Cypria *argument 10,* Pindar's Olympian Odes 2 *lines 79-83,* The Fall of Troy by Quintus Smyrnaeus Book 14 *lines 127-134.*

Antilochus: reportedly, Poseidon was the father of Neleus, who was the father of Nestor, who was the father of Antilochus—Homer's Iliad Book 6 *lines 30-36,* Book 10 *lines 1-24,* Homer's Odyssey Book 11 *lines 235-259.* Antilochus was killed by Memnon (reportedly, a son of the supposed female immortal called Dawn), who was killed by Achilles: Homer's Odyssey Book 4 *lines 183-202,* Greek Epic Fragments Aethiopis *argument 2,* The Fall of Troy by Quintus Smyrnaeus Book 2 *lines 1-592.*

Other major bouts between descendants of believed immortals:

Aeneas vs. Achilles—Homer's Iliad Book 20 *lines 156-352* (no winner).

Ajax vs. Hector—Homer's Iliad Book 7 *lines 206-312* (no winner).

Hector vs. Achilles—Homer's Iliad Book 22 *lines 131-394* (Achilles killed Hector; Achilles was especially proud of this victory, because the Trojans had been in the habit of praying to his opponent, as if he was a god).

Many others can be cited.

[1] Helen was reportedly incomparably beautiful and the focus of the war: Homer's Iliad Book 2 *lines 155-181,* Book 3 *lines 15-461,* Book 9 *lines 135-140, 272-282,* Apollodorus' The Library Epitome *chapter 3:1-6,* Euripides' Andromache *lines 103-116.*

Helen was reportedly the daughter of Zeus by Leda (the wife of Tyndareus): Apollodorus' The Library Book 3 *chapter 10:6-7,* Euripides' Helen *lines 16-30, 211-216,* Hyginus' Fabulae 77.

An alternative is that Helen was the daughter of Zeus and Nemesis, and was subsequently adopted by Leda (same last Apollodorus reference and Pausanias' Description of Greece Book 1 *chapter 33:7-8*). Either way, Helen was still reportedly a daughter of Zeus.

War fell within the approximately 400-year period during which the Hebrews fought against other giants as well as regular humans to inherit the Promised Land[1]—the different conflicts separated in distance by just a thousand miles. So what secrets does Troy hold? After all, Achilles, Priam, Ajax and Hector were all supposed to have died there.[2] I can add to Sam's thoughts.

---

[1] See Timeline and Chapter 3 pgs 65-71 with relevant footnotes regarding this topic.

[2] Achilles: Homer's Odyssey Book 3 *lines 102-119*, Book 24 *lines 35-97*, Greek Epic Fragments Aethiopis *argument 3*, The Fall of Troy by Quintus Smyrnaeus Book 3 *lines 1-185*. There is a dispute as to whether or not Achilles' bones were buried in his tomb at Troy, the latter possibility being that after his body was cremated, his mother removed the bones to Leuce Island (White Island, Zmiinyi Island) in the Euxine Sea (Black Sea). Achilles' tomb at Troy was visited by Alexander the Great in 334 BC. Greek Epic Fragments Aethiopis *argument 4*, Sack of Ilion *argument 4*, The Fall of Troy by Quintus Smyrnaeus Book 3 *lines 709-742*, Arrian's Anabasis of Alexander Book 1 *chapter 12:1-2*, Plutarch's Lives Alexander *chapter 15:4-5*, Library of History by Diodorus Siculus Book 17 *chapter 17:1-3* (Alexander also visited the tomb of Ajax at Troy).

Ajax: Apollodorus' The Library Epitome *chapter 5:4-8**, The Fall of Troy by Quintus Smyrnaeus Book 5 *lines 482-663**, Homer's Odyssey Book 3 *lines 102-119*, Pindar's Isthmian Odes 4 *lines 31-36b*.

*Ajax's bones were buried in Rhoeteium, which was Trojan territory.

Priam: The Fall of Troy by Quintus Smyrnaeus Book 13 *lines 216-250*, Virgil's Aeneid Book 2 *lines 506-558* (after Priam's death in Troy, he was observable as a massive headless corpse on the beach).

Hector: see earlier in this chapter pg 315 and footnote regarding the descendants of immortals fighting each other. Hector's bones were buried outside of the city of Troy: Homer's Iliad Book 24 *lines 776-804*. Hector's bones might have been later exhumed, transported to
FOOTNOTE CONTINUED ON THE NEXT PAGE

Concerning the warriors Achilles, Agamemnon, Ajax, Odysseus, Aeneas and Hector, although their heights are not stated in the Iliad or the Odyssey, they were portrayed by Homer as being of much greater physical stature and strength than the men of normal human lineage, and wielded weapons to match (when described).[1] The great statures of some of the descendents of Zeus who fought at Troy—and occasionally their huge weap-

CONTINUED FOOTNOTE PRESENT

Greece and buried in Thebes: Pausanias' Description of Greece Book 9 *chapter 18:5.*

[1] Homer's Iliad:

Achilles was described as enormous and powerful. His spear was so massive (in size and weight) that amongst the Greeks only he could wield it. Book 16 *lines 130-144,* Book 20 *lines 430-437,* Book 21 *lines 526-536.*

Agamemnon was described as an enormous fighter who was mighty and tall—Book 3 *lines 161-180.*

Ajax was described as mighty, enormous and of a height greatly surpassing the other Greeks (Achilles was not present amongst the troops at that time). Ajax threw a rock comparable to a millstone at Hector. The rock broke Hector's shield and knocked him to the ground. Book 3 *lines 225-233,* Book 7 *lines 206-282.*

Aeneas was described as powerful, and he used a strong and exceedingly long spear. In battle he easily wielded in one hand a stone that two normal men together would not be able to lift. Although Homer does not directly comment on Aeneas' height, the description of the spear's length and the use of the stone indicate enormous height accompanying extraordinary strength. Book 2 *lines 819-823,* Book 20 *lines 259-308.*

Hector was described as enormous and the possessor of unconquerable strength. He used a spear that was 11 cubits (16½ feet) in length. Book 6 *lines 312-322,* Book 11 *lines 819-821,* Book 22 *lines 90-98.*

Homer's Odyssey:

Odysseus was described as extremely tall and muscular. Only he could string his bow; his wife's suitors were unable. Book 21 *lines 1-342, 376-423.*

ons—were described by Quintus of Smyrna. In his 14 books, collectively called the Fall of Troy, Achilles, Ajax, Aeneas, Odysseus and Neoptolemus (the son of Achilles), who joined the war after his father's death, are all referred to as giants.[1] The geographer and historian Pausanias wrote that the skeleton found in Ajax's tomb in the territory of Troy was abnormally large. To demonstrate this Pausanias relayed that the size of a kneecap was equal to that of a discus used in competition by boys.[2] From this one can estimate that Ajax was 16 feet tall.[3] Homer reported that amongst the Greeks who fought at Troy, Ajax was second only to Achilles in physical stature.[4] It wasn't only Achilles' stature that secured his legend. It was reported that he could run faster than horse-drawn chariots—a swiftness that when combined with his other attributes, namely his great size and strength, would have

---

[1] The Fall of Troy by Quintus Smyrnaeus:

Achilles—Book 1 *lines 494-528*, Book 2 *lines 202-207*, Book 3 *lines 383-434, 720-742*, Book 5 *lines 110-120* (Achilles' massive spear and armour are described; the spear was as long as a pine tree).

Ajax—Book 1 *lines 494-528*, Book 4 *lines 214-235,* Book 5 *lines 598-620, 636-652*.

Aeneas—Book 11 *lines 352-430*.

Odysseus—Book 3 *lines 308-321*.

Neoptolemus—Book 8 *lines 195-216* (Neoptolemus was able to effectively wield Achilles' spear in battle), Book 9 *lines 222-246, 310-320*.

[2] Pausanias' Description of Greece Book 1 *chapter 35:4-5*.

Near the tomb was a temple to Ajax and also a statue of him—the location of all in Rhoeteium, which was historically Trojan territory: Strabo's Geography Book 13 *chapter 1:30*.

[3] The width of the kneecap of a six-foot-tall man is approximately 6 cm; the diameter of a boy's discus is approximately 16 cm; therefore, the approximate height of Ajax was 16 feet.

[4] Homer's Odyssey Book 11 *lines 465-486*, Book 24 *lines 15-18*.

made him a formidable fighter.[1] It's notable that despite the well-broadcasted deaths of Achilles and Ajax, both were later worshipped by those fully aware of their demise.[2] Regarding other descendants of the king of Olympus, according to Herodotus the historian, Hercules' footprint was two cubits in length,[3] which would have made him approximately 18 feet tall. Hercules was widely reported to have been a son of Zeus,[4] lived one generation before the Trojan War[5] and was deified after his death.[1] Orestes

---

[1] Homer's Iliad Book 22 *lines 21-25*, Euripides' Iphigenia at Aulis *lines 206-230*.

[2] After Achilles' death, temples and statues were erected to him and sacrifices were made to him. Furthermore, Leuce Island (Zmiinyi Island, in the Black Sea) was considered sacred to Achilles. Pausanias' Description of Greece Book 3 *chapters 19:11-12, 20:8-9, 24:4-5,* Strabo's Geography Book 7 *chapter 3:16,* Book 11 *chapter 2:6,* Dio Cassius' Roman History Epitome of Book 78 *chapter 16:7,* The Fall of Troy by Quintus Smyrnaeus Book 14 *lines 246-323* (according to this reference, after Achilles' death he was declared to be a god, and his son, Neoptolemus, sacrificed one of Priam's daughters on Achilles' tomb), see also previous footnote in this chapter pg 317 regarding the death of Achilles in Troy.
After Ajax's death, temples and statues were erected to him. Alexander the Great made an offering to Ajax during a visit to his tomb in Troy (334 BC). Strabo's Geography Book 13 *chapter 1:30,* Pausanias' Description of Greece Book 1 *chapter 35:1-4,* Library of History by Diodorus Siculus Book 17 *chapter 17:1-3.*

[3] Herodotus' The Persian Wars Book 4 *chapter 82* (it was a man's footprint).

[4] Homer's Iliad Book 14 *lines 312-328*, Hesiod's Theogony *lines 306-318,* Apollodorus' The Library Book 2 *chapter 4:8,* Hyginus' Fabulae *29.* These are just a few of a host of possible references.

[5] According to Homer's Iliad, Hercules' son Tlepolemus fought in the Trojan War on the side of the Greeks. Two of Hercules' grandsons, Pheidippus and Antiphus, also came to assist the Greeks, but it is Tlepolemus' battle against Sarpedon that made Tlepolemus the most famous of Hercules' offspring in the war. Sarpedon was
FOOTNOTE CONTINUED ON THE NEXT PAGE

(the son of Agamemnon), reported to have been five generations from Zeus,[2] according to the same historian, was 10½ feet tall—the length of Orestes' corpse within his coffin was seven cubits.[3] All the abovementioned heights are worth relaying, as Pausanias and Herodotus have clearly attempted precision to inform their readers of the veracity of the extraordinary heights of these individuals, which cannot be said of many other mythographers and historians.[4]

CONTINUED FOOTNOTE PRESENT

---

reportedly the son of Zeus and Laodameia. Book 2 *lines 653-670, 676-680*, Book 5 *lines 627-667*, Book 6 *lines 191-199*.

[1] After his death, Hercules was believed to be a god and was widely worshipped as such (temples, sacrifices, etc.) by the ancient Greeks and Romans: Homer's Iliad Book 18 *lines 112-126*, Homer's Odyssey Book 11 *lines 601-616*, Apollodorus' The Library Book 2 *chapters 7:7-8:1*, Library of History by Diodorus Siculus Book 4 *chapters 38:1-39:1*, Pausanias' Description of Greece Book 1 *chapters 15:3-4, 19:2-3, 31:6*, Book 4 *chapters 8:1-3, 23:10, 30:1*, Book 5 *chapter 4:6*, Book 9 *chapter 24:3*, Livy's History of Rome Book 1 *chapter 7:3-15*, Book 32 *chapter 9:1-5*, Dionysius of Halicarnassus' Roman Antiquities Book 7 *chapter 72:13-14*. See also further on in this chapter pg 327 and footnote regarding the poisoning and then pyre of Hercules.

[2] Homer's Iliad Book 9 *lines 114-148, 262-290*, Euripides' Orestes *lines 1-28*, Apollodorus' The Library Epitome *chapter 2:16*, Hyginus' Fabulae *101, 119*. See also previous footnote in this chapter pg 315 regarding the lineage of Agamemnon.

[3] Herodotus' The Persian Wars Book 1 *chapters 67-68*.

[4] Furthermore, the heights are comparable to those of Goliath (whose height is precisely known) and Og (whose height one can easily estimate) found in the Bible. For their heights and further comments, see Chapter 3 pgs 65 and 65 with accompanying footnotes regarding respectively their heights and the possible Anakic ancestry of Goliath.

It should not be overlooked that much larger giants than Hercules are likely to have existed. They are indicated to in Numbers 13:33, in which some of the Hebrew spies said that they were like

FOOTNOTE CONTINUED ON THE NEXT PAGE

Sam wondered how much the enemy knew about all these different places. They knew much more than he realized. And what of the unofficial excavations throughout Turkey, which Sol Hodaviah had spoken about? Sam then thought about the Arkwood fragment that had been discovered in his denim shirt. They hadn't asked him about the fragment. Or perhaps they hadn't had the chance. Surely it was too small for someone to identify, unless maybe they'd seen something like it before.

At that stage Sam had the option to initially head back to Batman and then make for the coast and escape from Turkey via the Mediterranean Sea, the latter perhaps by hiring a boat and sailing to one of the Greek islands. Eventually, he decided that the stakes were too high for him to give up. Furthermore, others had already risked their lives to help him. He also supposed that if the enemy truly thought that he was headed for Ararat to find the Ark of Noah, then they too must believe that there was something there, or they wouldn't be trying so hard to prevent him from finding it. After burying some unnecessary items and packing the ones that he needed, he started his 160-mile trek to Doğubayazıt, continuing to travel exclusively at night and hiding in the ground during the day.

Heading northeastward, Sam once again shunned the shores of Lake Van. He passed ruins of Urartian fortresses from a distance. After skirting Lake Erçek east of its shore, he continued toward Doğubayazıt, still in a northeasterly direction. There were ample sources of fresh water along the way except for a precarious 50-mile stretch, during which he'd wished that he'd brought more water bladders. He managed to avoid numerous Kurdish villages overnight and their dispersed occupants during the day. He also tried to keep well away from Iran. At one point the terrain led

---

CONTINUED FOOTNOTE PRESENT

grasshoppers in comparison with the sons of Anak, and in Amos 2:9, in which the heights of the Amorite giants are compared to the heights of cedar trees.

him to within two miles of the border, which was much closer than he'd intended.

On the eighteenth night since landing in Batman, Sam reached the southern perimeter of Doğubayazıt (1,600 metres in altitude). It was here that his climbing equipment had been hidden: buried by the House of Hodaviah. Unable to find the stones that marked the equipment's presence overnight, he dug a hole for his bed in preparation for the day's sleep in an area that he'd estimated was the correct general location. His intention was to riskily use dawn's light to locate the equipment, which was inside a new backpack, which was buried beneath the stones.

Dawn arrived and Sam saw Mount Ararat for the first time. It was only 12 miles away. The snowy peak appeared as a conical cloud suspended in a dark-blue sky. Awestruck, he tarried, watching for sunrise's enhancement. When the sun rose, its radiance drifted downward and the peak received its true recognition as the white crown of a vast mountain domain. Great Ararat's tremendous height relative to the surrounding area, besides its smaller neighbour, makes it a rise surpassed by only a few mountains in the world. If he hadn't been travelling solely at night, he would have seen the mountain a day before. Observing from the southwest of the mountain, he strained his eyes in an attempt to distinguish details on the southern glacier. Reportedly, it was there that Kurdish rebels had used hideouts within the glacier to evade the Turkish military. There were rumours that these lairs had been found and not constructed by the rebels, and were made of ancient wood. Furthermore, the rumours related that the rebels had somehow been expelled from their hideouts. Although Sam could see the glacier's downward course, he was too far away and viewing from too low an angle to discern any specific features. His pair of binoculars didn't help. However, the southern glacier wasn't his first intended destination. According to the information that he'd received from the House of Hodaviah, the perpendicular ridges were on the surface of the northern glacier. His plan was to investigate the northern glacier first, and if he couldn't find anything there, he would head to other candidate locations.

Sam found the new backpack after ten minutes of searching. Without examining its contents, he placed it into the sleeping hole. He buried himself and slept until night.

The Bible tells us that the Nephilim, those men of renown, were part of the pre-Flood corruption and delivers accounts of their harmful influence in the post-Flood era. The biblical narratives are correct, because they are inspired by God. All other sources of the Nephilim are inferior to the Bible in accuracy; however, they clearly demonstrate that these men of legend walked the Earth. What is worrying is that for millennia popular retellings of the nonbiblical accounts have demonstrated censorship of the source material, focusing much on the Nephilim's superhuman feats and often hiding their dreadful deeds. Even the accounts on which the popular stories are based are undoubtedly softened and romanticized representations of the facts, yet the true nature of these individuals still rings through. They were also renowned for their malevolence. In the following summary Greco-Roman accounts are recalled more than those of other cultures, because the ancient Greeks and Romans made copious detailed records, many of which have been preserved. The existing accounts of similar beings amongst the early Germanic and Indic peoples are recalled to a lesser extent, because the stories are fewer in number and more embellished respectively in comparison with the Greco-Roman records. Although accounts that have other origins are not recalled, it should be stated that within practically every cultural group on Earth there exists both written and oral narratives of fearsome gigantic humans, often referred to as gods, demigods or heroes. It seems that no culture has escaped the Nephilim's corrupting influence, either directly (owing to their historical presence within a particular culture) or indirectly (from a particular culture being influenced by or blending with another culture or cultures that had previously had Nephilim present). Their former widespread presence is also evidenced by the fact that their giant skeletal remains have been discovered throughout the globe. Included in their atrocious acts are extreme-cruelty, licentiousness and infanticide, sometimes directed against one another. Nephilim are not to be admired. Regarding all of the nonbiblical accounts, their veracity can be questioned. The following has been reported, interspersed with comments.

During Zeus' existence on Earth he had one of his own cousins, Prometheus, bound to a pillar. Whilst restrained, Prometheus was tortured by an eagle that pecked at his liver. The reason for the sentence imposed on Prometheus was that he had tricked Zeus and had assisted normal humans.[1] If Prometheus conferred any benefits on mankind, then they came at a high price, for he still set himself up as a god, thereby distracting people away from God, their true creator, and leading those who followed him to Hell.[2] This is the case for any of the Nephilim who set themselves up in like manner. Zeus ravished women.[3] He also

---

[1] The punishment: Hesiod's Theogony *lines 517-531.*

The crime was twofold. Firstly, to trick Zeus into accepting the lesser parts of an animal that was to be sacrificed to him (bones instead of meat) and secondly, the trigger for the punishment, to give fire to regular humans—Prometheus having been in the habit of giving them methods of advancement, e.g., building techniques, sailing, etc. Hesiod's Theogony *lines 535-572,* Aeschylus' Prometheus Bound *lines 101-113, 436-471.*

Reportedly, the fathers of Zeus and Prometheus were Cronus and Iapetus respectively, brothers and Titans: Hesiod's Theogony *lines 126-138, 453-465, 507-514.*

[2] According to some accounts, Prometheus was the creator of men, but not women: Apollodorus' The Library Book 1 *chapter 7:1-3,* Hyginus' Fabulae *142.*

[3] Aegina: see footnote in Chapter 9 pg 206 regarding licentiousness of the Nephilim.

Europa was reportedly deceptively abducted by Zeus and carried by him to Crete, where he had three children by her: Hesiod's Catalogue of Women *fragment 89,* Ovid's Metamorphoses Book 2 *line 843-*Book 3 *line 5,* Book 6 *lines 103-107,* Apollodorus' The Library

FOOTNOTE CONTINUED ON THE NEXT PAGE

had sexual relationships with women married to other men. His son Hercules was the result of Zeus' seduction of Alcmene, the wife of Amphitryon.[1] Hercules married a princess called Megara, his first wife, by whom he had three children—all of them sons, whom he later killed. It was because of this murderous act that his Labours were imposed.[2] He had at least two adulterous

CONTINUED FOOTNOTE PRESENT

Book 3 *chapter 1:1,* Library of History by Diodorus Siculus Book 4 *chapter 60:2-4,* Book 5 *chapter 78:1,* Hyginus' Fabulae *178.* Minor variations of the account are given in the above references.

Callisto was reportedly overcome by Zeus against her will; their son was Arcas: Apollodorus' The Library Book 3 *chapter 8:2,* Ovid's Metamorphoses Book 2 *lines 401-475,* Hyginus' Fabulae *176.* Pausanias briefly reported the account and perhaps as a result mentioned only that Zeus had intercourse with Callisto: Description of Greece Book 8 *chapter 3:6-7.*

[1] Apollodorus' The Library Book 2 *chapter 4:8,* Library of History by Diodorus Siculus Book 4 *chapter 9:1-7,* Hesiod's The Shield *lines 1-56.* See Chapter 21 pg 463 and footnote regarding Zeus seducing women in different forms.

[2] Apollodorus' The Library Book 2 *chapter 4:11-12* (three sons). See also variant accounts: Library of History by Diodorus Siculus Book 4 *chapters 10:6-11:2* (children—number not reported), Euripides' Heracles *lines 621-1038* (three sons). Euripides differs in that he reported that Hercules' Labours preceded the slaying of his sons. Diodorus reported that the Labours were requested of Hercules, but on account of his pride, he didn't initially undertake them; however, after being brought low by having slain his own children, he finally submitted.

Hyginus (Fabulae *32*) and Euripides (above) reported that Hercules killed Megara along with their sons (two sons rather than three in the Hyginus' reference). Apollodorus and Diodorus did not report that Megara was killed at this time but that she lived beyond Hercules' Labours, after which he gave her to another man: Apollodorus' The Library Book 2 *chapter 6:1,* Library of History by Diodorus Siculus Book 4 *chapter 31:1-2.* See also footnote in Chapter 9 pg 206 regarding the violence of the Nephilim.

affairs, both whilst married to his last wife, Deïanara.[1] Hercules was so jealous of the horses of Iphitus that he stole them. While Iphitus was searching for the horses, he approached Hercules. Iphitus was invited by this son of Zeus into his home for a meal. There Hercules killed his guest in order to retain possession of the horses.[2] Hercules was poisoned by Deïanara when she

---

[1] The following two affairs Hercules had while married to Deïanara: with Astyoche (daughter of Phyleus, king of the Thresprotians) to father a son called Tlepolemus; and then with Astydameia (daughter of Amyntor, king of Ormenium) to father a son called Ctessipus. Apollodorus' The Library Book 2 *chapter 7:5-8,* Library of History by Diodorus Siculus Book 4 *chapters 34:1-37:5* (this reference also reports that Hercules had an affair with the daughter of Phylas, king of the Dryopes, to father a son called Antiochus—timed between the affairs with Astyoche and Astydameia).

If Megara was not slain by Hercules at the same time that he killed their children and was given by him to another man after his Labours, then whilst still married to her Hercules had an affair with a woman in Scythia (three sons were born to him: Scythes, Agathyrsus and Gelonus), because this relationship reportedly occurred during the Labours. Herodotus' The Persian Wars Book 4 *chapters 8-10,* Apollodorus' The Library Book 2 *chapter 6:1,* Library of History by Diodorus Siculus Book 4 *chapter 31:1-2.*

[2] Homer's Odyssey Book 21 *lines 11-41.* Other accounts differ: (i) Apollodorus reported that Eurytus (the father of Iphitus) held an archery contest, the victor of which would be given his daughter Iole in marriage. Hercules won but was refused Iole because of concerns that he would kill the future children—his past was known. Iphitus was the only member of his family to support Hercules' claim. Later on some cattle were stolen, and although Hercules was suspected, Iphitus denied this as a possibility. Indeed, they were stolen by another man. Iphitus asked Hercules to help find the cattle. However, having agreed, Hercules threw Iphitus to his death from the walls of a city called Tiryns. The Library Book 2 *chapter 6:1-2.* (ii) Diodorus reported that Hercules was denied consent to marry Iole by her father, Eurytus (no archery contest

FOOTNOTE CONTINUED ON THE NEXT PAGE

learned of his plans for an affair with yet another woman. On account of the intolerable pain caused by the poison, Hercules arranged for a pyre to be built on which his misery could be terminated through a fiery death. This was done.[1] During his life

CONTINUED FOOTNOTE PRESENT

---

mentioned). The same concern as above was cited. As a consequence, Hercules drove off Eurytus' horses. When Iphitus (son of Eurytus) searched for the horses, Hercules took Iphitus to a high tower in Tiryns and asked him if he could see them—a ruse to endanger him. There, Hercules expressed his indignation, claiming that Iphitus had blamed him for stealing the horses. Hercules then threw Iphitus to his death. Library of History Book 4 *chapter 31:1-4*. All the above accounts display Hercules' treachery.

[1] The correct view would be that Hercules then died, as the mortal he was. However, after the pyre was lit and he was yet still alive on top of it, embellishment took his story further on different routes. Apollodorus reported that Hercules was then taken up to heaven in a cloud (The Library Book 2 *chapter 7:7*). The account in Hyginus' Fabulae *36* is similar. Diodorus reported that lightning struck the pyre, and then because Hercules' bones weren't found, it was presumed that he'd been taken to be with the gods (Library of History Book 4 *chapters 38:1-39:1*). Homer, writing earlier than the above three, reported in the Iliad that Hercules did die (Book 18 *lines 112-126*), but in the Odyssey that he is immortal and with the gods despite his phantom being in Hades (Book 11 *lines 601-635*)—a muddled story. The reports that Hercules became truly immortal are wishful fantasy, albeit certainly he was believed to have become immortal by men. Indeed, in Diodorus' account the men who witnessed Hercules' pyre, although they were of the opinion that he was caught up to be with the gods, they still considered him to be a dead hero and honoured him thus, rather than as a god. The account continues to state that later the Athenians elevated Hercules to the status of a god and made sacrifices to him suitable for a god. They subsequently promoted Hercules' god cult among the rest of the Greeks, then beyond. See also previous footnote in this chapter pg 320 regarding Hercules' deification.

he fathered over sixty children with numerous women.[1] Some of Hercules' descendants founded royal lines in locations—mostly cities—in the Mediterranean, including in the Peloponnese and Asia Minor, now in modern-day Greece and Turkey respectively. Some of these descendants achieved their founding of sovereign dynasties by conquering with the assistance of armies that they'd gathered, whilst others accomplished theirs without battle.[2]

Theseus was the son of Poseidon and Aethra.[3] Poseidon had slept with Aethra on the same night that Aegeus, the king of Athens, had lain with her.[4] When Theseus was a young man, whilst travelling from Troizen to Athens, he killed Sinis the Pine-bender, another son of Poseidon. Sinis would flex two pine trees

---

[1] Apollodorus' The Library Book 2 *chapter 7:8*.

[2] Locations that were dominated by the descendants of Hercules: Sparta, Argos, Teuthrania, Sardinia, Rhodes, Sardis, Messene and others. Apollodorus' The Library Book 2 *chapters 7:6, 8:2-5*, Library of History by Diodorus Siculus Book 4 *chapters 29:2-6, 33:7-12, 57:1-58:8*, Herodotus' The Persian Wars Book 1 *chapter 7*, Book 4 *chapters 8-10*, Book 7 *chapter 208*, Book 9 *chapter 33*, Pausanias' Description of Greece Book 2 *chapters 6:5-7, 13:1-2, 18:5-9*, Book 3 *chapter 1:5-9*, Book 4 *chapter 3:3-10*, Strabo's Geography Book 8 *chapters 5:4, 7:1*, Book 14 *chapter 2:6*.

[3] Bacchylides' Dithyrambs 17 *lines 1-46*, Plutarch's Lives Theseus *chapter 36*, Library of History by Diodorus Siculus Book 4 *chapter 59:1*, Pausanias' Description of Greece Book 1 *chapter 17:3*, Book 2 *chapter 33:1*.

[4] Apollodorus' The Library Book 3 *chapter 15:6-7*.

An alternative origin is reported for Theseus—he having been the actual son of Aegeus: Apollodorus' The Library Book 3 *chapter 16:1*, Plutarch's Lives Theseus *chapters 3-4*.

Whether the son of Poseidon or Aegeus, Theseus was still reportedly the son of Aethra, a great-great-granddaughter of Zeus (reportedly, Zeus was the father of Tantalus, who was the father of Pelops, who was the father of Pittheus, who was the father of Aethra). Aethra's lineage: Apollodorus' The Library Book 3 *chapters 15:6–16:1*, Epitome *chapter 2:10*, Euripides' Orestes *lines 1-27*.

and tie travellers to both whilst still under tension. He derived his pleasure from the travellers being torn apart when the trees were released.[1] At the death of Aegeus, Theseus took the throne[2] and later abducted Helen with the intention of forcibly marrying her to him—the latter not achieved.[3] As mentioned, Helen was a daughter of Zeus—the result of his affair with Leda, the wife of Tyndareus.[4] Helen was rescued from Theseus by her brothers.[5]

---

[1] Library of History by Diodorus Siculus Book 4 *chapter 59:2-4*, Bacchylides' Dithyrambs 18 *lines 16-30*, Pausanias' Description of Greece Book 2 *chapter 1:3-4*.

Alternatively, Ovid reported that Sinis propelled men through the air by releasing pine trees that he had bent to the ground (Metamorphoses Book 7 *lines 440-442*).

It has also been reported that Sinis had a different father, Polypemon (Apollodorus' The Library Book 3 *chapter 16:1-2*), whose surname was Procrustes (Pausanias' Description of Greece Book 1 *chapter 38:5-6*). This Polypemon Procrustes was reportedly a son of Neptune (Poseidon) (Hyginus' Fabulae *38:3*—Polypemon Procrustes referred to as Procrustes). Therefore, according to the records, Sinis was a close descendant of Poseidon (either a son or grandson) and thus undoubtedly a giant capable of the feats of pine-bending.

On Theseus' journey to Athens he also killed Polypemon Procrustes, who was another danger to travellers: Apollodorus' The Library Epitome *chapter 1:3-4* (referred to as Polypemon), Library of History by Diodorus Siculus Book 4 *chapter 59:5-6* (referred to as Procrustes), above Pausanias (second) and Hyginus references.

[2] Apollodorus' The Library Epitome *chapter 1:10-11*, Library of History by Diodorus Siculus Book 4 *chapter 61:6-9*, Plutarch's Lives Theseus *chapter 22:1-3*.

[3] Apollodorus' The Library Epitome *chapter 1:23*, Library of History by Diodorus Siculus Book 4 *chapter 63:1-5*, Plutarch's Lives Theseus *chapter 31:2-3*.

[4] See relevant previous footnote in this chapter pg 316.

[5] Apollodorus' The Library Epitome *chapter 1:23*, Library of History by Diodorus Siculus Book 4 *chapter 63:5*.

She was later seduced by Paris,[1] with whom she eloped whilst married to Menelaus[2]—the act that triggered the Trojan War, wherein there was countless loss of life.[3] Theseus was deposed from his position as king of Athens and later killed whilst in exile on the island of Scyros.[4] His enormous bones were exhumed seven centuries after his death.[5]

The so-called god Loki was a son of the giant Farbauti. Although unprovoked, Loki vented his spite on another supposed god called Baldr, who was well liked amongst their peers, by arranging for him to be killed.[6] Loki had sexual relationships with the wives of Thor and Tyr.[1]

---

[1] Another son of Priam and a full brother of Hector: Homer's Iliad Book 6 *lines 503-519*, Apollodorus' The Library Book 3 *chapter 12:4-5*, Hyginus' Fabulae *91, 270* and see earlier in this chapter pg 314 with footnote regarding the lineage of Priam and Hector, reportedly descendants of Zeus.

[2] Brother of Agamemnon: Homer's Iliad Book 2 *lines 581-590*, Apollodorus' The Library Epitome *chapter 3:12* and many more.

[3] Apollodorus' The Library Epitome *chapter 3:1-7*, Homer's Iliad Book 2 *lines 173-181*, Book 3 *lines 1-77*, Book 6 *lines 312-368*, Ovid's Metamorphoses Book 12 *lines 1-10*, Book 13 *lines 196-204* and many more.

[4] Apollodorus' The Library Epitome *chapter 1:23-24*, Plutarch's Lives Theseus *chapter 35:1-5* (this reference reports that Theseus was either killed or died by accident).

[5] Plutarch's Lives Theseus *chapter 36:1-4*. A spear and sword were found buried with him in his coffin.

[6] The death of Baldr by the scheme of Loki: The Prose Edda—Gylfaginning (The deluding of Gylfi) *chapters 49, 50*.

Loki, son of the giant Farbauti, was believed to be a god: The Prose Edda—Gylfaginning (The deluding of Gylfi) *chapters 33, 44*.

Loki's wife, Sigyn, was believed to be a goddess: The Elder Edda—Völuspá (The prophecy of the seeress) *stanza 35;* The Prose Edda—Gylfaginning (The deluding of Gylfi) *chapter 33*, Skaldskaparmal (Poetic Diction) *1*.

FOOTNOTE CONTINUED ON THE NEXT PAGE

Krishna the giant,[2] eventual adviser to the Pāṇḍava brothers, lived, from infancy to early adulthood, in a pastoral community made up of male cowherds and their families. As a young man, Krishna had intercourse with: many of the cowherds' wives and also with many of the cowherds' daughters—all of these females were young women. This clear transgression was explained away by: a reliance in the doctrine that Krishna was the incarnation of the god Vishnu, believed to be in every living thing; the belief that Krishna had graced the women by his act; and the belief that the relevant male cowherds were so mesmerized by Krishna's

---

CONTINUED FOOTNOTE PRESENT

In Germanic mythology gods and giants were often related, and gods and giants were known to have sexual relations across groups. Examples: (i) The giantess Grid and the god Odin had a son called Vidar, who was a god: The Elder Edda—Völuspá (The prophecy of the seeress) *stanzas 53-54;* The Prose Edda—Gylfaginning (The deluding of Gylfi) *chapters 29, 51,* Skaldskaparmal (Poetic Diction) *4, 6.* (ii) See chapter 3 pg 71 and footnote regarding the lineage of Thor: he having been a god descended from a giant and having had a son with a giantess.

Baldr's death (above) and the predicted future event, Ragnarok, in which gods will die, demonstrate the gods' mortality: The Prose Edda—Gylfaginning (The deluding of Gylfi) *chapters 51, 52.*

Giants were reported to have died (see Chapter 3 pg 72 and footnote regarding Thor slaying giants).

Clearly, gods and giants were separated only by the name given to each group, and the members of each group were arbitrarily assigned.

[1] The affairs of Loki: The Elder Edda—Lokasenna (Loki's home-truths) *stanzas 40, 54.*

Tyr was believed to be one of the Aesir gods, like Thor and Odin: The Prose Edda—Gylfaginning (The deluding of Gylfi) *chapter 25.*

[2] See Chapter 13 pg 285 regarding Krishna—the accompanying footnote expands on his gigantic size.

power that they never even realized that their wives had left them to be with him and therefore bore him no resentment.[1]

These are only a small sample of the nonbiblical presumed Nephilim's deeds. I should add that similar acts have also been perpetrated by normal humans—some of which are mentioned in the Bible, a book that does not avoid the truth. Furthermore, God is willing to forgive even these sins. Jesus died for our sins, so that if we ask Him for forgiveness, express a genuine desire to turn away from our sins and accept Him as our personal saviour, then we can have eternal life with Him. While on the cross, Jesus accepted a criminal who was being crucified next to Him. Unlike Jesus, who'd committed no sin, the criminal had been condemned to die by crucifixion for his wrongful acts. This man even admitted that he was receiving the just reward for his deeds.[2] There may be punishment on Earth for our sins, but if we put our trust in Jesus, there will be no condemnation from Him on the Day of Judgement.[3] There is no record of Nephilim repenting of their evil deeds and seeking forgiveness for their sins from the true God, either through the biblical sacrificial method that preceded Jesus' death and resurrection or via Christ's sacrifice. I strongly suspect that in this regard Nephilim

---

[1] For the origins of Vishnu and Krishna see Chapter 13 pg 285 and footnote. Krishna is believed to have been both an offspring and an incarnation of the god Vishnu.

Krishna was adopted by a cowherd called Nanda and his wife, Yaśodā: The Bhāgavata Purāṇa Part IV *Skandha 10 chapters 2:41-3:12* (in relation to the birth of Krishna, he is described as the incarnation of Vishnu), *3:50-53, 5:1-18.*

The seduction of the gopīs (wives and daughters of cowherds) and proposed justification: Bhāgavata Purāṇa Part IV *Skandha 10 chapters 29:1-33:40.*

[2] Luke 23:38-43.

[3] John 3:16-18, 3:36, 2 Corinthians 5:16-21, Galatians 3:13, Ephesians 2:1-9, 1 Peter 1:17-19, 2:21-25.

are similar to Satan and his fallen angels, who will never willingly place themselves under God's authority.

Before setting out that night, Sam buried any items that he deemed unnecessary for the next phase of the mission (including the bivvy bag) and packed the ones that he needed. He preferred his old backpack to the new one and therefore left the latter with the other discarded items. Inside his backpack he now had a pair of ice axes, ropes, pitons (metal pegs), a hammer, a harness, carabiners, crampons, thick socks, a coat, a wool hat, unlined leather gloves, a tent made of exceptionally thin material, a lightweight sleeping bag, a basic medical kit and other essentials. He wore the new climbing boots. All the new clothes were a light-grey colour. Camouflage for the mountain, he thought. The House knew that he wasn't there to be noticed, even in the event of a disaster. We'd also provided him with a helmet, but he left it behind. He was used to climbing with one; however, it restricted his vision and he suspected that the mountain wouldn't be the only challenge to his ascent.

Sam started to circumvent Doğubayazıt to the east of the town. This led him to within half a mile of the İshak Paşa's fortress. The sentry on the minaret was using a pair of night-vision binoculars to survey the valley below. In daylight he had good sight with the naked eye to 20 miles and could recognize specific individuals up to one and a half miles away with regular binoculars. Now lacking the ability to observe with the naked eye for people of interest whom he could focus on, he had to make methodical sweeps of the valley with the pair of night-vision binoculars. The result was that Sam passed unnoticed, oblivious to the threat above him.

Chapter 15   **The Shadows of Ararat**

It was midnight. Sam was two miles from the base of Mount Ararat (Great Ararat). For decades there had been three acknowledged points from which mountaineers could start their climb—and by progressing up the corresponding face, finish the climb if desired. The first, the southern starting point, was directly ahead of him. The second, the northern starting point, was located south of a village called Aralık. (Although north of the mountain, Aralık is in Turkey rather than Armenia.) These were the two routes permitted by the government. The third, the eastern starting point (located on the elevated region between Great Ararat and Little Ararat and therefore necessary to approach by climbing from either the north or south), provided the easiest climb, but civilians were prohibited from using this route. Sam thought that the enemy would be guarding the two permitted starting points. He'd read that the eastern route was forbidden, because it was the Turkish army's means of accessing the mountain for military exercises. He reasoned that his only option was to not take any of these three routes. Instead, he decided to start his ascent from the west of the mountain—and continue up the western face. There was a paucity of information on this approach except for the fact that the climb was technically much more difficult than the other three.

Sam's plan was to reach the summit of the mountain (5,137 metres in altitude), or get close to it, in three days. The climb itself can be completed in a single day. However, in the context of a rapid ascent without acclimatization, a climber will develop acute mountain sickness. This illness develops beyond an altitude of 3,500 metres. Slow acclimatization to the altitude is vital. Acute mountain sickness develops because of the thinness of the air at high altitude, which causes the body to be starved of oxygen. Symptoms from 3,500 metres and onward can include shortness of breath, fatigue, headache, decreased mental ability, chest pain, nausea and vomiting. If a climber ascends past 4,000 metres without a sufficient period of acclimatization, then there can be worse consequences: water can accumulate in the lungs, which can cause severe shortness of breath. Beyond 4,500 metres there is a small but serious risk of water accumulating in the brain, which can cause drowsiness and in the worst cases coma and then death. And beyond 5,000 metres there is a fifty-fifty chance of blood vessels bursting at the backs of the eyes, which can cause severe visual impairment.

Staying well clear of the southern starting point by over a mile, Sam walked to a suitable location to the west of the mountain. On the nineteenth night since landing in Batman and the forty-eighth since landing in Yeşilköy (near Istanbul) Sam reached the base of Mount Ararat. He slept in the open, being now without his subterranean sleeping equipment. Anyway, the ground was rocky hard underfoot and would have been near impossible for him to dig his usual hole. After two hours, his watch's alarm woke him a few minutes before dawn.

Sam intended to use the daylight to climb. He started his ascent. The initial slope was gentle and littered with loose rocks of varying sizes. Some were the size of mice, whilst others were boulders as large as a car. Sam imagined spewed rocks and lava raining down to create the unusual terrain. He looked up at the cold peak of Great Ararat. The mountain was serene and silent: hard to imagine as a tumultuous volcano during an upsurge. Nevertheless, the last eruption was in 1840, which had utterly destroyed a village on the northern face near a deep, scar-like chasm called Ahora Gorge. Between the loose rocks the ground supported only the tiniest blades of pale-green grass. There were no trees or bushes, and he felt extremely exposed. He'd become so used to the night that he found himself missing its protective dark shroud. The advantage that the daylight offered was a sure step, and this was too important a benefit to forego.

As Sam walked, he looked around him to survey the environment for human life. There was not a soul to be seen. There was a gentle wind at his back, encouraging him up the shallow slope. He was surprised at how cool the temperature was compared with the city of Van, which was only a little lower in altitude than the western base of Mount Ararat. He could see the mountain increase in steepness at well-defined levels ahead of him. As his eyes drifted upward, he observed that at each zone between two successive increments the rock face seemed to have a different character. This continued until the snowline at 4,000 metres, above which the rocky slopes were hidden from view. He thought: and what else is buried beneath that white mound?

As the sun rose further, it barely seemed to influence the temperature. Sam noticed a wispy, white mist far above him— frivolous vapour that seemed to emanate from the snowy peak. Within an hour, the mist had become an unbroken, thick, circular, white cloud that surrounded the summit. Although Sam could see only a fraction of the cloud, it was nonetheless an extraordinary sight, and from the curvature of its shape, he recognized it as part of a ring from having seen a geography book's picture, whose accompanying text described the halo cloud as a regular natural phenomenon on account of the unique topography of the mountain and the surrounding land.

Sam had already climbed past two of the rocky zones by 0830 hours and had reached a large plateau (2,600 metres in altitude) that hadn't been visible from lower down the mountain. To his left (northward) he passed two massive craters—the second bigger than the first. They were depressions in the plateau as if caused by the impact of two individual falling meteorites. He didn't stop to take in the scenery but pressed on to the next zone.

The plateau had been a gentle rest compared with the next slope, which was the first truly steep gradient. Sam looked upward. The circular cloud was thicker now and had grown a single vaporous extension, part of which happened to be directly above him. This tendril became wider and denser, and soon it cast its dark-grey shadow over his entire route. The shadow was accompanied by an unnaturally rapid temperature drop. His environment became so cold that he had to stop and put on the thick coat that we'd provided. He transferred the revolver from his trousers to his right coat pocket.

15 miles away in the bowels of the İşhak Paşa's fortress, the Guardian of Turkey sat at his desk, talking intently on the phone. He'd become frustrated with the search for March. The situation meant that the Guardian hadn't left the fortress for a whole month. This predicament had taken him away from his own business interests and more importantly from his other duties for the organization. No new information would perpetuate his confinement. He wished that March had abandoned the mission or even better was dead. Maybe the Guardian would receive a report from the British agents that March had returned to the UK. They could kill him there. Then there would be no question of a March repeat attempt to find the Ark.

"No," the Guardian said. He listened to the person's reply, then asserted, "After a fraction of that, they would have talked." His eyes commended the suggestion that followed, but he thought of a better approach. "Do as you did with . . ." One of the Guardian's men rushed into the room. Usually they would knock. The subordinate's face had the expression of one who'd just realized that he'd broken protocol but felt that justification would come if he was allowed to speak. The Guardian continued to hold the handle of the phone in his right hand, but he placed his left over the mouthpiece. "What is it?" he impatiently asked the subordinate.

"News from Russia, emir."

The subordinate had the undivided attention of the Guardian, who removed his left hand from the mouthpiece. "I'll speak to you later." He hung up the phone. "Well," he said.

The subordinate spoke confidently, "I've just received a transmission from Novgorod. The Soyuz R83 satellite passed over Mount Ararat ten minutes ago. They've picked up a new infrared signature ('heat signature') a third of the way up—human motion pattern."

"Could it be one of the troops?" the Guardian asked.

"The heat signature is on the western face. My military contact has confirmed that there are two squads on the mountain and all the men are currently accounted for at both camps."

"When will the satellite next be in range?"

"Around this time tomorrow." The subordinate looked down at a piece of paper that he clutched in his left hand. "At exactly 0955 hours for two minutes."

"Your military contact—can we use him?"

"He's in Ankara![1] I could ask him to send a report to the squads that there's a dangerous spy on the mountain, but they'll probably capture whoever it is and take him in for interrogation. Then who knows what they'll do?"

"The usual move would be to transfer the prisoner to a larger military base for further questioning by senior officers," the Guardian postulated.

"My contact could attempt to get to whoever's been captured as early as possible and find out who it is. If it is March, my contact could try to eliminate him."

"It's getting complicated. And who knows what March will tell them before your contact gets there?" The Guardian spent a few seconds thinking. "No, it's better that we use our own men. The lookouts at Aralık and Doğubayazıt—send both groups up."

"And if they come across the military?"

"Make sure they don't! It's a big mountain. Your contact can regularly update them by radio on the squads' positions. Now radio our men with the heat signature's exact location. I know it's him."

The breeze that had initially been at Sam's back gave way to a greater current of cold air that pushed against him. His ears were

---

[1] Capital of Turkey, located in the northwest of the country.

the first casualty of the new wind, which lowered the temperature to minus ten degrees Celsius. He stopped again: this time to remove the wool hat and leather gloves from his backpack. He put on the hat so that it covered his ears. He was loath to do that, as he'd planned to climb with a full array of unattenuated senses. The gloves were thin, because they were designed to maintain a climber's ability; therefore, they provided scant insulation. The circular part of the cloud became broader, and the tendrilous part wider and denser still, and his path darker. He was an adept climber, and even with the cold and increasing gradient, he was ascending well. He easily picked his way upward despite the cumbersome scree that lay scattered over that section of the mountain. Scree are loose stones, often flat, that can cause the foot to slide downward if stepped upon. Before long he felt a snowflake press itself against his right cheek. The flake was large and took seconds to melt. It was a herald of something greater, and soon there were driving snows that bore down onto him, as if they'd been conjured from the centre of an Arctic blizzard. He'd read that it was rare for Mount Ararat to experience snow in summer. Maybe it was the unusual weather or the swiftness of its onset that had first started to worry him. He looked up toward the higher reaches of Ararat. They were no longer discernible. His visibility had dropped to just 25 metres.

The snowstorm was severely limiting Sam's pace. The gradient was fifty-five degrees. He was now continually using both hands to stabilize himself. The snow had covered the rocks. He could no longer see the scree and had to step with slow diligent care. At the base of Mount Ararat his plan had been to climb the mountain with the minimum of evidence that he was there. Also, once he'd left, no evidence that he'd ever been there. This meant that he'd decided not to use any pitons and ropes, which could betray him in so many different ways. He'd been close to ditching those items owing to their heavy weight but had retained them for unexpected emergencies. He'd even intended to climb unaided (except for the use of the ice axes) on the more precarious sections of the western face above the snowline. The heavy snowfall was making this part of the plan almost suicidal. What's more, thoughts of fresh snow covering the perpendicular ridges on the northern glacier darkened his mood. He made the decision to continue to climb unaided—for now—despite the adverse weather conditions, which recommended the contrary.

Sam's first goal was to achieve an altitude of 3,200 metres, at which point he would stop for the day in order to acclimatize. His intention was to find a nook where he could stay out of sight for the rest of the day and night. However, at 3,200 metres the slope was open to the elements with no visible recesses. Instead of abating, the snow grew stronger, as did the wind and the cold. He still considered stopping, yet without secluded shelter, thoughts of an avalanche sweeping him down the mountain or waking up the following morning surrounded by the Turkish military began to plague his mind. It wasn't sensible to stop. He passed 3,250 metres. He would only stop provided that he found a rocky haven.

At 3,500 metres the snow had become so thick underfoot that Sam could barely feel the scree and was starting to slip on the snow itself. He strapped the crampons to his boots. He'd envisaged doing this at the snow line (4,000 metres in altitude) on day two, but the spikes were needed now. Before long his winter apparel felt as if he was wearing a T-shirt and short trousers, and movement was obligatory to prevent him from freezing. The snowstorm's fury inflicted an unremitting double impact of piercing cold and halting wind. Moreover, the mountain possessed ever-increasing gradients.

In one hour Sam climbed a height of just 200 metres. The next 200 metres took two hours. His brown face was hung low as gargantuan effort was put into each step. His face was numb from the bitter cold, and he felt the beginnings of a headache. Thoughts of avoiding frostbite crossed his mind. He was surrounded by conditions perfect for its genesis: the wind-chill had brought the temperature to minus forty degrees Celsius. He wondered why frostbite is so called, because from what he'd read it's acquired silently and painlessly. Maybe the thawing of frozen tissues causes the pain he considered. These simple thoughts turned over slowly in his mind.

A masculine voice spoke to Sam. It had come from the storm directly ahead. Sam forced himself to take cover by pressing himself flat against the mountain. He looked in front but saw nothing apart from the windswept snow. He looked around him for any signs of the person who'd called out the name Samuel March. Sam saw no one. He felt his face and adjusted the areas of the wool hat that covered his ears. He re-established his arduous ascent. He was sure that the voice had come from less than five metres away, well within his visual range.

"Samuel March, why are you on this mountain?" the voice asked; the words were spoken slowly and clearly.

Sam halted. His ears had localized the voice to an area directly in front of his face—a voice without a body. Sam wondered about the effect that the cold was having on him. He took off his right glove. His hand, although cold, was well perfused with no sign of frostbite.

The voice continued but now faster, "Do you take pleasure in being alone? If you succeed, you'll have nowhere to go—always hiding. Your enemies will hunt you on every continent—nowhere is free from their reach. Who wants to know somebody like that? What woman would partner herself to a man like that? If you feel alone now, wait until you have your prize."

Sam hadn't formally studied psychiatry yet. This subject would be dealt with in his penultimate year of medical school. However, he knew a little about auditory hallucinations and thought insertion as features of some psychiatric diseases.

"Why do I even talk to you about your future? You have none. The storm will grow stronger, and you will grow weaker. A frozen corpse is all you'll be. Your God has left you to die on this mountain."

The thought of developing a mental illness alarmed Sam. He thought about the immense amount of stress that he'd been under, recently combined with solitude. He didn't realize that his insight and reasoning in considering this diagnosis were sound and not therefore indicative of a mental illness. He focused his thoughts on the voice. Does it originate from inside my mind? Somehow it doesn't seem to be me. Either way, it has a point. Why would the enemy stop trying to kill me, even if I succeed? If evidence of the Ark's existence was published, they'd still try to murder me, but as revenge. I shall be a hounded man, probably needing to change my name and most likely unable to finish my medical studies. Some of these things he'd already considered, but he hadn't thought about the effect that the first objective if completed would have on him finding a wife. Even at his young age, to have a wife and family was a deep desire. And what manner of woman could live with a man who was surrounded by such danger, for she would share the same peril? How different would the future be if I leave this mountain now? Will the enemy relent? Sam replied to the voice with a thought that simultaneously slipped from his chapped lips as a barely audible whisper, "He hasn't deserted me. My Lord is with me. I can feel His presence, even on this mountain."

"But where is He? Let us hear His voice. We have voices."

Sam was shocked that the voice had answered. Sam intentionally froze his mental activity. He waited for something to intercede that would tell him that the voice wasn't real.

"Let us hear Him!" the voice commanded with malice in each word.

Sam loosened his mental restraint and again replied, now self-conscious that he might be talking to himself: "He's here. His presence is silent, yet His voice is more powerful than yours." He noted that the voice had used the words "we" and "us".

There was no reply. Sam climbed on. The incline increased further. The storm persisted. The wind whipped around him and whistled as it passed beneath him. He climbed a height of 50 metres in two hours. He removed one of the ice axes as a precaution—a valuable tool to arrest a slide if he slipped.

The next voice came, starting slowly like the first, although with more initial spite: "What makes you think that you're worthy to climb this mountain and show the world what it contains?"

Sam listened. The first voice had sounded human, but this voice, though still masculine, had an unearthly rasp like a heavy metal bar being scraped along an asphalt road in a dry, hot summer.

"I know your sins; we've seen them with our own eyes," the voice was accusatory: a trigger that caused introspection in the listener.

Sam delved inside his own consciousness. Those sins that were deep in his memory, almost forgotten, were dredged to the surface to join those in the forefront of his mind. There, His sins were declared one after the other.

Sam was physically drained from fighting the blizzard and the mountain. He'd also spent the best part of his mental reserve, which had driven him for the last two hours. It was at rare times like this that he mined deep inside himself for what he considered his last asset: a seam of confidence blended with vision that gave him the ability to extract the last drop of service from his body. But sin questions worthiness. And so the erosive voice took its toll. Sam's mind created a flat, sombre picture of each pro-claimed sinful event. The pictures were layered to form a vivid three-dimensional rotting carcass. From within this putrid image came intense feelings of shame and worthlessness. He'd never before felt such overwhelming remorse for his sins. The fetid stench made the seam recede. That precious amalgam of strong confidence and driving vision, which he was relying on, was gone.

Sam thought: who am I to ascend Ararat? Descent is all that I'm worthy of. There was no doubt of that in his mind. However, a Christian's true confidence is in the Lord.[1] Jesus was the rock and foundation that Sam had put his trust in,[2] not in himself or his own good deeds. And the Lord reminded him of this. Sam's answer came from his heart, set alight by God: "For these sins I have no defence. I am a sinner. I was born a sinner.[3] Without the Lord's sacrifice for me, at my death I would descend into Hell. But I've put my trust in Him. The Spirit of the Lord is inside of me. He gives me the confidence to continue, not myself. It is He who gives me the vision of my immediate and eternal goals.[4] Everything I am is because of God. Yes, I'm a sinner, but it's my duty to be on this mountain. Christ has made me worthy."

This was followed by more verbal silence. Sam's mind re-engaged with his physical dual against Ağrı Dağı, the Mountain of Pain. His thoughts about the voices soon returned. Is this acute mountain sickness? He'd climbed high mountains in the Andes and the Rockies but had always been careful to acclimatize and had therefore not experienced acute mountain sickness. He was aware that his mental faculties had slowed from the cold and exhaustion. He thought that if the voices were coming from his mind, then what he was experiencing could be a form of delirium caused by the altitude. Or was it something else? His thoughts drifted numbly to his experience in the caverns of Cappadocia.

The third voice came, "My, my, you're a valiant man, Samuel March. There are greater prizes in this world than anything you could find on this mountain and easier ways of getting them." The male voice was quick and charming yet had the potency of one who'd been given the authority to make deals. "Why risk

---

[1] Deuteronomy 31:1-8, Joshua 1:7-9, Acts 2:1-47, Ephesians 6:10-20, 2 Timothy 1:7.

[2] Deuteronomy 32:3-4, 32:17-18, 2 Samuel 22:32-51, Psalms 62:7, Matthew 7:24-29, Luke 6:46-49, Acts 4:10-13, 1 Corinthians 10:1-14.

[3] Romans 5:12-19.

[4] See Soul and Spirit.

that handsome face of yours or trouble that noble bearing further. We can give you everything that a man like you could want—more riches than you've ever dreamt of."

Sam involuntarily pictured a gleaming skyscraper in Manhattan and a sprawling country mansion in Britain. The thoughts registered on his face.

"Power as well as riches—the ability to influence the lives of many. We know that this is what you seek. And with this power comes women—as many as your heart's desire. We know that you're a passionate man in all things; not least is your lust for women. Or is it not many women, but one whom you want: one woman whom you long for above all others? Yes, that's it. You want just one. We can find this jewel for you—perhaps a woman like Prasseda."

Sam listened.

"You already know the truth of the world; you would be a great asset to our lord. There are others who have the same knowledge and intelligence, yet they work with us and are well rewarded."

Sam remembered that decreased mental ability is a feature of acute mountain sickness; however, the condition is unlikely to cause severe delusional confusion. He correctly estimated that he was just below a height of 4,000 metres and that he'd been between 3,500 and 4,000 metres for a maximum of six hours. This is the minimum threshold of time that a person can start exhibiting clinical features of acute mountain sickness. Collectively, these facts meant that he couldn't attribute the blame to acute mountain sickness. "Our lord" the voice had said. Sam concluded that the voices were an attack by invisible demonic forces.

Like Prasseda, not actually Prasseda. They didn't offer her to me, Sam thought. They could have lied. How curious. They're right about one thing. There are others who know the truth. But to know the truth and yet serve Satan—what tremendous judgement those individuals call upon themselves. The truth is that Jesus is the Light that shines in the darkness. However, instead of showing others the Light, these servants of Satan don't accept Jesus themselves and deliberately keep others in darkness, so that those these deceivers influence eventually end up in Hell with the deceivers.

Sam spoke out while the blizzard wrapped his body, "I will use whatever God has given me to reveal the truth to many. I will show them Jesus. I will hold Him up as a flaming torch in the darkest night, so that they can see Him. He will save their souls, because salvation is through the Messiah alone.[1] He is my Lord and would take no pleasure in me if I drew back.[2] And in His name I command you to leave my presence."

The three demons of Ararat left Sam alone. Abandonment, Discouragement and Temptation were their names, and that was the order in which they'd spoken. Discouragement had lied. None of them had seen Sam's sins. However, Discouragement's accusation had disrupted Sam's mind and had shaken loose the memories of his sins, their barbs spiking his conscience.

The wind virtually stopped, and Ararat became quiet again. Sam could now hear the crunching sound of snow as it impacted underfoot. The temperature improved quickly but remained well below the freezing point. The snow continued to fall, although at a tenth of the intensity as before. It fell vertically, settling softly on the mountain. His visibility improved greatly, and he could see the higher reaches of Ararat once more; the mountain itself blocked his view of the summit. His pace could now increase, only to reach an altitude of 4,000 metres was too great an ascent for one day. Now that the snowstorm had cleared, he planned to descend to an altitude below 3,500 metres to find a place where he could take refuge for the night and acclimatize before the next day's ascent. He was also in desperate need of rest for both mind

---

[1] See Chapter 9 pg 213 and Chapter 13 pg 294 together with their relevant footnotes regarding this topic. See Soul and Spirit.
[2] Hebrews 10:38.

and body. As he started his descent, a reverse of the ascent, that is, with his eyes still facing the mountain, he noticed the snow a few metres above him flick upward. It did it again directly afterward. On that occasion he recognized what had caused these peculiarities: impacting silenced bullets. He flattened himself against the slope, then quickly confirmed that there was no one ahead of him. He looked down the mountain. 300 metres from his position were five figures climbing upward, and a sixth was stationary, holding a pistol with both hands. The six figures were all men. Sam was very much out of the effective range of the pistol. Another shot missed him.

Sam resumed his ascent with new incentive but the same muscles. He wondered why they hadn't used a rifle—too much weight for the climb perhaps. Or maybe they had no silencers for their rifles and were afraid of attracting attention or starting an avalanche. Sam was equally worried about causing both of these potentially disastrous problems with his own revolver. As he climbed, he again cast his gaze downward. He wanted to absolutely confirm whether or not they possessed any rifles. Furthermore, there was something about the man at the front of the group that had been familiar the first time Sam had glimpsed them. He could scarcely believe his eyes. Even though the lead man was 300 metres away and beneath a thick coat, Sam recognized the distinctive gangly form and disproportionately muscular upper body of the Vulture.

"Not him again!" Sam said through gritted teeth. And to think of all the time that I wasted worrying about the fallout from that man's death, he thought. Sam could see no rifles.

These accursed people—it's as if they've got a copy of my itinerary. How do they know that I'm here? What have I left on the slopes? These were the first questions that Sam asked himself as he pushed on.

He was aware that he was now above an altitude of 4,000 metres. It's been only six and a half hours since I passed 3,500 metres, but I'm still ascending, he thought. Higher altitudes meant less oxygen and therefore increased impetus for acute mountain sickness. He looked at his watch. It was half-past five: four more hours of light to come. The next question that he asked himself was more pertinent. Are my pursuers already acclimatized? If that's the case, then I'm in serious trouble if I climb higher. I'll get sick and they'll catch me. He realized that if he started to move horizontally instead of upward, it wouldn't be long before he brought himself onto the eastern face of the mountain, and that meant the possibility of encountering the Turkish military. His thoughts were interrupted by a familiar sound. He'd heard one of his pursuers vomit. That partly answers my question, Sam thought; at least one of them isn't acclimatized. He inferred that they all weren't acclimatized and that the man who'd vomited was simply the first to exhibit symptoms.

Obviously, there wasn't going to be a gentleman's agreement that they all either descend or stay at their present altitudes for the night—and then resume their activities in the morning. Sam was being bitterly pursued by men with the single purpose of concluding his life. Moreover, they were being led by the Vulture, who had a personal score to settle. Sam decided to risk climbing higher. His new goal was to cross over the mountain at or near the summit and then immediately descend via the northern face into Armenia. The Ark would have to wait.

Sam pressed on. The snow continued to fall gently. He would occasionally look back to mark his pursuers. From where they were climbing Sam was still well out of the effective range of handguns and they seemed to have understood that fact as there were no more puffs of snow around him. After approximately half an hour, he noticed that they'd split into two groups. The Vulture now led only two men at the front, and the remaining three were lagging behind. The latter group was at a distance of approximately 500 metres from Sam. One of them was stationary and bent forward on a narrow ledge.

Sam soon developed his own symptoms of acute mountain sickness. He seemed to be taking deeper and more rapid breaths over and above what he would have expected for the altitude. He also started to feel nauseas. He was at 4,500 metres. It had to happen sooner or later, and it's only going to get worse, he thought.

The Vulture's leading group was still only 300 metres behind Sam. On flat ground and at low altitude, 300 metres would have been an insignificant distance: a little over half a minute's sprint for Sam. Yet at that moment on Ararat, Sam and these pursuers were as much as thirty minutes apart: the gradient was sixty-five degrees and the snow-covered mountainside demanded careful and steady negotiation. Despite this time lag, Sam was painfully aware of the need to maintain or increase the distance, because bullets had scant regard for terrain and altitude.

Sam started vomiting at 4,700 metres. He heard the men in the Vulture's group doing the same. Sam didn't stop. He merely allowed his vomit to spill onto the snow. The warm acid melted the surface layer. Some vomit had fallen onto his coat. The enemy persisted. And so the chase became surreal, as all had become sick but continued to climb. As everyone became more physically incapacitated, the time lag between Sam and the leading group increased to forty minutes, yet the distance remained at just 300 metres. It wasn't only the acute mountain sickness that affected them. The thinness of the air itself had a direct effect: less essential oxygen was being delivered to their working muscles and each gruelling step pushed them further into a more oxygen-depleted environment. Sam heard a low-pitched bellow of agony beneath him. He didn't turn to look.

Directly ahead of Sam the gradient increased sharply to an almost vertical incline and obstructed his view of the higher reaches of the mountain. He'd seen this near-vertical section a while back and had noted that there was an easier route that headed upward, albeit at a diagonal, that was to his left. This indirect route possessed a similar gradient to the slope that he was presently on, and he took this less-challenging alternative. His muscles felt as if they were burning—an odd sensation considering the temperature of his surroundings. As he climbed diagonally upward, he could see the enemy out of the corner of his left eye. Regarding the front group, a distance of approximately 20 metres now separated each man from the one closest to him. The Vulture continued to lead them. To Sam's surprise the rear group stopped, then started to slowly descend. Furthermore, one of them was moving awkwardly—clearly injured.

Having reached the top of the diagonal route, Sam could now see the summit itself. It was close. Too exhausted to continue ascending, he decided to circumvent the summit by moving laterally. To go from the west of the mountain directly to the north would have been ideal, except there was no immediately discernable route: only a sheer snow-covered rock face that plunged 70 metres to a hard, icy death. He moved in the opposite direction on a course that would first lead him to the southern glacier. Although no longer ascending, his fatigued muscles barely noticed the difference. The route first took him above the top of the near-vertical section that he'd avoided on his ascent. This obstructed part of his downward view, and the enemy was entirely out of sight. He assumed that they would be following his own path. His intention was still to descend into Armenia via the northern glacier. Circumventing the summit by way of the upper slopes, southern to eastern to northern, may also serve to lose the enemy, he thought. On the other hand, he hoped that the execution of this plan wouldn't attract any attention from the eastern face of the mountain.

Sam reached the upper section of the southern glacier. Considering the lag between him and his pursuers, he perceived that the snow wasn't falling fast enough to cover his footprints. As he started to cross the glacier, he noticed blurred dark dots at his feet. The dots were caused by objects beneath two inches of fresh snow; owing to the objects' high degree of blackness, they were visible through the snow. Soon the glacier appeared to be peppered with similar dots. While moving, he scooped up one of the dark objects and examined it. At first it simply looked like a piece of charcoal, but closer inspection revealed it to be similar to the wood of the talisman. The difference was that the piece of wood that he now held was blackened by more than just pitch. The wood had been additionally blackened by scorching heat. The Ark had clearly been blown to smithereens. And he had a good idea who might have been responsible. Yet they were still after him. He therefore wondered if there were still parts of the Ark buried within the southern glacier that hadn't been destroyed. The snowfall on the southern glacier had not nearly been like the blizzard that had accompanied the demons; however, the modest amount of snow that persisted would cover the charred wood fragments before nightfall. He looked around him for landmarks that he could commit to memory. And where had the explosion(s) been? He could see no crater. He wondered if he would live to return. He continued to circumvent the summit, but his route forced him to ascend again as he went from the south to the east of the mountain.

Sam could see much of Little Ararat, which was seven miles away to the east. The peak itself was obscured by the falling snow. As he climbed, he looked about him for his pursuers. They were still out of sight. This fact didn't comfort him. He actually felt more uneasy. Before, when he could see them, he had some measure of control: a way to gauge his danger. Maybe they've given up, he thought. He shook that notion off quickly. For sure they were still coming.

Whilst Sam climbed, he silently prayed:

My God and my Lord, King of kings, I'm begging You to help me.
Extend my life.
Let me survive this mountain.

At 5,100 metres Sam developed intermittent muscle cramps and was even more short of breath. He was now at such a high altitude that he was much less worried about being seen by the Turkish military. The pinnacle of Great Ararat was only 60 metres away and at an additional vertical height of 37 metres. Although the peak could offer strategic views, there was no necessity for him to go there.

Sam reached the upper section of the northern glacier at around quarter-past eight. So there he was at his intended target with neither the time nor the capacity to explore. The Armenian border was 20 miles to the north. On a clear day an observer positioned on Great Ararat's summit can see Yerevan, the capital of Armenia. Sam couldn't see the city, yet had no problem believing it was there. The gradient where Sam was now treading was not nearly as steep as the equivalent level of the western face. He pressed on. He was now descending, eyes directed forward. Despite this, his legs felt as if they would give way at any minute. If he had had time to investigate, he would have been looking for the two perpendicular ridges. He vomited again. His headache had never left and now worsened. His ears were ringing. He continued his descent.

Sam heard the puff of a man's breath behind him. Sam spun around while his right hand dove into his right coat pocket to grasp the revolver. At the same time as first glimpsing the tall figure, just 10 metres away, Sam felt a cold bullet enter his chest beneath his right collar bone. The Vulture's right arm was fully extended with a smoking silenced pistol held firmly in his right hand. As Sam fell backward, he saw another man coming into view in the distance, clumsily mounting a large snow-covered range of rocky outcrops. A short cut, Sam thought—as he hit the ground and fired his revolver. The bullet struck the centre of the Vulture's forehead with a resounding metallic clink. Although deflected by the metal plate in the Vulture's head, the bullet had enough force to knock him off balance. Yet he didn't fall. Sam fired again. The bullet hit the vulture in the chest. Blood instantly stained his coat, but still he didn't fall. The Vulture fired his pistol, which was poorly supported by a now flexed right arm— the bullet narrowly missed Sam. The Vulture retched. Sam's third bullet penetrated his acrid enemy's left eye and lodged in his brain. The Vulture toppled over onto his back. His last exhale was a gurgle, and that was the earthly end of him.

Sam struggled to his feet. His visible pursuer was at a distance, beyond the effective range of the revolver, but not so far that he wouldn't have seen what had just transpired. Sam was sorely tempted to climb back up the northern face and finish off this enemy as well. However, Sam knew that the third man of the leading group could step over the range of rocky outcrops at any moment. Sam would then be disadvantaged, worse than one against two; after all, he was injured and they weren't. He noticed that he was bleeding at an alarming rate. In his mind this was reason to perhaps risk his poor odds straightaway, because they would be deteriorating by the minute. If he finished the two men while he was still relatively strong, he could leave the mountain and tend to his wound at his own pace. If he tried to flee now, they could follow and simply wait till he was weak and kill him at their leisure.

Sam continued his descent. His mind was grinding through his options. He looked back and could no longer see his nearest living foe. Sam presumed correctly that this enemy had hung back to wait for the other, with the intention of them both pursuing together. As Sam staggered downward, he continually looked around him for a place from which he could ambush his foes. He should have been wondering what kind of attention from further down the mountain his three shots, if heard, could bring, but this wasn't on his mind. He pressed his left hand beneath his right collar bone to slow the bleeding. Toward the lowermost end of the northern glacier there was a large rock behind which he could hide. He headed beyond the rock for 20 metres, leaving his footprints in and drops of blood on the snow. After that, he climbed back up the glacier but along a path screened from those descending the mountain by the rock. As he climbed back up the slope, he vomited and stumbled. He vomited again and tripped face forward. As he tried to get up, both of his legs cracked the glacier, and he plummeted 28 feet through a chamber beneath the ice.

Sam landed on his back, the backpack taking the brunt of the fall. He was surrounded by pitch-blackness. Despite this, he could tell that the surface on which he'd landed was slanted—nearly parallel to the mountain's slope above—and wondered why he hadn't slid backward. He was facing upward. He stared intently at the only source of light, which was his entry point. It was a hole with a diameter of two feet. Forty-five minutes of light remained before nightfall. He stayed in the exact place onto which he'd fallen. He waited silently with his right arm pointing straight upward; the revolver was held firmly in his tremulous right hand as he aimed at the hole through the iron sights. His left hand was pressed tightly against the wound. The snow drifted down from the hole above. He lay there, not even moving to wipe the flakes from his eyes.

Chapter 17   **Sanctuary**

Sam awoke in the morning of the following day. It was ten o'clock. He was still lying on his back, his backpack sandwiched between him and the floor. His left hand covered the wound, although with little pressure applied. His right arm was no longer pointing upward but was outstretched beside him, the revolver loosely held in his right hand. As he raised his head, he felt lancing pain in his right upper chest. He looked up toward his entry point to the chamber—now a luminous blue disc bordered by blackness: the snow had covered the hole by completely bridging the gap yet was thin enough to let light shine through.

With sleep's compassionate oblivion locked away, Sam's other ailments began to quickly register. He was inordinately fatigued, dizzy, nauseas and the previous day's shortness of breath was ongoing despite the fact that he was now essentially motionless. He knew that he was still suffering from acute mountain sickness. He estimated that he was between 4,400 and 4,800 metres and therefore at risk of the further complication of water accumulation in the lungs and, if over 4,500 metres, water accumulation in the brain. Of even greater concern was whether the bullet had pierced his right lung and caused it to deflate. If the shortness of breath was solely due to acute mountain sickness, then descending should be the cure. A collapsed lung caused by a penetrating injury was a different problem entirely.

Sam lifted himself into a sitting position and removed his backpack. He examined his wound, then the surrounding area. His shirt was soaked with blood, the crimson stain extending downward to his belt, but he was no longer bleeding. He put the revolver into his right coat pocket and felt the ground with his right hand to detect if there was any more blood. He expected to feel ice. Instead, he felt a flat rough wooden board, whose surface did indeed have a few drops of his own half-dried, sticky blood. He turned himself so that he was on his hands and knees.

He felt the floor with both hands, becoming more and more excited by the second. The area around him was fabricated from the board and similar ones to form a hard, flat surface. Beyond his immediate vicinity the wooden surface had patches of ice. He stood up and shone his pen torch about the chamber. The light poorly illuminated the areas that it touched. He replaced the old batteries with two new ones. This strengthened the beam only slightly.

Sam was inside the Ark of Noah. He was in an empty compartment tilted approximately thirty degrees. Its original dimensions would have been: height 23 feet, width 27 feet and length 40 feet—capable of holding enormous creatures; however, the ceiling was crushed inward at the lower end, which significantly reduced the compartment's height in that location. He wished that he had a flare to light the compartment more effectively. The wooden walls, floor and ceiling were all stained with a type of pitch. There was a single giant doorless opening, which reached the ceiling and led outward to a large corridor. He saw huge structural timbers beneath the ceiling of the compartment—branches of the robust inner frame of the Ark. Icicles hung rigidly from different positions—more densely from the crushed area. As he looked more closely, he noticed that the wall opposite the opening had 18-inch-high panels at the very top, many of which were damaged. They'd been made with the ability to be opened.

Sam sat back down. He removed some items from his backpack. He washed his wound with water and then with antiseptic solution from his medical kit. Considering the amount that he'd bled, he was surprised at how small the bullet's entry site was. The absence of an exit wound meant that he had a metallic foreign body in his chest. Therefore, although he had a suture kit, he knew that it was best not to stitch the wound yet. He decided that he would try to prise the bullet out later; he anticipated that more sunlight would be transmitted through the snow-covered hole above in the early afternoon. He covered the wound with gauze and strapped on a tight diagonal bandage, which went under his right armpit and over an area between his neck and right shoulder.

The Bible states the Ark's dimensions in cubits. Sam knew them by heart: length 300 cubits (450 feet, 137 metres), width 50 cubits (75 feet, 23 metres) and height 30 cubits (45 feet, 14 metres). Noah was instructed to make the Ark with three storeys; however, there are no biblical details written on what height each storey was to be. Although likely that each storey was divided into compartments, this is not known. The Ark was made with a single door but to which level (storey) this gave entrance, again there are no details. The Ark had a single window, which could be opened and closed, a cubit (1.5 feet, 0.46 metres) high around the entire vessel directly below the roof. The Ark was made of wood and was covered inside and out with pitch.[1]

With the knowledge regarding the window already firmly in Sam's brain, he knew that the ceiling of the compartment that he'd fallen into was a part of the roof of the Ark.

Wood is preserved well by covering it with pitch, which makes wood waterproof, yet the Ark was over 4,000 years old, and Sam was worried that it would now be a fragile structure after that length of time. He was not keen on another fall, for even though he'd already plummeted through over half of the Ark's height, at the angle at which it was lying there remained the potential of a further drop—23 feet. He was in no fit state to go investigating but was extremely eager to see the inside of the Ark beyond the compartment that had received him. He removed the crampons from his boots. He arranged to take his backpack but emptied of everything except much of the climbing equipment, including the

---

[1] Genesis 6:14-16, 8:6.
The Ark also had a covering (probably made of leather), which would have served to protect the roof from the rain: Genesis 8:13.
The Ark's inner dimensions would have had to have allowed for the space taken up by the wood used in its construction.

harness, the rope, one of the ice axes, the pitons, the hammer and the carabiners. He didn't forget the camera and rolls of film.

Sam stepped with great care, first testing each board before applying his whole weight. He was surprised that there was no bounce in the wood, indicating its apparent thickness. With each step his confidence grew, and before long he'd left the compartment via the giant opening and had entered the corridor. Downward to his left there was a wooden barrier, which he realized was one end of the vessel. Opposite him, on the other side of the corridor, was another empty compartment. It was of similar magnitude to the first. The corridor continued to his right and was 18 feet wide. Similar to the first two compartments, as far as he could see, the corridor was also at an approximately thirty-degree incline, which was less than the gradient of the slope of the glacier in which the Ark was embedded. Taking into account the compartment he'd fallen into, the end of the corridor and the opposite compartment, it was evident that this end of the Ark was rectangular. Sam knew that the opposite end of the Ark would also be rectangular. Therefore, the Ark was unlike most pictorial representations, that is to say, nothing like a boat with projecting ends. The Ark was true to the instructions that God had given Noah. After all, it was designed only to float and not to sail.

Sam carefully made his way up the corridor's gradient, clinging to the wooden wall to his right. In effect, he was climbing back up the mountain inside the Ark. The tremendous inner frame of the vessel was evident, now visible along the corridor's ceiling as a central spine possessing perpendicular ribs. His wound, which had originally been acutely painful with each footstep, started to dull. He took several photographs of the corridor. He saw an even grander opening than those previously seen. It belonged to the next compartment to his right. He peered inside and shone the torch along the compartment's length. Within the huge space, there was supportive framework. The torch couldn't provide enough light to reach the wooden wall at the furthest distance, which was to his left rather than directly forward. He continued climbing, negotiating patches of ice. He remained surprised at the enduring preservation of the floor, although he encountered a few holes that could be easily skirted and a larger one that he needed his climbing equipment to traverse.

Sam soon met a purpose-built square five-foot-wide hole, which led to a deeper level via a ramp. He continued up the corridor with the intention of descending later. It wasn't until he'd climbed a further 70 feet that he found another opening on his right. Instead of being for the next compartment, this was another opening for the most recently found compartment on his right, which was over 140 feet long. He figured that all the Ark's compartments would be empty, as they had been so far. In his mind he pictured the long compartment full of a variety of creatures, including large dinosaurs and birds. He entered and took five photographs. He longed to see them, because the camera had used a flash, and hence the images would be better than what he was capable of seeing with his torch. He returned to the corridor. Opposite the 140-foot-long compartment, on the other side of the corridor, he'd passed four smaller compartments, although in their own right these were still very large. Further to the left the compartments ended and made way for a large door, which had been the entrance to the Ark. Beyond that the corridor continued for a further 20 feet, then stopped abruptly. This end was solid ice. He estimated that he'd travelled approximately half of the distance of the length of the Ark. He concluded that the other half had become embedded in the southern glacier.

As Sam retraced his steps through the Ark, he thought about the Vulture. Sam had previously spent a nerve-racking period in Alaşehir worrying over the Vulture's death—first death—and had no desire to go through that experience again. Sam now tried to examine the situation more rationally. The Vulture's death was justified in Sam's mind as an act of self-defence. In fact, both deaths were. Despite this, Sam had wanted his own life to pass without taking another's. In the past he'd tried to avoid situations where violence could easily spiral out of control with deadly consequence. However, on this occasion he'd accepted a mission that he knew would take him to a country that was hostile to Christianity: a place where the necessity to defend himself would be likely. He'd weighed this against the need to spread the truth. He'd already formed the opinion that a man shouldn't spend his life intimidated by other men. Indeed, he knew that the Bible is full of brave men and women who'd risked their lives so that others could understand that the God who created us is also the One who can save our eternal spirits. Sam now considered how many people there were not written about in the Bible who'd lived after the time of the New Testament apostles and who'd put themselves in mortal danger to spread this same truth. These brave people had collectively smuggled Bibles, translated Bibles and preached the Gospel—the message of salvation through only Jesus the Messiah[1]—to others throughout the world. Furthermore, Sam remembered Jesus' own recommendations to His disciples regarding their appropriate self-defence in anticipation of the period after His death and resurrection, when they would peacefully spread the Gospel—recommendations that were suitable for the time, place and the extreme peril that the disciples would face.[2] These thoughts gave a measure of reassurance to Sam's soul.

---

[1] Regarding salvation through Christ alone, see Chapter 9 pg 213 and Chapter 13 pg 294 and their relevant footnotes.

[2] Luke 22:35-54. Just before Jesus' arrest, He recommended a list of items that each of His disciples should travel with: a pouch of money, a sack (for items such as food) and a sword. Earlier in Jesus' ministry He had advised His disciples to each travel with neither a pouch of money, a sack nor shoes; a sword was not mentioned (see also Matthew 10:1-14, Mark 6:7-9 [sandals rather than shoes were permitted], Luke 9:1-6, 10:1-9). The change of recommendation was because of the tremendous danger that His

FOOTNOTE CONTINUED ON THE NEXT PAGE

Sam was in Turkey to find more evidence that supports the truth of the Bible: a truth that wicked men and demonic forces wish to stifle. He would show the evidence to the world. His intention was that more people in all parts of the globe would open their eyes and realize: that this Earth was and is a fantastic place; that past events in our collective history affect each and every day of our lives; and that the Bible is the greatest historical document known to humanity. As a result of this, he hoped that more people would discover that the Bible contains the answers that mankind seeks, including the way to eternal life in Heaven.[1]

With life, there is risk. Sam knew one part of his own future. He knew that when he died he would go to Heaven. He could only speculate on other aspects of his future. He could do things that made one outcome more likely than another, yet in the end what eventually came to pass he didn't have absolute control over.[2] Ultimately, the truth of Christ carries personal risk, both to those who accept Him and to those who don't. To accept Him is to put yourself in harm's way but with the ultimate prize as a reward—Heaven. To not accept Him is to live a life with or without strife but to have inevitable disaster as a consequence—

CONTINUED FOOTNOTE PRESENT

---

disciples would face after His death and resurrection. It is important to note that clearly at that time and place it was legal to carry a sword to physically defend oneself. Preparedness to defend themselves was appropriate to the threat faced and in accordance with the law of the land. There is no biblical mention of a disciple using a weapon to defend himself after Jesus' death and resurrection.

[1] Heaven, then eventually the New Heaven-New Earth. See: Chapter 7 pg 152 and footnotes regarding Heaven; Timeline; Dispensations (8); Soul and Spirit; and Chapter 20 pg 397 and Chapter 24 pg 536 with their relevant footnotes regarding the New Heaven-New Earth.

[2] Proverbs 16:1-3, 16:9, 27:1.

Hell.[1] With respect to Sam's enemies, he didn't know their precise futures while they lived; however, he knew exactly what would happen once they died if they stayed on their current path. He knew that they would go directly to Hell. He was sure of this, because they'd aligned themselves with an evil cause whose end was to suppress the truth. Until the moment of death, while they still had life, there was a chance for them to turn it around, but that was their responsibility. Sam's conclusion was expressed as an audible declaration to himself—a stamp to dispel all apprehension: "They have minds to reason and to recognize that they're on the wrong path. They're responsible for their own lives and actions. No one forced them to find me. No one forced the Vulture to climb this mountain to murder me. I needed to defend myself."

On the way to the ramp Sam took more photographs of the corridor and of some of the compartments. Once at the ramp, as a precaution he hammered a piton into the wood near to the square hole. To the piton he secured a rope and began to descend via the ramp to the next level. On his way down he couldn't help but notice the tremendous thickness of the wooden floor of the corridor that he was leaving. The Ark was an extremely sturdy construction. The next storey was less tall than the first and its corridor narrower. He estimated the current storey's height at approximately nine feet, which meant that the lower storey would probably be the same—taking into account the thickness of the wood between storeys and that of the roof and base of the Ark. He was gaining a good idea as to the plan of the Ark and how it had worked. The only door had given access to the upper level, so that this break in the Ark's continuity wouldn't have been under water once the vessel was afloat. The creatures that couldn't fly would have needed to embark by means of an external ramp if the Ark had been built on a large plain. The

---

[1] Hell, then eventually the Lake of Fire. See Dispensations (8). See Soul and Spirit.

largest kinds of creatures would have been kept in the top storey, together with some of the more numerous smaller kinds. Others of the latter kinds would have been able to descend to the lower levels. The spaces would have been used as economically as possible. Food had also been stored for the entire year and 10 days.[1] Even the corridors would have probably been used to keep animals and/or store food. Importantly, the overall weight would have been distributed in favour of the lower storeys to help keep the vessel steady.

Sam wondered why the Ark had broken in two: perhaps from structural stress during an earthquake caused by one of Ararat's own convulsions or from the decay that accompanies age—or both. The Ark would have been higher on the mountain, maybe at or near the peak itself: the two parts sliding downward in opposite directions. And when had the fracture happened?

The middle level was less intact than the level that Sam had left. As he ascended the corridor, he needed to watch his footing closely because of rot. The corridor began to decrease in height, because areas of the damaged floor had become lifted. Before long he had to stoop, as the height had reduced to less than his own. Holes in the wood beneath him sometimes revealed the damaged corridor below and other times only ice and splintered wood.

Sam was forced to stop, because the precarious flooring had caused him to slip and he'd almost fallen through to the next level. He wanted to go further, crawling on his knees, but his nausea and dizziness were worsening. He'd explored 60 feet of this level of the Ark's length and had passed several entrances to compartments, two of which contained small rooms. Maybe some or all of these rooms had been used as living quarters by

---

[1] Genesis 6:19-21, 7:11, 8:13-17.
Indeed, for the majority of the stay in the Ark food would have taken up substantially more weight than that of the animals and humans combined.

Noah and the other members of his family. Sam had taken many photographs. The insides of the other compartments were either deformed or filled with ice. He realized that this entire half of the Ark had been only fully buried by snow within the last 200 years and before long would be torn apart by the glacier.

Sam decided to return to the compartment that he'd first encountered. Before climbing the ramp, he noticed something engraved on one of the wooden walls. He wiped the wall to see if he could improve the clarity. What had been engraved were obviously horizontal lines of text; however, he was unable to identify the language and even the writing system used to relay the language. He took a photograph. He was determined that the wood on which the engraving had been made would be cut free to become his retrieved wooden board. He carefully chiselled the wall with an adze tool, which was at the reverse end of the ice axe. After half an hour, he held a two-foot-long piece of wood in his hand. The board was four inches thick and heavy. In addition to this, he retrieved two sturdy, plain pieces of Ark wood only for a different purpose.

It was late in the afternoon. The sun was bright on the surface, but below ground only artificial light illuminated the large office. Four men stood in front of the Guardian, who was sat behind his desk. The four were all still sick, although a little better since returning to a lower altitude. One of them was injured. The Guardian stared at them. There was yet another man in the room, who stood to the Guardian's right. This subordinate had a pistol in plain view, which was holstered near his left armpit.

"So where's March?" the Guardian asked the four men opposite him. His voice was even and cool-tempered. He wanted as much information from the four as possible without provoking them to lie. He'd heard the basic facts already, but there was no substitute to receiving a report firsthand. He had a habit of saying: "Truth surfaces in the flesh."

Of the central two men, the one nearest to the group's left flank spoke: "We found him on the western face. Everyone became sick. Duman continued on with Bayram close behind. I managed to follow Bayram but from a distance . . . I was so sick that . . ." No excuses, he thought. He tightened his report: "Duman's dead. March shot him. Bayram saw it. Duman shot March before dying."

"Did Bayram see that happen?"

"Yes, he did."

"And did he intercept March?"

"No."

"Where's Duman's body now?"

"On the mountain in the same place where he was shot. Bayram's still near the summit. When I last saw him, he was sick—although not as bad as we were. He's searching for March's body."

"March's body—you assume that he's dead."

"He was shot in the chest, emir. His blood was on the snow."

Kurtbek was the surname of the man standing next to the Guardian. Kurtbek was the head of communications. He and the Guardian had spoken with one another earlier in the day. The Soyuz satellite had again passed over Mount Ararat for two minutes. There had been only one visible heat signature near the summit of the mountain. That heat signature had corresponded exactly with Bayram, who'd confirmed his position by radio.

"Go back up the mountain. Join Bayram, and don't return until you have March's body. And while you're there, pick up Duman as well. We don't leave evidence."

The group of four left.

The Guardian turned to his head of communications. Kurtbek spoke, "There was a lot of snow overnight. Duman's body was buried by it. March's will be as well."

"I don't care. I need to see his body. They'll just have to do some digging. Oh, and before they go back up, make sure that they have hacksaws with them."

"Yes, emir."

The Guardian continued, "I've contacted my counterpart in Iran. He'll have agents waiting at the border."

"You think March could still be alive?" Kurtbek asked.

The Guardian pressed his fingertips into his temples. His elbows dug into the polished wooden table. "Maybe. Who've we got in Armenia?"

"I can think of one man who could assist. He won't respond to a call from us though."

"Then I'll get one of the non-Turkish members to contact him."

Sam sat with his back to a wall. He'd returned to the first compartment. He cleaned the wound, then attempted to sterilize the blade of his penknife with antiseptic. He'd missed the best of the sun while exploring the Ark. Despite the scanty light from above, he probed the wound with the tip of the blade in an effort to fish the bullet out. The area was tender and started to bleed anew. He was hoping to either hear the scrape of metal on metal or to eventually feel hard resistance to the blade as he probed inward. He persisted for an hour until finally giving up. He slumped back in frustrated exhaustion. He rested for a few minutes before cleaning and redressing the wound. He could feel the bullet as if it was near the surface but had come to the conclusion that it was lodged much deeper.

The day melted into night inside the Ark. Sam's acute mountain sickness was ongoing. He thought that the symptoms would have waned. They hadn't. He should have been thankful that they hadn't worsened. He was still nauseas, heavily fatigued and short of breath. He knew that he needed to make a move. He was in no condition to make a perilous descent in darkness, so he planned to descend at first light.

Sam's alarm woke him at half-past two in the morning. It was pitch-black outside but wouldn't be for long. Because of the high altitude, the dawn would arrive earlier than at the base of the mountain. He quickly set to work clearing the signs of his occupation. In order to illuminate his tidying efforts, he'd removed the casing from around the bulb of the pen torch and wedged the opposite end into a broken section of flooring, so that the torch looked and worked like a candle. While folding his sleeping bag, he realized that he felt a little better. He was becoming acclimatized.

Sam looked upward at the barely visible occluded hole. In his right hand he held one of the ice axes, which now had a long length of rope secured to both the handle and the adze tool. He pressed his left hand against his wound to test his right arm's limitation before use. His coordination with his left arm was too poor for what he intended. He looked down at the head of the ice axe. Even in the low light, the blade looked lethal. He flicked his eyebrows upward, an indication that he doubted his plan, and then flung the axe up toward the obstructed hole, his aim being to break the snow in the centre. The first throw seemed to be on target, but the axe was repelled and fell back down. He respectfully stepped out of its way before it struck the floor. He looked up at the blocked hole and wondered if the axe had hit the wooden rim. The torchlight was so attenuated by the distance that he couldn't be sure of what he'd seen of his effort.

Sam picked up the axe. The pain of the wound had been exacerbated by the first swing. He ignored the pain. His second attempt was a complete miss. The third hit the target; he was sure of it, yet the axe returned without an offering. The snow occluding the hole had transformed into ice. He felt momentary apprehension as he considered how thick this layer of ice could be. An alternative plan quickly came to mind. If he couldn't break the ice from his current position, he would climb to the obstructed hole by placing pitons into a wall of the compartment and then the ceiling. He could hack away at the ice while suspended from the ceiling. However, this plan would cost him time and he would probably have to leave the following day.

Sam persisted and achieved a breakthrough on the ninth throw. The falling axe was followed by shards of ice and chunks of snow. By using his entire weight and refining his efforts with the hammer, he managed to deform the blade of the axe into a hook. He threw the altered axe toward the hole. On the fifth throw the axe found a purchase. He wondered if it had hooked wood, ice or a combination of both. He pulled hard on the rope, first with his right arm and then tugged with both. The axe didn't move. He climbed onto the rope and shook himself—no movement. He packed away the hammer and the torch, placed his backpack onto his back and started his painful ascent.

It was still dark as Sam climbed out of the Ark. He recovered the rope and the now useless ice axe. While he waited for the dawn, he packed snow and ice into the water bladders. He patched the hole with the two sturdy, plain pieces of Ark wood, then covered them with rocks, ice and snow.

Sam made a move as the first light of day touched the peak of Mount Ararat. He descended down the northern face to the right of Ahora Gorge. He observed that the ravine's centre was dark and appeared to have not accepted the recent snow, unlike the terrain round about. He could see Little Ararat to the east. The day was clear with not a single cloud in the sky. Furthermore, looking toward the distant north, he saw a metropolis that he was sure was Yerevan.

As Sam approached the identifiable base of Mount Ararat, he began to feel cold. At first he couldn't understand the sensation, because it was much warmer there than higher up the mountain. The descent had been rapid, taking Sam only four hours to complete. A few minutes later he began to sweat. He then felt unsettled and physically weak: symptoms he could now easily comprehend. They were the herald of practically every infective illness that he'd experienced, from gastroenteritis to malaria. He

tested the wound with his left hand. It had become extremely
tender. He had neither time nor shelter to undo the dressing and
examine the area. Anyway, he had a good idea of what he'd find,
and it was something that would be impossible to definitively
treat in the field. He had a wound infection due to a foreign body:
a complication that he'd tried to prevent by his attempts to
remove the bullet whilst in the Ark. The germs infecting the area
were likely to be of one type of bacterium from a small number
of different types of bacteria found normally on the skin. The
particular type would have been introduced as the bullet
penetrated the skin or soon after because the skin was broken.
The most likely type of bacterium implicated wasn't usually
sensitive to the antibiotic that he had in his possession. He
stopped to remove the medical kit from his backpack. Inside
the kit were the antibiotic tablets: two courses of the same
medication used to combat travellers' diarrhoea. He took double
the first recommended dose. He had little to lose but much to
gain if the antibiotic worked. He ran on.

The Armenian border was approximately 15 miles away. Sam
had no intention of crossing in the day. He also wanted to put as
much distance between him and the mountain. A balance would
have to be found. Although remote, the area he was currently
traversing was exposed and, according to the map, would
continue that way even beyond the border. He craved for his
underground refuge.

Before long Sam developed a swinging temperature. During
the cold phases his body shivered, and throughout the hot phases
he felt light-headed. His latest symptoms were confirmation that
he'd developed an abscess. Even if he had taken an antibiotic
that was active against the offending type of bacterium, the
medication wouldn't work, because it wouldn't be able to
penetrate deep inside the collection of pus. There was a general
rule that he'd heard from a number of different surgeons: "If
there's pus about, let it out." And that was exactly what needed
to happen. In addition to extracting the pus, the foreign body

would also have to be removed or the pus would return. For this procedure he needed a hospital and soon.

Six miles from the Armenian border Sam stopped. He'd found a relatively isolated location between two hills, although it was still somewhat exposed. He didn't erect the tent. He laid the sleeping bag and the backpack on the ground. He camouflaged them with as much surrounding matter as he could scavenge. He prayed for God's protection and then lay down, hoping to sleep for the seven hours of light that remained of the day. He awoke repeatedly, drenched in sweat. The pain in his right upper chest had become constant, the throbbing ache invading his dreams for the brief periods when he managed to fall asleep. He hadn't any pain relievers. The snow and ice that he'd packed into the water bladders had melted; therefore, he had plenty to drink: enough to match his losses.

Sam was already awake when his alarm sounded. It was eight at night. Although the Armenian border was now just six miles away, the centre of Yerevan was a further 14. He had a long way to go. As he considered the distance and felt the weight of his backpack, he realized that he wouldn't reach his intended destination that night with a heavy load: he was ill and knew that he would be getting sicker as he progressed. He made the decision to discard all the climbing tools, the tent, the sleeping bag and some of the heavier items of clothing. He was tempted to leave them in the open, as he was minus a spade, but his wish to leave as little evidence as possible won. Using his bare hands with the occasional help of the remaining unaltered ice axe, he laboriously dug a hole, and then buried the items. A lighter yet sicker Sam started running northward. The run became a short dash, because after a few seconds his body forced him to continue at a much slower pace.

One and a quarter hours later Sam crossed the Armenian border. He'd done this without realizing, as there were no demarcations, such as fences, or indications of human life in the area. Half an hour later he was sure that he was no longer in Turkey. His mind and body wished that the crossing represented a watershed between peril in Turkey and safety in Armenia. He reminded himself that he couldn't be sure of that, but a sliver of relief slipped through anyway. Perhaps he needed this small feeling of hope to push on. He put his watch forward by two hours to Armenian time.

Two hours later Sam met civilization. Nevertheless, he avoided close contact. The language on signs and buildings was Armenian. A few minutes later he noticed that some important signs included Russian and English. He was conscious of the way that he must have looked. He felt his unkempt beard and imagined dirt and grime on his face. He used a convenience at a petrol station to clean himself up, which included brushing the bulk of dirt from his black trousers. They were the pair that he'd worn since Cappadocia except for his brief excursion to the city of Van. The trousers were fatigued but not torn. Despite his efforts, he still looked a mess: not much tidier than the unfortunate homeless whom he'd met in London. Maybe my appearance will work to my advantage, he thought; the majority of people will certainly make every effort to avoid me. He then thought about what an Armenian policeman would think. Would I be arrested as a vagrant?

Sam left the petrol station and continued on toward Yerevan. He followed the roads from the distance of adjacent fields when able, and in areas that were built-up he walked along the pavements. He'd decided against using public transport. Besides, he had no Armenian currency and his odour would alienate other passengers—both warrants for ejection. He had the gold ingots though; someone would be willing to accept this universal currency such as a taxi driver. He decided to keep this option in reserve. He wanted no human interaction before reaching a hospital. He grieved his own ruling as a night bus passed him.

The directions to Yerevan's major general hospital were helpfully signposted throughout the capital in the three languages, and Sam found the complex without difficulty. It was five in the morning. He stood across the street from the hospital. Its twenty-four-hour main entrance was well advertised by a bright fluorescent sign that glared at the night. The lobby had a glass front and was spacious. A single uninterested guard sat behind a large reception desk. Six people stood, divided into two equally-numbered groups, in the lobby; none of them appeared to be staff or ill. They were probably patients' relatives waiting for their lifts but not from the taxi parked in the forecourt with its engine running.

Sam started to circle the large hospital complex. The main hospital building (that is, the building directly involved with delivering care) was the tallest structure in the entire complex at four storeys. This building had an external patients' entrance for the emergency department (emergency room), as was customary in the UK. He wasn't going to use that entrance. In addition, there were staff entrances as well as bays for emergencies arriving by ambulances, two of which were parked nearby. There were numerous other buildings, some of which, he thought, probably had teaching and research functions. Having completed his circuit, he furtively left his backpack in a large refuse bin in a backstreet next to another public building, then walked slowly toward the main entrance of the hospital.

As ever, timing was everything, and Sam hung back until the attention of the guard was diverted by a lady who'd asked him a question. As Sam approached the main door, he noticed two laterally-located closed-circuit television cameras. The door opened automatically, and he entered. He initially headed in the direction of the emergency department along a suitably signed route (written in the three languages) for its internal entrance. His footsteps were resonated by the clean sheer walls of the corridor. He saw a tired doctor enter the corridor from a side room 20 metres ahead. Not long after, the doctor dipped into another side room. Sam confirmed that he was then the only occupant in the corridor, after which he broke off to head in a different direction, along an adjoining corridor.

The laundry was in the basement and easy to locate. Sam used water from a sink to cursorily wash himself while standing. He donned a two-piece set of green theatre clothes and a crisp clean white lab coat. The pain from the abscess spiked, and he stood still to contain the attack of the noxious spur. The pain reduced somewhat after a few minutes. He placed his pen torch into the left top pocket of the lab coat and stashed his own dirty clothes in a dark recess. He climbed back up the stairs to take full advantage of the immunity that a white coat afforded in the hospital setting. His new target was the cardiac catheter laboratory. He hoped that in this hospital the laboratory would be located on the ground floor as this type of department would be in the UK, owing to the nature of the emergency services provided.

The signs for the departments besides the emergency department were written only in Armenian. Sam had never seen the characters of the Armenian alphabet before that night. They had no resemblance to Latin letters, and therefore searching for a word or a segment of a word that related to the heart was proving impossible.

As Sam explored, he made every effort to mask any signs of pain. He walked with the purposeful steps and furrowed questioning brow of a hospital doctor pondering the diagnosis of a difficult case between wards. He passed two tearful relatives of a patient. They paid Sam no mind. He saw a hospital porter wheeling an empty trolley. The porter lifted his eyes toward the new night doctor. Sam gave the porter a respectful out-of-hours nod, which was returned.

There were only two occupied wards on the ground floor. Most of this level was filled with empty outpatient clinic rooms and administrative offices. Sam began to consider whether he needed to go up a floor. However, he'd been methodical in his exploration, and after fifteen minutes he located the cardiac catheter laboratory at the very end of the outpatient department. He'd recognized from the exterior of the laboratory that he was in the correct place because of the posters on the wall. Some of the posters pictured: clogged atherosclerotic arteries in cross section together with unhealthy foods; cigarettes with large red "X"s through them; and other various public warnings of how to avoid a heart attack. Next to this cornucopia of healthy advice were posters that illustrated the treatment of narrowed coronary arteries (the heart's medium-sized arteries, which supply this organ with blood): balloons used to expand the arteries and mesh coils to keep them open. It was these images of treatment that were the conclusive indicator of what lay behind the laboratory's double door. The next thing that he noted was a combination lock with 14 labelled buttons: 10 numbers and 4 letters. The doors of the double door were wooden with metal-filament-reinforced-glass windows in both upper sections. The unlit laboratory was clearly vacant, and the small amount of light from the corridor in which he was positioned was unable to adequately illuminate even the first two metres inside. He'd experienced a similar type of lock before. The combination would be known only to members of that specific department for rapid keyless access and would be six characters made up of letters and numbers. He didn't have a week to input every conceivable combination.

Sam gently pushed the door that possessed the buttons in order to test the bolt. To his surprise the door opened. The last person to leave had forgotten to slide the metal clip to activate the lock. This was one of the signs of a busy department. Sam entered and activated the lock behind him.

There were three separate operating rooms in the laboratory. They were placed in series, and Sam chose the one furthest from the entrance. Once inside this operating room, he covered the glazed porthole of the room's main door with three thick sterile drapes, then switched on the lights.

The room was meticulously sanitary with light-blue walls that curved inward to meet the floor for easier and superior cleaning. An operating table, which resembled a bar of dark chocolate, was positioned in the centre. There was a doorless annex, where the cardiologists and other staff could scrub their hands. In addition, there was a door that led to a small room, where supplies were kept. Sam saw the device that he needed—the X-ray image intensifier—in a corner of the operating room. An X-ray image intensifier is a machine that's capable of delivering a low-strength, continuous X-ray beam, which is shone through the patient. Low-strength X-rays are used, because they're required over an extended period; standard-strength X-rays used to take single pictures would be dangerous. The images acquired using low-strength X-rays would be of poor quality if not altered, and so they are strengthened (intensified) by the machine. The images, displayed one after the other to produce a movie clip, are viewed on a monitor, which looks like a television. The movie clip is shown in real time, which means that the doctor can be guided by what he or she is seeing of the insides of the patient whilst operating. Cardiologists use the machine to correctly place catheters (tubes) into coronary arteries. The cardiologists inject dye, via the catheters, into the arteries to locate the pathological narrowings—the dye being visible to the machine. These narrowed areas can then be opened with the help of the image intensifier. The length of the movie clip is determined by the cardiologist, who activates the machine by a foot pedal. Sam had seen an X-ray image intensifier operated on many occasions in Zambia but had had no hands-on experience. Even so, he set to work, hoping that no one would be admitted with a heart attack in the following two hours.

The first thing that Sam did was put on a pair of latex gloves. He switched on the X-ray image intensifier, which started to emit a low hum. He positioned the monitor, which was a separate unit possessing a stand with wheels, so that it faced the foot of the operating table. He lifted the foot pedal, another separate unit, from off the floor and placed it onto the operating table. The monitor and the foot pedal were connected to the largest part of the image intensifier by wire cables. X-ray image intensifiers are composite devices. Even though made by numerous different companies, many X-ray image intensifiers resemble one another, especially in that one major unit of each of these similar-looking devices closely resembles the letter C. This unit can be tilted and raised and is connected to a heavy supporting platform with wheels. The bottom end of the C emits the X-rays, while the top end receives them. The patient is positioned between the two ends. Together the C and the platform constitute the largest part of the image intensifier—and a hefty part at that.

The medicines in the supply room had statements of contents in Russian. Sam knew almost no Russian but was acquainted with the pronunciations of the Cyrillic letters. Pharmacological names are a worldwide medical lingua franca, and he had no problem identifying what he needed. Other required items—all easily recognizable—were either in the supply room, the operating room or the annex. Whilst the image intensifier continued to warm up, Sam positioned a trolley next to the operating table. He spread out a sterile drape over two-thirds of the top of the trolley. On the drape he placed sterile equipment, which included more drapes, gloves, syringes, needles, dishes, scalpels, tweezers, forceps, saline, scissors, absorbable sutures and plenty of gauze. Away from the sterile equipment but still onto the top of the trolley he put a large plastic bottle containing an iodine-based sterilizing solution, and several small glass ampoules containing sterile local anaesthetic—the outer surfaces of all these containers were not sterile. He raised the back support of the operating table. Next he carefully positioned the C of the image intensifier so that the X-ray emitter was behind the tilted back support of the operating table at an angle that would direct the beam toward where he was planning for his right shoulder to be. Therefore, the receiver was above the operating table.

Sam tested the image intensifier by pressing the foot pedal with his fist for three seconds. He heard a click from the C but saw nothing on the monitor. He switched on the monitor. Again, he pressed the foot pedal. This time he could see a clear X-ray movie clip of nothing very much: the operating table was designed so that X-rays would pass through it unhindered. He removed the lab coat and the V-necked theatre shirt to expose his chest. He painfully mounted the table and placed the foot pedal beneath his right thigh, so that he could activate the device by pushing his leg downward.

Sam rested his back onto the slick, black plastic-covered padding. The operating table was surprisingly comfortable for such a firm-looking structure. He slowly removed the dressing, which had become adherent to the wound. The last layer of gauze was coloured pink and yellow: a mixture of blood and pus. The wound itself was raised and red compared with the surrounding skin. He replaced his gloves with a sterile new pair. He'd sweated so much into the first pair that he donned the new with sticky difficulty.

Sam activated the image intensifier. He shifted himself slightly to his left, so that the area of interest was displayed in the centre of the picture. He could clearly see the collection of bones that made up his right shoulder and upper chest. He could also see two pieces of metal. One of them was smaller than the other. The movie clip was two-dimensional, but by moving his right shoulder and pressing the wound he determined that the smallest piece was the more superficial. He was frustrated to further observe that his right lung had partially collapsed. The lung was not visible at the top of the right half of the chest cavity, the wound clearly affecting the lining of the chest cavity there, which had allowed outside air to enter. He knew that he would have to be extra careful, as a mistake could result in collapse of this entire lung. If he managed to avoid this complication, eventually the lung should naturally re-expand. He released the pressure on the pedal, and the picture disappeared.

Sam poured some of the sterilizing solution into a large dish. He broke open four of the glass ampoules and changed his gloves yet again. He washed the entire area of the wound and the surrounding skin, first with saline and then with copious amounts of the sterilizing solution. The latter—a dark-brown liquid because of the iodine—covered the right side of his chest. Some spilled onto the floor. He prepared three needle-tipped syringes. He positioned a drape with a square hole, cut by him, so that the wound remained exposed. The drape had sticky edges, which adhered to his skin. He cleaned the wound again but with only a fraction of the liquid used before and then changed his gloves once more. He drew two ampoules worth of clear local anaesthetic solution into one of the ten-millilitre syringes. He proceeded to anaesthetize the wound by injecting the local anaesthetic, superficially at first and then more deeply using the full length of the three-centimetre-long needle. He was used to saying to patients that the local anaesthetic is the most painful part of a procedure; however, he anticipated that digging around the wound would be much worse. What he was about to attempt would normally be performed under a general anaesthetic. He used an amount of local anaesthetic that he thought would be the perfect balance between effectiveness and safety: after all, he couldn't risk passing out from the pain—from using too little; but neither would he want to fall unconscious from the anaesthetic that would seep into his circulation—from using too much.

Sam viewed his right shoulder and upper chest with the image intensifier to briefly reacquaint himself with the challenge ahead. With the device off, he picked up a pair of blunt dissection scissors—in addition to the two short blunt blades, the scissors had two long handles for precise control of the blades. Whilst viewing the wound directly, he started to push aside tissue using the scissors with the blades unified. Keeping the unified blades of the scissors in the most profitable position, he re-engaged the image intensifier, and then he probed further. He disengaged the device and dug deeper with direct inspection, sometimes having to cut soft tissue. He repeated these actions, and in this manner he set about finding the two metal pieces. The blunt dissection scissors were ideal for the task, because it would be difficult to mistakenly cut a rubbery artery with this instrument. He'd used a similar pair of scissors to explore a cadaver during his first year at medical school. He was careful to use short bursts of X-rays to minimize his exposure, pressing his thigh onto the pedal only when necessary.

Sam reached the smallest piece. He easily plucked it out with a large pair of tweezers. The largest piece was more stubborn, and as it was extracted, a large collection of pus was released. He held the latter piece in the tweezers. He examined this piece closely. It was surrounded by different fabrics, which he recognized as shreds of his clothes. He wondered if there were any other shreds of fabric still inside. None of the different fabrics were of sufficient density to be detected by the image intensifier, so he explored the wound further with the blunt dissection scissors and irrigated the area with plenty of saline. He couldn't find any more shreds of fabric, although this was inconclusive as to whether any still remained. He was pleased to have not seen any major arterial damage, because he wouldn't have been able perform the tiny stitches required for the repair.

Sam cleaned the wound again with the iodine-based solution. He then started to close the wound with absorbable sutures. He made three deep stitches and four superficially. He'd been careful not to tie each suture too tightly; if there was pus still present, he wanted it to be able to easily track out from the wound. If pus was confined, it could become another abscess. A plastic drain that could be removed later would have been ideal, but he wouldn't be able to look after it on the run.

Sam looked at his handiwork and tested each of the superficial sutures. He left the operating table and walked to the scrub room. He washed himself with wet paper towels and shaved off his beard with one of the sterile razors that had been on the ECG trolley. He placed a dressing onto his treated wound. In the supply room he found some ampoules containing an antibiotic that would be much more likely to kill the type of bacterium that he was infected with. He gave himself two deep intramuscular injections, one into the front of each thigh, with the expectation that the antibiotic would be slowly released into his bloodstream from that moment on up to a period of about five to seven days.

Sam placed all the minor metallic items that he'd used into a half-full yellow plastic bin (designed for the disposal of sharp items), which was in the adjacent operating room, and he gave the bin a shake to mix the contents. He washed the operating table and scrubbed the floor thoroughly—while also collecting the minor nonmetallic items that he'd used, all of which he put into a large, yellow clinical-waste bag. By the time he was finished, the operating room looked the same as when he'd entered—except for a few missing trivial medical items, whose loss would either never be noticed or not detected for days.

Sam discarded the yellow bag into an appropriate bin in the empty outpatient department, returned to the laundry, changed his clothes and left the hospital by way of an unalarmed fire exit, where he met the seventh hour's staunch daylight. He collected his backpack from the refuse bin and promptly left Yerevan.

That morning Yerevan University Hospital was visited by a government official. He arrived at the same time that the clerical workers started their shift. He said that he was from the Department of Health and had the documentation to match his claim. He asked for the registration records stretching back six months of all foreigners who'd attended or were attending the hospital. His aim, he said, was to determine what proportion of them had travel insurance. He politely explained to the female clerk who'd been assigned to assist him that he wished to determine the burden to the health service that had been created by those without insurance who'd been unable to pay for their treatment. Unknown to the clerk, the official was interested in only the previous two days and took special notice of the records of male foreigners who were still inpatients.

Sam travelled northward by coach, past Abovyan and on to Hrazdan. He secured lodgings in a cheap hotel early that evening. At ten o'clock he left the hotel to make a telephone call. He dialled one of the numbers that he'd memorized—one of two that were not directed to a Turkish mobile phone. The number started with the international dialling code for France.

"Oui," the female voice said.

"It's me. I need to speak to him." Sam knew a little French but was too tired and frustrated to utter even a single Gallic word.

"He will call you back in exactly one hour, using the same number that you're calling from."

Sam left the phone box. He returned fifty-eight minutes later.

"So you're still with us," Sol Hodaviah said. He'd arrived in Finland two days previously and had made the call from there.

"Just about."

"If there's someone with you who's forcing you to make this call, indicate by asking me how I am," Sol Hodaviah requested.

"I'm not with anyone," Sam replied. "I was shot. Don't worry about the details; I've taken care of it."

"What do you mean, don't worry? Do you need some assistance? If you want, we could send someone to help you. It will take her at least twenty-four hours to get to . . ."

"I've taken care of it."

"If you say so. The dialling code told me what country you're in. Does that mean that you've completed the first objective?"

"Yes, it does: in its entirety and more besides."

"Congratulations! You've no idea how pleased I am to hear that."

"Thank you."

There was no room for further fanfare. Both of them understood that. Next Sol Hodaviah asked Sam to briefly list the people whom he'd come up against—since Hodaviah and Sam had last spoken together. Sam did this in around a minute.

"Now about the second objective—do you think you can go on?" Sol Hodaviah asked.

"That depends on what the second objective is."

"That's not how this is going to work. Are you fit enough to attempt the second objective or not—and do you want to attempt it?"

"Does it involve climbing any more mountains? I'm going to need some time to heal before I'm 'match-fit' again."

There was a pause on the line. "All you need to say is whether you'll attempt it or not. I'm not going to persuade you after I tell you what it is."

"I'm willing and able. Is that what you want to hear?"

"Exactly! This is how it is. You're now in a unique position to complete the second objective. The people you've come up against are of exceptional interest to us. You've brought them to the surface by your first objective. You see, there's another mystery in Turkey and I . . . we think that they're connected with it. We want you to go back into Turkey to a place called Bergama."

"Bergama?"

"The name Bergama is a Turkish adaptation of the name Pergamos. Bergama is a town that occupies the site of the ancient city of Pergamos. The book of Revelation states that Pergamos contains the throne of Satan—and that Pergamos is the location in which Satan resides.[1] Although this book was written almost 2,000 years ago, we strongly suspect that Satan's throne is still there. Many think that the book of Revelation and the other prophetic books of the Bible are just full of symbolism and should never be viewed or interpreted in a literal sense. However, things that were written have already come true, and others are quickly becoming a reality. For example, Israel has been revived in the original site of the ancient Kingdom of the Hebrews.[2] For centuries even those who correctly interpreted the prophecies wondered how that could ever come about. But praise God it's happened. On the downside, a new Babylon is about to be constructed on the exact same site as the original city,[3] in Iraq.[1]

---

[1] Revelation 2:12-13. In verse 13 the Greek word translated as "seat" is "thronos", which is a stately seat of a ruler: literally, a throne.

[2] Jeremiah 16:11-17, Ezekiel 11:13-17, 36:19-24, 37:21-22 (furthermore, the return of the Hebrews was predicted to result in one nation, which it is today, rather than divided into two kingdoms, Judah and Israel), Amos 9:14-15.

[3] A future Babylon is referred to in the Old and New Testaments. It will be a physical place in that: it is called a city; it will have a king; it will have great wealth, possessing tremendous physical luxuries (from fine spices to precious metals) and the epithet "the golden city"; and it will be vulnerable to earthquake activity as well as fire, and when its destruction comes, it will be seen burning from a distance. A concept cannot be endowed with these properties or have these things happen to it in the above ways. Isaiah 14:1-11, Revelation 14:8-12, 16:16-21, 17:1-18, 18:1-19:3.

FOOTNOTE CONTINUED ON THE NEXT PAGE

For centuries Babylon has been in ruins, and now—now after all this time, it's going to get a new lease of life. Once again, it will be the political and commercial centre of the world.[2] Within the city, the false religions of the world will be united into one.[3] We

CONTINUED FOOTNOTE PRESENT

Babylon is Babylon and no other place. Babylon is called Babel in Hebrew throughout the Old Testament. Babylon was one of the cities of Nimrod (lived around 2400 BC), although this particular city he was unable to complete, because during its construction God converted the people's one language to many, so that they wouldn't understand one another's speech, and then He scattered them over the face of the Earth: Genesis 10:8-10, 11:1-9. Babylon was the capital city of Nebuchadnezzar II's kingdom (Nebuchadnezzar II lived around 630–561 BC): 2 Kings 24:1-11, Ezra 5:12-14, Daniel 1:1-2, 4:1-37. At the time of the writing of the New Testament the city of Babylon still stood, and indeed, there was an early Christian community there (mentioned in 1 Peter 5:13). These three Babylons and other historical Babylons were all in the same place, and there is no reason to assume that the future city of Babylon will be in any other place. See Timeline.

[1] The location of Babylon is approximately 60 miles south of Baghdad.

[2] The future Babylon is described as: a city without comparison; a great city having immense secular power and reigning over all the kings of the Earth; and a city conducting such lucrative trade that the merchants of the Earth have become rich from doing business with it. Revelation 17:1-18, 18:1-19:3.

[3] The future Babylon is described as: deceiving all nations with its sorceries; a great city with tremendous religious influence, making all the nations of the world "drink of the wine of the wrath of her fornication" (the fornication is idolatry—see below*); "THE MOTHER OF HARLOTS AND ABOMINATIONS OF THE EARTH", in other words, the head and chief promoter of idolatry; and a city killing many genuine Christians both inside its borders and throughout the Earth. Revelation 14:8-12, 17:1-18, 18:1-19:3.

*Idolatry is a biblically declared type of fornication, because idolatry is a rejection of our creator God for beings and objects that

FOOTNOTE CONTINUED ON THE NEXT PAGE

know which countries are planning to build Babylon anew, but the order has come from a source more malevolent and purposeful than mankind. There must be a supernatural driving force. If these places are real, then the throne of Satan must also be real. We think that the origin of the command to resurrect Babylon is coming from Bergama."

"How?" Sam had more than an inkling of the answer to his own question yet wanted to hear Sol Hodaviah's view.

"The Bible demonstrates that demons are the inspiration of false religions on the Earth.[1] To the casual observer these religions appear to be started by men, except this just isn't the case. There must be purposeful demonic-human interfaces, that is, interfaces above that of the aimless conjuring of demons by mediums."[2]

"I wish I had time to tell you about my experience in Cappadocia."

"Cappadocia?"

CONTINUED FOOTNOTE PRESENT

---

didn't create or sustain us (Exodus 34:14-17, Leviticus 17:7, 20:6-8, Judges 2:17, Ezekiel 6:1-14, 16:1-39, 23:30, Hosea 4:6-19). The origin of all false religions is the angelic rebellion, which promotes the replacement of worshipping God with other beings and objects, which is idolatry (see Chapter 13 pgs 284-294 and the many relevant footnotes).

[1] Leviticus 17:7, Deuteronomy 32:16-17, Matthew 4:7-10, Luke 4:4-8, John 8:12-44, 2 Corinthians 11:13-15, Ephesians 2:1-5, 1 Timothy 4:1-3, Revelation 9:20-21, 12:9, 13:1-15, 20:2-3. The Catholic doctrine of forbidding marriage to certain individuals (Roman Catholicism—all priests; and Eastern Orthodoxy—bishops and higher positions) is a doctrine of devils, made evident in the above passage of 1 Timothy.

[2] Demonic possession of a human is another type of demonic-human interface, which can be either purposeful (*) or aimless (‡).

*See Chapter 20 pg 396 and footnote regarding Satan's possession of Judas Iscariot.

‡Mark 5:1-20, 9:17-29, Luke 8:27-39, 9:38-43.

"Yes, I came across one of these purposeful interfaces."

"Really?"

"Yes, really. There was a demon there who'd used one of the most influential members of the community to turn many of the people away from the true faith. In short, the demon was wreaking havoc. Don't worry; he's gone."

"Well, although I've previously not known anyone who's witnessed anything like this, I'm not surprised. I can name some men who've started false religions, each of whom claimed to have met an angel who gave him instructions. Muḥammad[1] and

---

[1] Muḥammad claimed to have received the Koran from the angel Gabriel: The Koran 2 The Cow (Al-Baqarah):97-99. However, even Muḥammad doubted that this was the case. The alternative was that he received the Koran from a demon, one of the jinn. The belief with some doubt: The Koran 26 The Poets (Ash-Shu´arā'):192-212, 81 Shrouded in Darkness (At-Takwīr):15-25. Within these two references, after statements that the Koran had been given by a trustworthy spirit and a noble messenger respectively (both believed to be referring to Gabriel) there are then denials that the supernatural being has come from the jinn and is a demon respectively. More doubt: Sīrat Rasūl Allāh by Ibn Isḥāq *chapter: The Gospel Prophecy of the sending of the Comforter (subchapter: The Prophet's Mission)*. According to this account, after Muḥammad was visited by a spirit who claimed to be Gabriel, Muḥammad was concerned that he was possessed and considered throwing himself off a mountain but was prevented from this action by the spirit. The spirit returned repeatedly, and the concern that this supernatural being might be a demon persisted. The spirit could be seen only by Muḥammad. His wife Khadījah performed a test to determine the character of the spirit. When the spirit was present, she made Muḥammad place himself inside her garment and asked him if the spirit had left as a result of this action. Muḥammad said that the spirit had left. She reassured Muḥammad that the spirit was an angel rather than a demon.

Joseph Smith, the founder of the Mormons,[1] are examples.

---

[1] Joseph Smith, the founder of the Mormons, claimed to have received holy writings from a supernatural being from Heaven called Moroni—the first visitation being on 21st September 1823. Smith referred to Moroni as an angel. However, via the gold plates, which Moroni reportedly disclosed the hidden location of to Smith, it is revealed that this supernatural being was the resurrected son of a prophet called Mormon. The prophet Mormon was meant to have written on the gold plates, which before his death he gave to his son (around 385 AD). Moroni is believed to have added more writing to them and then hid them in around 421 AD before dying. Smith declared that he found the gold plates beneath a large stone on a hill in New York and that the Book of Mormon was his translation of the plates. References for this paragraph are found in [α], below.

One of many doctrinal problems with this religion is the belief that there are three tiers of salvation. The first (top tier) requires belief in Christ, baptism and acquisition of the Holy Spirit by the laying on of hands of someone ordained by their clerical system; those who adhere to these conditions become priest-kings. After death, they would, at some point, be resurrected in the form of gods comparable to God. The second (middle tier) does not require belief in Christ whilst alive on Earth but acceptance of Christ after death while in a spiritual prison, the result of which is that the individual would be given a lower resurrected form than those in the top tier. The third (bottom tier) requires no belief in Christ whilst alive. Neither do they accept Him after death. They go to Hell. However, they do receive the Holy Spirit and are eventually given a resurrected form lower than those in the middle tier. These three groups are believed to all receive salvation in that no one receives eternal punishment and all receive a glorified everlasting body, although the level of glory is dependant on tier. The people's ongoing relationship (close or far) with God in their glorified forms is also dependant on tier. References for the above are found in [β], below. Notice the combination of a small amount of truth with copious invention. Salvation does indeed come through Christ but through the Christ of the Bible, not an interpretation of Him based on unbiblical doctrine.

FOOTNOTE CONTINUED ON THE NEXT PAGE

Clearly the angels weren't angels at all—quite the opposite in fact. There have probably been lots of these purposeful demonic-human interfaces in the past. Many were undoubtedly in different locations. However, we believe that there is a grand interface

CONTINUED FOOTNOTE PRESENT

Note two purgatory-like systems not too dissimilar from the purgatory found in Roman Catholicism. According to Mormon doctrine, after death both a spiritual prison and Hell itself are places from which an individual can receive salvation. Purgatory is not mentioned in the Bible, nor is there an equivalent mentioned under another name (for a fuller explanation see footnote in Chapter 7 pg 152 regarding those who go to Heaven). Our life on Earth is the only chance we have to receive salvation.

Two other doctrinal problems worth mentioning are related to salvation. Firstly, regarding the Mormon elders (specifically, those ordained into a type of senior priesthood), when claiming direction by the Holy Spirit, whatever they say is equal with Scripture, is the will of God and even has the power to salvation [γ]. This gives no room for criticism from a biblical standpoint. Secondly, those who accept the Book of Mormon in faith will receive a crown of eternal life, whereas those who reject this book will be condemned [δ]. This is another method of salvation that is not biblical.

[α] The Book of Mormon: Introduction—*The Testimony of Eight Witnesses, Testimony of the Prophet Smith;* Books—Words of Mormon *chapter 1:1-2*, Mormon *chapters 6:5-6, 8:1-14*, Ether *chapter 5:1-6*, Moroni *chapters 1:1, 10:1-34*. Doctrine and Covenants (a book believed to be a compilation of divine revelations of the leaders of "The Church of Jesus Christ of Latter-day Saints"): *sections 2:1-3, 20:1-8, 27:5*. The Pearl of Great Price (a collection of articles that relate particular features of the doctrine and faith of "The Church of Jesus Christ of Latter-day Saints"): Joseph Smith—History (an autobiographical piece) *1:27-75*.

[β] Doctrine and Covenants *sections 76:50-119, 138:53-60*.

[γ] Doctrine and Covenants *section 68:1-5*.

[δ] Doctrine and Covenants *section 20:1-16*.

Note some relevant information can be found in the introductions to the above chapters and sections.

located in one place. Your second objective could be truly revealing."

"No kidding."

"That's right—serious stuff."

"Now before I forget, can you make an anonymous donation to the Yerevan University Hospital for the equipment that I used?"

"Physician, heal thyself, eh?"

"With God's help I treated my wound, but ultimately all healing is in His hands."

"Well said. Estimate the cost of the equipment for me."

"Hmm . . . Six hundred US dollars."

"I'll multiply that figure by five."

"Thanks, and please do it once I'm clear of Armenia."

"It'll be sent in four weeks. And I now need detailed descriptions of all the enemies whom you've confronted since we last spoke."

"Fine, although first of all can I add something about my chief interrogator that I forgot to mention during our previous call? For someone who clearly isn't a Christian he has more than a superficial understanding of the faith, and he can use this against us." Sam then answered Sol Hodaviah's request. He first described Prasseda and Livia. After that, he revealed as much as he could about the appearances of the various men who'd hunted him but with whom he'd never conversed.

"I'll see if I can put that information to some good use," Sol Hodaviah said.

"Is that it? Anything else?"

"No, that's it. We're praying for you. Goodbye."

Chapter 19   **Anthony Burrows**

Sam spent another two days in Armenia. During this time he travelled northward. He crossed the border into Georgia as Anthony Burrows. From there he journeyed westward to reach a port on the coast of the Black Sea. After a day of careful scouting, he bought passage on a small ship whose ultimate destination was Cyprus.

The ship travelled slowly. Sam didn't mind. His wound needed time to heal. The ship's itinerary while sailing through the Black Sea was to stop at various northern Turkish ports. Sam's intention was to remain on board during these extended pauses. At first he mostly kept to himself, using the time to catch up on sleep and gather his thoughts for the mission's second objective. He imagined possible traps that may be set for him and how to evade them. What's more, he started to devise a strategy to find the throne of Satan and the presumed surrounding chamber, where the sovereign demon met and commanded his subjects.

After three days, Sam began to spend less time in his room, surfacing to eat in the same hall as the other passengers. They were a diverse ethnic and cultural mix: Russians, Georgians, Turks and Greeks making up the majority but also people from other parts of the world. While in the canteen, a group of young Muslim Turks who'd boarded at Sinop introduced themselves in a friendly gesture to get to know him. They consisted of three women and two men. Sam introduced himself as Anthony Burrows. He played cards with them that evening owing to their continued insistence. It would have been more awkward and suspicious if he'd declined, because he'd told them that he was travelling alone.

Sam made up Anthony's persona from no one except himself. All of the alternative identities that Sam hid behind were a part of him. He simply accentuated a particular facet of his character beyond what he normally found comfortable. Like numerous medics, he possessed broad aptitude, and hence at university he could have studied subjects within one of a variety of different fields but had chosen medicine. Medicine appealed to him, because it satisfied his own search for understanding and moreover the knowledge gained would be directly used for the betterment of mankind. Medical studies had a way of consuming large volumes of time, yet he managed to maintain an interest in subjects outside his field of learning. He did this in an economical fashion, placing understanding ahead of memorizing trivial details, although he often remembered minutiae nonetheless. He felt that to best understand something one should try to discover the root from reliable facts. After that, it was easy to tag on the finer points as they arrived. Accordingly, Anthony Burrows studied geography and was from Alberta, a province that Sam had visited in Canada. Anthony's Canadian accent was more than adequate for his audience.

Sam found it difficult not to share his faith with his new friends. If it was a different time, then he would have spoken freely. He was convinced that they weren't directly allied with his enemy. His concern was if they were questioned at a later time, especially if he was still in Turkey. Consequently, he kept his conversations superficial and simply enjoyed their company. He hadn't laughed with people his own age for a long time. He met with them for another evening prior to the ship passing through the Bosporus. Whilst in this strait, they'd disembarked at Istanbul. His experience with them strengthened his understanding of why Emin felt that he couldn't leave his native country despite the persecution that he suffered. Somebody had to reach the non-Christians in Turkey, and Emin himself had benefited from someone like his future self when he'd found Christ. In fact, the perseverance of all the Turkish Christians whom Sam had met reminded him of a sermon that he'd heard in church about "neighbours". Jesus tells us to love our neighbours as ourselves. He instructs His followers to love more than just their relatives and friends. Christians should also love those who hate them and persecute them: Christians should pray for, help and bless their enemies. When Jesus was asked by a lawyer to define the term neighbour, He told him about a man who'd been robbed, beaten and left half-dead on the road. The victim's own kin passed him by. The man who eventually helped the victim was of a different religion. This helper cleaned and bound the victim's wounds, carried him to an inn, looked after him there and paid the fee for his stay. Jesus presented this helper as an example of the way that we should behave.[1]

---

[1] Matthew 5:43-48, 19:19, Luke 10:25-37. The main text summarizes the account of the "Good Samaritan" told by Jesus. The victim was presumably a Judaean (a person of Judah*): having travelled from Jerusalem. His helper was a Samaritan. It was the Samaritan's behaviour and attitude toward the victim that Jesus commended, not his religion.

To understand the above passage in Luke properly it is important to understand who the Samaritans were at the time that Jesus told the story. The following relates to the Samaritans from their origin, which was after the Assyrian defeat of Israel (723 BC), up to the time of the writing of the New Testament. The Samaritans were the descendants of different peoples (including from Babylon, Cuthah, Ava, Hamath, Susa, Erech and Sepharvaim, i.e., not Hebrews except for a priest who'd been exiled and then returned, although it's unknown if he had descendants) placed by the Assyrians in Israel after the majority of the Israelites were exiled AND Israelites (Hebrews) who'd escaped the Assyrians. For centuries there was enmity and at least one conflict between the Samaritans and the Judaeans. The Samaritans' worship was contrary to that set forth in the Old Testament, idolatry being one of the transgressions. 2 Kings 17:5-41, 18:9-12, 1 Chronicles 5:18-26, 2 Chronicles 30:6-27, Ezra 4:1-6:13, Matthew 10:5-6, John 4:1-43, Josephus' Jewish Antiquities Book 10 *sections 183-184,* Book 12 *sections 9-10,* Book 13 *sections 74-79,* Book 20 *sections 118-136,* Josephus' The Jewish War Book 2 *sections 232-246.* See Chapter 14 pgs 312-313 and footnotes regarding the so-called "Ten Lost Tribes of Israel" and the
FOOTNOTE CONTINUED ON THE NEXT PAGE

The ship cruised along the northern coast of the Sea of Marmara, then through the Dardanelles. From there the ship followed the western coastline of Turkey, travelling past Troy, Ayvalık and Aliağa. Sam's journey continued for another 50 miles until the ship reached İzmir, the ancient site of Smyrna, where he disembarked. After a brief telephone call and a two hour wait, he was driven to an area near Ephesus.

CONTINUED FOOTNOTE PRESENT

---

fact that all the twelve tribes are still represented in the Jewish people today (*together the main text and the footnotes explain the origin of the people of Judah, Judaeans). See Timeline and Dispensations (5).
Other passages related to neighbours: Mark 12:31, Luke 10:27, Romans 13:9-10, Galatians 5:14.

Chapter 20   **The Ephesian**

The Messiah God existed in the beginning with God the Father and the Spirit of God. They are the Trinity, the three in one who together constitute the Most High God.[1] The Messiah is the part of God who created the universe and everything in it, including Lucifer, who served God in Heaven before his mutiny.[2] It was always the intention of God the Father that the Messiah God would eventually come to Earth as a man.[3] Although the Messiah existed before us, He was born among us: the Son of man and the Son of God.

Satan prefers to be a ruler for a limited time with none above him rather than to be in the service of God for all eternity, no matter how elevated the position he'd been given. Satan made that decision over 6,000 years ago, and we humans have been living with the consequences ever since.

I can only begin to imagine how Satan must have felt when he realized that Jesus the Messiah (Christ) had risen from the dead. Maybe Satan saw the event with his own eyes, or it was reported to him by one or more of his demons. The Bible doesn't say how Satan found out, but it's clear that he knew of the event. Either way, his reaction would have contained anxiety, frustration and a crushing sense of defeat, because Jesus' resurrection is critical to his own eventual demise.

Over the centuries there have been numerous misunderstandings about Satan, many of which I have already identified and corrected. Some believe that Satan doesn't read the Bible. This is yet another misconceived notion. It is evident that he has a profound knowledge of what lies within its pages. Satan even

---

[1] Genesis 1:1-2, Micah 5:2, John 1:1-34, 1 John 5:7, Revelation 1:8-18. See Timeline.

[2] Ezekiel 28:14-16, John 1:1-18, Colossians 1:12-17.

[3] Isaiah 9:6, Daniel 7:13-14, Micah 5:2, John 8:23-59.

quoted a passage during Jesus' temptation by him in the wilderness.[1]

Before Jesus was born, Satan would have read about the Messiah's future in the Old Testament as the individual who would undo his work. Satan would have read about the future character and accomplishments of the Messiah. In particular, he would have discerned two descriptions. The first describes a Messiah who would be born on the Earth as a child yet would be known as the mighty God. He would suffer and be killed, but because He was without sin, His death would take away the sins of the world in one day. He would then rise from the dead and take His place at the right hand of God the Father.[2] These events would defeat death that Satan had brought into the world, because all who believe in this Messiah (Christ) and put their trust in Him will have eternal life with Him after death.[3] The second describes the Messiah as a God King who will come to the Earth as an adult man. This Messiah will defeat the enemies of Israel, then go on to rule the entire Earth from Jerusalem (Zion).[4] Satan knew that the acts of the Messiah within both of these descriptions would be linked to his own downfall.

---

[1] During Jesus Christ's temptation Satan quoted from Psalms 91:11-12 in order that Jesus might recklessly put Himself in mortal danger and to test His authority over the angels, who would save Him. Jesus rebuked Satan with another quote (from Deuteronomy 6:16—for the events at Massah see Exodus 17:1-7), which states that you should not tempt God. Jesus illustrated that Satan's quote was not balanced by other Scriptures and had been applied maliciously. Matthew 4:1-11, Luke 4:1-13.

[2] Psalms 110:1-7, Isaiah 9:6, 53:1-12, Micah 5:2, Zechariah 3:1-10. See Timeline.

[3] John 3:14-16, 5:19-29, 8:51, Romans 5:10-21, 6:3-23, 1 Corinthians 15:3-58, 2 Timothy 1:7-10, Hebrews 2:1-14, Revelation 5:1-14, 20:4-6, 21:1-22:16.

[4] Daniel 7:13-14, Zechariah 14:1-21. See Timeline and Dispensations (6-7).

Before Jesus was born, humans had also read these prophecies. And many people thought these predictions contradictory. These people didn't realize that the prophecies could be explained by two comings of the same Messiah. Needless to say, many preferred the king who reigns and sets all to right over that of the suffering servant. However, the suffering servant was vital, because by suffering and dying the Messiah took away the sins of the entire world, so that if any believe in Him, then they can have eternal life in Heaven.[1]

When the Messiah came to Earth as a human, Satan tried to destroy His mission. Satan used different methods. He tried to invalidate Jesus' existence by tempting Him.[2] If Jesus sinned as a result of Satan's trap, then the Messiah wouldn't have been able to take away the sins of the world, because He would have no longer been a perfect sacrifice. Jesus resisted the temptation. Satan also tried to bring about Jesus' death,[3] because he thought that if he could remove the Messiah, then his own reign would continue either for a longer time or perhaps forever. Satan initially failed but eventually succeeded through his possession of Judas Iscariot, the betrayer of the Messiah.[4] However, it was written that the Messiah would be killed.[5] Indeed, Jesus was

---

[1] Isaiah 53:1-12, Matthew 16:21-23, 17:10-13, Luke 9:22, John 3:13-17, 8:23-59, 10:25-30, 11:25-27, 12:32-37, 14:6, Romans 6:23, 11:26-27, 1 John 3:1-5. Currently Heaven, the home of God, then the New Heaven-New Earth when the old are replaced (see Chapter 7 pg 152 and footnote regarding Heaven).

[2] Matthew 4:1-11, Luke 4:1-13.

[3] Matthew 4:5-7, Luke 4:8-13.
Humans also tried to bring about Jesus' death (Matthew 2:1-20, Luke 4:18-30, John 10:30-39—these instances were unrelated to His crucifixion; Jesus escaped all of these attempts).

[4] Matthew 26:1-27:54, Mark 14:10-15:39, Luke 22:1-23:47, John 13:1-19:38. It is clearly written in all these references that humans assisted in bringing about Jesus' crucifixion.

[5] Isaiah 53:1-12, Daniel 9:26.

aware that it would happen and permitted it.[1] And therefore everything came to pass that had been predicted. Jesus rose from the dead, and Satan was outdone.[2] Jesus is now at the right hand of God the Father.[3] He will return to the Earth in the future as an adult. He will not come into the world again as a baby.

Satan will now also have read the New Testament prophecies that continue in detail beyond the Messiah's victory over the enemies of Israel and after His rule of the Earth from Jerusalem as the God King. According to the New Testament, once Israel's foes are defeated, Jesus will reign as the God King for a thousand years, during which time Satan will be bound in the Abyss. After the thousand years are finished, Satan will be released for a short while and will lead his last rebellion. Satan will then be defeated and cast into the Lake of Fire for all eternity.[4] After this, God will do away with the Heaven and the Earth. He will create a New Heaven and a New Earth. From the New Heaven will descend the New Jerusalem, which will rest on the New Earth. The New Jerusalem is referred to as "the holy city" and "the tabernacle of God", His sanctuary. In other words, the most important part of Heaven will come to Earth. From this vast city, the New Jerusalem, God the Father and God the Son will reign for all eternity. People will literally reside in the New Heaven-New Earth.[5] To trust in Jesus is to look forward to an eternity

---

[1] Matthew 16:21-23, 26:1-68 (*), Mark 8:31-33, 14:1-65 (*), Luke 22:1-71 (*), John 2:19-22.

*Be that as it may, according to Jesus, the man who betrayed Him would have a terrible fate.

[2] Matthew 28:1-20, Mark 16:1-20, Luke 24:1-53, John 20:1-21:25.

[3] Matthew 22:43-46, 26:64, Mark 16:19, Luke 22:69-70, Acts 2:32-33, Romans 8:34, Hebrews 12:2.

[4] Revelation 19:11-20:15. The Abyss is the Bottomless Pit. See Chapter 4 pg 104 and footnote regarding the Abyss. See Timeline and Dispensations (7).

[5] Revelation 21:1-22:16. See Timeline and Dispensations (8).

with Him. Satan knows this, and he will try anything and everything to lead us into the Lake of Fire.[1]

Jesus said that He will come again.[2] Satan knows that the second coming of the Messiah is as the both religiously and secularly triumphant King of kings, the God King, and that this event spells the end of his reign.[3] Satan realizes that he's running out of time. He can feel the threat to his ambitions. Almost 2,000 years ago he saw many of the first Christians (mostly Jews but also some Gentiles) leave Judaea and spread the good news about Jesus. Some of them went from country to country, proclaiming the salvation that comes from Jesus the Messiah to Jews and non-Jews alike, continuing to fulfil the prophecies that the Messiah did not come only for the Jews but would also be a Light to the Gentiles.[4] Both Jewish and Gentile Christians continued forward. Satan feared this Christian movement. He tried to kill the Christians, and in many cases he succeeded. This is still one of the methods he uses today. However, the persecution and subsequent flight of Christians spread the Gospel even further. Nevertheless, Satan has many methods of achieving his goals. He can prevent people from knowing Christ by more than just physical force.

One of Satan's most effective tools is deception. The principle that the most persuasive lie is a combination of truth and lie is fundamental to his deceptions. Satan is the father of lies,[5] who's

---

[1] In front of the Great White Throne the inhabitants of Hell will be judged by God, and then they will be cast into the Lake of Fire: Revelation 20:10-15. The aspect of God who will be the judge is Jesus, because the Bible declares, "For the Father judgeth no man, but hath committed all judgment unto the Son": John 5:22, and read on from 23-30. See footnote further on in this chapter pg 442 regarding judgement by the Messiah. See Soul and Spirit.

[2] Matthew 24:3-31, 26:64, Mark 13:26, John 14:1-3.

[3] 1 Timothy 6:14-16, Revelation 17:14, 19:11-20:2.

[4] Isaiah 42:5-6, 60:1-3.

[5] John 8:44.

been in power for over 6,000 years. He's been able to test and refine his ability while watching many of his lies being propagated through numerous human generations. In order to distract people from the truth, Satan inspired men to create counterfeit churches (institutions) and other religions.[1] These have been some of his greatest deceptions. The churches, the institutions, call themselves Christian but are actually opposed to what is written in the Bible. In this manner, the leaders of these churches use the name of Jesus and other biblical characters, yet these leaders never encourage their followers to read the Bible themselves and independently find out about the individuals inside its covers. The church leaders repeatedly read only a limited number of passages that never contradict these leaders' own doctrines. The result is that the saving truth about Jesus is lost. There are many different so-called Christian churches that fall into this description. Of these, the institutions that come under the general title of Catholicism[2] collectively have the greatest number of adherents. Instead of telling their congregations about the salvation that comes only from Jesus,[3] the church leaders promote idolatry as a way to God, which includes the worship of Mary (Jesus' earthly mother) and the other saints.[4]

---

[1] Satan has achieved this directly, and he has accomplished this indirectly through the demons he commands. See Chapter 13 pg 293 and footnote regarding demons being the inspiration of false religions and receiving the worship. See Chapter 18 pg 385 and footnote regarding demons being the inspiration of false religions on the Earth.

[2] Roman Catholicism and Eastern Orthodoxy (the Orthodox Catholic Church)—the latter has many branches. See Chapter 5 pg 111 and footnote regarding Eastern Orthodoxy.

[3] Regarding salvation through Christ alone, see Chapter 9 pg 213 and Chapter 13 pg 294 and their relevant footnotes.

[4] Being aware of the criticism that praying to Mary and other saints—with or without the assistance of an image (statue or picture)—is idolatry, the Catholic Church proposed that their practice is used to: give honour to the individuals whom the images

FOOTNOTE CONTINUED ON THE NEXT PAGE

The result is that the leaders of these churches and their followers will be condemned to an eternity in the Lake of Fire.[1] So too will

CONTINUED FOOTNOTE PRESENT

---

represent; gain from those deceased individuals intercession with God on the behalf of the living; and receive mercy from those they pray to [α]. All the above is still outright idolatry, for Mary and other saints are not God, cannot receive prayers in Heaven, are unable to intercede for us and have not been given any authority in Heaven to grant us mercy. There is nothing in the Bible to support this Catholic practice and numerous passages against it [β]. Praying to idols of Jesus (which is also promoted by the Catholic Church [α]) is also idolatry. Praying to Jesus is what God the Father wants. Jesus is God, is sinless, died for us (no one else was the perfect sacrifice) and is capable of receiving prayers in Heaven [γ].

[α] The Seven Ecumenical Councils of the Undivided Church: The Seventh Ecumenical Council (787 AD)—*Extracts from the Acts Sessions I, IV; The Decree of the Holy, Great, Ecumenical Synod, the second of Nice.* Within this section of the book, can be found the Excursus on the Present Teaching of the Latin (Roman Catholic—i) and Greek (Eastern Orthodox—ii) Churches on the subject: (i) Decree of the Council of Trent (third convocation) (1562–1563 AD) (*Sess. XXV)* and Catechism of the Council of Trent (1566 AD) *(Question III God and the Saints addressed differently, Question IV In what Manner we may beseech the Saints to have mercy on us)*; and (ii) The Orthodox Confession of the faith of the Catholic and Apostolic Church of the East (1640 AD) (*P. III. Quæstio LII, LIV-LVI).*

[β] Exodus 20:1-6, Leviticus 19:4, 26:1, Numbers 33:51-53, Deuteronomy 29:17, 1 Samuel 15:22-24, 1 Kings 21:26-27, 2 Kings 23:23-25, 2 Chronicles 33:1-11, Habakkuk 2:18-19, 1 Corinthians 10:19-21, 2 Corinthians 6:16-18, Galatians 5:19-21, 1 John 5:21, Revelation 9:20, 22:14-15.

[γ] Psalms 2:1-12, John 1:1-34, 8:2-59, Romans 8:31-39, Hebrews 7:22-8:2, 9:24-28, 10:5-21, Revelation 5:1-14.

[1] Matthew 7:13-29, Luke 13:23-28, 2 Corinthians 11:9-15, 1 John 2:18-29, Revelation 20:11-22:21.

those belonging to the other counterfeit churches and other religions. And this is exactly what Satan wants.

At the time of my writing and for the last approximately 1,600 years, the counterfeit churches (institutions) have globally outnumbered the genuine Christian church (body of true believers with Christ at the head) to such an extent that the true Christians are just a small percentage of what an uninformed statistic would declare to be the total number of Christians in the world. This is evident in that when someone who doesn't understand the Bible thinks of the word Christian, he or she often thinks more about a member of a counterfeit church than one of the true Christians.

Satan has read about Israel's future role in the end times in both the Old and the New Testaments. God has not forgotten Israel. In the end times there will be 144,000 Jewish men who will be specially selected by God the Father to faithfully serve Jesus, the Messiah God, before His second coming near Jerusalem.[1] Israel will also have a central role in the Messiah's Kingdom during His 1,000-year reign.[2] Therefore, Satan thinks that he can also prevent his own demise by obliterating Israel.[3] Throughout history he's repeatedly tried to destroy the Jewish people with devastating consequences. More often than not, Satan has used counterfeit churches, mostly Catholic institutions, to this end. Satan has never fully achieved his genocidal goal and will not.

Sam and Mûsâ hadn't conversed much during the journey. When they did talk, their conversation had been light. Even so, by the time that they'd reached the villa, Sam had worked out that Mûsâ wasn't a Christian.

---

[1] Revelation 7:1-8, 14:1-5.

[2] Deuteronomy 30:1-10, Isaiah 66:15-24, Zechariah 8:1-23.

[3] Meaning the Jewish people, whether living inside or outside the country Israel.

Mûsâ's villa was in a remote place between two notable locations separated by 10 miles: the ruins of ancient Ephesus and the coastal town of Kuşadası. The position of the villa was ideal. It was broad daylight, yet Sam was comfortable that no one had seen him get out of the car and into the villa. He was also at ease with his host, partly because he knew that the House of Hodaviah trusted Mûsâ and also because of his general demeanor. Mûsâ spoke with the battle-hardened frankness of a man who'd overcome tough times on many occasions. Despite these reassurances, Sam still wanted to know how Mûsâ was connected with the House. Mûsâ closed the door of the villa and beckoned Sam down the hallway.

"No, please, after you—it's your home," Sam said.

Mûsâ led Sam to the lounge area. "Would you like a drink? You must be thirsty," Mûsâ said.

"A glass of water would be fine, thank you."

The lounge was furnished with a cotton-cushioned wicker sofa, four similarly styled single-seat chairs and a wooden coffee table. Sam sat on one of the single-seat chairs. The walls were light orange, which gave the room visual warmth. Mûsâ walked to the open-plan kitchen and poured some water into a clear glass tumbler and poured himself a glass of apple juice. He handed the water to his guest. Sam had observed that the kitchen work surfaces were bare and the fridge virtually empty. The villa didn't look lived in.

"Sol Kadmiel is dead," Mûsâ said. "It seems that he was killed a few days ago. I was asked to tell you."

"Murdered, you mean?" Sam was genuinely appalled by the news about Sol Kadmiel, but Sam's voice also betrayed his own concern for himself and the mission.

"Probably, they didn't give me the details."

"You knew him?"

"Barely: we met only once. I knew he had a family."

"I wish I'd known him. How's his family taking it?"

"As I said, I haven't got details."

"Well, he's truly in a better place now."

"Sure."

"Mûsâ, how did you get mixed up in all this?" Sam asked with his own brand of candour.

"You're on a mission for them; you're why Sol Kadmiel was here," Mûsâ replied.

"That's correct."

"You won't be discussing that mission with me. In the same way, I can't discuss my link with them with you."

"True, I won't be discussing the mission, but I still want to know the motivation of my host. All the other contacts here in Turkey have been Christian. You're not. I can tell from some of the comments that you made on the journey here—and just now. Don't get me wrong, I trust some people who aren't Christian and distrust some who say they are. It's just that you're a departure from what I was expecting—particularly considering the mission that I happen to be on. They must have told you who I am. I'd feel more at ease if I knew a little about you."

"The name 'Mûsâ' is Arabic for 'Moses'. In Hebrew it's pronounced Moshe. I'm Jewish."

Before leaving the villa, Mûsâ gave Sam a sealed package that had been left by Sol Kadmiel. It contained maps of Bergama, each issued by a different publisher than the others. In addition, Mûsâ gave Sam provisions and other items. All had been hidden in the villa. Sam diligently studied the maps over a couple of days, noting the subtle differences between them.

Mûsâ was in his early eighties. He and his family lived in Selçuk, which is a village that borders the ancient ruins of Ephesus. From there he still ran his business, selling stationery. Despite his age, he was both physically and mentally fit. The villa was his family's second home. They rarely used it as such and rented it out to tourists in the most popular months. It was close enough to Selçuk for the family to check regularly and maintain when necessary. No one had stayed there since Sam had entered Turkey in case it might be needed. Sam's plan was to remain there for a week, then move on to Bergama. Mûsâ shuttled back and forth from Selçuk to the villa.

Mûsâ and Sam would eat together and talk in the evenings. They both had lots to learn from one another. Sam asked many questions about Jewish history and what it meant to be Jewish. He was often fascinated by the answers and how they related in his own mind to the origin of Christianity. He was equally interested in Mûsâ's life experiences. Mûsâ was born in Cairo. He and his family were driven out of Egypt in 1956 at the time of the Suez Crisis. Mûsâ was a teenager at that time. Instead of following many of his relatives to Israel, he went to live in Turkey. He had an uncle there and joined his business. Although Mûsâ settled in Turkey, he still visited Israel on a number of occasions and had many adventures in parts of North Africa. As for Mûsâ, he was pleased to have further contact with one who called himself a Bible-believing Christian. For many years Mûsâ had noticed distinct differences in the attitudes toward Jewish people and Israel between various groups who call themselves Christian. The opinions of certain groups were, to his mind, often diametrically opposed to those of others. He'd never truly understood why these differences existed, and in the past he'd tried not to think too much about it. However, Sol Kadmiel's brief visit earlier that year had brought the puzzle to the fore, and since then Mûsâ had made his own efforts to find an answer. What both surprised and pleased him about his guest was the deep faith and understanding that Sam had in the entire Bible—the Old and the New Testaments.

On the third evening they'd again eaten together and had taken their conversation with them to the lounge. Both of them were reclined in their respective chairs, facing one another. Mûsâ took off his black plastic reading spectacles, cleaned them and then perched them back on his nose. His tanned skin was only a shade lighter than Sam's. Beneath Mûsâ's grey eyes were small bags, which looked like water-filled sacs. He had a well-trimmed beard and a moustache, both of which were whiter than the hair on his head. An unopened Bible rested on the coffee table. The curtains were closed, covering the lounge's large glass doors, which led to a terrace, which overlooked an orchard.

"I just can't accept that Jesus is God. That's what it says in the New Testament, isn't it?" Mûsâ said.

"That's correct," Sam answered.

"The whole thing just sounds like paganism—that a man can be God," Mûsâ replied. The forthrightness of their first day had continued, and neither took offence at the other's words.

"The New Testament says that the Messiah is God, but this is also found in the Hebrew Old Testament," Sam countered.

"Are you sure?"

"Let's take a look shall we?"

"That's why I brought it," Mûsâ said, reaching for his Bible. "Which book?"

"Let's take a look at Isaiah first. If you go to chapter nine, starting from verse six. Let's read this verse and the one that follows."

Mûsâ's page shuffling ceased. "Here we are."

Mûsâ's Bible contained only the Old Testament. It was printed in Hebrew and had a bordering English translation. Mûsâ also had a copy of the New Testament back in Selçuk. It had been given to him by Sol Kadmiel yet never opened.

Mûsâ started to read:

"For unto us a child is born, unto us a son is given: and the government shall be upon his shoulder: and his name shall be called Wonderful, Counsellor, The mighty God, The everlasting Father, The Prince of Peace. Of the increase of *his* government and peace *there shall be* no end, upon the throne of David, and upon his kingdom, to order it, and to establish it with judgment and with justice from henceforth even for ever. The zeal of the LORD of hosts will perform this."

Mûsâ wanted to say something contradictory but realized that what he'd thought couldn't refute what he'd read. "What's the next one?"

"The next one is about the Messiah appearing near Jerusalem during great turmoil. You can find it in Zechariah chapter fourteen. We'll read from the beginning up to verse sixteen."

Mûsâ began to read again:

"Behold, the day of the LORD cometh, and thy spoil shall be divided in the midst of thee."

"Sorry for interrupting, but can I just confirm with you that where the English reads 'LORD', each letter of the word in the capital form, the Hebrew actually says 'Yahweh'?" Sam asked.

"Yes, that's correct. That's the exclusive name of God. We refer to this word as 'ha Shem', which means 'the Name'," Mûsâ elaborated. "We say this so as to not say the name of God. I recognize this passage already. I read it many times when I was a boy. It's about the Messiah arriving at the Mount of Olives. I'll continue.

"For I will gather all nations against Jerusalem to battle; and the city shall be taken, and the houses rifled, and the women ravished; and half of the city shall go forth into captivity, and the residue of the people shall not be cut off from the city. Then shall the LORD go forth, and fight against those nations, as when he fought in the day of battle. And his feet shall stand in that day upon the mount of Olives, which *is* before Jerusalem on the east, and the mount of Olives shall cleave in the midst thereof toward the east and toward the west, *and there shall be* a very great valley; and half of the mountain shall remove toward the north, and half of it toward the south. And ye shall flee *to* the valley of the mountains; for the valley of the mountains shall reach unto Azal: yea, ye shall flee, like as ye fled from before the earthquake in the days of Uzziah king of Judah: and the LORD my God shall come, *and* all the saints with thee. And it shall come to pass in that day, *that* the light shall not be clear, *nor* dark: But it shall be one day which shall be known to the LORD, not day, nor night: but it shall come to pass, *that* at evening time it shall be light. And it shall be in that day, *that* living waters shall go out from Jerusalem; half of them toward the former sea, and half of them toward the hinder sea: in summer and in winter shall it be. And the LORD shall be king over all the earth: in that day shall there be one LORD, and his name one. All the land shall be turned as a plain from Geba to Rimmon south of Jerusalem: and it shall be lifted up, and inhabited in her place, from Benjamin's gate unto the place of the first gate, unto the corner gate, and *from* the tower of Hananeel unto the king's winepresses. And *men* shall dwell in it, and there shall be no more utter destruction; but Jerusalem shall be safely inhabited. And this shall be the plague wherewith the LORD will smite all the people that have fought against Jerusalem; Their flesh shall consume away while they stand upon their feet, and their eyes shall consume away in their holes, and their tongue shall consume away in their mouth. And it shall come to pass in that day, *that* a great tumult from the LORD shall be among them; and they shall lay hold every one on the hand of his neighbour, and his hand shall rise up against the hand of his neighbour. And Judah also shall fight at Jerusalem; and the wealth of all the heathen round about shall be gathered together, gold, and silver, and apparel, in great abundance. And so shall be the plague of the horse, of the mule, of the camel, and of the ass, and of all the beasts that shall be in these tents, as this plague. And it shall come to pass, *that* every one that is left of all the nations which came against Jerusalem shall even go up from year to year to worship the King, the LORD of hosts, and to keep the feast of tabernacles."

Mûsâ looked up from the text to Sam. "I must have read that a hundred times or more, yet I never properly understood it."

Some of what Sam was about to explain, Mûsâ was already beginning to understand for the first time. "At this coming of the Messiah all the armies of the Gentile nations[1] will have been

---

[1] In Hebrew they are Goyim, who are Gentiles: Zechariah 14:2, 14:3, 14:16.

gathered against Jerusalem to battle. The city will have already been defeated and half of the people taken into captivity. The Messiah will fight against those armies. The passage explains that the Messiah, the LORD, will strike them with a plague that works so rapidly that it will consume their flesh while they're still standing. He will also cause them to be confused and attack one another. On the same day He will stand on the Mount of Olives and be the ruler of the whole Earth. Throughout this chapter the Messiah is repeatedly referred to as Yahweh. He's also referred to as: the King, Yahweh of hosts; and Yahweh my God."

"Let's assume that this is correct. There's a problem. How is it that some passages in the Tanakh (Old Testament) say that the Messiah will come to Earth by being born as a child, yet others indicate that He will come as an adult? The two passages that we've just looked at demonstrate this. I remember reading that He will be born in Bethlehem."[1]

"Because there are two comings. His death and resurrection make this possible. At His first coming He was born. I'm speaking in the past tense, because this coming has been completed. The aim of this coming was to work miracles, teach the people and then die for the sins of the world. He subsequently rose from the dead and later went to Heaven. He will come back, but as an adult. He can be born only once. It will be at this second coming that He will return as the king and judge of all mankind on Earth. The Old and the New Testaments state that the Messiah is God and that He has been alive since everlasting; however, I'm talking about the Messiah's first and second

---

[1] Micah 5:2.

coming as the character of Jesus.[1] Jesus is one hundred percent man and one hundred percent God."[2]

"How is that possible and why?"

"God has made this possible. Why—because He couldn't fulfil His aim of defeating death unless He had a mortal body. He lived amongst us, felt the things that we've felt, suffered the things that we've suffered and experienced temptation over and above anything that we've experienced, but He never sinned. He died, and at His resurrection death was defeated."[3]

"Maybe I should take a look at that New Testament that Sol Kadmiel gave me. I haven't read it, because I've always thought that it's an anti-Semitic work."

"Quite the opposite—all the first disciples were Jewish, as were most of the earliest people to accept Jesus as their Messiah after His death and resurrection. The majority of the books of the New Testament, or perhaps all, were written by God-inspired Jewish men.[4] And there are prophecies about Israel's role toward the end of this age before Jesus returns—plus in the era after His return."

---

[1] Isaiah 9:6-7, Micah 5:2, Matthew 26:63-65, John 1:1-51, 10:24-33, 17:1-5.

[2] See Chapter 8 and footnotes regarding the same topic (pg 185) and God born into this world as mortal flesh to be a true sacrifice for our sins (pg 185).

[3] For examples of Jesus' experiences, including His temptation by Satan, see Chapter 7 pg 155 and footnote regarding Jesus feeling what we've felt.

Jesus did not sin: 2 Corinthians 5:18-21, Hebrews 7:22-28, 9:24-28, 1 Peter 2:21-25, 1 John 3:4-5.

Jesus defeated death: Matthew 27:50-28:20, Mark 15:37-16:20, Luke 23:46-24:53, John 19:30-21:25, Romans 6:3-10, 1 Corinthians 15:3-58, 2 Timothy 1:7-10, Hebrews 2:1-14, Revelation 1:17-18.

[4] Luke the physician, God-inspired author of the books Luke and Acts, was possibly a Gentile.

"If Jesus is the Jewish Messiah, why is it that so many Jews have been persecuted and killed over the centuries by His followers, who call themselves Christians? I'm referring to the Crusades, the Inquisition, the Pogroms in Russia, and the Holocaust. Hitler was born into a Catholic family, as were most of the other leaders of the Nazi Party. Even in your country, we were expelled in the thirteenth century."

"Please define those Christians more closely for me."

"Followers of Roman Catholicism and Eastern Orthodoxy.[1] They blame us for the death of Christ. This is always the accusation that they use to justify what they do to us."

---

[1] One must separate the original term "the Catholic Church" from the institution "the Catholic Church".

The original term "the Catholic Church", potentially applicable between 33 AD and 312 AD, simply means the general or universal (catholic) group of believers (church) with the same faith in Christ.

The institution called "the Catholic Church", which developed from the time of Constantine I's reign, the name being potentially applicable from 312 AD onward, contains ornate churches, extreme material wealth and the worship of beings who are not God, which together are combined with some features of New Testament Christianity and Old Testament priestly hierarchy. The Catholic Church is characterized by: the worship of statues, icons, angels, Mary and other saints; the belief that the Jewish people are mostly responsible for the death of Christ rather than every human being on the Earth whether Jewish or Gentile, each individual being as responsible as the next; doctrines, dogmas and laws that are not endorsed by the Bible, such as (i) celibacy of clerics (Roman Catholicism—all priests; and Eastern Orthodoxy—bishops and higher positions) (the Bible in fact denounces this—1 Timothy 4:1-3), (ii) transubstantiation (in Roman Catholicism) and sacramental change (in Eastern Orthodoxy), which are doctrines that the communion bread and wine are literally converted into the body and blood of Christ rather than merely being a representation of His sacrifice so that we can remember what He has done for us (Jesus could not be in three places, in His own body and in the bread and
FOOTNOTE CONTINUED ON THE NEXT PAGE

"Just because someone calls himself a thing, does it mean that he is that thing?" Sam asked.

"No."

"As defined by the New Testament, they aren't Christians. Even the Old Testament gives us an indication of how future followers of the Messiah would behave—absolutely the opposite of Catholic Christians."

"Why aren't they Christians?"

"For a start, to be a Christian is to accept that Jesus died for your sins. The Bible makes it clear that He died for the sins of the entire world: both for those people at the time of His death and for people in the future. One of the signs of false Christianity is that the leaders and members of those churches, institutions, lay the blame on the Jewish people, taking little, if any, responsibility for the death of Jesus. He died for me. I'm responsible for Jesus' death along with the rest of the world—all nations without exception. If I never sinned, then I wouldn't need Him to die for

CONTINUED FOOTNOTE PRESENT

---

wine, and therefore was speaking symbolically about the bread and wine being His body and blood respectively—Matthew 26:26-29, Mark 14:22-25, Luke 22:19-20, 1 Corinthians 11:23-26), (iii) the doctrine that priests can forgive sins (only God can do this—Leviticus 6:7, 19:22, Psalms 85:1-2, 130:1-8; Jesus forgives sins because He is God—Matthew 9:2-8, Luke 5:20-26, Luke 7:44-50, Acts 26:15-18, Ephesians 1:5-7), and (iv) the doctrine, specifically in the Roman Catholic Church, that the decrees of the pope are on par with biblical truth (papal infallibility)—even when they contradict the Bible. The institution did not contain all these features from its beginning, but they were accumulated and adapted over time. 312 AD can be considered as the year of the institution's birth.

The Catholic Church meaning the institution has eclipsed the original term the Catholic Church meaning the general group of believers with the same faith (complete trust) in Christ, for there is no faith in Christ in the institution. There was a period of overlap for perhaps as much as 100 years, i.e., from 312 AD to around 412 AD.

me. Everyone except Jesus has sinned, so He needed to die for us all."[1]

"But does the New Testament say that He died at the hands of my ancestors?"

"Yes, it does and also at the hands of the Romans.[2] The Old Testament states: that the Messiah would die;[3] that He would be Jewish from the line of King David;[4] and that He would be born, live and preach in places where your ancestors lived.[5] Most of those places are now within the borders of modern Israel. The Old Testament declares that He would walk in the Temple in Jerusalem.[6] In the light of these facts, where do you think that He'd die?"

"Specifically, in Judaea, much of which is now within modern Israel."

"Correct; however, we don't need to dwell on this, because one of the signs of true Christianity is that we believe the Bible. It says that Jesus is not dead but alive and at the right hand of God the Father. It says this in the New Testament.[7] In the Old Testament there are prophecies that the Messiah would die for the sins of the world, then rise from the dead.[8] And this is exactly what happened. Therefore, why mourn over Him as if He's lost to the world. He's alive. He's the one who died for you and me, so that if we believe and trust in Him, then we can have salvation

---

[1] Isaiah 53:1-12, Romans 3:22-26, 1 Corinthians 15:1-8, Galatians 1:3-5, Hebrews 9:28, 1 Peter 2:21-25, 1 John 2:1-2, 4:9-10, Revelation 1:5.

[2] Matthew 26:1-27:54, Mark 14:10-15:39, Luke 22:1-23:47, John 13:1-19:38, Acts 2:22-43.

[3] Isaiah 53:1-12, Daniel 9:26.

[4] Jeremiah 23:5-6.

[5] Isaiah 9:1-2, 61:1-3, Micah 5:2.

[6] Malachi 3:1.

[7] Mark 16:19, Acts 2:32-33, 7:55-60, Romans 8:34, Hebrews 12:2.

[8] Psalms 16:10, Isaiah 53:1-12, Daniel 9:26.

from everlasting torment and eternal life with Him and God the Father."

"And what of those Old Testament indications of how future followers of the Messiah would behave?"

"The Old Testament predicted that they would be people who make a covenant with God in their hearts, put their trust in His Son and obey the Word of God."[1]

Mûsâ made no comment on Sam's last answer. "So where does Catholicism come from? To us Jewish people, from the outside, it appears that its members are worshipping idols—and mere men and women. They call themselves Christians. How come they don't stick to the Bible in the way that your brand of Christianity does?"

"To best answer that, we have to look at the origins of the Catholic churches. Tell me, what name do the religious heads of the Roman Catholic Church call themselves?"

"The pope."

"That's true, but can you think of another?"

"The pontifex maximus."

"Let's take a close look at that title. Did you know that it existed for hundreds of years before the birth of Jesus?"

"No, I didn't."

"The pontifex maximus was the chief priest of the pagan religion of ancient Rome. This religion included the worship of many different gods such as Jupiter[2] (Zeus) and Mars[3] (Ares). The pontifex maximus oversaw everything from the creation of

---

[1] Genesis 22:18, Deuteronomy 30:1-6, Psalms 2:12, Isaiah 40:3-5, Jeremiah 4:4.

[2] King of the gods, identified with the Greek god Zeus. See Chapter 13 pg 290 and footnote regarding Jupiter, king of the gods.

[3] God of war, identified with the Greek god Ares. He was reportedly a son of Zeus (Jupiter). Hesiod's Theogony *lines 921-923, 933-937* (Ares, a defeater of battle lines in war), Homer's Iliad Book 5 *lines 846-908* (Ares, described as a god devoted to battles), Apollodorus' The Library Book 1 *chapter 3:1,* Hyginus' Theogony *20.*

religious laws to the punishment of those who broke them, whether they were priests or private citizens. As a judge, he administered the laws, the interpretation of which was in his hands. Not surprisingly, in religious matters he could neither be prosecuted nor punished and was not answerable to the Senate. He held the office for life and had the most powerful role of any single individual in the republic.[1] The Roman Republic started at around 500 BC, but the office of the pontifex maximus had its origin even before then. Before the republic, Rome was ruled by a series of kings—seven in all. The second king, Numa Pompilius, created the position of 'pontifex', high priest, which was held by a man who had similar authority and widely encompassing religious duties to the future pontifex maximus, also high priest."[2]

"What does pontifex maximus mean?"

"The word pontifex literally means 'bridge-builder'. It seems that the early high priests of Rome, the pontifices, conducted

---

[1] In addition to his duties already written in the main text, his responsibilities included overseeing the dedication of temples and the discipline of the Vestal Virgins. References for all the above: Dionysius of Halicarnassus' Roman Antiquities Book 2 *chapter 73:1-4*, Book 3 *chapter 67:2-4*, Plutarch's Lives Numa *chapters 9:4-12:2*, Livy's History of Rome Book 3 *chapter 54:1-15*, Book 4 *chapter 44:11-12*, Book 8 *chapter 9:1-8*, Book 9 *chapter 46:5-8*, Book 22 *chapter 10:1-10*, Book 27 *chapter 8:4-7*, Book 28 *chapter 11:5-7*, Book 37 *chapter 51:1-7*, Dio Cassius' History of Rome Book 49 *chapter 15:3-4*, Book 54 *chapter 27:1-3*.

[2] Numa Pompilius (reigned 715–673 BC) was the king who ruled after Romulus (founder of Rome): Livy's History of Rome Book 1 *chapters 20:1-7, 32:1-3*, Dionysius of Halicarnassus' Roman Antiquities Book 2 *chapter 73:1-2*, Plutarch's Lives Numa *chapter 9:1* (Plutarch mentioned that Numa was reportedly the first of these high priests, therefore being both king and high priest).

For a proposed, much earlier year of commencement of the office of the pontifex maximus see Chapter 24 pg 544 and footnote regarding Julius Caesar and the Julian clan.

sacrifices at a sacred wooden bridge, which spanned the River Tiber, and this is how some think their name came about.[1] Alternatively, I suspect that it means that the high priests were believed to be people who built bridges between the gods and men; that is to say, the high priests were mediators between the gods and men. At some point the title pontifex stopped being the exclusive name for only the high priest, and it was then used to refer to any one member of a group of specially selected priests . . ."

"And to distinguish the high priest, the 'maximus' was added to indicate that he was the greatest of these individuals, these priests,"[2] Mûsâ said.

---

[1] Plutarch's Lives Numa *chapter 9:1-4*. Plutarch related that he was unsure of the exact derivation of the title pontifex. He was highly sceptical that the pontifices could be named after their sacrifices at the bridge. He preferred the opinion of some that within the word pontifex is the Latin word for "potent" and that this expressed the pontifices' priestly duties to the potent (mighty) gods. Dionysius concurred with Plutach in that Numa initiated the high-priestly office but wrote that the name pontifices was derived from the fact that they had the duty of repairing the bridge and simultaneously conducting sacrifices if it was ever damaged. However, Dionysius stated that this bridge was constructed by Ancus Marcius (Dionysius of Halicarnassus' Roman Antiquities Book 2 *chapter 73:1-2*, Book 3 *chapter 45:1-2*). Ancus was the fourth king of Rome (reigned 640–617 BC) and grandson of Numa (reigned 715–673 BC), which reveals a chronological error in Dionysius' reasoning, in general highlighted by Plutarch, unless the high-priestly office originally had a different name that was later replaced by the title pontifex.

[2] The high priest being referred to as "pontifex" then later "pontifex maximus" is evidenced by ancient authors: Plutarch moved seamlessly from referring to the high priest as pontifex to pontifex maximus, chief of the pontifices (Plutarch's Lives Numa *chapter 9:1-4*); there were multiple pontifices in 304 BC (probably four at this time—exact number not stated but see 300 BC below) and their

FOOTNOTE CONTINUED ON THE NEXT PAGE

"Exactly, he was their leader, the chief priest. Julius Caesar[1] recognized the power of the pontifex maximus. It was Julius Caesar's dictatorship that played a key role in bringing an end to the republic. During his rise to supreme power he must have realized that no matter how powerful his position in military or other secular affairs, he could potentially be brought down by the head of Rome's religion: such was the pontifex maximus' influence over the people. Consequently, Caesar ran for and was elected to the role of pontifex maximus and held it until his death.[2] His adopted son, Augustus,[3] the first Roman emperor

CONTINUED FOOTNOTE PRESENT

---

leader was the pontifex maximus (Livy's History of Rome Book 9 *chapter 46:1-8*); there were four pontifices in 300 BC and the number increased to eight that same year (Livy's History of Rome Book 10 *chapters 6:1-9:2*); at some point the group became known as the college of pontifices (known as this in 204 BC—Livy's History of Rome Book 29 *chapter 20:9-10*); and the system continued, wherein pontifex was used to refer to any one member of the group of pontifices and the leader was the pontifex maximus (183 BC—Livy's History of Rome Book 39 *chapter 46:1-2*).

[1] Lived 100–44 BC.

[2] Dio Cassius' Roman History Book 37 *chapter 37:1-3*, Book 44 *chapter 17:2-3*, Plutarch's Lives Caesar *chapter 7:1-4*.

After Julius Caesar's murder, the office of the pontifex maximus first went to Lepidus, one of the Second Triumvirate, which included Mark Antony and Octavian (future Augustus Caesar, emperor), who together with Lepidus defeated Julius Caesar's assassins. Lepidus held the position till his death. Dio Cassius' Roman History Book 44 *chapters 52:1-53:7*, Livy's History of Rome Summaries Book 117.

The next pontifex maximus was Augustus Caesar. See what follows in this chapter and footnote regarding Augustus being elected to the role of pontifex maximus.

[3] Augustus Caesar (lived 63 BC–14 AD). His birth name was Gaius Octavius. Today the man before taking the title Augustus in 27 BC is often referred to as Octavian. Although Octavian was adopted by

FOOTNOTE CONTINUED ON THE NEXT PAGE

following the republic, was also elected to the role.[1] From the time of Augustus—and for a long while—the titles and offices of emperor and pontifex maximus were indivisible."

"How does that get us to today's position?"

"It was during the rule of the emperor Tiberius, which ended in 37 AD, that Jesus was crucified. The Christian movement spread to Asia Minor, northern Africa, Syria, Greece, Spain and Gaul—all parts of the Roman Empire. It also spread to Rome itself. Throughout the Roman Empire, but especially in Rome, Christianity was persecuted, often with torture and death.[2] One of the

CONTINUED FOOTNOTE PRESENT

Julius Caesar, they were related. Augustus' maternal grandmother was Julius' sister.

[1] Dio Cassius' Roman History Book 54 *chapter 27:1-3*, Book 55 *chapter 12:5*.

[2] A few of many examples from Eusebius' Ecclesiastical History: in Rome Nero was the instigator of mass killings of Christians (Book 2.25:1-5); the martyrs of Smyrna (including Polycarp), some of whom were whipped so that their internal organs were visible (Book 4.15:1-39); the martyrs of Gaul, some of whom endured prolonged torture before being killed (Book 5.1:1-63); in Caesarea a rich Roman military man of high rank called Marinus was beheaded for adhering to Christianity and not engaging in emperor worship (Book 7.15:1-5); and an entire Phrygian town (in Asia Minor) was burnt with the occupants inside, because they professed Christianity and eschewed idolatry (Book 8.11:1).

Eusebius' Ecclesiastical History and Life of Constantine are valuable historical documents regarding events of the early Christian Church and the life of the emperor Constantine I. However, these books also relay to us that Eusebius, the bishop of Caesarea, revered the relics of Christian martyrs (relics are the dead remains of individuals deemed special and objects that they had had close contact with) and wholeheartedly embraced the changes to the church brought about by Constantine, including the rapid acquisition of abundant material wealth. Neither did he criticize Constantine's promotion of saint worship and institutional anti-Semitism.
FOOTNOTE CONTINUED ON THE NEXT PAGE

main reasons for the persecutions, frequently initiated by the emperors, was that the Christians had rejected the immortal gods of the Romans' ancestors, of whom Jupiter (Zeus) was the head.[1] The Christians would neither worship nor offer sacrifices to the idols of these gods, and as a consequence many were killed as punishment. Yet their numbers continued to grow. Sadly the church itself had some internal problems. There are recorded disputes over matters of doctrine. However, it was vital that many of the disputes took place, as they were countering false doctrines that were emerging within the church.[2] As made clear

CONTINUED FOOTNOTE PRESENT

Ecclesiastical History Book 2.25:5-8, Book 10.4:1-72, Life of Constantine Book 3.18:1-20:1, Book 4.58-60:5, Book 4.71:2.
Eusebius was also a supporter of the incorrect doctrine of Arius, demonstrated in the Documents of the Early Arian Controversy: documents 4, 9, 10, 15, 20 and 24 (for referencing of documents see Bibliography). See Chapter 11 pgs 253-255 and relevant footnotes.
[1] Read within Eusebius' Ecclesiastical History: the proconsul's declaration and the mob's shouts before the martyrdom of Polycarp (Book 4.15:18-28); the edict of the emperor Galerius (Book 8.17:1-11); the broadcasting by the prefect Sabinus of the resolution of the self-proclaimed emperor Maximinus (Book 9.1:1-6); the full account regarding the curator of Antioch called Theotecnus, who built a statue to Zeus and drove the Christians away, claiming that they were enemies of this god—acts approved by the emperor Maximinus (Book 9.2:1-4:3); and the emperor Maximinus' Tablet at Tyre against Christianity (Book 9.7:3-16).
[2] During the period of the apostles there was a dispute over whether Gentile believers in Christ should be circumcised or not (Acts 14:27-15:32). The problem was that some had declared that without circumcision the Gentiles cannot receive salvation. This was resolved at that time, and it was declared that they do not need to be circumcised; however, the issue recurred. The Galatians had received people who were subverting the Gospel of Christ by preaching that for salvation it is necessary to be circumcised (Galatians 1:1-6:18). Paul appealed to the Galatians that salvation is
FOOTNOTE CONTINUED ON THE NEXT PAGE

in the Old and New Testaments, there are those who mix with the faithful with the intention of drawing believers away from God.[1] It was during the reign of Constantine I that a new religion was born. He reigned from 312–337 AD.[2] This new religion, which developed with time, became an amalgamation of the Roman worship of the pantheon of gods with Christianity. The idolatrous worship of the so-called gods Jupiter, Mars, Mercury, and the like were replaced with St Peter, St Paul and other apostles. And the cults of the mother goddess Cybele and other goddesses were replaced with St Mary."

"How did it happen?"

CONTINUED FOOTNOTE PRESENT

---

through faith in Jesus and that neither circumcision nor uncircumcision would benefit anyone further with Christ beyond His gift of salvation.

After the period of the apostles, false doctrines were also opposed within the church (between around 100 AD and 300 AD); examples of such are as follows (references to Eusebius' Ecclesiastical History). Menander claimed that he was the saviour sent from above to bestow immortality on those who believed in him. Whilst preaching this, he professed Christianity. Book 3.26:1-4. Saturninus' doctrine was similar to that of Menander. Carpocrates held magical rituals, which included performing incantations to call forth familiar spirits. He taught that only by engaging in these rituals can a person avoid certain perils on Earth. While Saturninus and Carpocrates spread their doctrines, they professed Christianity. Book 4.7:1-14. Artemon, while professing Christianity, claimed that Jesus was only a man (and not simultaneously God) and that this doctrine had been preached by the apostles: Book 5.28:1-6. Paul of Samosata, the bishop of Antioch, espoused the doctrine that Christ was only a man: Book 7.27:1-30:19.

[1] Exodus 32:1-35, Ezekiel 22:18-31, Matthew 7:15-29, Acts 20:28-31.

[2] See footnote in Chapter 5 pg 114 regarding "the city of Constantine" for details regarding the years of Constantine I's reign.

"In the period just before Constantine officially became emperor the Christians had suffered some of the worst persecution that they'd experienced in their almost three hundred-year-history.[1] Constantine was the first emperor to boldly profess Christianity, and not surprisingly he was almost unconditionally embraced by the church, especially its leaders.[2] However, Constantine did many things that were contrary to biblical Christianity,[3] which

---

[1] The Roman emperors were the chief instigators of this period of persecution, the first wave of which was initiated by Diocletian in 303 AD. The relevant emperors are as follows: Diocletian, emperor of the East (reigned 284–305 AD); Galerius, emperor of the East (reigned 305–311 AD); Maximinus, emperor of part of the East (reigned 308–313 AD); and Maximian, emperor of the West (reigned 286–305 AD). Maxentius, emperor of the West (reigned 306–312 AD), can perhaps also be included. He initially feigned Christianity early in his reign in order to obtain favour from the people of Rome (there clearly being a significant proportion of Christians present at that time), but then toward the same city he became an indiscriminate murdering tyrant and was revealed to be an adherent of witchcraft. Eusebius' Ecclesiastical History Book 7.30:22-Book 9.11:8.

[2] Eusebius (bishop of Caesarea), from Book 9.9:1 of his Ecclesiastical History to the end (Book 10.9:9) and throughout the 4 books of his Life of Constantine, extols the virtues of Constantine I and promotes him as the champion of the Christian Church.
At the Council of Nicaea in 325 AD, attended by over 250 bishops, Constantine was seated on a gold chair and headed the meeting; indeed, it was he who had summoned the clerics because of their disputes: Eusebius' Life of Constantine Book 3.4-14.

[3] The Old Testament books accepted as Holy Scripture, which we have today, were well recognized at the time of Constantine I. The books of the New Testament accepted as Holy Scripture, which we have today, were split into two groups by Eusebius in around 311 AD*: (i) recognized; and (ii) highly regarded (in that they were widely read and well respected but there was still discord as to whether or not they are Holy Scripture). The books were in the two

FOOTNOTE CONTINUED ON THE NEXT PAGE

should have been criticized.[1] For instance, on defeating Maxentius, a tyrannical ruler of Rome, when Constantine entered the city, his first act was to build a statue of himself with a cross in one hand and an inscription that stated that with this sign he'd saved the city from a tyrant, thereby immediately combining Christianity with idolatry.[2] Emperor worship was so widespread in the Roman Empire that this act would have served only to promote it further. Constantine could not have been innocent or ignorant of this, as even his own father, the emperor Constantius Chlorus, had been deified.[3] The following year Constantine

CONTINUED FOOTNOTE PRESENT

---

groups as follows: (i) Matthew, Mark, Luke, John, Acts, Romans, 1 & 2 Corinthians, Galatians, Ephesians, Philippians, Colossians, 1 & 2 Thessalonians, 1 & 2 Timothy, Titus, Philemon, 1 Peter, 1 John and Revelation; and (ii) Hebrews, James, 2 Peter, 2 & 3 John, and Jude. Put another way, there were those who correctly recognized that all the above listed books are Holy Scripture and used them as such, but some people disagreed. The choosing of the collection of books as Holy Scripture that make up the Old and New Testaments is as inspired by God as the words within each book. Eusebius was a doubter, evident in his approach. Eusebius' Ecclesiastical History Book 3.24:17-25:7.

*311 AD is the approximate year of the earliest book written by Eusebius within his Ecclesiastical History.

[1] The Bible demonstrates that it was not beyond men of God to criticize rulers. Some rulers responded well (e.g., King David) and others poorly (e.g., Herod the Tetrarch). 2 Samuel 11:1-12:25, Matthew 14:1-12. Other examples: 1 Samuel 15:1-35, 1 Kings 21:1-29.

[2] 312 AD. Eusebius' Ecclesiastical History Book 9.9:9-11, Life of Constantine Book 1.39:1-41:2.

[3] Constantius Chlorus was deified after his death (died in 306 AD): Eusebius' Ecclesiastical History Book 8.13:12-13.

Constantine I's understanding and behaviour in this regard did not improve. Later in his reign (after 324 AD) he had a statue of himself erected in Constantinople, into which he placed wood that was

FOOTNOTE CONTINUED ON THE NEXT PAGE

issued an edict of toleration, so that his subjects were free to worship whatever religion they wished,[1] but he then contradicted the spirit of this ruling by promoting to high office mostly Christians. Those similarly elevated who were non-Christians he did not permit to sacrifice to the traditional Roman gods.[2] This would have resulted in a multiplicity of responses, which included people feigning Christianity for worldly advancement.[3] Having no genuine incentive to follow the doctrine of the Bible, fertile ground for error, many would have been unwilling to give up their old gods and the manner in which they worshipped them. Therefore, a combination of Christianity and idolatry emerged in which prayers were made to many rather than to one. This would have been compounded by the fact that Constantine then issued a general prohibition that forbade sacrifices to the traditional Roman gods,[4] and later in his reign he commenced the destruc-

CONTINUED FOOTNOTE PRESENT

---

reputedly from the cross of Christ. Socrates Scholasticus Book 1 *chapter 18 The Emperor's Mother Helena having come to Jerusalem, searches for and finds the Cross of Christ, and builds a church.* Indeed, Constantine's desire that people worship him deteriorated even further and continued to his death (see further on in this chapter pg 426).

[1] Known as the Edict of Milan (313 AD), which was issued by Constantine I and Licinius (Eastern emperor). It did more than grant religious freedom (for individuals to worship in accordance with their own desires); the issuers also stated that they gave this liberty, so that their desire would be fulfilled that all the gods that people prayed to would assist the Roman Empire. Neither man understood Christianity. Eusebius' Ecclesiastical History Book 10.5:1-14.

[2] Eusebius' Life of Constantine Book 2.44.

[3] During Constantine I's reign some people feigned Christianity as part of an overall masquerade of loyalty to him, presumably to gain positions of power: Eusebius' Life of Constantine Book 4.54:2-3.

[4] This was one major aspect of a law that Constantine I enacted against religions that he didn't agree with: Eusebius' Life of Constantine Book 2.45:1.

tion of the statues, shrines and temples of this polytheistic religion.[1] Christianity should not be imposed. To follow Jesus is a personal choice. Neither should there be any financial enticement. If people want to follow another path, that's up to them—and their religion should be tolerated."

"And what did Constantine do to the Christian Church itself?"

"In response to the fact that many churches were destroyed by the persecution that preceded his reign, Constantine not only used the imperial funds to rebuild churches[2], but he over-compensated by dedicating vast sums of money, from the imperial funds and his own pocket, so that many churches could be enlarged—or built anew on a grander scale—and be made visual spectacles of ornate craftsmanship.[3] Furthermore, he gave money directly to bishops,[4] and the practice of having thrones in

---

[1] Eusebius' Life of Constantine Book 3.1:5, Book 3.54:1-58:4.

[2] Eusebius' Life of Constantine Book 2.45:2-46:4, Eusebius' Ecclesiastical History Book 10.2:1.
Constantine I also ensured that the churches (places of assembly) be restored to their rightful owners if during persecution they were seized (even if additionally given away or sold), which was in itself a good action by him: Eusebius' Ecclesiastical History Book 10.5:9-17.

[3] Eusebius' Ecclesiastical History Book 10.2:1, Eusebius' Life of Constantine Book 1.42:2, Book 2.45:2-46:4, Book 3.47:4-50:2.
Constantine I also financed new grand churches (see last reference).

[4] Eusebius' Ecclesiastical History Book 10.2:2. It is proper to judiciously give donations to ministers who preach in a single church or wander from church to church; however, in Eusebius' time bishops were a major part of a hierarchical clerical system, which is against Jesus' plan for the Christian Church. Giving money to bishops encouraged something that was wrong with the Church. Acts 4:32-37, 1 Corinthians 9:1-18, see Chapter 21 pgs 446-448 and the four accompanying footnotes regarding the doctrine of the Nicolaitans.

churches for high-ranking ministers was started[1]—ministers then additionally called priests.[2] Consequently, the church rapidly became materially very wealthy, as did its leaders, which is not the way the church should be, made clear in the New Testament.[3] With regard to idolatry, he built huge shrines to revere prominent

---

[1] Eusebius' Ecclesiastical History Book 10.4:1-68. This reference mentions thrones for leading clerics in a newly built basilica in Tyre.

Eusebius states that James, a brother of Jesus, had a church-related throne; however, this is undoubtedly a fiction used to justify the later thrones during Eusebius's time: Ecclesiastical History Book 7.19:1.

[2] The title of priest was added after the start of Constantine I's financial injection into church-related buildings—ministers earlier being referred to as such or as pastors: Eusebius' Ecclesiastical History: Book 3.36:5, Book 6.43:2, Book 7.3:1, 7.27:2-30:2, Book 8.1:1-2:3, 8.13:3, Book 10.3:1-4, 10.4:1-2.

Regarding an event before the defeat of Maxentius, in Eusebius' Life of Constantine (Book 1.32.3) ministers are referred to as priests; however, this work was completed later than the Ecclesiastical History (around 337 AD and around 324 AD respectively) and the author, being later accustomed to refer to ministers as priests, had clearly lost when in time the title priest was added.

A minister being called a pastor is valid (Ephesians 4:7-12), whereas a minister being called a priest in order to distinguish him from his congregation is not (see footnote in Chapter 21 pg 448 regarding hierarchical clerical systems damaging churches).

[3] Matthew 6:19-24 demonstrates that Christians should not be laying up earthly treasures and that we cannot serve both God and wealth (mammon), for ultimately we shall despise one and love the other. 1 Timothy 6:3-11 shows us that Christians should: avoid those who claim that earthly wealth follows godliness; be content with food and clothing; understand that those who seek to be rich will be caught up in senseless and harmful desires that lead to destruction; and understand that the root of all evil is greed, which leads to grief and errors in faith.

dead Christians (many of whom were martyrs)—individuals who dedicated their lives so that people could focus on Jesus' gift of salvation and who wouldn't have wished for the spotlight to be taken off their saviour and onto them.[1] Contrary to the way of the Bible, due to Constantine's influence and example, he was almost certainly the initiator of the trend of constructing statues of biblical characters."[2]

"I'm getting the picture. He was denying the people their right to worship their own gods and was simultaneously replacing them with others. He was clearly an idolater and recognized that his subjects would more readily accept Christianity if he replaced their religion with another that had a similar system of worship."

"Constantine was also extremely anti-Semitic, demonstrated in his universal letter sent to the churches after the council of Nicaea, claiming that the Jewish people were the killers of Christ, their nation rejected and that the churches should have

---

[1] Eusebius' Life of Constantine Book 3.47-48:1, Book 4.58-60:5. Places were also revered such as the reputed site of the tomb of Christ (the Holy Sepulcher) and a specific site believed to be Mamre, where the Messiah appeared to Abraham (Genesis 18:1-33) before He came to Earth as Jesus; at Constantine I's order both sites had newly constructed basilicas connected with them. The former place is still frequently visited and greatly revered. It is the Messiah who should be revered, not the places where He might have lain or stood. Book 3.25-40, Book 3.51.1-53.4.

[2] Constantine I's influence was tremendous, as was the example that he set for his subjects in his empire. The statue specifically mentioned related to Constantine was of the biblical character Daniel. It was a bronze statue covered in gold leaf with lions similarly constructed and adorned. Eusebius' Life of Constantine Book 3.49. Although this reference doesn't mention that anybody worshipped the statue, its construction was still contrary to what is written in the Bible regarding making graven images. Before long images of biblical characters became widespread, and many images of characters from the New Testament began to be worshipped.

nothing in common with them.[1] Before Constantine's death, he built a massive ornate shrine to the twelve apostles in Constantinople containing twelve memorial tombs (sepulchers), one for each apostle. Six were on either side of his own intended grave. His intention was that when people came to the shrine to worship the apostles, he too would receive this worship as well as the prayers to them.[2] He obviously wasn't a true Christian."

"And did they put him in this grave when he died."

"Yes, they did."[3]

Mûsâ motioned for Sam to continue.

"And this was just the beginning of the new religion. I'm sure that some genuine Christians would have left, unable to accept the changes, continuing in their faith outside of this organized religion. You see, true Christianity follows what the Bible says: that salvation is through the Messiah alone.[4] The true Christians who remained, hoping for this religion to revert back to the previous state, would have either been marginalized and then ejected or cowardly suppressed their own faiths for the new emerging alternative. The false Christians, including many freshly drawn to the new religion, would have increased in relative comfort. As each subsequent generation arose, the general population would have either met or been brought up in

---

[1] Eusebius' Life of Constantine Book 3.16-20:2.

[2] Eusebius' Life of Constantine Book 4.58-60:5, Book 4.71:2. The words used regarding people's behaviour toward the apostles are worship, invoke and honour. The first two are direct evidence of a belief that the apostles receive prayers. The apostles can neither receive nor answer prayers.

[3] Eusebius' Life of Constantine Book 4.69:1-70:2, Ecclesiastical History of Socrates Scholasticus Book 1 *chapter 40 The Funeral of the Emperor Constantine,* Ecclesiastical History of Sozomen Book 2 *chapter 34 Death of Constantine the Great; he died after Baptism and was buried in the Temple of the Holy Apostles.*

[4] John 14:6, Acts 4:10-12, Colossians 1:13-20, 1 Thessalonians 5:9-10, Hebrews 2:9-10.

the deception of the new religion (sponsored by the Roman Empire[1]), which still carried the name of Christianity.[2] Attracting people to or holding them by the truths that remained and the falsehoods that no longer made it Christianity, the religion was a huge success. The new religion was Catholicism,[3] that is, the institution known as the Catholic Church[4]—in an early form. In 379 or 380 AD the office of the pontifex maximus was refused by the emperor Gratian when it was ceremonially offered to him.[5] By 381 AD the title pontifex had been taken up by the head

---

[1] After Constantine I, the majority of emperors supported Catholicism in its various doctrinally shifting forms. His nephew Julian was a notable exception, who promoted the old Roman gods.

[2] The adherents to Catholicism called themselves Christians as Catholics do today.

[3] The universal religion of Catholic Christianity.

[4] See footnote earlier in this chapter pg 410 that differentiates the original term "the Catholic Church" from the institution "the Catholic Church". The year of the birth of the institution known as the Catholic Church can be considered to be 312 AD (the beginning of Constantine I's reign). The institution developed from that time onward.

[5] Zosimus' New History Book 4 *section 36*.

Gratian was emperor from 367–383 AD. The office of pontifex maximus would have undoubtedly accompanied his accession to emperorship (the office of pontifex maximus being shared with the emperors Valentinian and Valens); however, only later, perhaps when a suitable opportunity presented itself, was the office of pontifex maximus ceremonially offered to him by the traditional pontifices. 379 and 380 AD are the possible years for Gratian's refusal (actually a discarding) of the office of pontifex maximus, because at the beginning of 379 AD he was still pontifex maximus* and by referring to Damasus, bishop of Rome, as a pontifex in an edict of 380 AD‡, Gratian was slighting the traditional pontifices and would have no longer been their chief.

*Ausonius Book 20 *sections 9-10*.

‡See next immediate footnote.

of the new religion, the pope, who was—and still is—the bishop
of Rome.[1] By 420 AD, which was before the supposed fall of the
Roman Empire,[2] other bishops were additionally known as
pontifices, and, although not known as the pontifex maximus at
that time, the pontifex of Rome continued to be their chief.[3]
Today both titles, pontifex and pontifex maximus, refer to the
pope—this has been the case for over five centuries.[4] After 420

---

[1] In 380 AD the emperors Gratian, Valentinian II and Theodosius I
issued an edict that stated that Damasus, the pontifex of Rome, was
one of two prominent leaders of the Catholic Church and indicated
that Damasus had precedence over the other leader, Peter, the
bishop of Alexandria, as the latter was named second and called a
bishop rather than a pontifex. An edict on the profession of the
Catholic Faith, 380 (Codex Theodosianus XVI 1.2), document 112,
Creeds Councils and Controversies.
At the Council of Constantinople of 381 AD, the Second Ecumenical
Council, a decree stated that the bishop of Constantinople (another
prominent leader) was second in honour to the bishop of Rome, thus
confirming the authority of Rome and raising Constantinople above
Alexandria. Seven Ecumenical Councils of the Undivided Church:
The Second Ecumenical Council (381 AD)—*Canon III.*
[2] 476 AD. The fall of the Roman Empire is widely considered to be
that of the fall of the Western Roman Empire, thereby ignoring the
Eastern Roman Empire. Sam's "supposed" was for a different
reason though, explained further on.
[3] By 397 AD other bishops were known as pontifices. Ongoing
submission to the pontifex of Rome is demonstrated by the fact that
in 419 AD he had authority over the pontifices of Africa (part of the
Western Empire) and the Eastern Empire. The Seven Ecumenical
Councils of the Undivided Church: The Code of Canons of the
African Church—*Canons XLIX* (397 AD) *and CXXXIV* (419 AD).
[4] The book Lives of the Popes by Bartolomeo Platina was presented
to Pope Sixtus IV in 1474, after which, in 1475, Platina was made
prefect of the Vatican Library by Sixtus. The book has been
subsequently published in numerous Latin editions. The title of the
first printed edition, of 1479, refers to the popes as the pontificum
FOOTNOTE CONTINUED ON THE NEXT PAGE

AD, other features that we recognize as Catholicism emerged, such as the perpetual virginity of Mary and her elevation to become the co-redeemer with Christ;[1] in fact, she is often preferred over Jesus as the saviour of souls."

"And what of those true Christians who stuck to their faith," Mûsâ asked.

"They clearly persevered but as a persecuted minority. However, not sponsored and suppressed, they probably didn't keep many records of their activities, unlike the Catholic Church. And if their records were found, they would have most likely been destroyed or confiscated. In fact, evidence of their ongoing existence comes from the copious records of the Catholic Church regarding decrees that denounced those espousing Christianity who were not in agreement with the Catholic Church."[2]

CONTINUED FOOTNOTE PRESENT

(pontifices). The title of Filippo Pincio's edition, of 1511, refers to the popes as the maximorum pontificum (pontifices maximi). Bartolomeo Platina's Lives of the Popes Volume I: Introduction; Note on the Text and Translation; and Bibliography.

[1] Although not an official Catholic doctrine, this is how she is often regarded.

[2] This is revealed in the documentation of some of the Ecumenical Councils of the Catholic Church between and including 381 AD and 787 AD. The councils imposed decrees that denounced and expelled clerics or lay people (nonclerics) who attended their churches if they opposed, contravened or were not in agreement with the doctrines laid down by the Catholic Church. In addition, these decrees would have affected lay people who had already left the church of their own accord; they would be denounced. The decrees with an asterisk* would have also affected lay people who were never part of the church; again, they would be denounced.

The summarized decrees are as follows: clergy or laymen who bring charges against a cleric related to faith will themselves first be investigated, especially with a view to whether they were previously expelled for a faith that contradicted the Catholic Church or they in professing that they hold the true faith have set up competing

FOOTNOTE CONTINUED ON THE NEXT PAGE

CONTINUED FOOTNOTE PRESENT

churches (381 AD); a ruling against any man who brings forward (verbally or in writing) a different Christian faith to rival that put forward by the Catholic Church* (431 AD); a ruling against clergy or laymen who interact in a benign way with Jewish people or receive medical help from them* (692 AD); a ruling against laymen for preaching or teaching Christianity publicly* (692 AD); and a ruling against clergy or laymen who criticize the worship of icons (pictures), statues and relics of martyrs (relics are the dead remains of individuals deemed special and objects that they had had close contact with) for being idolatry, and furthermore any writings of these critics must be confiscated and locked away with other alleged heretical works* (787 AD).

From these we can see that some people, both clerical and lay: declared that they adhered to the true Christian faith, separated themselves from the Catholic Church and brought charges against Catholic clerics regarding matters of faith; whilst espousing Christianity, they disagreed with doctrines instituted by the Catholic Church; if Gentiles, they interacted with Jews in a benign way (as they should because the revelation of Jesus the Messiah was given initially to the Jews, Jesus is Jewish and the Gospel is to the Jew first then the Greek [Gentiles]—Matthew 1:1-16, Luke 3:23-38, Romans 1:16 and the entire New Testament; these truths are recognized by genuine Christianity); and criticized the worship of icons, statues and the relics of martyrs, which the people stated correctly was idolatry, even if a statue or image of Jesus. Moreover, laymen preached and taught Christianity publicly in defiance of the Catholic Church.

The above are exceptionally strong clues to ongoing genuine Christianity, not absolute proof. Of course, there were many who were ruled against by the above decrees who possessed doctrines contrary to biblical Christianity. For example, a document[‡] reveals that some of those who were opposed to the worship of images of Mary and other saints still prayed to these individuals except without the use of images.

FOOTNOTE CONTINUED ON THE NEXT PAGE

Sam's explanation of the origins of Catholicism had triggered Mûsâ own memory regarding the history of where he lived. "I know that the Roman Empire was so large that in the 3rd century it was divided into Western and Eastern Empires,[1] each ruled by its own emperor. Today we refer to the eastern half as the Byzantine Empire. I also know that a schism of the Catholic Church occurred in the 11th century: essentially dividing it into Roman Catholicism in the west and the Orthodox Catholic Church (Eastern Orthodoxy) in the east.[2] To my mind, they have more similarities than differences, and yet the schism still isn't healed despite numerous attempts over the centuries. The eastern

CONTINUED FOOTNOTE PRESENT

References for documents are as follows. The Seven Ecumenical Councils of the Undivided Church: The Second Ecumenical Council (381 AD)—*Canon VI*; The Third Ecumenical Council (431 AD)—*Canons VI and VII*; The combined Fifth and Sixth Ecumenical Council (Quinisext Council) (692 AD)—*Canons XI and LXIV* (principally of the Eastern Church, as the pope, representing the Western Church, did not attend or sign the decrees); The Seventh Ecumenical Council (787 AD)—*‡Epitome of the definition of the Iconoclastic Conciliabulum, held in Constantinople, A.D. 754; The Decree of the Holy, Great, Ecumenical Synod, the second of Nice; Canon IX.*

[1] Divided by Diocletian in 286 AD. Although Diocletian preceded Constantine I, the latter ruler during part of his reign was emperor of both Western and Eastern Empires (324–337 AD). Before this time, from 312–324 AD, Constantine was emperor of only the Western Empire.

[2] Probably the most critical event that precipitated the schism was in 1054 AD, when the representatives (legates) of Pope Leo IX clashed with the patriarch of Constantinople (Michael Cerularius), each opposing side excommunicating the other. Note that Leo had died approximately three months before his legates, lead by Humbert, excommunicated Cerularius.

branch no longer recognizes the pope as their head.[1] They have patriarchs as their leaders instead. Now let's just go back again for a moment. Why did you say 'the supposed fall of the Roman Empire'?"

"Because the Roman Empire went through some tough times but never truly fell,[2] and it still exists today, although it's not as uniformly powerful as it once was."

"In what way does it still exist?"

"The office of the pontifex maximus is considered to be the oldest surviving monarchy in the world. The leaders of the

---

[1] Before the East-West Schism, the pope (bishop of Rome) was the official head of the entire Catholic Church, including over the bishop of Constantinople (a position that later became patriarch of Constantinople), although in practice this was occasionally resisted in varying degrees, generally escalating over time, by the East. The following are present in the pre-schism documentation of the Ecumenical Councils: the decree that the bishop of Constantinople has the special right of honour after the bishop of Rome (381 AD); the pope is referred to as the "guardian of the faith" (431 AD); the declaration that all the popes are the successors of the apostle Peter, whom the Catholic clerics believe to have been the head of the apostles and the foundation of the Catholic Church (431 AD); and the pope is addressed as the "chief priest" (primus sacerdos) (787 AD). The Seven Ecumenical Councils of the Undivided Church: The Second Ecumenical Council (381 AD)—*Canon III*; The Third Ecumenical Council (431 AD)—*Extracts from the Acts Session II (continued), Session III*; The Seventh Ecumenical Council (787 AD)—*The Divine Sacra sent by the Emperors Constantine and Irene to the Most Holy and Most Blessed Hadrian, Pope of Old Rome.*

[2] The proposed fall was in 476 AD, the year in which the last Western Roman emperor, Romulus Augustulus, was deposed by the Germanic soldier Odoacer, who had previously been in the Roman army. Odoacer became king of Italy. His reign as king was the start of a long trend of rulers in Italy of Germanic origin, who wielded varying amounts of power.

Roman Catholic Church are proud of this fact. This office is over two thousand five hundred years old. It may not be associated with the title of emperor at present, but the office of the pontifex maximus maintains great influence over all countries whose populations are predominantly Roman Catholic and has done so for centuries. Tell me, who bows when they meet: the pope or the head of state of one of these countries?"

"The head of state bows."

"And imagine if the pope withdrew his support for that sovereign, prime minister or president."

"They'd be in a lot of trouble. However, I know that that hasn't been the end for some of them. Henry VIII was a classic example—his daughter Elizabeth I was another."

"That's true," Sam agreed as he pondered over some more examples in his mind.

Mûsâ poured them both a sweet mint tea. "Please go on."

Sam continued, "The prophet Daniel was used by God to reveal that the Roman Empire will continue to exist until the Messiah comes to set up His kingdom.[1] In the dream of King Nebuchadnezzar,[2] the interpretation of which was given by God to Daniel, it's the Roman Empire[3] that's represented by iron within the image."

---

[1] Daniel 2:1-45.

[2] Nebuchadnezzar II.

[3] The dream refers to kingdoms; however, a kingdom can be thought of loosely as any state or connected states led by a ruler or rulers. In this way, the Kingdom of Rome applies to all of the following: the regal period, when the kingdom was ruled by kings (one at a time) [753–509 BC]; the republic, ruled by two consuls or occasional dictators [509–27 BC]; the empire, ruled by emperors, empresses, kings, queens or political leaders. The empire is currently a diverse group of mostly secular states, each with its own ruler and each with a religion that the other states have in common and that possesses varying degrees of influence from state to state [27 BC–?].

FOOTNOTE CONTINUED ON THE NEXT PAGE

"Can we take a look at this?"

"Yes, if you turn to Chapter 2 of the book of Daniel—verses 31 to 45 will do."

Mûsâ read:

"Thou, O king, sawest, and behold a great image. This great image, whose brightness *was* excellent, stood before thee; and the form thereof *was* terrible. This image's head *was* of fine gold, his breast and his arms of silver, his belly and his thighs of brass, His legs of iron, his feet part of iron and part of clay. Thou sawest till that a stone was cut out without hands, which smote the image upon his feet *that were* of iron and clay, and brake them to pieces. Then was the iron, the clay, the brass, the silver, and the gold, broken to pieces together, and became like the chaff of the summer threshingfloors; and the wind carried them away, that no place was found for them: and the stone that smote the image became a great mountain, and filled the whole earth. This *is* the dream; and we will tell the interpretation thereof before the king. Thou, O king, *art* a king of kings: for the God of heaven hath given thee a kingdom, power, and strength, and glory. And wheresoever the children of men dwell, the beasts of the field and the fowls of the heaven hath he given into thine hand, and hath made thee ruler over them all. Thou *art* this head of gold. And after thee shall arise another kingdom inferior to thee, and another third kingdom of brass, which shall bear rule over all the earth. And the fourth kingdom shall be strong as iron: forasmuch as iron breaketh in pieces and subdueth all *things:* and as iron that breaketh all these, shall it break in pieces and bruise. And whereas thou sawest the feet and toes, part of potters' clay, and part of iron, the kingdom shall be divided; but there shall be in it

CONTINUED FOOTNOTE PRESENT

For the derivation of the date 27 BC for the transition of republic to empire see Chapter 8 pg 182 regarding Cybele becoming one of the most important deities in the Roman Republic and then the Empire—the accompanying footnote contains the explanation.

of the strength of the iron, forasmuch as thou sawest the iron mixed with miry clay. And *as* the toes of the feet *were* part of iron, and part of clay, *so* the kingdom shall be partly strong, and partly broken. And whereas thou sawest iron mixed with miry clay, they shall mingle themselves with the seed of men: but they shall not cleave one to another, even as iron is not mixed with clay. And in the days of these kings shall the God of heaven set up a kingdom, which shall never be destroyed: and the kingdom shall not be left to other people, *but* it shall break in pieces and consume all these kingdoms, and it shall stand for ever. Forasmuch as thou sawest that the stone was cut out of the mountain without hands, and that it brake in pieces the iron, the brass, the clay, the silver, and the gold; the great God hath made known to the king what shall come to pass hereafter: and the dream *is* certain, and the interpretation thereof sure."

Mûsâ started, "I know that Nebuchadnezzar was the king of Babylon and that this empire is the head of gold. Babylon was defeated by the Medes and the Persians. Hence, the empire of the Medes and the Persians is the breast and arms of silver. They were defeated by the Greeks, whose empire is therefore the belly and thighs of brass. This brings us to the Romans,[1] who defeated the Greeks. Their empire is the legs of iron. It's the next part of the image that I don't understand—the feet made of a mixture of iron and clay?"[2]

"This is still the Roman Empire, but as Daniel states, it's a mixture of the strong and the broken. Some regions are clearly much stronger than others—the weaker ones broken perhaps by ravaging disease, poverty or war. Over the centuries the fragmented Roman Empire, which was and is made up of countries dominated by Catholicism, has tried to unify more strongly. The methods used include: peace treaties; and conditional alliances

---

[1] The Greeks were defeated by the Roman Republic.

[2] See Timeline.

triggered when the relevant nations entered a war. Yet many of the wars were between countries that were once part of the uniformly strong, completely iron Roman Empire. Another method was the forging of marriage alliances between different royal families, yet this didn't always result in cohesiveness. Earlier, you mentioned Henry VIII.[1] He married the Spanish Catherine of Aragon, and then the subsequent annulment of this marriage, driven by him, led to England's break with Rome. Even when the marriage alliances fared better, this didn't necessarily result in the couple's subjects displaying harmony. The Holy Roman Empire, which was an empire supported mostly by ruling Germanic peoples, lasted from 800 to 1806 AD.[2] It was typified by such treaties and alliances. Incidentally, this particular empire is also known as the First Reich—Reich meaning empire."

"I've read about the Holy Roman Empire. Charlemagne, a Frankish king,[3] became the first of its emperors. I wasn't aware that this empire lasted so long—a thousand and six years. I can see where Hitler got his inspiration for his planned thousand-year Third Reich."

"I'm sure you're right. Regarding the First Reich, I should say that although it had been named the Holy Roman Empire, it was only part of the even bigger actual Roman Empire, which included the Byzantine Empire. Although the Eastern Roman Empire is today mostly called the Byzantine Empire, its people thought of themselves as Romans until just beyond the defeat of Constantinople by the Ottoman Turks in the 15th century.[4]

---

[1] King of England from 1509–1547 AD.

[2] Although the Holy Roman Empire had its beginning in 800 AD with the crowning of Charlemagne as emperor by Pope Leo III, it was not called so until 1254 AD.

[3] The Franks were a Germanic people.

[4] Kritovoulos' History of Mehmed the Conqueror Part 1 *sections 3, 102-255,* Part 2 *sections 1-3,* Doukas' Decline and fall of Byzan-
FOOTNOTE CONTINUED ON THE NEXT PAGE

Incidentally, the Byzantine Empire's—Eastern Roman Empire's—last emperor was called Constantine (XI), who died in the battle.[1] Furthermore, through Catholicism, whose origins are

---

CONTINUED FOOTNOTE PRESENT

---

tium to the Ottoman Turks* *chapters 31:1-40:1,* Sphrantzes' Chronicon Minus *chapters 35:1-39:8, 43:4-5* (these two preceding references show that Sphrantzes, regarding events in 1459 and 1466 AD, still referred to the people as Romans, even after the defeat of Constantinople, the capital of the empire, in 1453 AD).
*A modern descriptive designation—see Bibliography.
Even the historian Laonikos Chalkokondyles (lived around 1430–1490 AD), who strongly emphasized the Greek character of the Eastern Empire, conceded that the people of the Greek city Byzantion (which became Constantinople), having become citizens of a capital of the Roman Empire and mixing with Romans, permanently stopped calling themselves Greeks and their rulers kings of the Greeks but instead called themselves Romans and their rulers emperors of the Romans (The Histories Book 1 *section 5*). Once the position of emperor was destroyed and Constantinople defeated, the people no longer had an emperor or control of the renowned city, and thus the prestige of the name Roman was diminished; consequently, calling oneself a Roman would have rapidly declined.
Kritovoulos, Doukas, Sphrantzes and Chalkokondyles were Eastern Romans.
[1] Kritovoulos' History of Mehmed the Conqueror Part 1 *sections 102-252, 272-276,* Laonikos Chalkokondyles' The Histories Book 8 *sections 3-30,* Sphrantzes' Chronicon Minus *chapter 35:1-10.*
Doukas considered Constantine XI's brother, John VIII (reigned 1421–1448 AD), to be the last valid emperor of the Romans rather than Constantine, who succeeded John in 1449 AD and whose reign was ended at the fall of Constantinople in 1453 AD. Doukas' reason for the preference was that Constantine was never crowned*. However, according to Sphrantzes, Constantine was crowned as emperor of the Romans in Mistra, today in Greece, in 1449 AD. Moreover, Doukas himself repeatedly referred to Constantine as emperor and Doukas' text demonstrates that Constantine was
FOOTNOTE CONTINUED ON THE NEXT PAGE

in Rome, the actual Roman Empire—regardless of the names that
come under it—expanded way beyond the bounds of when it was
considered to be pure iron. Roman Catholicism spread to South
America, Eastern Orthodoxy to Russia, and both to many other
regions throughout the globe.[1] And I suspect that the empire will
get bigger."

"So the Roman Empire is vast, yet as the passage says, it's
'partly strong, and partly broken'. And the stone that destroyed
the statue and grew into a mountain—is this the Messiah?"

"Yes, the stone represents the Messiah, who will come and
make an end of the four kingdoms.[2] And His kingdom will last
forever."

Mûsâ sipped his tea slowly. "You know, Sam, I went to Rome
a few years ago with my wife. We were on holiday in Italy, and
we wanted to see Saint Peter's Basilica and other places within
Vatican City—just out of interest. I could scarcely believe the
number of idols!"

"And many of those idols are worshipped in a similar way to
how idols were worshipped in ancient Rome."[1]

CONTINUED FOOTNOTE PRESENT

---

recognized as the emperor of the Romans by the Romans themselves and by his chief enemy, Sultan Mehmed II, whose troops
killed Constantine. Doukas' Decline and fall of Byzantium to the
Ottoman Turks *chapters 20:5, 28:7, 33:1, 33:12-39:13 (*found in
34:2), 40:3,* Sphrantzes' Chronicon Minus *chapters 28:7-29:5.*

[1] See Chapter 5 pg 111 and footnote regarding Eastern Orthodoxy
for its current self-governing institutions.

[2] The fact that the Messiah clears away four kingdoms rather than
one (the last) indicates that despite the fact that three kingdoms
were consecutively defeated, each of these three has in some way
persisted in the fourth. The manner of their persistence may be
culturally religious and/or culturally secular. For example, the
Roman Empire is strongly influenced by the ancient Greek religion
and system of government.

"Yes, I remember seeing people bowing and praying to them."

"I can imagine how the apostles would feel about having statues made of them—about being prayed to, bowed down to and worshipped. Peter and Paul would undoubtedly tear their own clothes in utter dismay, as this practice represents so much of what Jesus strove to save people from. Mary would certainly do the same. Jesus said, 'I am the way, the truth, and the life: no man cometh unto the Father, but by me.'[2] Peter and Paul believed this and told others the same.[3] If anyone attempted to worship them, they immediately exclaimed that this was wrong, because they were just men.[4] Jesus accepted worship, because He is God.[1]

CONTINUED FOOTNOTE PRESENT

---

[1] The obvious difference is lack of animal sacrifice, although sacrifices are made in the form of monetary donations. For ancient Roman animal sacrifice see Chapter 13 pgs 289-291 and footnotes regarding Diana, Jupiter and Mercury. Monetary donations were also made in ancient times to the Roman gods.

[2] John 14:6.

[3] Peter: 1 Peter 1:1-10, 5:10, 2 Peter 1:1-11.
Paul: Romans 5:1-9, 6:22-23, 8:34, Galatians 3:26, Ephesians 1:2-3, 1 Thessalonians 5:9-10.

[4] Peter stopped Cornelius, who had fallen at Peter's feet and had started to worship him. Peter helped Cornelius to stand up, and Peter said that he too was a man. Acts 10:25-26.
A crowd of people in Lystra proclaimed that Paul and Barnabas were both gods, Mercury and Jupiter respectively, and started to prepare a sacrifice to these two men. Paul and Barnabas stopped these Lystrans. Indeed, both men tore their clothes in horror at what the crowd had said and were planning to do, declaring that they both were men like the Lystrans and that these people needed to turn to the Living God. Acts 14:8-18.
There is no biblical record of anyone attempting to directly worship Mary during her lifetime, and therefore no biblical documentation of her countering this. The closest thing regarding a rebuke against Mary worship is when a woman shouted to Jesus: "Blessed *is* the womb that bare thee, and the paps which thou hast sucked." (Paps

FOOTNOTE CONTINUED ON THE NEXT PAGE

Praying to men and women (alive or dead), angels or stone representations of any of these beings won't lead to your salvation. My heart really goes out to people who are born into Catholicism and indeed any false religion. But with God's grace the message of Jesus the Messiah can reach them. There are many real Christians throughout the world who were born into these other religions yet found the truth and put their faith in the Messiah."

Mûsâ was thinking carefully. He then spoke, "But becoming a Christian . . . accepting Jesus. It feels like I'd be traitor to my own people. In fact, I've called people who have become Christians that very name."

"You feel that way because of what false Christianity has done; however, you owe it to yourself to investigate the truth about Jesus."

"What do you mean?"

"We have a saying: 'Don't throw the baby out with the bath-water.' The Catholic churches, the institutions, along with many of the leaders of those countries who profess that religion have persecuted your people for centuries—the Crusades, the Inquisition, the Russian Pogroms. I can add that these institutions and these leaders have persecuted people such as me as well: people who believe the truth of the Bible and can see through their lies. False churches have many roles. Distraction from true Christianity by attracting people to false Christianity is one such role. Repelling certain people from Jesus by misrepresenting His name is another. You're one of the 'certain people' being

CONTINUED FOOTNOTE PRESENT

---

are breasts.) Jesus replied: "Yea rather, blessed *are* they that hear the word of God, and keep it." He was clearly stating that adhering to the Word of God brings about blessings, thereby rightly bringing attention to this and away from His mother. Luke 11:27-28.

[1] Matthew 2:2, 2:11, 8:2-3, 9:18, 14:33, 15:22-28, 20:17-21, 28:9-17, Mark 5:33-34, 7:25-26, Luke 5:8, 5:12-13, 17:16-19, 24:45-52, John 9:1-38.

repelled. What this means is that you're still being manipulated at the cost of your eternal soul."[1]

"You talk in absolute terms."

"I do, although I'm sure that you understand that the minds of individuals are more complicated and that I understand this too. During World War II there were some Roman Catholics in Germany who hid Jewish people, so that they wouldn't be rounded up for extermination."

Mûsâ said, "I'm aware of this. And this despite Vatican neutrality throughout the war[2] . . ."

"At a time when right and wrong were so well demarcated," Sam interrupted.

". . . and despite Pius XII's[3] deficient opposition to Nazism, anti-Semitism and the slaughter of my people," Mûsâ completed.

Sam continued, "Some of these German Catholics lost their own lives as a result of their actions. So they did these acts in defiance of their secular leaders and traditional Catholic anti-Semitism. Nevertheless, the devastating momentum of the Holocaust was driven by the leaders of those countries concerned, and many of the people colluded or submitted. However, leaders are more responsible. The people look to them for guidance and often follow the path on which the leaders steer them. Secular leaders understand this!"

"I agree."

"In a similar way, the responsibilities of those persons who've been funded by the people to study the Bible and relay what it says to them—well, perhaps each of these leaders carries an even greater responsibility. Consequently, when they disregard what's

---

[1] See Soul and Spirit.

[2] Note that since 1929 Vatican City has been an independent nation (with the pope at its head), which is capable of making its own policies.

[3] Pius XII, Eugenio Pacelli (pope from 2nd March 1939 to 9th October 1958).

written on its pages and do the opposite, and worse still, persuade their followers to do the same, then the leaders call great judgement on themselves from God. I pity any young man desiring to be a Catholic priest who enters 'the church' with the genuine intention of finding God and sharing Him with other people. Imagine how he must feel if or when he reads the entire Bible and finds out that it contradicts his own church. What must go on in his head? Imagine the conflict!"

"Imagine the pressure to conform to Catholic dogmas: from his teachers, from society and from his family," Mûsâ added. He understood.

"And more probably, yet Christ still expects him to make a stand—as he expects us all to."

Mûsâ was thinking deeply about his own situation, clearly challenged by Sam's last statement.

Sam continued, "We aren't a herd of zebra being hunted by a lion. There's no safety in numbers. One day each of us will stand alone before Jesus the Messiah and be judged.[1] We can't hide

---

[1] Believers will be judged separately from non-believers, but all will be judged.

Believers will be judged based on their works, as Christ will not condemn them for their sins, because during their earthly lives they believed in Him. Jesus died for everyone's sins, but a person needs to ask Him to forgive his or her sins and accept Him as his or her personal saviour to not be condemned. John 3:16-18, Galatians 3:13, 1 Peter 1:18-19. Specific judgement references below.

Non-believers will be condemned to the Lake of Fire, and the judgement is to determine the degree of punishment based on their deeds, both good and bad, in their lives. As non-believers, they will have been brought from Hell to be judged. The Lake of Fire will be the permanent place of punishment.

Believers will be judged at the Judgement Seat of Christ and non-believers at the Great White Throne. All judgement is given by God the Father to Jesus, God the Messiah (John 5:22-30).

FOOTNOTE CONTINUED ON THE NEXT PAGE

behind other people or use them as an excuse. The truth is that Jesus is the Messiah. He's the hope of all Israel and the rest of the world. I know some Christians who are Jewish. They've retained their Jewish identity—indeed, it's intensified in them; they're proud of their backgrounds and support Israel. They're believers in the Jewish Messiah, yet they often struggle to be understood by their own kin. All Christians face trials in this life, whatever their background, but Jesus has promised us that if we stand up for Him, then one day He will stand up for us."[1]

"Why can't I just worship God alone? Surely He will have pity on me at the time of judgement and overlook the fact that I didn't worship His Son."

"He has taken pity on you—on you and the rest of the world, whether Jewish or Gentile. God became a man, Jesus, and died for your sins, so that if you believe in Him, then you can have everlasting life in Heaven."[2]

"Hmm," Mûsâ muttered.

"Let's put it another way. Imagine you had a son who in his life did no wrong at all. Imagine that he died a horrific death to save many people who'd all been condemned to death for crimes that they'd committed. Wouldn't you want them to acknowledge

CONTINUED FOOTNOTE PRESENT

Believer's judgement: Romans 14:10, 1 Corinthians 3:10-15, 2 Corinthians 5:7-10.
Non-believers judgement: Matthew 10:15, 11:20-24, Mark 6:11, Luke 10:12-15, Revelation 20:4-21:1.
See Soul and Spirit.
[1] Matthew 10:32-33, Luke 12:8-9.
[2] See footnote in Chapter 7 pg 152 regarding Heaven. A believer's current destination is Heaven, the home of God, but the ultimate destination is the New Heaven-New Earth when the old are replaced. The New Jerusalem, the Holy City, will descend from the New Heaven to rest on the New Earth. See earlier in this chapter pg 397 and Chapter 24 pg 536 with their accompanying footnotes regarding this topic.

what your son had done? Wouldn't you want them to be thankful and honour his name?"

"Yes, I would."

"Then is it a surprise that God has declared that salvation is through faith in Jesus?[1] And as I've mentioned already, Jesus himself said: 'I am the way, the truth, and the life: no man cometh unto the Father, but by me.'"[2]

And the conversation went back and forth until the early morning hours.

Mûsâ joined Sam for dinner on two more evenings, at which times they'd again talked late into the night. Sam spent an entire week in the villa as he'd planned. This time combined with the seven-day cruise from Georgia had allowed him to fully heal and regain much of his strength. With the week complete, Sam bid farewell to Mûsâ, that old friend of mine, who saved my life in Tripoli when I was just a child. A few days later Mûsâ looked at the Bible—both Testaments. He did what few people are brave enough to do: that is, to investigate for oneself whether or not the Scriptures clearly identify Jesus as the Messiah, the Son of God and Himself God. In truth, in Mûsâ's heart of hearts, he knew that the Scriptures would, but until that time he'd been afraid of what would follow—troubled by the inevitable confrontation to his soul. The Old Testament confirmed that Jesus is indeed the Messiah as described in the New Testament. Mûsâ carefully counted the cost of being a follower of Jesus. Mûsâ then asked Jesus to forgive his sins and put his trust in Him, and in doing so, my own prayers were answered.

---

[1] Romans 1:16, 2 Timothy 2:10, 3:15-16. See also earlier in this chapter pg 426 and footnote regarding salvation through the Messiah alone.

[2] John 14:6.

Chapter 21   **Bergama**

The Revelation of Jesus the Messiah was given to John while he was on Patmos, one of the Greek islands. Concerning Pergamos (Pergamum, Bergama) he wrote:

Revelation 2:12 And to the angel of the church in Pergamos write; These things saith he which hath the sharp sword with two edges;

INTERPRETATION: This is the beginning of Jesus' address to the church (group of Christians) in Pergamos. Earlier in the book of Revelation Jesus is described as the one with the two-edged sword.[1] Jesus instructed John to write the message to the angel who'd been given the responsibility of watching over the church.

13 I know thy works, and where thou dwellest, *even* where Satan's seat *is:* and thou holdest fast my name, and hast not denied my faith, even in those days wherein Antipas *was* my faithful martyr, who was slain among you, where Satan dwelleth.

INTERPRETATION: Jesus first commended the church for their faith and determination to stay true to Him, despite the fact that they were located where Satan resides and has his throne. In this instance the Greek word used in the New Testament for "seat" is "thronos", which is a stately seat of a ruler, literally a throne.

14 But I have a few things against thee, because thou hast there them that hold the doctrine of Balaam, who taught Balac to cast a stumblingblock before the children of Israel, to eat things sacrificed unto idols, and to commit fornication.

---

[1] Revelation 1:12-16.

INTERPRETATION: But the church had within their congregation people who knew the truth yet nonetheless plotted the downfall of other members by willfully tempting them to sin. These deceivers resembled a man called Balaam, who lived around the time of the Exodus of the Hebrews from Egypt (1446 BC). Before the Hebrews entered the Promised Land, they were opposed by a Moabite king called Balac (Balak). This king tried to recruit Balaam to place a curse on the Hebrews. However, God spoke to Balaam, ordering him not to curse them. With a measure of reluctance, Balaam obeyed but afterward devised an alternative way to make the Hebrews stumble. For money he advised King Balak to use his female subjects to entice the Hebrews into idolatry and sexual sin.[1] The plan worked and many of the Hebrews were led astray, which angered God. Therefore, the doctrine of Balaam is an erroneous blending of Christianity with idolatry and sexual sin.

15 So hast thou also them that hold the doctrine of the Nicolaitans, which thing I hate.

INTERPRETATION: They (the church) also had within their congregation followers of the doctrine of the Nicolaitans—a doctrine that Jesus hates. Unlike the doctrine of Balaam, the doctrine of the Nicolaitans is not expansively explained in any biblical passage. However, the best answer is derived from the name itself, which is a combination of two Greek words: "nikao" meaning "to conquer" and "laos" meaning "people". Christian ministers conquering the laity (the people) is almost certainly what is meant here. Elevation of the clergy over the congregation leads to exploitation, and this has never been Christ's intention

---

[1] Numbers 22:1-25:18 (a Midianite woman was also involved), 31:8, 31:15-16, 2 Peter 2:15, Jude 1:11.

for the church. When the disciples argued over who was the greatest amongst them, Jesus' instruction was that in contrast to worldly leaders, Christian leaders should not lord themselves over the people but serve them humbly.[1] Whilst with us, Jesus demonstrated this by washing the feet of His disciples and said that this is what they themselves should do for one another.[2] If the clergy are elevated, they become incapable of being criticized by the laity. The members of an individual church can consequently be harmed directly by their minister if that person is in error. The clergy also seek to elevate themselves over one another. The ultimate outcome is a hierarchical clerical system in which individuals at the top have authority over many churches. This results in centralized policies that are disseminated, and if incorrect, the laity are then led into false doctrine.[3] To not follow the doctrine of the Nicolaitans means that if the minister of one church is in error, then the members, not being subjugated, can criticize him from a biblical standpoint to bring him out of error. If the minister didn't then preach in accordance with the Bible, he would potentially lead only one church astray (sad as that is), but its members could leave and find another church in the same area that was not so affected. Alternatively, the members could dismiss the minister. The doctrine of the Nicolaitans makes all of

---

[1] Luke 22:24-27. See also Mark 9:35.

[2] John 13:4-17.

[3] An alternative, poorer interpretation, of the doctrine of the Nicolaitans is as follows. Within Eusebius' Ecclesiastical History, there is a quote from the writings of a man who lived at an earlier time, Clement of Alexandria (lived around 150 to 215 AD), that indicates that sexual sin was possibly involved (Book 3.29:1-4). However, this would be a repeat of the doctrine of Balaam in Revelation 2:14. Revelation 2:15 starts with "So hast thou also", indicating that there was another problem to contend with, and ends with "which thing I hate", indicating that this problem, the doctrine of the Nicolaitans, evokes its own emotion from Christ.

these avenues difficult to impossible, depending on the extent to
which it is employed. It appears, therefore, that even during the
lifetime of the apostle John, the combined practices of clerical
suppression of the laity and clerical hierarchy were damaging the
Christian Church. By 300 AD this combination was commonplace and paved the way for the institution known as the Catholic
Church. For once a clerical hierarchy was in place, it needed only
to adopt false doctrine that was then disseminated and enforced
to make a new religion that was not in fact biblically Christian.
The truth is that for Christians seeking God-approved doctrine,
what's already in the Bible is all that's necessary, and when
further doctrine is unnecessarily added, misery results. Similar
clerical suppression of the laity and hierarchical clerical systems
exist today, which damage churches that still have genuine
Christian members.[1]

---

[1] Hierarchical clerical systems include bishops, who are an integral
part of their workings. Bishops—who are elected from the rank of
ministers—rank above a minister of a single church (group of
Christians who gather in the name of Christ), have authority to
supervise many different churches in a locality, ordain ministers and
implement doctrine (even create doctrine). The New Testament
does contain the word "bishop" (episkopos in Greek); however, the
role except for implementing doctrine is different from the above
and the requirements to fulfil such a position are collectively
different from those stipulated by hierarchical clerical systems. Role
according to the New Testament—a supervisor who takes care of a
church (a single assembly of Christians). Requirements according to
the New Testament—he needs to: be a mature Christian; be
blameless; be married to only one woman; be the head of his house
of obedient children (for otherwise he would be a poor candidate to
supervise the church); be a teacher; be patient; have a good report
from non-Christians in the community; be hospitable; and not be
prone to violence, greed or jealousy. Acts 20:17-28, 1 Timothy 3:1-
7, 3:14-15, Titus 1:7-9. Although bishops should teach, a minister
(the Greek word translated mostly as minister is "diakonos",
FOOTNOTE CONTINUED ON THE NEXT PAGE

16 Repent; or else I will come unto thee quickly, and will fight against them with the sword of my mouth.

17 He that hath an ear, let him hear what the Spirit saith unto the churches; To him that overcometh will I give to eat of the hidden manna, and will give him a white stone, and in the stone a new name written, which no man knoweth saving he that receiveth *it.*

INTERPRETATION: Jesus finished His address by telling them to turn away from the things that He'd highlighted that were

CONTINUED FOOTNOTE PRESENT

---

deacon, which means "servant"; deacon is also used directly) should be the principal preacher of a church. (In most hierarchical clerical systems a deacon is an assistant to a minister.) On Earth Jesus was a minister, as were the apostles, including Paul. A minister should be a servant of a church, or a servant who wanders from church to church. Matthew 20:26-28, Mark 10:43-45, Luke 1:2, Acts 1:13-26, 6:1-4, 12:25-13:52, 26:14-18, Romans 1:1, 15:8-19, 1 Corinthians 3:5, Galatians 1:1, Ephesians 3:1-21, Colossians 1:23-25, 1 Thessalonians 3:2, 1 Timothy 3:8-13, 4:6. Nowhere does the New Testament say that bishops should have authority over many churches. Cardinals and popes are not in the New Testament.

Regarding Christianity (rather than the Old Testament covenant, which had a Levitical priesthood), the role of priest, as stated in the New Testament, belongs to all genuine Christians (whether ministers or members of the laity) who tell others about Jesus. For in this way, they all act as intermediaries between mankind and God. 1 Peter 2:1-9. Therefore, to distinguish one person over others with the title priest is wrong. Note that none of these intermediaries (alive or dead) should be prayed to for intercession. Christ is Himself the High Priest, the ultimate intermediary between God the Father and mankind because of what Jesus did for us on Earth. Jesus can be prayed to for intercession, because He is God. Hebrews 3:1-4, 4:14-15, 5:5-10, 6:20-7:26, 8:1-2. See Chapter 9 pg 213 and footnote regarding Christ being our only intercessor.

wrong with the church, or punishment dispensed by Him would result. He encouraged them with a promise that those who overcame the problems would be rewarded with special gifts.

Some have said that the reason why the Bible states that the throne of Satan is in Pergamos is because the worship of Aesculapius, the Greco-Roman god of medicine,[1] was prevalent in this city when the book of Revelation was written—in imagery Aesculapius was often portrayed as a male figure holding a staff with a serpent coiled around it.[2] However, this is a weak deduction, and Pergamos was also the centre of worship for a variety of

---

[1] Aesculapius was reported by Ovid to be a god who brought health. Aesculapius' dedication to healing human ailments was related by Diodorus. Ovid's Metamorphoses Book 15 *lines 622-744*, Library of History by Diodorus Siculus Book 4 *chapter 71:1-4*.

Temples and worship in Roman-controlled Italy (including Rome), Greece and elsewhere: Dio Cassius' Roman History Book 47 *chapter 2:1-3*, Livy's History of Rome Summary of Book 11, Book 38 *chapters 4:1-5:3*, Book 43 *chapter 4:6-8*, Book 45 *chapter 28:1-4*, Strabo's Geography Book 16 *chapter 2:22*, Pausanias' Description of Greece Book 3 *chapter 26:10* (the temple of Aesculapius at Pergamos is mentioned), Dionysius of Halicarnassus' Roman Antiquities Book 7 *chapter 72:13-14*.

Because of a contagious disease in Rome, a serpent representing Aesculapius was transferred from Greece to Rome (290 BC), a recommendation based on a Sibylline prophecy—similar to the transfer of Cybele: Strabo's Geography Book 12 *chapter 5:3*, Livy's History of Rome Book 10 *chapter 47:6-7*, Summary of Book 11, Book 29 *chapter 11:1*.

[2] Ovid's writings similarly describe Aesculapius (Metamorphoses Book 15 *lines 622-744*). In Pausanias' Description of Greece Book 2 *chapter 27:1-2* there is a detailed description of one of Aesculapius' statues, which was of a seated man holding a staff in one hand whilst the other hand was held above a serpent (a variant of the above).

other gods, including Zeus, Demeter, Apollo, Dionysus, Athena, Nike, Hera and emperors.[1] John's vision was of Jesus. Jesus told John that Pergamos is the location of Satan's throne.

Bergama is a quiet unassuming town. To Sam it hardly seemed to be the place where Satan's throne would be located. Sam had arrived in Bergama two weeks previously, having travelled the short distance of 85 miles from Mûsâ's villa. He sat on an armless wooden chair that faced the window of his rented apartment. This flat was on the third floor and overlooked the entrance of Bergama's busiest hotel. The window had two thin white veils hung side by side, which together prevented distant

---

[1] Based on archaeological evidence of the ruins (A) and/or written history (H): Zeus (A and H)—Pausanias' Description of Greece Book 5 *chapter 13:8*; Demeter (A); Apollo (H)—Pausanias' Description of Greece Book 8 *chapter 42:7*; Dionysus (A and H)—Pausanias' Description of Greece Book 10 *chapter 18:6*, Dio Cassius' Roman History Book 41 *chapter 61:3-4*; Athena (A); Nike (A and H)—Strabo's Geography Book 13 *chapter 4:2*, Library of History by Diodorus Siculus Fragments of Book 28:5, Polybius' The Histories Fragments of Book 16 *chapter 1:1-9*; Hera (A); the emperor Augustus Caesar (H)—Dio Cassius' Roman History Book 51 *chapter 20:6-9*, Book 59 *chapter 28:1-2*; and the emperor Trajan (A).

It is likely that the worship of the majority of these deities coincided. This would be in keeping with the polytheism of Greece, Rome and Asia Minor. The above historical reference of Polybius supports this by mentioning multiple, simultaneous places associated with the city for the worship of the so-called gods. Regarding emperors, relative latecomers to be worshipped in Pergamos, Caesar (Octavian) would have been added to the other deities after his temple was erected in 29 BC (see first Dio Cassius reference regarding his worship—note that it wasn't until 2 years had passed that he received the title Augustus). As for Trajan, he would have been added even later.

onlookers from seeing inside. Occasionally he would gently move aside one of the veils where they met with an index finger to gain clearer views of the people who were arriving at and departing from the hotel. When required, he would raise his pair of binoculars to his eyes.

There were a few clues that the quiet town of Bergama had been something greater in the past. The modern town can be thought of as being between two sets of ruins: one to the east and the other to the west. On the hill to the east lie the relics of the Attalid city of Pergamos, the capital of a once powerful kingdom. It became a city of international renown in the era when, after the death of Alexander the Great, many Greek monarchs ruled over Macedonia and areas that he'd conquered and Greek culture permeated non-Greek nations in parts of Europe, the Middle East and western Asia (from 323 to 30 BC). During this period the Attalid dynasty built Pergamos into a great city and formed a close bond with Rome. This bond came about as follows. As is often the way, a common enemy can bring people together, and in the case of Rome and Pergamos this uniting foe was Philip V (leading the Macedonians), who, in fighting both, brought them to somewhat good terms.[1] Added to this, during Rome's second war with Carthage the first Attalid king, Attalus I (reigned 241–197 BC), received the Roman ambassadors and arranged for them to take the sacred stone of Cybele from Pessinus (230 miles east of Pergamos) back to Rome, so that, according to a Sibylline prophecy, the Carthaginians under Hannibal could be defeated.[2] Subsequently, Pergamos became even more closely allied with Rome, continuing to jointly fight battles against mutual enemies. Eventually, the last king, Attalus III, bequeathed the kingdom to Rome. At his death (133 BC) Pergamos became part of Rome's

---

[1] Livy's History of Rome Book 27 *chapters 29:9-30:17,* Book 29 *chapter 12:8-16*, Strabo's Geography Book 13 *chapter 4:1-2.*
[2] Livy's History of Rome Book 29 *chapters 10:1-11:8.* See also Chapter 8 pgs 181-182 and footnotes regarding the same topic.

expanding realm—the Attalid city's bond's zenith having been complete assimilation by the dominant power.[1] After this time, the city was relocated to the plain below. The majority of the remains of the Roman city are now beneath the modern town except for an area to the west. It was this Roman Pergamos[2] that was current at the time that John received the Revelation.

The history of the habitation of the area extends much further back, though, than what is related above. The ancient people of Pergamos (in around 170 AD and undoubtedly earlier) believed that they were the distant descendants of Greeks who'd migrated to Asia Minor with Telephus.[3] Reportedly, Telephus, a son of Hercules, became the king of the region in around 1200 BC; the kingdom at that time was known as Teuthrania.[4] Furthermore, two generations later Pergamos, a grandson of Achilles, defeated the then ruler of Teuthrania, a man called Areius, in single combat, thereby winning the kingdom and naming the city after himself.[5]

---

[1] Strabo's Geography Book 13 *chapter 4:1-2*, Livy's History of Rome Book 32 *chapters 8:9-16, 23:1-13,* Summaries Book 58.

[2] The Roman (Latin) version of the name is Pergamum.

[3] Pausanias' Description of Greece Book 1 *chapter 4:5-6.*

[4] Apollodorus' The Library Book 2 *chapter 7:4,* Book 3 *chapter 9:1,* Hyginus' Fabulae *99-101* (Telephus was a contemporary of Agamemnon and Achilles), Library of History by Diodorus Siculus Book 4 *chapter 33:7-12,* Strabo's Geography Book 13 *chapter 1:69.*

As a son of Hercules, Telephus was therefore a grandson of Zeus (see Chapter 14 pg 320 and relevant footnote for the lineage of Hercules and the footnote in Chapter 9 pg 206 regarding licentiousness of Nephilim for Telephus' conception).

[5] Pausanias' Description of Greece Book 1 *chapter 11:1-2*— reportedly, Achilles was the father of Neoptolemus (also known as Pyrrhus), who was the father of Pergamos. See Chapter 14 pg 314 and relevant footnotes for the lineage of Achilles.

Bergama's main hotel was far from resplendent, and Sam's apartment block even less so. The hotel had a glass double door that led to a large lobby. From his window during the day he could clearly see the first four metres of the lobby, but further inspection faded rapidly into darkness. At night the lobby was well lit, and the only limitation was then his viewing angle. The hotel's outside walls were painted in a neutral lime-green colour and rose to complete just two floors above ground level. Despite this lack of height, he could see that the hotel was large. Its red-tiled roof spread backward to a distance of over 150 metres. The roof had a single large rectangular recess within the structure. He guessed that this break in continuity contained an outdoor swimming pool that wasn't visible from his window. The style of roof was similar to that of the majority of other buildings in this Mediterranean town, and if it weren't for the pool, a loftier observer would have had difficulty recognizing the hotel's function as such. In contrast, his apartment block was grey and characterless. It had been designed and built stringently with few accoutrements. His flat's interior was no less Spartan. There was no lounge, but the bedroom permitted an area near the window to entertain a guest, which he'd met containing two single-seat chairs facing one another. There was a plain en suite bathroom and a small functional kitchen, which was separate from the bedroom.

Sam hadn't left the flat in the day. He'd also mostly remained in the apartment at night except for two occasions when he'd had to stock up on groceries. He'd spent the days and much of the nights staring out of the window, not just at the hotel entrance but also along the length of the adjacent street. He now felt impatient with what seemed to be fruitless surveillance. Most of the people who came and went were simply tourists, the majority of whom were families. He'd chosen that flat because of the hotel. He'd decided to stake-out the establishment that would receive the largest number of visitors to Bergama. He'd already questioned his choice; however, he couldn't think of an alternative site that had a higher probability of a result.

Sam now contemplated deeply on the following questions, some of which he'd already raised, as he maintained his vigil. What if the people I'm looking for have somewhere else to stay that was set up specifically for that purpose? What if they're low-level members of the conspiracy and know nothing of Pergamos? If they are part of what may be going on here, what if they meet once a year or once every ten years, and I've missed them? What if Satan has changed the position of his throne? What if the passage in Revelation is symbolic rather than literal?

Mûsâ had bought Sam a Bible. Sam had specifically requested one at the villa to take with him. He'd thought that the next section of his mission would demand it. After all, it was the Word that had identified Pergamos as his destination. He decided to see if he could discover within the Bible's pages any clues as to the precise location of Satan's throne.

As Sam searched the Scriptures, he closely examined the many passages that make it clear that Satan and his demons are not in Hell but free to roam the Earth and still have access to Heaven. There was one chapter in particular that greatly aided his understanding of the other passages, because it contained an ordered sequence of events—Revelation 12. Each of the other passages related to this topic fits comfortably before, within or after the verses of this chapter without conflict. The same can be said of additional passages regarding critical events in our universe.

Revelation 12:1 And there appeared a great wonder in heaven; a woman clothed with the sun, and the moon under her feet, and upon her head a crown of twelve stars:
2 And she being with child cried, travailing in birth, and pained to be delivered.
3 And there appeared another wonder in heaven; and behold a great red dragon, having seven heads and ten horns, and seven crowns upon his heads.
4 And his tail drew the third part of the stars of heaven, and did cast them to the earth: and the dragon stood before the woman

which was ready to be delivered, for to devour her child as soon as it was born.

5 And she brought forth a man child, who was to rule all nations with a rod of iron: and her child was caught up unto God, and *to* his throne.

6 And the woman fled into the wilderness, where she hath a place prepared of God, that they should feed her there a thousand two hundred *and* threescore days.

7 And there was war in heaven: Michael and his angels fought against the dragon; and the dragon fought and his angels,

8 And prevailed not; neither was their place found any more in heaven.

9 And the great dragon was cast out, that old serpent, called the Devil, and Satan, which deceiveth the whole world: he was cast out into the earth, and his angels were cast out with him.

10 And I heard a loud voice saying in heaven, Now is come salvation, and strength, and the kingdom of our God, and the power of his Christ: for the accuser of our brethren is cast down, which accused them before our God day and night.

11 And they overcame him by the blood of the Lamb, and by the word of their testimony; and they loved not their lives unto the death.

12 Therefore rejoice, *ye* heavens, and ye that dwell in them. Woe to the inhabiters of the earth and of the sea! for the devil is come down unto you, having great wrath, because he knoweth that he hath but a short time.

13 And when the dragon saw that he was cast unto the earth, he persecuted the woman which brought forth the man *child.*

14 And to the woman were given two wings of a great eagle, that she might fly into the wilderness, into her place, where she is nourished for a time, and times, and half a time, from the face of the serpent.

15 And the serpent cast out of his mouth water as a flood after the woman, that he might cause her to be carried away of the flood.

16 And the earth helped the woman, and the earth opened her mouth, and swallowed up the flood which the dragon cast out of his mouth.

17 And the dragon was wroth with the woman, and went to make war with the remnant of her seed, which keep the commandments of God, and have the testimony of Jesus Christ.

As Sam read each verse, he referred to the other passages in the Bible, mentioned earlier, when and where appropriate. Revelation chapter 12 is heavy with symbolism but easily interpreted with many of the explanations within the passage itself.

Verse 1 starts with Israel. The ordered sequence of significant events before the time of Israel were: the creation of the angels;[1] the creation of the Earth and the living beings that populate it (including mankind);[2] the sin of Satan and his demons and the loss of their original roles;[3] Satan cast out of Heaven;[4] Adam and Eve succumbed to temptation in the Garden of Eden;[5] the Flood;[6] the attempted construction of the City and Tower of Babel in Shinar (an area now in Iraq), at which time everybody spoke the same language and lived together; God confounded the language and scattered mankind over the face of all the Earth;[7] the separation of the continents of the Earth during the lifetime of Peleg (fifth generation from the Flood), which therefore divided many of the new linguistic groups with water barriers;[8] and

---

[1] Job 38:4-7. See Timeline.

[2] Genesis 1:1-2:2. See Timeline.

[3] Isaiah 14:12-14, Ezekiel 28:12-17, Luke 10:17-18. See Timeline, and see Chapter 1 pg 25 and footnote regarding Lucifer cast out of Heaven with his rebel angels (demons).

[4] Luke 10:17-18.

[5] Genesis 3:1-24.

[6] Genesis 6:1-8:22. See Timeline.

[7] Genesis 11:1-9. See Timeline.

[8] Genesis 10:25, 11:10-19. See Timeline.

Abraham left Haran, having been selected by God to be His servant.[1] Jacob (a grandson of Abraham) had his name changed to Israel by God.[2] The woman in Revelation 12:1 represents the nation of Israel, as according to Joseph's dream in Genesis, the sun represents Jacob (the father of the twelve tribes of Israel), the moon represents Rachel (a mother of two of the tribes) and the 11 stars represent Joseph's brothers, the other sons of Jacob. Joseph was himself in the dream; hence 12 sons of Jacob are represented in the dream. In Revelation 12:1 the 12 sons are represented by 12 stars. The descendants of each son became a tribe of Israel.[3] Set in a period around the time of the beginning of the tribes of Israel, the book of Job demonstrates that Satan still has access to Heaven to meet with God when He meets with angels, except now to criticize those humans who are faithful to Him.[4]

Verse 2: Israel suffered, because she was both blessed and burdened by the prophecies of the Messiah to come, the child.[5] The prophecies were a burden, because Israel was targeted by Satan for at least approximately 1,000 years before the prophecies came to fruition.[6]

---

[1] Genesis 11:28-12:5, 18:1-5. See Timeline.

[2] Genesis 32:28.

[3] Genesis 35:5-26, 37:1-11. 49:1-28.

[4] Job 1:6-12, 2:1-7. Job was a post-Flood individual (for when he lived see footnote in Chapter 4 pg 97 regarding the delayed extinction of some large dinosaurs). Genesis 49:1-33—Jacob declared the tribal system before he died in 1859 BC (see Timeline).

[5] The earliest prophecy to the Hebrews regarding the Messiah coming from them was to Abraham the Hebrew (Genesis 14:13), an ancestor of the 12 tribes of Israel, approximately 2,000 years before Jesus was born. Genesis 22:18 (earliest prophecy as above), Isaiah 9:6-7, Micah 5:2, Zechariah 3:1-10.

[6] Counted from the earliest biblical documentation of Satan's direct opposition to Israel. 1 Chronicles 21:1-30 (this is the earliest, which occurred during David's reign as king, around 1000 BC—see

FOOTNOTE CONTINUED ON THE NEXT PAGE

Verse 3: There is a red dragon who is Satan (verse 9).

Verse 4: Satan and his angels still have access to Heaven. In a way the first "casting out" was a termination of their jobs, but they still have right of entry. They use their right of entry to cause trouble. However, events in Heaven were about to be less interesting for them than those on Earth. Satan drew his demonic crew to Earth, as their undivided attention would be needed there. At that time the demons who were still able to do his bidding made up a third of the angels (stars of Heaven).[1]

Verse 5: A great event unfolded on Earth and was a forerunner of more to come. From Israel came the Messiah. God was born on Earth as a man.[2] God the Father's purpose is that one day the Messiah will rule the whole Earth; however, this was not the objective of the Messiah's first coming. The New Testament reveals that during Jesus' time on Earth there was a huge amount of demonic activity in Israel: there were many rampant possessions and even a temptation of Jesus by Satan.[3] The aim of Satan was to destroy the Messiah and His mission. This was why he needed to draw his demons down to Earth. Jesus died for the sins of the world, came back to life and was taken up to be with God the Father in Heaven.[4]

CONTINUED FOOTNOTE PRESENT

Timeline), Zechariah 3:1-10. Israel continues to be targeted by Satan for other reasons related to God's favour toward this nation of people; some of these reasons are made apparent in Creation's Mutiny.

[1] See Chapter 1 pg 24 and footnote regarding the stars of God. The demons imprisoned in the Abyss were no longer under Satan's command (see Chapter 4 pg 104 and footnote regarding the Abyss).

[2] Isaiah 9:6-7, Micah 5:2, John 1:1-36, Romans 1:1-5, 1 Timothy 3:16, 1 John 4:1-4. See Timeline.

[3] Matthew 4:1-11, 4:24, 8:16, Mark 1:13, 1:32, Luke 4:2-13 and many more.

[4] Isaiah 53:1-12, Zechariah 3:1-10, Matthew 26:1-28:20, Mark 14:1-16:20, Luke 22:1-24:53, John 13:1-21:25, Romans 3:23-25, 1

FOOTNOTE CONTINUED ON THE NEXT PAGE

Verse 6: The passage leaps to a time in the future when Israel will be persecuted and needs to flee from civilization to a place that has been prepared for the people's safety by God.

Verses 7 to 9: There will be a war in Heaven (the Battle of Heaven). Satan, the great deceiver of our world, and his demons will be beaten by the angelic army of the archangel, Michael, and will lose their right of entry to Heaven forever.

Verses 10 to 12: Satan will no longer be able to visit God to accuse those humans on Earth who are faithful to Him. This is a task that Satan currently spends a great deal of his time doing, as he performs it day and night. The residents of Heaven will be glad that Satan no longer has access there. As a consequence of this loss of admittance, Satan will turn his full attention to affairs on Earth, and he will be angry, because he will know that his time as the ruler of Earth will be almost up.

Verses 13 to 16: Satan will focus his rage on Israel: specifically, the remnant of Israel, who are faithful to God and believe in Jesus the Messiah (verse 17). Satan will send his minions (the flood) out to attack this remnant of Israel, but his horde's mission will be thwarted. Indeed, they will be defeated by Jesus, who will return to Earth at this time to intercede. Furthermore, Jesus will cast the leader of Satan's human minions, the Antichrist, into the Lake of Fire.[1]

Verse 17: Therefore, Satan will personally go to war against the remnant of Israel. Satan will then be bound and sealed in the Abyss.[2]

CONTINUED FOOTNOTE PRESENT

Corinthians 15:1-9, Hebrews 10:10-14, 1 John 2:1-2. See Chapter 20 pg 397 and footnote regarding Jesus now at the right hand of God the Father.

[1] Isaiah 34:1-10, Zechariah 14:1-16, Revelation 19:11-21. See Timeline.

[2] Revelation 20:1-3. See Timeline. The Abyss is the Bottomless Pit (see Chapter 4 pg 104 and footnote regarding the Abyss).

Sam's search of the Bible had been thorough and methodical, yet no matter how deeply he delved, he couldn't find any information regarding the precise location of Satan's throne within Pergamos. The Bible simply states that Satan's throne is in Pergamos. Sam would have to continue investigating the hard way.

At the beginning of Sam's third week in Bergama he decided to venture out at night in the hope of finding the throne or clues to its location. It was then the 20th of August. The clinical studies in Cambridge were due to start on the 8th of September. He thought about Cambridge's flat green landscape as he walked silently up the hill toward the Attalid ruins. His life in Cambridge seemed so remote from his current situation. The university was purposefully sheltering and comfortable for its students: its goal was to allow them to focus on their studies. Turkey had been a place of danger, stress and pain, yet at the same time it had been a place that had galvanized his Christian resolve. If he returned to England, Turkey would stay with him. He was sure of that.

It was one o'clock in the morning. The hill was deserted, and no artificial light was there. A thin crescent moon provided a feeble glow, which softly illuminated the ancient upper city. Sam carried a torch but had no plans to use it except in case of an emergency. From the town below the light would be like a flare on the hill.

Sam's first stop was the altar of Zeus. It had been built around 2,200 years ago and devoted to the worship of the chief Greek deity. A large portion of it was excavated and transported to Berlin in the 19th century. In Bergama all that now remains of the altar is its extensive foundation. As Sam paced methodically over the site, he wondered about the being known as Zeus. Sam was already convinced that Zeus was a Nephil, one of the giants, one of those men of renown, who was now long dead. As a Nephil, Zeus would have dominated normal humans and had the first choice of women, the result of which would have been more giants. His direct offspring would have begat further giants, and they more giants, and this would have continued for a number of generations. Eventually, his descendants would have attained normal stature as a consequence of the dilution of their genes with regular humans.[1] Another notion then crossed Sam's mind: maybe Zeus was a demon who'd fathered many first-generation Nephilim. Sam remembered what he'd been taught in school about Zeus' origin. Within the legends, Zeus' birth and growth are described. A similar record exists for his father, Cronus, one of the Titans, which suggests that both were Nephilim. Perhaps fatherless Uranus—a being described as the personification of the sky, and the reported ancestor of both Zeus and Cronus[2]—was the demon, Sam thought. He pondered over the fact that Zeus, Cronus and Uranus were all thought of as gods.[3] From the

---

[1] See Chapter 14 and relevant footnotes regarding the heights of the descendants of Zeus [first number in square brackets is the height in feet; second number is the number of generations from Zeus]: Hercules [18, 1] (pg 320), Ajax [16, 3] (pg 319 for height, pg 315 for lineage) and Orestes [10½, 5] (pg 320).

[2] Reportedly, Uranus was the father of Cronus, who was the father of Zeus: Hesiod's Theogony *lines 126-822* (Uranus—no childhood, no father but born from a female Earth), Apollodorus' The Library Book 1 *chapter 1:1-2:1* (Uranus—no childhood, no father and no mother).

[3] Uranus was reportedly sacrificed to as a god: Library of History by Diodorus Siculus Book 5 *chapter 71:1-3* (the individual who performed the sacrifice was Zeus, who was seeking divine guidance!).

Cronus, regarded as the chief of the Titan gods fathered by Uranus: Hesiod's Theogony *lines 126-138, 163-210, 383-403, 630-733.*

Zeus, regarded as the king of the Olympian gods: Hesiod's Theogony *lines 886-7,* Homer's Iliad Book 1 *lines 493-510,* Book 8 *lines 1-27.*

The accounts illustrate the belief that the ultimate ruler over intelligent beings was first Uranus, who was supplanted by Cronus, who was subsequently supplanted by Zeus: Hesiod's Theogony

FOOTNOTE CONTINUED ON THE NEXT PAGE

record of Zeus' development to maturity Sam derived his conclusion, unaltered from previously, that this supposed god was indeed a Nephil—an opinion that Sol Hodaviah shared. However, there were a couple of things that neither Sam nor Sol Hodaviah had taken into account that favoured the possibility of Zeus the demon with a made-up human-like ancestry. Firstly, Zeus was believed to have seduced women in a variety of different physical forms.[1] The ability to change form is certainly

CONTINUED FOOTNOTE PRESENT

---

lines 126-210, 453-506, 617-735, Apollodorus' The Library Book 1 *chapters 1:1-2.1.*

[1] Reportedly, in the form of a shower of gold, Zeus seduced and had intercourse with Danae; the offspring from the union was Perseus: Apollodorus' The Library Book *2 chapter 4:1*, Ovid's Metamorphoses Book 4 *lines 604-611*, Book 6 *lines 103-114*, Hyginus' Fabulae *63*. Apollodorus' account also mentions the alternative possibility of Danae having been seduced by a descendant of Poseidon called Proetus (see Chapter 22 pg 490 and footnote regarding Nephilic manufacture for Proetus' reported lineage).

Reportedly, in the form of Alcmene's husband Amphytrion, Zeus seduced and had intercourse with Alcmene; the offspring from the union was Hercules: Apollodorus' The Library Book 2 *chapter 4:8*, Library of History by Diodorus Siculus Book 4 *chapter 9:1-7*, Ovid's Metamorphoses Book 6 *lines 103-114*, Pausanias' Description of Greece Book 5 *chapter 18:3*, Hyginus' Fabulae *29*.

Reportedly, in the form of a bull, Zeus seduced Europa; he abducted her to Crete by carrying her on his back and then had intercourse with her there; the offspring from the union were Minos, Sarpedon and Rhadamanthys: Apollodorus' The Library Book 3 *chapter 1:1-2*, Hesiod's Catalogue of Women *fragment 89*, Ovid's Metamorphoses Book 2 *line 843*-Book 3 *line 2*, Book 6 *lines 103-107*. An alternative is that Zeus abducted Europa, carrying her to Crete on a bull: Library of History by Diodorus Siculus Book 4 *chapter 60:2-4*.

Reportedly, in the form of a swan, Zeus seduced and had intercourse with Leda; their daughter from the union was Helen*:

FOOTNOTE CONTINUED ON THE NEXT PAGE

possessed by angels,[1] which is expected considering that they're spirits, who can take on solid form, but I think unlikely to be exhibited in their enormous human offspring, who existed in mortal solid form.[2] On the other hand, this morphing ability was also reportedly exhibited by some Olympians who were offspring of Zeus.[3] Maybe the Nephilim's devotion to sorcery and adept-

CONTINUED FOOTNOTE PRESENT

Apollodorus' The Library Book 3 *chapter 10:6-7*, Euripides' Helen *lines 16-22, 211-219*, Hyginus' Fabulae *77* (this reference states that Zeus ravished Leda). An alternative is that in the form of a swan, Zeus seduced and had intercourse with Nemesis; the offspring from the union was Helen, and she was adopted by Leda (same Apollodorus reference).

*It has been reported that Zeus and Leda also had a son called Pollux (same Apollodorus and Hyginus references) or two sons, Pollux and Castor (Homeric Hymns *17 To the Dioscuri lines 1-5, 33 To the Dioscuri lines 1-19*).

[1] 2 Corinthians 11:14.

[2] Regarding solidity, there is no mention of any of the Nephilim changing form in the Bible; however, it doesn't categorically say that they can't.

[3] Reportedly, in the form of vultures, Athena and Apollo watched the Trojans and the Greeks when Hector proposed a single-combat fight to the death with a Greek champion: Homer's Iliad Book 7 *lines 55-91*.

Reportedly, in the form of a dolphin, Apollo recruited his ministers: Homeric Hymns *3 To Apollo lines 387-543*.

Athena reportedly transformed herself into the form of Deïphobus (a brother of Hector) in order to trick Hector into a dual with Achilles: Homer's Iliad Book 22 *lines 224-259, 289-305*.

For Apollo's reported lineage see Chapter 8 pg 177 and footnote regarding his parentage.

Athena was reportedly an offspring of Zeus: Hesiod's Theogony *lines 886-900, 924-926*, Homer's Iliad Book 1 *lines 188-205*, Apollodorus' The Library Book 1 *chapter 3:6*, Homeric Hymns *28 To Athena lines 1-18*.

ness at it, inherent from being kin to demons, granted some of these giants special powers through demonic intervention that gave them either the ability to transform or the illusion of such to others. Secondly, mythographers reported that Zeus—who had a living daughter and son, Helen and Sarpedon respectively,[1] who were involved in the Trojan War—oversaw the conflict[2] and had living descendants who were as many as seven generations from him—such as Hector and Aeneas[3]—who were embroiled in the very same war, thus, in this instance, placing Zeus' influence over an approximately 175-year period, from 1375 to 1200 BC,[4] which falls in the era when the maximum age of humans was 120 years (1406 BC and onward[5]). This suggests that Zeus was a

---

[1] For Helen see earlier in this chapter pg 463 regarding Zeus' seduction of women—the accompanying footnote contains more details on her reported lineage.

For Sarpedon the son of Laodameia (not Sarpedon the son of Europa) see Chapter 14 pg 320 regarding Hercules having lived one generation before the Trojan War—the accompanying footnote contains more details.

[2] Throughout Homer's Iliad and Quintus Smyrnaeus' The Fall of Troy Zeus is reported to have been overseeing the Trojan War.

[3] See Chapter 14 pg 314 and footnote regarding the Trojans Priam, Hector and Aeneas all reportedly having been descendants of Zeus. Hector having had an infant son, Astyanax, is also mentioned in Homer's Iliad (Book 6 *lines 390-413*), which would make eight generations. Astyanax is not included in the math in the next footnote, as he was a minor during the war.

[4] This was calculated as follows. The Trojan War was around 1200 BC. Assuming that each generation was 25 years, then in 1375 BC Zeus fathered the first member (Dardanus) of the 7-generation aristocratic lineage of the Trojan royal house. Therefore, a span of 175 years would potentially separate Dardanus' birth from the Trojan War.

[5] The year of the death of Moses (1406 BC) marks the year of the establishment of the 120-year maximum age steady state. See
FOOTNOTE CONTINUED ON THE NEXT PAGE

demon who repeatedly manifested himself over a span of many
generations. The alternative is that Zeus was a Nephil with an
extremely long lifespan. Perhaps the demonic genes did more
than just magnify the size of humans but also their longevity. In
other words, maybe the changes to humanity following the Flood
that brought the maximum age from around 1000 years to 120
years could be counteracted by demonic genes. So conceivably
the Nephilim of the generations closest to the demons would live
much longer than the surrounding normal humans,[1] adding
further to some of these Nephilim's perceived immortality.[2]
Other possibilities are that the mythographers mistakenly
attributed the same name Zeus to different Nephilim or even to
different demons: perhaps easily done as he was portrayed as a
remote Olympian character.[3]

CONTINUED FOOTNOTE PRESENT

Deuteronomy 34:5-12, Joshua 1:1-2, Timeline and Chapter 4 pgs
94–95 and footnotes regarding this topic.

[1] And the effect could be maintained from generation to generation
if the giants procreated amongst themselves, thereby retaining the
demonic genes. Three of many possible examples are: Zeus himself,
who was reportedly a son of Cronus and Rhea, both Titans and
brother and sister; Apollo, who was reportedly the son of Zeus and
Leto, a daughter of Coeus and Phoebe, who were both Titans and
again brother and sister; and Ares, who was reportedly a son of
Zeus and Hera, once more brother and sister. All of the above
individuals were considered to be gods. Hesiod's Theogony *lines 1-
21, 126-138, 404-428, 453-506, 918-920, 921-923*, Apollodorus'
The Library Book 1 *chapters 1:1-4:1*. Homer's Iliad Book 1 *lines
43-52*, Book 5 *lines 846-908*.

[2] And regarding the Nephilim of the pre-Flood era, perhaps the
demonic genes could reduce the speed of aging and thus extend life
beyond 1,000 years.

[3] That is, residing on Mount Olympus in Greece and ruling over
those like himself: Homer's Iliad Book 1 *lines 568-611*, Hesiod's
Theogony *lines 35-52*.

Clearly Greek mythology is unable to provide a conclusive answer to the question of the exact nature of Zeus, being riddled with embellishments, imprecise chronology and inconsistencies.[1] However, the mythology indicates that supernatural beings had relations with humans, the result of which were giants with extraordinary abilities. Many of the characters within the mythology have been aggrandized by certain entities, thereby making gods of some of those who are actually the demon-fathers and some of their enormous human offspring. The Bible contains an accurate explanation of the origins of all these beings and reveals conclusively that none of them were gods.

Sam walked to the temple of Athena and after that to the library. In its day the library of Pergamos was inferior only to its rival in Alexandria. From there he explored the remains of the temple of the emperor Trajan and then moved on to the north-easternmost section of the Attalid ruins to investigate the palaces of the kings. Sam paused to survey the surroundings. To the east he could see the moon reflected in the meandering waters of the Kestel Çayi River. The modern town slept below him to the west. To the distant north and south were more hills. It was then almost five o'clock in the morning. Unable to properly explore the entire Attalid ruins in a single night, he returned on two successive nights. None of the three visits provided him with any new insights. Therefore, on the following night, instead of going east, he headed west to the remains of the Roman city.

Within the Roman ruins is the temple of healing dedicated to the god Aesculapius, a giant and a son of Apollo,[2] and it was

---

[1] The same can be declared for Roman mythology, which identifies Jupiter with Zeus. In addition to Greek records of Zeus, Roman records of Jupiter have been used in Creation's Mutiny to understand the individual known as Zeus.

[2] Aesculapius was reportedly a son of Apollo (and therefore a grandson of Zeus—see Chapter 8 pg 177 and footnote for the lineage of Apollo). Aesculapius' bones were worshipped and were described as being of human form but of exaggerated size. Note that
FOOTNOTE CONTINUED ON THE NEXT PAGE

there that Sam started his search. In the temple's day people came from far and wide, seeking treatments within it.[1] There is still a road lined with stone pillars that stretches from the temple toward the city centre. Within the temple, snakes had been held in a pit—as mentioned earlier, the serpent was a creature particularly associated with the worship of Aesculapius.[2] Sam explored the remains of this pit but found nothing of interest. He carefully searched the rest of the temple before moving on toward the Sacred Well, positioned further west.

On the previous three nights the illumination of Sam's work had mostly been provided by the moon, which had now waned to its full extent. As he approached the well, he noticed a flat array of artificial lights beyond the Roman ruins. The lights were 20 feet above the horizon and at a distance of less than 300 metres from him. He continued toward the well. He wondered if it led to a subterranean chamber similar to the ruins north of Afyon that were the cover for his place of torture. Instead of a deep well, he saw that the hole had been purposely filled with rocks to prevent tourists from injuring themselves. He'd deduced that if there was a physical throne of Satan, then it must be underground, and if

CONTINUED FOOTNOTE PRESENT

---

although he was widely worshipped as a god, the fact that he was reduced to dead bones clearly demonstrates a very mortal nature. Library of History by Diodorus Siculus Book 4 *chapter 71:1-4,* Pindar's Pythian Odes 3 *lines 1-62,* Pausanias' Description of Greece Book 2 *chapter 26:1-10,* Book 3 *chapter 22:9,* Hyginus' Fabulae *14:21.*

[1] In general, treatments were sought for and administered at the temples of Aesculapius: Strabo's Geography Book 8 *chapter 6:15,* Livy's History of Rome Book 45 *chapter 28:1-4,* Pausanias' Description of Greece Book 2 *chapters 26:1-27:6.*

[2] Pausanias' Description of Greece Book 2 *chapter 11:5-8.* See also earlier in this chapter and relevant footnotes regarding Aesculapius, the Greco-Roman god of medicine (pg 450), and Aesculapius' representation in imagery (pg 450).

humans were permitted to enter the presumed accompanying throne chamber, then there had to be a superficial entrance.

It was four o'clock in the morning by the time Sam had satisfied himself that the Roman ruins wouldn't further his cause. Before returning to the town, he decided to investigate the lights to the west. After covering a distance of 100 metres toward them, he realized that he was approaching a military base. He could make out a set of barracks and military vehicles. He lay flat on the ground. The terrain was even, and he leopard-crawled further in order to conceal his approach. As he came closer, he noticed uniformed soldiers patrolling the base. He stopped at a distance of 75 metres and observed what went on for the next hour. He noted the number of guards, and also the number of buildings and their probable functions. He worked out which building housed the electrical generator for the compound. What a perfect cover the base could be for the entrance to Satan's throne chamber, he thought. Guarded by the Turkish armed forces, the entrance would be off limits to inquisitive Turkish-civilians and tourists. Could the entrance be hidden inside one of the buildings? Perhaps only a few hand-picked high-level members of the military knew the precise location. He continued to consider the possibilities as he crawled stealthily away from the base.

Over the following five days Sam occupied himself with formulating a plan to enter the military base. During this time he'd returned at night on two further occasions with his pair of binoculars to more thoroughly scrutinize the site. On each of these nights he'd spent over four hours viewing the base from different angles. At first it had seemed utterly impossible for him to enter and investigate undetected, even for a few minutes. However, by the end of the third reconnaissance, he'd come up with a plan that made the venture a fraction less than suicidal.

Sam was back in the flat following the third reconnaissance. He ate breakfast, then watched the sunlight lift the night from the streets of Bergama. He thought of ways to improve his chance of success at the base. They wouldn't be expecting him. That much he knew. He envisaged ways to maximize this advantage: maybe by disabling the generator or creating a distraction. These thoughts took him to his bed, and he slept till two o'clock in the afternoon.

Sam arose and looked out of the window toward the hotel. He'd missed the early arrivals. The street was busy with traffic and pedestrians. A family of five stepped into a taxi near the lobby of the hotel. The day was approaching its maximum heat, and Sam turned away in order to head for the kitchen for a glass of water. As he did so, from the corner of his right eye, he saw a woman walking quickly toward the hotel.

"Well looky here, shouldn't you be in Singapore by now," Sam said as he fastened his gaze through the window again. The woman who'd called herself Prasseda was wearing a jogging suit and carried a gym bag in her right hand. Her hair was tied back in a pony tail, which bobbed as she walked. "Travelling alone are we? Where's your blonde friend?" Prasseda strode into the hotel and out of view.

Sam showered, then hastily dressed. He returned to the window.

That night Prasseda made a swift exit from the hotel and turned to her right to walk along the adjacent street. Sam scrambled down the stairs of the apartment block and calmly strode onto the street. Prasseda was already 50 metres ahead. Sam made no attempt to catch up but continued to pursue from a distance, as the streets were well lit and he wasn't disguised. He stayed on the opposite pavement to her. She was dressed smartly in a trouser suit and walked confidently, only turning her head to cross roads. Her high heels had predicted a short journey, which ended at a restaurant near the main shopping area in the heart of town. Sam hadn't been to this part of Bergama before. Although it was night, the location was busy. Many of the shops were still open. He became conscious of his vulnerability in this open area. Prasseda entered the restaurant. Sam didn't follow. He approached a nearby market stall that sold leather goods, which was seven metres away from the restaurant and slightly to the right of its façade (Sam's left). While pretending to examine the dealer's wares, Sam watched Prasseda through the restaurant's large front window. She talked with one of the waiters, then walked with him deeper into the dark candlelit interior; they weaved between occupied tables as they went. For a few seconds she disappeared, then re-emerged further still as an elegant figure beneath a bright outdoor light. Subsequently, she was guided away from this light and out of Sam's sight.

The outdoor light illuminated a paved alfresco area beyond the rear of the indoor section of the restaurant. This terrace was partly visible because of large windows and an open back door in the far wall of the restaurant's interior. There were tables and chairs on the terrace, which had a view of a pretty garden. The outdoor dining area was as busy as inside. Despite the bright light of the terrace, the features of those present were obscured by their relative distance from Sam. Furthermore, he became frustrated that Prasseda remained out of sight. He needed a better view.

The leather merchant muttered something to Sam, who placed the leather jacket that he held in his hands back onto its hanger. Sam moved away from the market stall and walked into the shop that was to the left of the restaurant's façade. As he entered, the young woman who sat at the cashier's desk said in Turkish: "We're closing in five minutes."

Sam looked at his watch. It was five to nine. The shop sold crockery, tableware and cooking utensils. The other customers were only a young couple, each of whom carried a basket that contained a few items. Sam drifted to the rear of the shop. In front of the rear window were backless shelves, on which glass tumblers and jugs were neatly stacked. The shop lacked the depth of the restaurant, and consequently he was able to see only a fraction of the outdoor dining area. He'd estimated that there were eight or nine outside tables, judging from the width of the restaurant, the depth of the terrace and the table density. He could see three whole tables. Prasseda was not seated at any of them. He maximized his viewing angle by walking to his right, which was in a direction away from the restaurant. He could visualize another whole table and half of another. He looked behind him at the cashier's desk. The couple were paying for their selected items. After that, the cashier's attention would turn to him. He still couldn't see Prasseda. The four whole tables were fully occupied. The half-table's visible occupant was a smartly dressed middle-aged man. He was talking to someone who must have been sat opposite him with his or her back to the indoor section of the restaurant. Sam could see the smart man clearly. This man—whom Sam estimated to be around fifty—was clean-shaven and possessed a full head of black hair. He wore an expensive navy-blue suit, which was thin enough for the heat yet well structured. He had thin lips, which lifted his early jowls as he talked. Sam thought that the smart man looked Mediterranean but not Turkish.

"We're closing now," the woman called to Sam. "Is there anything that you want to buy?"

"These glasses," Sam asked in his broken Turkish, "are they made here in Turkey?"

The woman got up and walked toward Sam. He'd bought himself some time. As the woman inspected the base of one of the glasses, he looked over her shoulder to view the terrace. He saw the unmistakable nose and mouth of Prasseda come into view. She was the person sat opposite the smartly dressed man. Visible for half a second, she then receded from view.

"No, they're from Italy," the shop assistant said.

Sam was sat in a dark recess of a cafeteria that was more or less opposite the restaurant but at a much greater distance than the leather-goods stall. Eight minutes earlier he'd watched Prasseda leave the restaurant alone and set off in the direction of the hotel. Sam had remained seated. It was now almost eleven o'clock, and the smartly dressed man left the restaurant. He walked in the opposite direction to Prasseda, and Sam followed.

Sam pursued the smart man from a distance and mostly from the shadows. Sam could have risked coming closer, as he and this middle-aged man had never met, yet wisely decided to hang back. The smart man walked for less than ten minutes before entering a town house with a well-kept exterior. Sam saw three lights switched on in succession. An hour later they were all extinguished.

Sam watched the house till two in the morning. Since going dark, there hadn't been the faintest stir from inside, so he returned to his apartment, having judged that nothing more would happen that night. He returned to the town house at dawn disguised as a street cleaner, biding his time in conspicuous view. He'd slept for only two hours. At midday the Mediterranean man left, wearing a crisp, new tan-coloured suit, which was completed with a white shirt and a light-pastel-blue tie. Sam found a concealed area, where he slipped out of his overalls to reveal typical tourist garb. He packed the overalls and his cleaner's cap into a small backpack. He quickly tidied his hair with his fingers and started his pursuit.

At a different restaurant, which was on the northern edge of Bergama, the Mediterranean man met two other men, neither of whom Sam recognized. They were both older than the man whom Sam had correctly deduced to be Italian. One of the two new men looked Japanese and the other German. The trio lunched at the restaurant. After they split up, Sam was presented with the option of following any one of the three. He decided to stick with the Italian.

The following day the Italian met another man, who was unmistakably an Arabian; their rendezvous was in a Range Rover. Sam could see them talking behind tinted glass. They were sat on the rear passenger seats. There were two other men in the vehicle, who occupied the driver's seat and the front passenger seat. They had the appearance of bodyguards but were not vigilant: clearly overly comfortable with their situation. The meeting was brief, lasting just over ten minutes.

The next day and night were uneventful. The Italian man hadn't left the town house and had had no visitors. There had been detectable activity, water draining from the plumbing and lights going on and off, but no exit. All the lights had been turned off by eleven o'clock. Sam had watched the house till midnight, after which he'd returned to his apartment.

It was then the fifth day of Sam's shadowing of the Italian man. Sam was wearing normal garb: a pair of beige chinos and a navy-blue polo shirt. The street on which the town house lay was immaculate after his efforts, and any further cleaning would arouse suspicion of madness as much as espionage. He loitered in a nearby street that provided a narrow view of the door of the town house. The Italian left at around midday, and Sam followed at a distance of 30 metres. The Italian was dressed in the dark suit that he'd worn to meet with Prasseda. He walked to a moderately busy restaurant in South Bergama. Sam watched as the Italian talked briefly with a waiter and then as the Italian sat at a small table near to the front window. There was no especially convenient location from where Sam could bide his time to discreetly watch the proceedings unfold. The street was wide and uncluttered. There were two shops with a view on the opposite side of the street. One of them sold shoes and the other provided a dry-cleaning service. Sam entered the former and started browsing the merchandise.

From the position of the shoe shop Sam was surprised to see the Italian man make his order while still alone. A bottle arrived two minutes later, and red wine was carefully decanted into a glass. One of the shop assistants asked Sam if he needed any help. Sam politely declined. Five minutes passed by. The Italian remained alone. Another of the shop assistants was hovering: this time a man. Sam was holding a pair of brown brogues in his hands and sent the assistant to find a pair of size nines. Sam sat down on one of the shop's benches. It was the only one that faced the shop window and hence the restaurant. Four minutes later and the shoes fit surprisingly well. The Italian still sat alone, and his hors d'oeuvre arrived. Sam asked the male shop assistant for the brogues in half a size larger. The Italian received a call on his mobile phone. He spoke for three minutes, then calmly put the phone back into his right jacket pocket. The shoes didn't fit well at all. Sam thanked the male assistant, left the shoe shop, crossed the road and walked into the restaurant.

Sam was greeted similarly to the Italian man. Sam was initially offered a table that was too close to the focus of pursuit. The Italian looked up at the newcomer. Sam was careful to not meet the Italian's gaze. Instead, Sam read the middle-aged man's eyes while swiftly scanning the restaurant in the pretence of trying to pick a table. There was indifference in the eyes. Sam pointed to a table in the dark and quiet rear of the restaurant. He'd also read something else in the eyes: lack of expectation. The Italian wasn't waiting for anybody.

Sam ordered a single-course meal. As his water in a sealed bottle was opened and poured, the Italian man's main course arrived. Sam was sat so that his passive sight was directly toward the Italian's profile. The middle-aged man took his time. He initiated two phone calls during his meal. Sam's lunch arrived. The Italian called a waiter.

The meetings of individuals with such diversity of nationalities had shown considerable promise to Sam's investigation. He thought: but what of today? Is this purely about the man passing time? Sam started to question his reasoning behind following the Italian. How important is this man in the overall scheme of things? The Italian paid his bill, after which he walked to the rear of the restaurant toward the sign for the toilets. Sam stared at the Italian's table. The bottle of wine was two-thirds full. I should have followed one of the other men, Sam thought. Tomorrow, if he meets anyone who looks to be a bigger fish, then I'll pursue him instead. If only I had a car, I'd have followed the Arabian.

Sam quickly finished his meal. He waited for the Italian man to return. Ten minutes went by, but no one came from the direction of the toilets. After a further five minutes, Sam got up and went toward them himself. As he walked, he noticed one of the waitresses cast a glance in his direction. There was slight curiosity in her eyes. The sign for the toilets led Sam down three steps and along a short corridor, which ended with a blank wall straight ahead and two opposing doors: one to his right and the other to his left. Sam turned right and opened the door with the bronze matchstick man attached. The revolver was in the right pocket of Sam's chinos. In the left pocket was the screwdriver, whose handle he ensured could be easily reached. No other customers had walked in the direction of the toilets in the last fifteen minutes, and therefore he was expecting to meet only one person inside. Instead, he found no one.

The men's room had a privacy partition after the door. Beyond this the room had two stalls to the right, both positioned at the back. The room was clean. There was a large mirror over two capacious sinks, which were situated to Sam's immediate left. To his right, before the stalls, the wall was blank. Although each stall's entrance faced the left wall, their doors were wide open, and the emptiness of the men's room had been evident the instant he'd walked past the partition. "Where on Earth did you go?" he said quietly to himself.

At the end of the men's room there was a single rectangular frosted-glass window, which was horizontally positioned at a level of six feet above the floor. The permeating light was unable to adequately illuminate the room, and four fluorescent lamps on the ceiling provided the majority required. Sam was having difficulty imagining the middle-aged man climbing up to the window and crawling through the tight space. The window was closed shut and had a lock that could be fastened only from the inside. Sam noted that the lock was indeed fastened. He was concerned. Maybe the Italian had caught on to the fact that he'd been followed and had used that exit, which had then been locked behind him by an as yet unseen accomplice. Or perhaps the Italian was in the ladies' room, hiding or already escaped. There'll be another day, Sam thought. After all, he knew where the man lived. But Sam would have to be much more careful from now on. He then perceived the full gravity of the possible situation of the Italian realizing that he'd been followed. If that was truly the case, then it was grounds to leave Bergama. Now Sam was anxious. The Italian would talk with the others.

Someone would recognize Sam's description, and they'd be looking for him. Maybe they were even on the way now.

There was another possibility. Sam decided to check the place carefully. He looked over the stalls. They were quite ordinary, each with nothing present other than a bowl and a cistern. The next item to be examined was the mirror. It was firmly bolted to the wall. He turned out the lights and could see no evidence of the mirror being two-way—although to better test this, he would need to also occlude the light from the window. He turned the lights back on. He looked around himself at the walls. They were covered with tiles. He was aware of the time that he was spending in the men's room. He didn't want to arouse any suspicion. He was also possibly burning into his escape time. The next thing that he did was to quietly perform "percussion" on the walls. Percussion is a technique used by doctors in order to determine the density of tissue beneath the skin of a patient. The doctor presses the palmar side of his (or her) left middle finger against the patient. He then gently taps his right middle finger on the upper surface of the left middle finger. This action produces a tone that signals what lies beneath. The tone can vary from resonant to dull. Air is resonant and water is dull. Percussion can be performed very gently and quietly, as the nerves along the length of the left middle finger can detect and distinguish the tone, even when inaudible. This is why percussion is superior to simply tapping with one finger, the tip of which would need to impact with more force to similarly ascertain the tone. Three of the walls were completely dull. The wall that he next tested was also dull except for a single square area, which was resonant. This section was four feet high, tiled like the rest of the wall and located in the blank section that had been to his right on entering the men's room (beyond the partition). He pushed the section hard. Although nothing opened, the centre of the square could be depressed by two millimetres, indicating that there was nothing immediately behind this tiled area.

Sam unlocked the room's window by releasing the catch. There were two hinges on the window's upper border. He pushed the window. It opened outward. The hinges were stiff. He stopped pushing once the window's lower edge was two centimetres from the frame. He walked back into the dining area, paid his bill and left.

It didn't take Sam long to locate the exterior of the window of the men's room. He was in a quiet alley, which contained two large refuse bins for the restaurant. The window was positioned at a level of three feet above the ground. He listened for sounds from within. When he was satisfied that no one was there, he pulled the window open and slipped inside.

Sam closed the window and locked it securely. Short of smashing the resonant panel with his foot, there appeared to be no way of opening the panel in the immediate vicinity. His aim was to leave no trace of having been there. He commenced a more careful search. He went back to the stalls. He looked inside the two cisterns, first into the one closest to the panel and then into the one furthest away. Although outwardly identical, there was a discrepancy between their internal mechanisms. He returned to the first cistern, which had an extra lever below the waterline. He dipped his right hand into the water. He tugged the extra lever and simultaneously heard a click outside the stall. He returned the hood of the cistern to its place and left the stall. The left edge of the panel had flipped open, and the right edge was now three centimetres deeper than the wall. He pulled the left edge toward him. In the centre of each of the upper and lower edges was a vertical pivot, which allowed the panel to smoothly rotate. The only illumination beyond the panel was provided by the light from the men's room. This light revealed a dark stairwell made of stone, which led steeply downward. He entered and closed the panel behind him.

Chapter 22   **Pergamos**

And no marvel; for Satan himself is transformed into an angel of light. Therefore *it is* no great thing if his ministers also be transformed as the ministers of righteousness; whose end shall be according to their works.

2 Corinthians 11:14-15.

Sam leaned his back on the wall that had been to his left in order to register his new surroundings. He was hunched, because the height of the stairwell was only four feet. Its width was the same. The air was still. There was a single sliver of light where the panel hadn't made a perfect seal. The light dissolved into the darkness round about. He felt a thin handle on the panel's interior surface. He began a half-test of an intended exit by pushing the handle downward. He stopped when the handle was tilted fifteen degrees. He'd felt the characteristic give after an increase in resistance, which was the sign that the panel would open if he pushed any further. He released the handle, then silently prayed.

Dear Heavenly Father, Almighty God, my faithful Lord, please forgive my sins.
Let Your mercy rain down on me.
Thank You for sending your Son, Jesus, to Earth.
I'm a sinner, but His blood has covered all my wrongs.
Thank You for the Turkish Christians who've helped me.
Please save them from harm.
Thank You for Mûsâ.
Touch his heart and mind.
Help him to see that Jesus is the Messiah God.
Give him the courage to choose your Son.
Thank You for the life that You've given me, the life that's in Your hands.

I want to live, yet there's no question in my mind that I need to follow this stairwell.

Please give me the strength to go on.

Help me.

Protect me.

Shield me from the prince of the power of the air and from his minions as I know You've done in the past.

You've given me a place in Heaven, not because I'm worthy, but because I believe in Your Son. Whatever I encounter, whatever happens next, I know that this can't be taken from me.

Merciful Jesus, intercede for me.

Oh, my Lord Jesus, God King, creator of the universe, I long for the day when You rule from Zion.[1]

Let that day come swiftly.

Sam's eyes had adapted to the darkness. The slice of light from the men's room now appeared to weakly illuminate his surroundings. He listened very carefully. He could hear a vague buzz that came from the restaurant and nothing else. Stooping, he slowly and quietly started his descent. At first he moved whilst holding his hands—palms facing up—flat against the stone ceiling to protect his head. After a few steps, he no longer needed to stoop, because the ceiling had descended less than the stairway. He was then surrounded by total darkness. He'd brought his pen torch but didn't dare switch it on. Before long only his fingertips could feel the stone with his arms stretched fully upward. He now placed his hands against the stone walls, one hand on each side, for guidance and to reduce the pressure of his weight on the steps and hence the sound of his footfalls. He soon developed a steady rhythm that allowed him to quicken his pace yet maintain his silence.

Once Sam had put the restaurant approximately 200 metres behind him, he stopped and listened. He heard nothing. He carried on. The stairwell progressed downward. Its width

---

[1] Jerusalem.

continued to be four feet across. His movements remained stealthy. After two minutes, he felt a breeze on his face. He looked upward but could see nothing. He stood on his tiptoes while stretching his arms upward. A strong current of cool air swept through his fingers. He touched a metal frame. His fingers searched and felt a metal grille within and firmly attached to the frame. Around the frame, which was square, he pressed stone. He resumed his descent. The breeze lessened until it was barely there. Every 25 metres he could feel the wind intensify and deduced that he was passing more vents.

Sam stopped. He thought that he'd heard a sound. He stood perfectly still and listened intently. He could hear the faint sound of footsteps ahead of him. He remained frozen in the darkness. An additional fifteen seconds allowed him to determine that the footsteps were headed away from him. When they'd completely faded, he recommenced his downward journey. He presumed that the person ahead of him was the Italian man. Sam now ensured that his own pace would be slower than that of the Italian.

Sam estimated that he'd walked half a mile at an angle that had varied irregularly between thirty-five and forty-five degrees. He wondered how far the stairwell would go. He'd hoped to see other stairwells or passageways on the way but hadn't. He'd seen no light and deduced that the Italian was so far ahead that his torch, if the man had one, wouldn't be visible—the variation in the angle of the stairwell prevented visualization of direct light beyond certain distances that depended on where a viewer was relative to the light source. At that moment Sam heard another sound. He halted his steps.

"Damn!" Sam whispered. Footsteps gaining in audible strength were coming from the stairwell behind him. He stood silently. He felt trapped, enclosed in the stone stairwell with the Italian somewhere in front and a newcomer descending from behind. Sam thought about continuing downward in the hope of finding options for evasion. He also considered, as the first part of an escape attempt, confronting the person who must have entered the stairwell from the restaurant after him.

Sam pressed on. He moved as fast as he could whilst making every attempt to maintain his silence. The footsteps from behind grew louder still. Sam felt the wind intensify and stopped. He reached up with both hands in the darkness and examined one of the sources of ventilation more closely with his fingertips. He paid greater attention to the frame of the grille this time. He felt the heads of four screws, one at each corner, that were securing the frame to its fittings. Each head would receive a screwdriver with a flat blade tip—exactly the type that he had with him. He immediately got to work. He didn't rush. He'd learnt from performing basic medical procedures that when under pressure, he performed best if he relaxed. From the sound of the footsteps he estimated that their owner was 150 metres behind. Sam turned his head to look. He could now see a hazy luminosity.

Sam carefully caught each of the screws in his left hand and placed them into his left front trouser pocket. Even with all the screws removed, the frame didn't fall. With the screwdriver at one of the edges, he tried to pry loose the frame. The grille was old and corroded. Particles of rust fell onto his eyes as the frame started to loosen. The darkness meant that he'd had no warning. He blinked repetitively. The torchlight was now clearly visible as an undulating yellow bulb moving rhythmically as its holder descended. The bearer was not visible behind the light. The frame came free at two of the four corners. Sam loosely reinserted one of the screws, fixing the associated corner, and pulled the rest of the frame free. The grille was welded to the frame, and they moved together. He jumped up to gain a purchase with his hands, then hoisted himself up into the tight tubular ventilation shaft, which had a diameter of just three feet and was made of stone, similar to the stairwell. There was barely enough room to turn around, yet he managed. He pulled the loose frame back into position by gripping the grille, his fingers passing through the mesh. The frame held in place, but he was concerned that a corner or corners might fall because of his earlier efforts to loosen the frame. He felt the four metal brackets that were attached to the stone shaft and had been designed to receive the screws used to secure the frame. The brackets wouldn't help him. He jammed a small coin between one of the edges of the frame and the stone that was opposite to tighten the fit.

The descent had reminded him of his night journey in Cappadocia. The difference was that the Cappadocian caverns were an intersecting network of passageways designed for multipurpose social interaction, whereas the Pergamene stairwell had every indication of leading toward a single goal. Within the ventilation shaft, the current of air, which had been travelling downward, changed direction to travel upward, although with less force.

Sam waited. He lay flat on his stomach with his eyes in the direction of the grille. The footsteps were now almost directly beneath him, and a soft indirect light entered the ventilation shaft. Seconds later he saw a man walking briskly below with a torch held in his right hand. Sam recognized the walker as the German whom he'd seen with the Italian three days previously. The German took no notice of the grille as he walked under it. His footsteps soon faded.

Sam wondered how many more people would be using the stairwell from the restaurant. He decided to continue his descent through the ventilation shaft in the hope that it would continue to follow the stairwell. And indeed the shaft did: parallel and at the same angle. His progress was slow, because he had to crawl. He stopped to listen for further footsteps at each grille that he met.

After 200 metres, the ventilation shaft gradually levelled off, that is, it became horizontal. Sam had expected to pass another grille 25 metres after the preceding one, but none had emerged. He continued to crawl horizontally. Soon he saw a faint yellow glow 35 metres ahead of him. He crept cautiously toward the radiance. He could see that there would be no more grilles beneath him before he reached the light.

10 metres on Sam could see an end to the shaft (25 metres ahead), demarcated by a vertical circular grille, and that the light actually originated from beyond the shaft. The circular grille was the entire width of the shaft and therefore much larger than the

square grilles. As Sam approached the circular grille, he became completely focused on what lay beyond.

Sam could see a vast oval-shaped hall, the floor of which was 30 metres beneath him. There were people present. The hall's size and Sam's relative position in his lofty perch reminded him of spectating in a sports stadium. However, there were no tiered seats and the hall was clearly designed to be a place of grim congregation. He estimated that the distance between the two furthest edges of the oval was 250 metres, which made the hall greater in size than any arena that he'd ever seen. He was positioned in the upper southern perimeter, a location at one of the two shallow curves of the oval. The hall's light was provided by four bowls of fire. Each bowl was a perfect half-sphere, roughly 5 metres across. None of them intruded into the central area. They were positioned on the floor, each being the point of a large imaginary rectangle whose location and dimensions optimized the illumination that the bowls of fire together provided. In spite of this, the overall light was dim owing to their small size relative to the enormous hall.

The people were positioned within the gloomy yet best-lit central area. The majority of them stood silently, while a few walked slowly about the group, whispering greetings. Sam counted the total number to be thirty-three—all men. They were dressed smartly, each man in attire that was individual to him— but all wore darkly tinted goggles. The goggles resembled the ones used by swimmers in that they each had two individual lenses and a tight rubber strap that secured them firmly to the wearer's head. Sam wondered how well the assembled men could see in the already dusky hall. He then got his answer as he saw one of them bump into another.

Sam noticed a man enter the hall from the east. As this man stepped toward the group, he turned off his torch and put on his goggles. He hadn't entered through a doorway in a wall. Instead, he'd negotiated his way between pillars. Sam saw that pillars stretched around the hall. Those at the front were well spaced, while those behind were progressively more tightly packed the deeper they were positioned, and ultimately he was unable to see beyond them. It was like looking into a forest from its periphery. He presumed that this was the situation for the entire circumference of the hall, although he couldn't see the pillars beneath him to 50 metres on either side. Another man entered except from the northwest, again switching off his torch and donning his goggles after he cleared the innermost screen of pillars. A few minutes later a woman in an emerald-green dress appeared from below Sam—he at first had looked almost vertically downward to see her. Her torch was off, and she was already wearing her goggles. Even in the poor light, Sam recognized her as Prasseda. The stairwell from the restaurant had continued downward as the ventilation shaft had levelled off and must have led to an entrance directly beneath him. Having seen different people enter from different points of the compass, Sam concluded that there were many entrances to the hall, which were fed from different locations in Bergama.

Within the central area, there was a single empty seat, which had the appearance of a throne. It was in an off-centre position with its back facing east. The people were assembled before it—vassals patiently waiting for their king. The throne was plain and distinctly uncomfortable. There were no cushions, and it appeared to be made entirely of stone. What troubled Sam was the throne's size. It was 12 feet in width. The actual seating area was eight feet wide, because each solid-stone arm had a width of two feet. Similarly, two feet of the throne's ten-foot depth was taken up by the back of the throne, which extended upward to an overall height of 15 feet.

The opposite side of the oval hall was 125 metres away and poorly lit. Sam's horizontal sight viewed a level where the upper portions of the innermost pillars met the base of a domed ceiling. He strained to distinguish any detail, but none was forthcoming. Besides the throne and the four bowls of fire, there appeared to be no other adornment within the austere hall.

Having surveyed the hall, Sam closely inspected the vertical grille. It was a hefty silver-white-metal lattice. Unlike the previous grilles, it showed no signs of corrosion. It seemed to merge into the circular wall of the stone ventilation shaft and had no visible screws or any other hints as to its fixity. Even in the low light, the grille had the appearance of being made from platinum. The holes of the grille were perfectly square, except at the edges; the squares each had a height and width of approximately three centimetres.

Two more men arrived to join the gathering. After this, the assembly faced the throne. They stood in silent expectation. The centre of the group was 70 metres from Sam's platinum grille as the crow flies. He recognized only those individuals whom he'd seen in the last few days. He was unable to characterize any new faces because of their tinted goggles, the lack of light and their distance from his position. However, he could tell that the assembly was made up of people of many different races and that Prasseda was indeed the only woman amongst thirty-seven men. The silence continued except for the occasional footfalls of a few of the congregation steadying themselves. The infrequent sounds travelled well in the stony hall. An hour passed by in this manner. Sam's anticipation didn't wane.

Sam started to feel a woe in the air similar to that which had accompanied the presence of Shezeren—no such disturbance had attended the demons of Ararat. Moments later Sam spied ethereal forms floating through the perimeter to enter the vast hall. They descended into position to form two orderly lines, which almost converged to resemble the letter V. The point of the V was the throne, which remained empty. In between the two lines were the humans. The demons solidified, relinquishing their wraithlike forms, to become like men. They were gigantic with heights ranging between 15 and 25 feet.[1] They stood absolutely still,

---

[1] How tall are angels in their untransformed originally created state? Impossible to determine but the following may be of interest.
Having received permission from God to build the Temple, Solomon made two cherubim of olive wood overlaid with gold: 1 Kings 6:11-38. Each cherub was 10 cubits (15 feet) in height. They

FOOTNOTE CONTINUED ON THE NEXT PAGE

each looking straight ahead at his opposite demon. The yellow
light and deep shadows held them in monochrome, and they

CONTINUED FOOTNOTE PRESENT

---

were placed in the area called the Holy of Holies with the Ark of the
Covenant. There is no record of them ever being worshipped, and
their purpose was probably to simulate the situation in the greater
Temple in Heaven, where living cherubim are present. One can
possibly infer that a height of fifteen feet is exhibited by some
angels.

In Revelation 21:9-17 one of the seven angels who had each poured
out a plague onto the Earth from a vial (Revelation 15:1-16:21)
talked with John. This angel was manifest having the same height as
a regular man. In Genesis 18:1-19:15 two angels loyal to God on
missions manifested themselves as men to humans. Three beings
visited Abraham and were referred to as men. Two of the three
beings went on to Sodom to meet Lot and were identified as angels.
The other being was God. These two passages (not bracketed) are
perhaps less useful than the passage in 1 Kings, because the angels
are likely to have transformed to prevent overwhelming intimida-
tion. The other possibility is that some angels have not only the
basic appearance of men but are also of similar height.

The kinship between demons and Nephilim could help determine
the heights of angels. In other words, perhaps special angelic genes
that determine gigantic height are passed on to the offspring, and
these genes also determine the heights of the angel-fathers themselves. This is a likely situation. (This comment, rather than those
before it and after it, carries the most weight in providing an answer
to the question.) Alternatively, it could be that there is no relationship between the heights of Nephilim and angels, and the gigantic
offspring are simply the result of the bizarre combination of angelic
and human genes; this is a less likely situation. A combination of
both of the above situations may also be a possibility.

All of the above comments are speculative. The heights of the
angels in the sentence of the main text that this footnote accompanies are speculative; the heights reflect a blending of all the above
comments.

looked like two rows of statues designed to intimidate the human assembly. There were 26 demons in all. Some of the humans looked to their left and right to view the spectacle. The majority kept their eyes fixed on the throne.

The four bowls of fire were slowly extinguished, as if the flames had been deprived of fuel. Now there was complete darkness. It lasted long enough for Sam to speculate on whether demons can see a wider spectrum of light than humans and therefore see in the apparent blackness of the hall.

Light returned slowly like the dawn. Instead of multiple sources, there was then just one, which was located above the seat of the throne. The source of light was an orb, but the inexorable increase in brightness soon obscured its form. Sam saw that the humans had already bowed themselves low to the ground. They were on their knees with their heads facing downward, noses almost touching the floor, and their arms were thrust out frontward. The demons were also on their knees, though they continued to face one another. They were no less a formidable portrayal of physical power than when standing. They'd not turned in the direction of the throne, because they were on parade to demonstrate their obedience to their leader and therefore his potency. This was a day when humans met their master. The demons' meetings were held at other times.

The light's origin lengthened vertically and became so bright that Sam's eyes began to hurt. His overriding curiosity compelled him to continue staring, only the light became too intense, and he had to turn away. His eyes were cast upon the hall, which he now noticed was far from plain, although still austere. Having passed from the obscurity of darkness to clarity, within seconds the hall was then returned to obscurity by the blanching effect of the intensifying white light. Sam tried to look toward the throne again. Before he could fix his gaze, his mind and body forced his face away as they do when one attempts to stare at the midday sun.

The source of light took the form of a man and was Lucifer. He was sat on his throne, emitting as much radiant splendour as he could generate. He uttered a single word, and all the beings in the hall rose to their feet. Sam made another effort to look directly at the light's origin, hoping that his eyes would have adapted to the level of brightness. He had to divert his gaze a third time. He noticed that even some of the men below, in spite of being goggled, had to look away until their eyes became accustomed to the light.

Despite Sam's inability to stare at the centre of attention, his eyes had adjusted enough to view the hall in detail again. The floor was made of marble with a most peculiar natural design. The pattern was symmetrical yet lacked repetition, so that it seemed to have been created by the splaying out of two halves of a single stone that had been split down the middle. His eyes were drawn to the intricate pattern, which would have suited a serpent's back. The multitude of cylindrical pillars, which bordered the hall, were each made of a single block of polished light-grey stone and reached a height of 30 metres. A single canal ran vertically up each of the innermost pillars. Each canal was filled with solid gold. The canals didn't cease at the pillars' summits, but each canal branched into new channels, which radiated into the domed ceiling: a crisscrossing array forming triangles, squares, diamonds, hexagons, octagons and other geometric shapes. The dome was made of black granite, and the web of gold gave the ceiling a strangely disturbing vitality. Sam could see that there were sporadic circular interruptions in some of the gold-filled canals at the base of the dome. The interruptions were positioned immediately after the canals had extended from the pillars but before the branching. He noticed circular grilles within the interruptions. The grilles were identical to the one that covered his ventilation shaft. He counted fifteen of these grilles beyond his own. He inferred that there were more, which were out of sight, and that each circular grille, whether visible or not, led to a shaft that communicated with its own stairwell. There were no other interruptions to the continuity of the gold-filled canals. At first the grilles had been barely noticeable, as the width of the canals was the same as the width of the circular interruptions, which gave an indication as to the tremendous overall breadth of each pillar. All things considered, he deduced that the hall had not been made by ordinary human hands, unlike the stairwell and ventilation shaft through which he'd descended. Sam knelt at the interface of that which was of normal human construction and that which was of either demonic or Nephilic manufacture.[1]

---

[1] Regarding Nephilic manufacture:

Teuthrania and early Pergamos were both reportedly ruled by descendants of Zeus: Telephus and Pergamos respectively (see Chapter 21 pg 453 and relevant footnotes regarding these topics). Consider two ancient cities that were reportedly ruled by descendants of believed immortals and the great walls of which were built by either supposed immortals or Cyclopes.

(i) Troy was ruled by Laomedon, believed to be a descendant of Zeus (see footnote in Chapter 14 pg 314 regarding his son Priam having been a descendant of Zeus). The wall of Troy was reportedly built by Poseidon and Apollo. Apollodorus' The Library Book 2 *chapter 5:9*, Hyginus' Fabulae *89,* Homer's Iliad Book 7 *lines 442-453,* Book 21 *lines 434-461* (in the first reference of Homer it is reported that both Poseidon and Apollo built the wall, but in the second Poseidon alone).

(ii) Tiryns, in Greece, was ruled by Proetus, reportedly a descendant of Poseidon (Poseidon was the father of Belus, who was the father of Danaus, who was the father of Hypermnestra, who was the mother of Abas, who was the father of Proetus). The wall of Tiryns was reportedly built by seven Cyclopes from Lycia (today a region of Southwest Turkey). They were a different group of Cyclopes from Polyphemus and his brothers, who were reportedly sons of Poseidon and lived on an island (see footnote in Chapter 3 pg 73 regarding Neptune having been the father of colossal giants). Pausanias' Description of Greece Book 2 *chapters 16:1-7, 25:8-9,* Apollodorus' The Library Book 2 *chapters 1:4-2:2,* Strabo's Geography Book 8 *chapter 6:11.*

Were parts of Teuthrania and/or early Pergamos similarly constructed?

Sam was unprepared to view Satan in all his glory as Heelel, son of the morning.[1] Sam quietly adjusted his position and sat awkwardly with his back against the curved wall of the ventilation shaft. He had no sunglasses with him at that time or at any time on the mission. They were an indulgence and restricted his vision, a limitation that might have proved fatal. He removed a banknote from his wallet and put a single pinhole through one of the darkest sections. He raised the banknote to his right eye, closed his left and knelt to peer through the platinum grille once more. The pinhole worked by occluding the greater proportion of light at the expense of overall clarity.

Comparing Satan to the attendant demons, Sam estimated that the prince of demons was around 21 feet tall. Perfect in beauty, the Bible states.[2] Indeed, the preeminent angel was formidably handsome and faultlessly proportioned, yet at the same time he possessed a profoundly individual character. He had a crown on his head. His armour of gold, decorated with precious stones, extended from neck to knees. He was barefooted.

"Grand Inquisitor," Satan said; his voice was singular, deep and clear.

A man stepped forward a few paces, separating himself from the human assembly. He was the Italian man, who'd met with Prasseda. Before speaking, the Grand Inquisitor bowed again: this time while on one knee. Satan spoke to the bowed man in Latin, asking him to rise to his feet.

The Grand Inquisitor spoke in English with an Italian accent, "Mighty lord, god of the Earth, perpetual one, we come before you today in worship. We're grateful that you deem humanity worthy to stand in your presence and receive your guidance. We thank you for the powers that you've bestowed on us, and we profess our eternal loyalty to you." He followed this with a few

---

[1] Isaiah 14:12.

[2] Ezekiel 28:12-17. See Chapter 1 pg 23 and footnote regarding Lucifer having been the anointed cherub for sacred duties for a detailed explanation of the passage in which these verses reside.

sentences in Latin, then briefly bowed his head. Instead of returning to his original position, he remained close to the huge throne. From this spot, with a gentle beckoning of his left hand, he invited the next man to make his address.

The second man stepped forward more boldly than the first. Sam hadn't heard a title to introduce this man. Sam wondered if he'd missed something, because he now faced the Grand Inquisitor's back. The second man also bowed while on one knee. Satan nodded, and the man stood. This man has been here many times before, Sam thought. Whilst studying the second man, Sam noticed a momentary flash of pale-blue light discharged from the direction of Lucifer. Sam refocused on Satan, but the blue light was gone. Now looking toward the human assembly, Sam saw that some of its members were recovering from having recently shrunk back. The second man spoke in English with a Turkish accent. He spent the first five minutes commending Lucifer on his attributes and thanking him for the gifts that he'd given to the human congregation during their lives. The Turkish man then started to make various cursory accounts of recent world events (the majority of which Lucifer undoubtedly had prior knowledge of) but occasionally went into greater depth where he thought necessary. He relished his own speech. While he addressed his god, now and then the Turk would turn to different members of the human assembly when he referred to things directly relevant to them. Sam presumed that this speech was more for the Turk's human comrades than for Lucifer. Nevertheless, Sam had been able to tell that at least three of the finer details Lucifer hadn't already known, judging by his subtle change in expression on hearing them. With this round-up of world events complete, the Turk proceeded to praise Lucifer.

Despite the goggles, Sam noticed a striking similarity in the Turk's physical appearance to another man, who'd stood to the right of this speaker before he'd stepped forward. Sam removed the banknote from his right eye and held up his right hand to block the light emanating from Lucifer. With both eyes, Sam examined the two similar-looking men more closely. They were both slim and of medium height, though the speaker was slightly taller than the other man. They were clean-shaven. Their hair was dark brown, but the speaker was starting to go bald, whereas the other man was not. Sam noticed subtle differences in their profiles, which were more variations on a theme rather than contrasting characteristics. The features of their faces that most distinguished them from others were the pair's similarly pointed noses and thin lips. Although Sam correctly deduced that they were brothers, he couldn't determine the eldest. They both had the appearance of being in their early fifties. There was also something about the current speaker's voice that was slightly familiar; however, Sam was positive that he'd never heard this Turk speak before.

Lucifer interrupted the balding Turk and spoke to him in Turkish. Sam understood a third of what Satan had said but wondered if the rest of the human assembly had. The balding Turk replied in Turkish. After his lengthy discourse, he returned to his original position, next to his brother. The Grand Inquisitor remained. Sam returned the banknote to his right eye and closed his left again.

The next man to step forward was the German. The protocol was for each human to bow whilst on a single bended knee before being asked or motioned to stand. The German did likewise.

"Mighty lord, for eighty-five years Pergamos has been open to all the nations of the world; you've been gracious to allow this," the German proclaimed in English. I'm sure that modern travel has something to do with it as well, Sam thought.

"So here we are representing the peoples of the Earth." Despite the excellent acoustic properties of the hall, Sam was straining to hear what the German was saying. The German spoke at a lower volume than the preceding two men. "The eighty-five years have seen one of the world wars and numerous lesser conflicts."

Sam thought it logical to assume that before this time the throne of Satan had been open to humans of Mediterranean Europe and the Middle East. He considered the Assyrian, Babylonian, Persian, Greek, Roman and Ottoman Empires—each either close to Pergamos or possessing the city within its boundaries.

"Now there are a lingua franca and technology that link us all. But our steps to unite have been thwarted by events that cannot be fully accounted for by the actions and machinations of men alone."

"It will happen. When the time is right, it will happen," Lucifer said.

Satan continued with his reassurances. As Sam was looking directly at the cherub, the blue light materialized. It was lightning that cracked around Lucifer's glowing body. The lightning lasted for less than a quarter of a second and left this angel with a dramatically changed appearance. He'd transformed into a dragon, seated on the throne, his tail curling from the base of his spine to lie motionless at his clawed feet. He had seven heads, each attached to a strong neck. The seven necks united at the summit of a widened upper torso. On each head was a crown. The shapes of his limbs still resembled that of a man only covered in crimson scales. He wore the same armor, notwithstanding his altered frame. The heads looked similar to one another except that three possessed two horns, while the rest had only one, making a total of ten horns.[1] The heads brought to mind those of predatory dinosaurs that Sam had seen illustrated in books but didn't exactly correspond with any of the species that he'd seen displayed. The chief difference was the proportionally larger size of the Dragon's eyes, which were highly intelligent in appearance. The central head's mouth moved in accordance with what the human-shaped mouth had been articulating, and there was no interruption in Satan's dialogue. This head's eyes remained on the German. The mouths of the other heads were closed and silent, yet the many eyes of these heads actively scanned the human congregation. The semblance of the Dragon lasted for a whole second. No one below had drawn back this time; Sam could sense their fear though. He was

---

[1] Revelation 12:3.

convinced that Satan could have suppressed this dragon visage but had purposefully decided not to. Lucifer wanted to demonstrate that beneath his angelic form lurked a monster. This would serve to magnify his own perceived complexity and instill dread in those who witnessed the Dragon.[1]

"Persist with these efforts toward unification, but you must never lose sight of why you do this: to prepare the way for the king of Babylon. Work to this end," Satan said, widely addressing all the human congregants. "The One who died talks of a harvest of Christian souls.[2] You need to continue to plant seeds for His opposite incarnate. This opposite, the king of Babylon, will also one day reap a harvest. The conditions must be right before he steps forth. Continue to place the right people into the right positions. Those people can't be choked by weeds. Undermine the Christians. Create laws to marginalize them. Use those laws to strike their bodies, and their spirits will fail them. You'll receive help from my angels in all of these things."

"Yes, my lord."

Even if only one individual was talking with Satan, this demon's address was potentially to all the humans in the hall—whom his communication was meant to instruct was determined by the content. However, all could be "illuminated" by even a specific address to one person—if they understood the language.

Lucifer continued, "You wish to communicate with me about the Balkans; even as we speak, the conflict rages in Macedonia. The Dutch troops are close to being wiped out. Your combined French and German forces will be destroyed tomorrow by the infantry division of General Yavorov. You didn't send enough men. You underestimated him. He's planning to move swiftly

---

[1] Satan has both the appearance of a man and of a dragon, and as he is able to transform, he may have other appearances: Isaiah 14:12-17, 2 Corinthians 11:14, Revelation 12:3-17, 13:2-4, 16:13, 20:2. Satan's created appearance is that of a man. See Chapter 1 pg 22 and footnote regarding this topic.

[2] Luke 10:1-2, John 4:34-38. See Soul and Spirit.

against you before dawn—south of Skopje. You can avoid this defeat and shame—and remain in power—by withdrawing your troops to the mountains. Execute precision missile offensives overnight, then attack them at midday."

The German thanked Satan for the advice and proceeded to report other matters. At various times they spoke together in German but mostly they conversed in English, the lingua franca. Sam thought about people who believe that Satan is in Hell. How wrong can they be? The place that Sam saw was expensively constructed. Yet it was sparse and lent little to comfort. However, one would expect Satan to use Pergamos infrequently, because he's an angel who dislikes being still, preferring to: roam the Earth, engaging in the affairs of nations and even individual men and women; and make accusations in Heaven against the Creator's faithful people on Earth.[1]

The next man to present himself spoke Spanish with an Argentinean accent. He was the first person to make his address entirely in his native language. Lucifer had conversed with the Argentinean in Spanish—clearly able to reply in whatever language a person spoke. The next man was Nigerian and spoke Hausa. Sam had recognized a few Spanish words but couldn't understand a word of Hausa.

Subsequently, the Arabian man who owned the Range Rover stepped forward to present himself. He was clean-shaven except for a thin moustache and wore a dark suit. After a short exchange with Lucifer, the Arabian was joined by five other men of various nationalities. One of them was the Grand Inquisitor, who'd merely needed to step forward two paces in order to add himself to the group.

Satan spoke first, "I approve of the latest revisions to the Babylon plans. The world is more than ready for the city to rise

---

[1] 1 Chronicles 21:1-30, Job 1:6-22, Isaiah 14:12-17, 1 Peter 5:8, Revelation 12:10, 20:2-3. See also Chapter 1 pg 25 and Chapter 21 pgs 459-460 as well as any relevant accompanying footnotes regarding right of entry to Heaven for Satan and other demons.

again. Still, there will be opposition, not just from Christians but also from some within your own religions." Satan had directed his last statement toward the Grand Inquisitor, two men with long thick beards—one of them was another Arab and the other was Slavic—and an Indian man. The garbs of the latter three spoke volumes as to the religions that they represented.

"This is the way of things, but the city will be built as a concerted effort by you all; this should be made public regardless of the opposition that you'll encounter," Satan directed this statement with its accompanying instruction toward everyone within the group. Now to the entire human congregation, "It will be the greatest city on Earth, eclipsing all others as it did before. Economic stability will radiate from it and permeate the Earth. Eventually, a united religion will flourish in Babylon. Discord will become accord."

Some of the men in the six-man group then briefly conversed with Satan in English, the content adding little to what Satan had already declared.

Four of the men withdrew to the general congregation and the Grand Inquisitor returned to his previous position. A tall, blond man remained. His attire resembled that of a financier. He spoke in English with a strong American accent. The majority of topics that he discussed with Satan were indeed related to financial matters, even when they touched on Babylon again toward the end.

Once the American had been dismissed, five new men sequentially presented themselves, representing different sections of the world. Their reports had been secular, as was their attire, and these things they had in common with the German, the Argentinean, the Nigerian, the secular Arab of the Babylon group and the American. Following the withdrawal of the most recent man, the secular Arab presented himself again to complete the discussion of his region. So in all the secular representatives were ten. Each had spoken about a territory greater than his country of origin. Sam inferred the territories to be: North America; South America; Australasia; the Far East; southern

Asia; Russia and affiliated states; the Middle East; Africa; eastern Europe; and western Europe.

After the secular Arabian had resumed his position, it was then the turn of a different faction to step forward. Satan introduced the next set of discussions with the following preamble: "In Pergamos you are united against the Creator. The world sees you as antagonists. The present situation will continue for a short time more. However, soon the world will see you advance together as one with a unified purpose. The least to the greatest will be won over. Persist with your preparations for this." He'd said these words in a manner that suggested that he'd repeated them for years, even generations. The men who would now present themselves were representatives of a diversity of the world's religions. If more than one man represented one religion, they would address Satan as a group.

The first of these religious representatives stepped forward alone. "I'm pleased to report that within the Western world the theory of evolution has been accepted by mainstream society."

Sam had recognized this religious representative before he'd even reached the words "theory of evolution" because of his distinctive voice. He was a goggled Arthur Hamilton—celebrated atheist and media personality. Hamilton called himself a secular humanist, and it was well known that he'd given some of his fortune to charitable organizations.

Hamilton continued, "Although not necessarily the greatest in numbers, we represent the fastest growing religion on the globe. Our efforts have meant that people even believe that evolution is a scientifically proven fact. And many have combined it with their own religions. We continue to press for the indoctrination of children in those schools that remain resistant. Conditioning as early as possible is imperative. But you already know this, all-seeing god."

"And what of those scientific reports that show that the Bible is the truth?" Lucifer asked. "There are more discoveries coming to the fore. I personally watched five of them being uncovered for the first time."

"Master, you've been here from the start. The Earth has seen only a few thousand years; proven science points to this fact—it's inescapable."

"And I commend you and your colleagues on your interpretive manipulation of the raw data."

"We continue to ensure that scientific facts regarding the origin of life on Earth, the origin of the planet itself and what has transpired here over time are drowned in theories. That will be how these facts will continue to appear in the scientific journals. Even now the facts are so buried by the theories that only the most scrupulous of scientists are able to tease out the truth. As for the material for the public domain, it will continue to contain an even smaller percentage of fact and the rest of what's written will be palatable simplifications of our theories—stated as facts, of course."

"Some of your colleagues are digging too deep. Their curiosity has gotten the better of them. Some have turned away from us to the One who died."

"Yes, but so few, master. They're unsupported voices crying in the wilderness."

"Suppress them!"

"Yes, my master."

Two Hindu priests presented themselves next,[1] one of whom had previously stood with the group who'd discussed Babylon. The Hindu priests were followed by a Buddhist cleric, who stood alone.[2] They'd all spoken in languages that Sam couldn't understand.

The next group consisted of four Muslim clerics. That was immediately obvious to Sam because of their beards and characteristic clothing. One of them had already been part of the Babylon group. Sam had figured that this cleric was an Iraqi mufti.

---

[1] See Chapter 13 pg 285 and footnote regarding Hinduism.
[2] See Chapter 13 pg 285 and footnote regarding Buddhism.

"I accept your human sacrifices—not just those who destroy themselves for your faith but those they take with them as well," Satan directed his words to all four clerics in English. There was another revelatory glimpse of the Dragon.

"The Jews now have control of Jerusalem. Our spies tell us that their preparations to rebuild the Temple on the Mount are complete," a cleric—evidently Palestinian and probably a mufti—said in English. "They're planning to act soon. They will rebuild it in no other place than on where the two successive Jewish Temples once stood: where Qubbat aṣ-Ṣakhrah[1] and the Al-Aqṣā Mosque now stand. We'll lose one of our holiest sites, and even worse, the Jews will claim a great victory over us, having firmly established themselves in the land once more. What do you advise, my lord?"

Satan answered, "Do these three things. Do as the rich man does with ample funds at his disposal, as is the case with you. Money will buy men and arms. Also, do as the man does who is poor and desperate. Sympathy will draw popular support. Finally, do as the trickster does, using deceit to achieve his end. Make and break deals when it suits you best."

"In what order shall I attempt this, master?"

"Do all three things together, except make your methods known to only those closest to you."

"Yes, my lord."

Sam's pity was great for those under the yoke of such a man.

"Hold off this Jewish venture for as long as you can, and you will be greatly rewarded," Satan said.

Of the next three, the first two spoke to Lucifer in Arabic. Sam hadn't understood their conversations but had been able to pick out some proper nouns that confirmed that the first, the Muslim cleric of the Babylon group, was indeed a mufti from Iraq and the second was from Saudi Arabia. These two had each spoken at length. They'd received their replies from Satan in Arabic. The final Muslim cleric spoke in Persian.

---

[1] The Dome of the Rock.

The Roman Catholics followed and had four members, including the Grand Inquisitor. Their discourse was in Latin. While they were speaking, Sam occasionally glanced at Prasseda to detect her reaction to Satan conversing with representatives of her professed religion. Throughout the discourse she stood steadfast, and although goggled, she was magnificent in her beauty. The Eastern Orthodox clerics came next, speaking in Russian. There were three members, one of whom had already presented himself in the Babylon discourse yet had said nothing at that time. The Catholic conversations lasted an hour and a half. Sam was dismayed at how much information he'd missed. As previously mentioned, in school he'd learnt to read and write Latin, but it hadn't been taught as a spoken language. Nevertheless, he'd picked out a few words of possible interest and had noticed that one of the Roman Catholic clerics had a Spanish accent and another had a German accent. All of the spoken Russian had been a complete loss.

The Catholics were followed by a single Church of England cleric, who spoke in English. Firstly, for his efforts to reconcile the Church of England with the Roman Catholic Church,[1] he was commended by Satan. The true aim was that the reconciliation would be followed by a merger of the two churches, with the Roman Catholic Church as the dominant organization. The

---

[1] The Church of England (which is the origin of the Anglican Churches) was initially a breakaway section of the Roman Catholic Church (a consequence of the schism of 1534, precipitated by Henry VIII, see Chapter 20 pg 436), then later became a Protestant institution. However, features of Roman Catholicism remain such as: infant baptism (a person cannot become a true Christian if it's not his or her will to do so); baptism by sprinkling water onto the individual—note that some Church of England churches, as an optional alternative to the sprinkling of water, baptize adult converts by full immersion (see Chapter 11 pg 242 and footnote for both baptism topics); and in some churches there is idolatry in the form of statues and icons of Mary.

English cleric was then warned about eight evangelical clerics within the Church of England who were resisting the reconciliation and had already identified him as the chief instigator of the movement. The eight were each named individually, one of whom was a bishop. Although not directly said, from the discourse Sam thought that the man who stood directly before Lucifer most likely carried the rank of bishop.

A Mormon[1] followed then a Jehovah's Witness.[2]

Then came the turn of the representatives of the secret societies—six men. Having been invited by the Grand Inquisitor, they approached the throne as a group, and their leader addressed Satan as Beelzebub.[3] The leader spoke in English with a British accent. He was the first of the whole assembly who'd called Satan by a specific name. The name Beelzebub means Lord of the Flies—the flies almost certainly referring to demons. The other men spoke in English but with accents different from their leader and from each other. Five of them, including the leader, were chiefs of Masonic Grand Lodges. The other headed a secret society that although not as extensive as Freemasonry, the members were highly influential. Satan spoke to all six about cohesiveness and brotherhood. He referred to them as the bond between nations, even when at war. Both secular and religious matters were discussed.

Now practically everyone had at some point presented themselves before Satan. The exceptions were the brother of the Turkish orator and Prasseda. Speaking to the entire human congregation, Satan commenced a tirade against churches and

---

[1] For more information regarding the origin and doctrine of the Mormons see footnote in Chapter 18 pg 387 regarding Joseph Smith, the founder of the Mormons.

[2] For more information regarding the doctrine of the Jehovah's Witnesses see the whole of Chapter 11 and the accompanying footnote where the Jehovah's Witnesses' stance on Jesus is mentioned (pg 249).

[3] Satan is Beelzebub: Mark 3:22-27, Luke 11:14-20.

institutions that he wished to have destroyed or made ineffective. He explained the various methods to be employed. His aim was then to deliver an even tighter address about people who were to be targeted. He started by highlighting the importance of individuals who'd been used by the Creator to thwart his plans, explaining the knock-on effect that their influence had had in their lifetimes and even after their deaths. The individual was never to be ignored. Various members of the human assembly who resided in and/or represented those parts of the world in which the targets lived came forward. It wasn't only Satan who spoke, but there was an exchange of plans and goals. The human assembly was orchestrated by the Grand Inquisitor unless countermanded by the enthroned cherub.

Sam noticed that many of the methods that were being discussed consisted of ways to discredit the targets, yet some individuals still advocated imprisonment, torture and assassination. Mostly true Christians were being targeted. Sam also observed that the speakers referred to their organization with Satan at its head simply as "the Throne". They also referred to the entire hall and Satan's throne within it as "the Throne". The correct meaning, the organization or the place, was made clear by the context. The brother of the Turkish orator was asked to step forward.

"You've been busy over the last three months," Satan said.

"Work that I gladly do for you, my master. The Ark remains a fable."

Sam had instantly recognized the voice as belonging to the chief interrogator of the dungeon located north of Afyon.

"Have you seen the body of March with your own two eyes?"

"No, but he must have died on Ararat," the Guardian of Turkey replied.

"My angels haven't found his body. The Creator has angered me with this one. For three months we've been unable to see March except for those instances when he's come into direct view within the domains of angels. He was last seen by the Ararat Three. Edorth-Ban had warned them that he may be seen there." There was a restrained nod toward one of the demons arrayed to Satan's right.

So that's how they knew that I'd met Prasseda, Sam thought. He'd not questioned himself about this before.

Satan continued, "March was exhausted and thought that he was hallucinating. He made the mistake of conversing with them. He finally resisted, and they were forced to leave him alone. When they returned, they found nothing. His corpse wouldn't be the first that the Creator has hidden from us,[1] but this doesn't mean that he's dead. There have been other people's paths that have been temporarily concealed from us; they've always been on an errand for the Creator—or connected in some way. Be that as it may, they're not invisible to the eyes of men, and their flesh can be struck by you and have been. Since March's departure there have been clouds of confusion over parts of England and spiritual barriers placed around certain people. They're still there. There have been battles with the Creator's angels, several of which have lasted for months.[2] In Turkey some angels have been unable to report to me—blocked. Even Fazarn, the angel whom I assigned to March after he became a Christian, was thwarted in

---

[1] Deuteronomy 34:5-6.

[2] There are struggles between angels and demons that take place in the background but are directly related to human activities on Earth. Daniel 10:1-21 reveals that a Messenger fought a demon called the Prince of Persia for 21 days. The Messenger was helped by Michael, the archangel, allowing Him to reach Daniel. Daniel bowed before the Messenger and called Him "my lord" (properly "my Lord"), therefore identifying Him as the Angel of the LORD, the Messiah. Verses 5 and 6 describe the appearance of the Messenger. The appearance of the resurrected Jesus the Messiah is similarly described in Revelation 1:4-18. The passage from Daniel reveals that there is another demon called the Prince of Greece (verse 20). From this passage the Prince of Persia and the Prince of Greece can both be identified as demons, because they are spirit-adversaries to both the Messenger (the Messiah) and Michael.

England.[1] I visited him there a while ago and the Ararat Three a week after their encounter with March. He'd become much stronger since being in Turkey. If March lives, he'll become a powerful opponent. I've seen a similar pattern before. I hope for your sake that he's dead."

"Yes, my lord."

Later on in the targeting discussion the House of Hodaviah was mentioned. Four of our founding members' real names were announced. One of those real names belongs to Sol Kadmiel, whose recent murder was lauded. So much for our anonymity—may God protect us!

After this discourse, which had named over a hundred people spanning the entire globe, Lucifer made it known that the meeting was at an end. As the Grand Inquisitor was tying up the proceedings, Lucifer disappeared and with him the light. The last few words of the Grand Inquisitor were uttered in absolute darkness. Within a few seconds, thirty-eight torches were switched on, and Sam could see a random display of flickering lights bobbing up and down in the central area. The two rows of demons were gone, and the bowls hadn't been relit. The humans on the marble floor now looked like spirits, being both silhouetted and lit by the hovering beams. Sam saw them holding their goggles in their hands. Slowly and without talking, the assembly dispersed in different directions. Their nodding lights radiated outward and drifted between the pillars. Their footsteps echoed in the vast hall. As they departed, the deep darkness gradually returned.

The proceedings had lasted over eight hours. It was eleven o'clock at night. Sam waited in silence. He'd become uncomfortable, having knelt in one position for such a long period of time. He quietly lay down on his stomach. His intention was to wait for

---

[1] It stands to reason that as Satan is not omnipresent and yet regularly attends meetings in Heaven to make accusations against Christians (Revelation 12:7-10), then he must assign to watch certain individuals demons who report back to him.

a further four hours. He contemplated all that he'd seen and heard. He divided the human assembly into the following three divisions: the ten world-sector representatives, the clerics and the representatives of the secret societies. However, there had been substantial crossover during the meeting, made most evident in the six-man Babylon discourse. The men who'd stepped forward on that occasion had been the North American representative, the Middle Eastern representative, a mufti from Iraq, an Eastern Orthodox cleric, a Hindu priest and the Grand Inquisitor (representing the interests of the Roman Catholic Church). There were three people who could not be easily placed within the three divisions: Prasseda, the Guardian of Turkey and his brother. The only woman present had not said a single word. Sam knew that she hadn't been there for decoration. She was an agent of the Throne, yet he'd not reached a conclusion as to her exact role.

At three o'clock in the morning Sam quietly started to leave by the way he came. Before long he arrived at the vent through which he'd entered the shaft. The coin was still wedged in place. He couldn't remove it with his fingers. He gave the grille a gentle punch, and it fell together with its frame at all the corners except the one with the screw. He climbed down onto the stairway and was careful to retrieve the coin. He returned the metal frame (with the grille intact) to its original position and secured it tightly with all four screws. He left the empty restaurant via the men's room's window and pushed it firmly closed from the alley. His only regret was that the internal lock remained unfastened. He wondered if he should have continued following the ventilation shaft upward rather than the stairwell. But who knows where that would have led? Anyway, he was out.

Chapter 23　　**Altitude**

Sam was stretched out in a metal coffin—a bitter reminder of his journey from Batman to Ararat. He needed no snorkel this time, because the coffin had been modified with concealed ventilation slits. He could feel that the plane was still climbing to reach its cruising altitude. There had been some turbulence after takeoff, and to experience this while lying flat in the dark had been disconcerting.

The noise in the cargo hold, which was where Sam was located, was much louder than in the insulated passenger cabin. The metal coffin attenuated much of the sound, but he could still hear the background hum of the two engines as they propelled the 250-seat airliner to its destination. Inside the coffin he'd hidden the four rolls of film. Also hidden was the engraved piece of wood from the Ark. He'd enveloped this precious item in a tight opaque plastic wrapper for its preservation. The revolver was buried in Turkey. He wore a black suit, white shirt and black tie. The coffin's interior had been checked visually at the airport in Cyprus. The inspection had been perfunctory, and Sam had played his brief role of "the deceased" with aplomb.

Sam was cold. The cargo hold was pressurized and heated but not maintained at the same temperature as the passenger cabin. It wouldn't do for a dead man to be wearing a coat, so before donning his funereal finery he'd put on many layers in preparation for the impending chill. It was five degrees Celsius, and he'd not made adequate provision.

From Bergama Sam had travelled by coach to the port of İzmir on the west coast. Under the identity of Anthony Burrows, Sam had taken a ship to Cyprus, where he'd met one of our contacts, Andreas, a Greek Cypriot. Andreas had provided Sam with the coffin. Andreas was an undertaker and skilled metal worker. He'd altered the coffin over a period of two days. During this time Sam had remained hidden in Andreas' home. In addition to the ventilation slits, Andreas had made panels with concealed internal catches, so that the coffin could be opened from the inside. There were two panels that could be moved to effect an exit: one that made up the majority of the upper lid and the other was part of the side of the coffin to Sam's right. The latter was in case the coffin was placed beneath cargo. Of course, this particular air coffin was illegal. All air coffins have to be hermetically sealed, so that an aircraft's ventilation system won't be contaminated by gases emitted from putrefaction or by microorganisms that can cause communicable diseases. The plan was for Sam to be flown to Heathrow Airport, where he would be received by another undertaker. From there he would be driven to a mortuary, where he'd be picked up by a relative of the deceased, a certain Dr Michael Burrows. Michael Burrows, a false identity, would be the individual known to Sam as Sol Hodaviah.

The cargo hold was open, that is, completely lacking partitions. For that reason the cargo hold appeared much larger than the passenger cabin, even though the former was smaller in volume than the latter. The luggage was stacked in seemingly randomly-distributed piles. Each pile had been placed on top of a flat square platform designed for transport. The luggage was secured to the platforms with strong, yellow plastic ribbons. The platforms were held to the floor with metal clips. Within the long, hollow space of the cargo hold, the piles, many of which were well over six feet high, formed a simple maze.

The Guardian of Turkey moved quietly through the cargo hold. He was wearing a heavy parka and held a plastic semiautomatic pistol in his right hand. The pistol had a high-velocity plastic round in the chamber, seven more in the clip and a silencer attached to the muzzle. He advanced slowly. His furtive footsteps were inaudible owing to the din of the engines. He checked piles of luggage. He spent variable amounts of time at different mounds, sometimes dismissing one at a glance, whilst at others he prowled around trying his best to determine what was held with greater visual focus. Occasionally he would push pieces of soft luggage with the tip of the silencer to gain a better view of what lay behind or beneath. He spent most of his time examining piles with larger items. He continued in this vein for thirty minutes, gradually making his way toward the front of the cargo hold. He intermittently cast a glance over one or other shoulder, worried that he might have missed something.

The Guardian wore a pair of black, fingerless leather gloves. He was too warmly dressed and was sweating from both this over-insulation and the tension of the search. He was unshaven with a stubble length that betrayed more than his confinement in the crate that he'd been packed into eight hours before. Within the crate, labelled as lost luggage, he'd been flown from Turkey to Cyprus and had then endured a long wait at the airport. His packers, his accomplices, had done only what had been asked of them, having been wholly ignorant of his goal. He'd kept them uninformed, unwilling to reveal to anyone within the organization that March was alive. He would see to March personally. As for the man who'd reported to the Guardian that March was still alive, his body was now being seen to by worms and his soul by fire.

Like a man who spots gold and ignores what had previously occupied his attention, the Guardian disregarded four stacks of luggage, two to his right and left, having seen a mound containing a silver-grey metal coffin 10 metres ahead of him, which was not far from the front of the cargo hold. With his target selected, he now walked even more stealthily. He held in both hands the pistol, which he'd thrust out in front of him. He briefly released his left hand to wipe the sweat from his brow; his mind was deep in concentration. The coffin-containing mound had peaks of varying heights. The pile was made up of rigid luggage stacked in three sections. The coffin was at the top of a section that reached four feet, whilst directly behind the middle section's luggage reached a height of six and a half feet. The coffin had two heavy clasps, which would need to be released before the lid could be opened. Each clasp possessed two screws, which would need to be loosened before it could be raised. Each screw had a handle, which resembled a pair of mouse's ears for ease of turning. The Guardian removed a plastic penknife from his left coat pocket and opened the main blade. He placed the penknife onto a nearby piece of luggage. With the pistol in his right hand, he very slowly loosened the screws on both of the clasps with his left. Once complete, he used the penknife to cut the two yellow securing ribbons that would prevent the lid from opening. He returned the penknife to his left coat pocket. Continuing to use his left hand, he gently released the first clasp. He positioned the tip of the silencer to face the junction between the lid and the main body of the coffin. He took a deep breath, then quickly released the second clasp. There was a hiss of air. He hastily lifted the lid by two inches, thrust the first inch of the silencer into the coffin and discharged three bullets. The black gap smoked. As the Guardian started to further raise the lid of the coffin to examine his handiwork, he felt a hard cylinder pressed firmly into his back.

"Drop it!" Sam commanded. The Guardian had his back to Sam. Despite this, Sam could tell that the Guardian knew who the speaker was.

The Guardian still held his pistol in his right hand. His entire body was frozen except for his right arm. This arm moved downward as if complying with the order, but two successive small twitches indicated to Sam that the Guardian was thinking about a different course of action. With a firmly clenched right fist, Sam struck the Guardian's right forearm. It was a strong, sharp, downward blow, which forced the Guardian's pistol to the floor. Sam kicked the plastic pistol away. His left hand continued to press the thick metal pipe into the Guardian's spine. Sam injected the contents of a prepared syringe into the back of the Guardian's right thigh. The Guardian had flinched at the surprise of the needle. Sam pushed the metal pipe with more vigour to discourage any foolish behaviour. He quickly looked around him for any other would-be assailants.

"Been a while a since you've done anything like this, hasn't it?" Sam spoke to the back of the Guardian's head while sustaining the pressure of the pipe against his back. "You know, I would have liked to have had a little talk with you, but there are others on board and you'd resist once you knew that yours was the only gun."

The Guardian's mind told his body to turn around, except it was too late: the contents of the syringe had taken effect. The beginning of a sluggish attempt at rotation was the result. Sam pushed the Guardian back into position.

"And you're hardly the type who loves his neighbour as himself—so I've given you a taste of your own medicine," Sam explained as the Guardian slowly collapsed onto the floor, slipping into unconsciousness.

Sam put the needle inside the syringe, placed the syringe inside the pipe and put the pipe into his left jacket pocket. He picked up the Guardian's plastic pistol. Sam held the weapon firmly in his right hand. He stood above the Guardian, who was lying on the floor breathing shallowly. "How did you know that I'd be on this plane?" Sam asked uselessly.

The Guardian's eyes were closed. Sam checked the Guardian's pulse, which was present and strong. Sam searched the entire cargo hold for any other hostiles and to discover where the Guardian had sprung from. There was no one else present. To the rear of the cargo hold Sam had found a large, open wooden crate labelled as lost luggage. Written on the upper surface were two addresses: one for a warehouse in Hackney, in London, and the other for a factory in Hungary. Both addresses Sam committed to memory; the former was supposedly the crate's intended destination.

Sam returned to the Guardian and proceeded to drag him from where he lay to the rear of the cargo hold. Having achieved this task, Sam looked at his watch. There was just over an hour left of the flight. Sam injected the Guardian with another dose of the tranquilizer, rechecked his pulse, tied up his hands and legs, and gagged him with a clean, white handkerchief.

"I should finish you off," Sam said as he stuffed the Guardian back into his crate. "I know you came here to kill me and that you'll keep coming for me in England or wherever I go—only I'm not like you." Sam placed the Guardian so that he was sat upright with his knees next to his chest and his arms around his knees. Sam noticed that the well-worn crate had many small cracks that would allow for ventilation yet not reveal the contents. He removed the plastic rounds from the pistol and damaged each one individually. He wiped the pistol and placed it into the crate. He carefully scattered the unusable remains of the rounds, now cleaned, inside the crate before resealing it.

Sam returned to the metal coffin. He peered inside and saw the punctured unbloodied corpse. Sam wondered who the young man was as the lid was closed, the clasps re-engaged and the screws tightened. Sam did his best to secure the pile, even though he was unable to unite the two cut ends of each of the two yellow ribbons. He calmly walked toward the very front of the cargo hold. He passed another metal coffin on the way, then returned to his own.

Day 1

"It's good to finally see you without a mask," Sam said. "Same voice, yet I never would have thought that you look the way you do."

Sol Hodaviah and Sam were sat together at a table, eating a meal of vegetables and roasted lamb. They were in the dining room of a house that was in a village somewhere between London and Oxford. The house had the look of a place that was lived in but not by the person who was talking with Sam. Sol Hodaviah had picked up Sam's coffin at the West London Mortuary. Hodaviah had come alone in an old American station wagon (estate car) and had extended the trunk's space by folding down the rear seats. The coffin had fitted with ease. In the garage attached to the house the late Anthony Burrows had been resurrected as Sam March and Sol Hodaviah had removed his mask.

"Well, this is me," Sol Hodaviah replied. "You'll get used to this face and come to realize that it matches both my voice and personality only too well."

"I was sorry to hear about Sol Kadmiel."

"As were we all."

"How have things been for the rest of you?" Sam asked.

"Our troubles have escalated." Sol Hodaviah knew that he could trust Sam with more. He even wanted to—perhaps another day. "Now we should really get down to business. The quicker we get the films developed, that marvellous piece of wood analysed and the basic facts about your discovery of Noah's Ark published the better. They'll need a picture of you as the intrepid explorer." He removed a small glossy picture from his shirt pocket and turned it to face Sam. "I've selected this photo taken last year while you were in South America. Do you mind if we use it?"

Sam looked at the picture. "That one will be fine."

"Good." Sol Hodaviah looked as if he was about to continue but delayed as he was contemplating where best to start.

Sam interrupted Sol Hodaviah's train of thought, "I had some trouble on the flight. The man who was in charge during my interrogation tried to kill me. I incapacitated him and returned him to his crate. Its destination is a warehouse in Hackney—at least that's what was written."

After Sam had imparted the full address, Sol Hodaviah rose, left the room and made a long telephone call.

On Sol Hodaviah's return, Sam resumed: "I'd have thought that his people would have received the crate immediately on arrival. Do you think that he'll use them to continue his mission here?"

"Maybe, although on the other hand, they may not know why he's here. He'll certainly come after you though."

Day 2

The day was Sunday the 7th of September, the day before Sam's clinical studies were due to start. He made two calls that morning: one to a pair of concerned parents; and the other to the medical faculty, informing them that he would be late for the start of his studies for personal reasons.

After breakfast, Sam sat in a comfortable leather chair in the lounge. Sol Hodaviah handed Sam a newspaper. "Read the second article on page five."

Sam started to read. There was a grainy black and white picture that accompanied the piece.

A would-be hijacker was found after the landing of flight CG715, from Larnaca (Cyprus) to Heathrow. The solitary male was in the cargo hold in possession of a plastic gun. He escaped soon after his arrest, having been aided by outside accomplices. The police don't know his name but suspect that he is an Islamic fundamentalist. There was no passport or any other identifiers in his possession. He's thought to be in his late forties or early fifties. This poor-quality picture from a closed-circuit-television recording of him on the way to be questioned is the best image available. Formal pictures were yet to be taken. He and his accomplices are at large and should be considered extremely dangerous. All the passengers were temporarily detained for questioning. We interviewed some of them, who were clearly relieved that the man did not go through with his plans . . .

"That was a vague report," Sam said. "'A would-be hijacker'— they forgot to mention that they found him tied up. And I wonder how those 'outside accomplices' managed to get past the Heathrow security."

Day 3

. . .

Day 4

"Tell me about the man who appeared to be running the human show," Sol Hodaviah asked.

"They, including Satan, called him 'Grand Inquisitor'," Sam replied. "Are they referring to the Inquisition? I thought that that was all over."

"The Inquisition took place in many Roman Catholic coun-tries,[1] however, most intensely in Portugal, Spain, France and

---

[1] Countries include: Spain, France, Italy, Mexico, Portugal, Colombia*, Peru, Belgium*, Holland*, Sicily, Czech Republic*, *FOOTNOTE CONTINUED ON THE NEXT PAGE*

Italy. It was initiated at the command of Pope Gregory IX in 1231 AD. The most brazen of its many activities continued until the middle of the 19th century. It was supposedly developed to root out heresy."

"Heresy to what exactly?" Sam knew part of the answer to his own question but wanted to hear the response of a more-experienced Christian.

"They defined heresy as the belief in and observance of a religious doctrine contrary to any of the Roman Catholic dogmas. Of course, many of their dogmas are in direct opposition to what's written in the Bible. This meant that if you believed the Bible and stuck by what it said, then you'd fall foul of the Inquisition. It had many aims. To destroy Bible-believing Christians was one of them. It devastated false Christian groups who were different from Roman Catholicism as well. The Inquisition was also extensively used to eliminate or drive out Jewish people from areas dominated by Roman Catholicism. Muslims, too, were expelled or killed. Some Jews and Muslims were given the option to convert to Roman Catholicism. Their conversions didn't necessarily save them though."

"Yes, and I've read that at times the Inquisition even killed people professing Roman Catholicism whose ancestors generations before had been followers of Judaism or Islām and had converted to Roman Catholicism," Sam stated.

"That's correct. And as you've seen for yourself, the Inquisition is ongoing. Its continued existence is not denied by the Roman Catholic Church. At the same time they don't advertise it either. The Inquisition was first renamed 'the Supreme Sacred Congregation of the Holy Office' by Pope Pius X in 1908. Then in 1965 Pope Paul VI changed the title to 'the Congregation for the Doctrine of the Faith', which is the name that the Inquisition

CONTINUED FOOTNOTE PRESENT

Austria, Germany*, Guatemala*, Nicaragua*, Costa Rica*, El Salvador*, Honduras*, Brazil, Cape Verde.
*Modern names of countries are used.

goes by today. Its activities may not be as overt, but they're clearly not sleeping. One day I'll tell you about some of the other things that they're up to now. It's revealing that they're using the old title for the heads of the Inquisition. 'Grand Inquisitor' hasn't been used openly for over two centuries. There were multiple simultaneous Grand Inquisitors, each with authority over the areas that fell under his jurisdiction. I expect that there's only one Grand Inquisitor now, the area he covers being the world."

Day 5

"There have been criticisms levelled at you all—that the House of Hodaviah is kind of a secret society?" it was mostly a question; however, Sam intended it to be a fraction accusatory.

"On the contrary, we're anything but secret," Sol Hodaviah replied. "We're completely accessible to all, willing to give advice to anyone who asks."

"Anyone with a few pounds to spare?!"

"You're not aware of all the work that we do. We offer a free advisory service as well. But those with means should pay. This is partly a business, and we need to pay the staff of advisers, who include ourselves, and spend money on technology—and so on. The only reason why we haven't publicly revealed who the seven founding members are is because of the inherent danger to ourselves of doing so."

"And what about your profits? I'm asking, not to find fault but for my own edification."

"We give thirty percent of our profits to charity. We don't publicize this, because the Bible says that if you give to charity and then tell everyone about it, you're showing the world how good you are, and as a result the world's praise is all the reward that you'll receive.[1] We work for a reward that we'll receive in

---

[1] Matthew 6:1-4, 1 Corinthians 13:4.

Heaven from God, who sees every secret charity. What's left after tax we feed back into the infrastructure (personnel, equipment, premises, etc.) and the security of everyone who works for the House—we treat security separately, even though it's tied up with most aspects of infrastructure. Please keep all of this to yourself. The reason why I tell you is so that you can fully understand what we do and our goals. Your pay came from the infrastructure fund."

"Do you think that you should have sent someone who speaks more languages?" Sam asked, changing the subject.

"We can't have everything. As time passes, you'll realize that although there are many individuals with an abundance of skills and gifts, very few wish to engage themselves in matters that champion God. His work is a great divider of persons! And with regard to this mission, to our knowledge there was no one else who could have completed both objectives."

"If I spoke more languages, I could have told you more about their plans."

"Before you set out, we might not have known the exact things that they discuss or the manner in which demonic spirits converse with men to ambitiously plan, but we had a good idea as to what things they would be scheming. The Bible has laid out Satan's modus operandi and his ultimate goal."

Day 6

"Based on your descriptions of the members of the Throne, we've amassed a large number of pictures for you to look at. Maybe you can identify some of the members. The first pile is an assortment of political leaders of many different nations. The next is of high-ranking Freemasons. We're still compiling pictures of clerics of the various religions. Who would have thought that all we needed to do was follow Arthur Hamilton to find the Throne?"

Sam recognized two of the ten representatives of the world divisions.

Day 7

"Here we are, Sam. You're in two national papers. The geographical magazines are to follow next week." Sol Hodaviah handed Sam the two newspapers. "I'll have a collection of international papers for you tomorrow."

Sam held the first paper between his hands. The relevant article started in a small section on the front page and continued on the fifth. The second paper reported Sam's discovery on the second page. He spent half an hour thoroughly reading the articles.

Both papers had a picture of the engraved wood fragment. The writing had been examined by four linguistic experts, each from a different country. With the aid of computers, the experts had deciphered the majority of the script, and the consensus was that what was written was a list, probably one of many, of different creatures together with each one's feeding program. Some of the words that named certain dragons (dinosaurs) had similarities to Archaic Sumerian. The huge volumes of these creatures' daily diets confirmed their sizes. The experts' summary was reported in each paper.

Day 8

Sam's discovery of Noah's Ark was in five international newspapers. All had a picture of the engraved wood fragment and the linguistic experts' summary.

Sam was also handed a London paper later that day. "Take a look at this," Sol Hodaviah said. As Sam read silently, Sol Hodaviah watched for Sam's reaction.

The body of man with several bullet holes has been found in Knightsbridge. Police suspect that the slaying was an assassination related to organized crime. His identity is unknown, as his hands and head had been cut off, but it has been estimated from his remains that he was approximately fifty years old. Preliminary racial DNA studies localize the man's origin to the Mediterranean with an 80% probability that he was of Turkish origin. The Police are following leads . . .

"Do you think that it's him?" Sam asked.

"I don't think—it has to be him. Too much coincidence not to be—the day after your discovery had gone public. He failed and paid the price."

"What did you find at the warehouse?"

"Not much. It really is just a storage facility: part of a chain owned by a British man. We're doing some checks on him. I don't think that they'll lead anywhere though. I suspect that that address was used just to legitimize the crate. I doubt that it would have made it there."

"Do you think that the police will identify the body?"

"For that they'll need a record of his DNA. And let's say for a moment that he had a DNA record in Turkey because of some crime or other—the Turks would first have to give it up to the British authorities. Anyway, that's irrelevant: he was so well connected that there's no way that a record of his DNA would be on their system."

"And what about me? Do you think the Throne will still come after me in England?"

"It's possible; they definitely have people here. We've made some provision for that though. We'll be posting two bodyguards for your protection when you go back to your studies. They won't be the type who shields you in close proximity. They'll observe you and your surroundings from a distance. Their job will be to recognize trouble and act before it strikes. If they fail to do this, then you'll have to deal with the up close, immediate dangers yourself. They'll then provide assistance. I'll show you their pictures before you leave. Don't approach either of them. Only in emergencies will they approach you."

"How long will they be shadowing me?"

"Let's try it for a year. In that time they'll discover if the enemy is seeking revenge."

"Thank you."

"You don't need to thank me. Think of it as a reward for your efforts."

"And don't tell me, the money is coming from the House of Hodaviah's security fund?"

"Now you're getting the picture."

Day 9

"I've got some more photographs for you to look at, Sam. The first pile is of Roman Catholic bishops. The second is of top-ranking Jesuits. The third is of various Muslim religious leaders; and the fourth of notable Hindu and Buddhist religious leaders, and prominent figures of other persuasions such as the Jehovah's Witnesses."

Sam saw another two envelopes containing further sets of pictures. He looked toward them.

"They're for later. I want you to see if you recognize any of these men first." Sol Hodaviah motioned to the pictures that he'd already uncovered.

Sam identified a few of the clerics, one of whom was the Palestinian grand mufti of Jerusalem, who'd stepped forward to discuss the future Jewish Temple.

Later on the first of the two reserved envelopes was opened. Sam recognized the man in the third picture of the pile.

"He's the Grand Inquisitor! Who is he?" Sam asked.

"He's Giovanni Ezzelino. We don't know much about him, but we do know that he used to be a prominent Vatican lawyer about ten years ago."

"What's his pile?" Sam inquired as he flicked through the rest of the pictures.

"Vatican nonclerical staff. The Roman Catholic Church has a host of secular people working for its interests. They include lawyers, bankers, etc."

"Isn't it unusual that he's not a priest?"

"Our information on him is rather old. Based on what you saw, he's undoubtedly a priest now. We'll confirm this though. The head of the Congregation for the Doctrine of the Faith is always held by a high-ranking priest. At the moment the official head, the prefect, is a Cardinal."

"Well, it appears that Ezzelino is the real head and clearly does more for the Vatican now than simply looking after their legal interests."

"This last pile is of particular significance to us. It's far from complete. Take a look anyway. We'll have the rest of the pictures in a couple of days."

Sam looked through the ten pictures that had come from the second reserved envelope. "None. I don't recognize any of these men. Who are they?"

"They're members of one part of our so-called 'Protestant Church': a few bishops and some prominent vicars whom we've had our eye on. You said that you weren't certain that the Church of England cleric held the rank of bishop."

"Why do you say 'so-called'?"

"Because 'Protestant' is a name that came about in the sixteenth century for those people who opposed the pope and the Holy Roman emperor. The essence of it is that these people were being forced to obey the pope, which meant that they couldn't obey God, because both could not be obeyed simultaneously. They chose God. Obviously, from the time of the resurrection of Christ until then there had been true Christians with the same kind of faith, but they weren't called Protestants."

"And today?"

"Today Protestantism is represented by a group that encompasses Anglicans, Pentecostals, Baptists, Presbyterians, Methodists and others. As you well know, Protestantism isn't what it used to be. The problem is that many of the churches aren't interested in what the Bible says. Some of the ministers don't even believe that Jesus is God and tell their congregations as much. They preach about Jesus as merely a man who did good deeds during His lifetime. They omit to tell their congregations that they need to acknowledge that Jesus died for their sins, ask His forgiveness, recognize that He is God and put their trust in Him.[1] As a consequence, the people miss out on the salvation that comes from Christ. Even so, there are still ministers who keep the faith and whose congregations adhere to the truth of the Gospel. Anyhow, the result is that the Protestant Church as a whole has a mixture of people who are genuine Christians and those who aren't. Within each individual church, amongst those professing Christianity, there is a certain proportion of people who are actually true Christians; the proportion varies from church to church. In some of these churches there are no true Christians at all, not even in the pulpit."

"It sounds to me that the cause of this is from the pulpit."

"Yes. It's truly sad when the disbelief becomes institutional-ized, producing ministers who have no faith in Christ."

"Which is exactly what Satan wants."

Day 10

"And Prasseda—isn't it odd that there were almost forty men in the chamber and only one woman, plus she didn't say a thing," Sam remarked.

"I've wondered about her myself. She doesn't seem to be a regular operative. In the Bible there are hints that the Antichrist will be more than just a normal man—instead, part man and part

---

[1] John 3:13-21, 14:1-11, Acts 3:1-26, 4:10-12, 5:29-31, 13:33-38, 26:15-18, Ephesians 1:2-14, Colossians 1:12-14, 1 Peter 1:3-4.

demon.[1] And the demon-part may originate from Satan.[2] The Bible states that the Antichrist will come about through the working of Satan (the Dragon).[3] In Revelation the Antichrist is most often referred to as the Beast.[4] This beast, this dangerous animal, is described in a similar way to Satan in that the Beast has seven heads and ten horns; however, he is portrayed as a leopard with bear's feet and lion's mouth rather than as a dragon.

---

[1] During the Antichrist's life on Earth he will die (a human quality) and then be resurrected: Revelation 13:1-12, 17:8. However, whilst dead he will be placed in the Abyss (Bottomless Pit), which is a place of incarceration for demons: Revelation 11:7, 17:8, and see Chapter 4 pg 104 with footnote regarding the Abyss. The son of perdition (the Antichrist, the Beast) is referred to as a man: 2 Thessalonians 2:1-12, Revelation 13:18.

[2] There was a prophecy-curse placed on the talking serpent, which deceived Eve, found in Genesis 3:1-15. This serpent once walked on the Earth similar to other land creatures. The prophecy states that the serpent will have seed (offspring). The sire of the seed is certainly the physical serpent, as it was an animal that was cursed to slither on its belly thus becoming a snake. In addition, the sire of the seed may also refer to the spirit Satan, because he possessed the serpent and gave it the ability to speak, evidenced by the fact that Satan is referred to as "that old serpent" and was present in Eden (Ezekiel 28:12-16—see Chapter 1 pg 23 and footnote regarding Satan having been the anointed cherub for sacred duties; 2 Corinthians 11:3; Revelation 12:9, 20:2). The prophecy-curse also states that there will be enmity between the serpent's seed and the woman's seed. The serpent's seed can refer to snakes but perhaps also to Satan's actual offspring. The woman's seed can refer to mankind in general but also specifically to Christ. There will certainly be enmity between Christ and the Antichrist, ultimately resulting in the latter's defeat (2 Thessalonians 2:1-9, Revelation 13:6-7, 19:11-21).

[3] 2 Thessalonians 2:8-9. The Dragon will also give power to the Beast: Revelation 13:4.

[4] Revelation 13:3-18, 14:7-11, 15:2, 16:2-13, 19:19-20, 20:4.

The Antichrist and Satan are alike but not the same, perhaps as a son is to his father.[1] In the Antichrist's case, as he will have a human appearance, his bestial description is symbolic rather than literal."

"Symbolic of what?"

"Of his authority and behaviour.[2] In contrast, because Satan is a spirit, his portrayal as a dragon is both symbolic and literal—one of his forms.[3] We did a search based on your description of Prasseda. I've got some pictures of some women here. Why don't you take a look at them?"

"Surely you didn't select them based on my description alone?" Sam asked as he held the stack of glossy prints. He slowly sifted through the pictures, placing those that he'd already inspected to the back. He was still thinking about Sol Hodaviah's comments concerning the Antichrist and what possible relevance they had to Prasseda.

"They're Roman Black Nobility."

"Black Nobility?"

"That's right."

"I can already see that whatever that means, it's nothing to do with the colour of their skin."

"They're members of the Roman hereditary nobility who've historically remained faithful to the popes—black because of the

---

[1] Revelation 12:3, 13:1-2 (presumably, this beast has seven leopard-heads, each with a lion's mouth).

[2] Revelation 13:1-18, 17:3-18, 19:19. This will be dealt with further on in this chapter and in accompanying footnotes regarding the Antichrist's authority (pg 530) and his behaviour (pgs 531-533) during the seven-year Tribulation period.

[3] Revelation 12:9-17, 16:13, 20:2. Symbolic in that Satan is the spirit who has control over the Earth, which is already biblically divided into ten divisions (see further on in this chapter pg 532 and footnote regarding Satan being worshipped and the Antichrist deriving his power from Satan). Furthermore, Satan's behaviour is that of a ferocious death-dealing dragon.

colour of priestly garments. A few of these dynasties are descended from ancient Roman families.[1] The Black Nobility have had close ties with the papacy for centuries. In fact, many of the popes have been elected from the ranks of the Black Nobility."

"This is her. Who is she?" Sam held up the picture for Sol Hodaviah to see.

"Her real name is Alessandra Pinari. She's the granddaughter of a count—he's her father's father. She's not just a pretty face either. She studied architecture at the University of Rome. She came second in her class."

"What's she been doing since she graduated?"

"She works for an architectural firm in Rome."

"How old is she?"

"Twenty-six."

Sam was looking closely at the picture. He remembered how her face moved as she talked.

Sol Hodaviah continued, "Sam, there's a prophecy in the book of Daniel about the destruction of the Temple in Jerusalem. Daniel received the prophecy while he was in exile in Babylon.[2] The First Temple, built by Solomon, had already been destroyed by Nebuchadnezzar,[3] the Babylonian king. Daniel's prophecy was about a Temple that would be built after the Jews returned from their captivity in Babylon. Regarding the people who would come and destroy that temple, it was predicted that from them will eventually arise the Antichrist.[4] That temple was the one that was destroyed in 70 AD by the Romans."[1]

---

[1] That is, a few of these dynasties' origins preceded the fall of the Western Roman Empire in 476 AD*. Indeed, a few of the dynasties' origins also preceded the birth of Jesus (6–4 BC).

*The Roman Empire never truly fell. See Chapter 20 pg 428 and pgs 432-438 with relevant footnotes regarding this topic.

[2] Daniel 1:1-6, 9:1-27.

[3] Nebuchadnezzar II. See Timeline.

[4] Daniel 9:26-27. The Antichrist is the "prince that shall come" within this passage. The "prince that shall come" has to be the
FOOTNOTE CONTINUED ON THE NEXT PAGE

Antichrist, because in verse 27 he is the one who makes a deal with many for a "week" (7 years, which is the seven-year Tribulation period—see below) and is the ultimate cause of the abomination of desolation being set up in the Temple in the middle of the 7 years. Daniel 12:11 also predicts that after the Temple sacrifices are stopped, an abomination of desolation will be set up.

Matthew 24:7-27 refers to the abomination of desolation being set up in the holy place (an area within the Temple—1 Kings 8:1-10, 2 Chronicles 5:1-11). See also Mark 13:14-26. These passages in Matthew and Mark refer directly to the book of Daniel's prediction regarding the setting up of the abomination of desolation (above) and place this event in the Tribulation period.

Revelation 13:11-18 reveals that the abomination of desolation will be an image (idol) of the Antichrist. It will be set up by the Antichrist's colleague, the False Prophet, who is presented as being symbolically a lamb (his appearance mimicking Christ's sacrificial aspect known as the Lamb [Revelation 5:6-7:17, 17:14, 19:1-21]), but this person will speak like a dragon. The False Prophet will do great miracles and direct people to worship the Antichrist and his image. Indeed, it is the False Prophet who will institute the death penalty for people who will not worship the image of the Antichrist. One of the False Prophet's miracles will be to make the image speak.

The Antichrist and the False Prophet will together be thrown into the Lake of Fire by Jesus: Revelation 16:13-14, 19:20-21, 20:10.

See Timeline and the footnote accompanying the year of Jesus' death and resurrection for an explanation of a broader passage, Daniel 9:24-27. As well as the ancestry-of-the-Antichrist prophecy, this passage contains a prophecy that predicted the year of the Messiah's death during His first coming, from which in conjunction with Daniel 12:11 it can be deduced why the above "week" represents 7 years.

[1] Josephus' The Jewish War Book 6 *sections 249-287,* Dio Cassius' Roman History Book 65 *chapters 4:1-7:2.*

"Hence, the Antichrist will originate from the Romans!" Sam stated.

"Yes, he will be born into the descendants of the Romans."

"So are you saying that Alessandra is having relations with Satan?" Sam's mind slowly absorbed his own words as he stared at Sol Hodaviah. Sam looked at Alessandra's picture again.

"Probably not yet. But she may do in the future. Obviously, we're now assuming that Satan will be the father of the Antichrist based on those few biblical hints. Alternatively, the Antichrist could have an entirely human father, another Roman, and Alessandra could simply be that man's future wife—if this is indeed her role."

Sam's unalleviated expression of horror seemed to indicate that he'd ignored Sol Hodaviah's last two sentences. "The descendants of the Romans are now spread across the entire world. They're not just in Rome."

"That's true," Hodaviah said, "and this woman has a limited lifespan and an even shorter reproductive time. It may be that every decade or so they choose a woman from somewhere in the world where there are descendants of Romans and offer her to Satan. By all accounts, it appears that he hasn't slept with any of them yet."

"Why do you think that?" Sam asked.

"Satan has a restriction. If he took one of the women to procreate, he would then be subject to the same judgement by God that the other demons received—and suffer the same punishment. After those demons had taken human wives, they were imprisoned by God in the Abyss—confined until the final judgement so that they couldn't commit that particular sin again."[1]

"How long was it between the sin and the punishment?"

---

[1] Genesis 6:1-4, 2 Peter 2:4 (the Abyss is used to refer to the Bottomless Pit and Tartarus—see Chapter 4 pg 104 and footnote regarding the Abyss), Jude 1:6-7.

"The Bible doesn't say how long the time period was. Revelation clearly shows us that Satan will participate in the life of the Antichrist and will receive human worship during this time together with the Antichrist.[1] Therefore, Satan's punishment wouldn't be immediate. It's only after the defeat of the Antichrist that Satan will be bound. Satan has read Revelation and knows that he too will one day be imprisoned in the Abyss (Bottomless Pit). The duration of his internment will be for a thousand years.[2] Of course, the main reason why God will imprison Satan is to prevent him from having any direct influence over humanity for the thousand-year period, the Millennium."[3]

"So when Satan feels the time is right, he'll take a woman to procreate—to father the Antichrist, Satan's very own Nephil-son."

"If the Satan-father premise is correct," Sol Hodaviah was keen to remind Sam of their shared speculation. "Then yes, he'd want to be precise in his timing. World conditions would need to be suitably advantageous to his cause before he took one of these women to produce his son."

"I've read in the Bible that before the Millennium there will be a seven-year Tribulation, the period when the Earth will experience tremendous troubles.[4] The Antichrist, whether the son

---

[1] Revelation 13:2-4.

[2] Revelation 20:1-3 (see Chapter 20 pg 397 and footnote regarding Satan's incarceration in the Abyss), 20:7. See also Chapter 4 pg 104 and footnote regarding the Abyss.

[3] See Timeline.

[4] Matthew 24:4-30, Mark 13:4-26, Revelation 7:14. See Timeline and the footnote accompanying Jesus' death and resurrection for how the length of 7 years is derived.

This is a useful place to mention the Rapture (the transfer of all Christians from the Earth to Heaven by Christ), which will happen and is very likely to take place at an unknown time before the Tribulation. After the Rapture, some people will become Christians from among the people left on the Earth. Matthew 24:31-51, 1

FOOTNOTE CONTINUED ON THE NEXT PAGE

of Satan or not, will feature greatly during this period and would therefore have to be an adult when it starts."[1]

"Yes, indeed, and he will become the most prominent person in the world during those seven years. People will even know that he is the Beast.[2] At the start of this period there will be ten leaders (kings) who will control the different parts of the world.[3] The Antichrist will be a powerful individual, the king of Babylon, but not one of the ten world-division leaders. However, they will give their power and strength to him.[4] As a consequence, he will be the effective world leader through them. Similar to the situation now, the world will focus its attention on events in Israel: specifically, Jerusalem.[5] In addition to the resurrected city

CONTINUED FOOTNOTE PRESENT

Corinthians 15:50-54, 1 Thessalonians 1:10, 4:13-18, 5:1-11, 2 Peter 3:10, Revelation 3:10. See Timeline for the time of the Rapture and the accompanying footnote.

[1] Daniel 11:31-12:11, 2 Thessalonians 2:1-14, Revelation 11:7-19:20.

[2] Revelation 13:4.

[3] Revelation 17:12-18. Or put another way, they will be the kings of the Earth whose provinces together will encompass the entire globe. See also footnote further on in this chapter pg 532 regarding the Antichrist seizing the authority of three of the kings.

[4] Revelation 17:1-18. The city of Babylon, the Antichrist and the ten kings will be closely associated. The Antichrist is portrayed as a blasphemous beast. He has seven heads, which represent seven preceding kings of Babylon; and he himself is the eighth king. The 10 horns represent the 10 world-division kings, and a woman riding on his back represents the city of Babylon. The relationship between the city, the Antichrist and the 10 kings will not always be in accord. From the Revelation passage one can read that the 10 kings will at some point hate and attack the city of Babylon, having previously been ruled by it and having previously given their power to its king, the Antichrist.

[5] Jerusalem will be a burdensome stone to all the peoples of the world: Zechariah 12:1-3. The following is undoubtedly one of the

FOOTNOTE CONTINUED ON THE NEXT PAGE

of Babylon, one of the other features of this seven-year period will be another Jewish Temple in Jerusalem. In this temple people will again offer animal sacrifices for their sins.[1] This will demonstrate that many will lack the understanding of the New Testament (the New Covenant between God and man), which states that it's only through Jesus' sacrifice, the ultimate sacrifice, that sins can be forgiven.[2] Anyhow, the Antichrist, for his own gain, will forcibly stop the sacrifices in the Temple. An idol of himself will be set up in the Temple, and a policy of killing all those who don't worship him and his image enforced."[3]

CONTINUED FOOTNOTE PRESENT

---

reasons for this future focus. There will be two witnesses who will prophecy in Jerusalem. God will give them: power to defend themselves with fire from their mouths, which will consume their assailants; and the ability to cause droughts and plagues on the Earth until their testimony is complete. The Antichrist will succeed in killing them, and the world will be so glad that people will even exchange presents. The witnesses' unburied bodies will be resurrected by God and taken up to Heaven in the sight of their enemies. Revelation 11:3-13.

[1] This temple will be in Jerusalem, the city where Jesus the Messiah was crucified: Revelation 11:1-8. It is this temple that will have its sacrifices stopped and the Antichrist's image (idol) placed inside. See earlier in this chapter pg 526 and footnotes regarding the ancestry of the Antichrist.

The Western Wall was not part of the Temple but part of the Temple Mount, a supporting structure that allowed for a greater flat area for the Temple complex (which included the various courts). Some have made an idol of the Western Wall in that they pray toward it and leave money and letters to God between the stones, believing that the wall has special properties as a conduit to Him.

[2] Acts 5:25-42, 26:14-18, Ephesians 1:1-23, Colossians 1:12-20, Hebrews 9:1-28, 10:1-24.

[3] See earlier in this chapter pg 526 and footnotes regarding the ancestry of the Antichrist. One of the footnotes also comments on the False Prophet; it also refers the reader to the part of the Timeline

FOOTNOTE CONTINUED ON THE NEXT PAGE

"He'll effectively be worshipped as a god," Sam added.

"Precisely. And people will also worship Satan, knowing that it is from him that the Antichrist derives his power.[1] Clearly, it won't be enough for the Antichrist to simply control the world through the ten leaders. At some point he'll defeat three of them and seize their authority,[2] thereby directly ruling three of the world divisions."

CONTINUED FOOTNOTE PRESENT

---

regarding the year of Jesus' death and resurrection—the accompanying footnote contains an explanation of Daniel 9:24-27.

[1] Revelation 13:1-8. Satan will be the spirit-ruler behind the physical ruler of the world, the Antichrist. This is one of the reasons why Satan's dragon semblance has ten horns (Revelation 12:3): the ten horns are symbolic of the ten kings, each of whom will reign over his own world division during the seven-year Tribulation period (Revelation 17:12, 17:18). The Antichrist symbolically has ten horns, because the ten kings will give their strength and power to him (Revelation 17:12-13). Satan will be the power behind the Antichrist's command over the ten world divisions. The Antichrist is not yet reigning over the world, but Satan is ruling as the chief malevolent spirit and has been for thousands of years. This is why Satan already had the ten horns when Mary gave birth to Jesus (Revelation 12:3-5—see Chapter 21 pg 455). Therefore, the Bible already represents the world in ten divisions, which Satan has control over (See Chapter 1 pgs 26-27 and footnotes regarding Satan becoming the temporary ruler of the Earth).

[2] Daniel 7:1-25. The fourth beast described in this passage is different from the Beast of Revelation 13:1-2 and 17:1-18. However, the former beast is similar to the latter in that the former also has 10 horns, which represent 10 kings who will rule over the whole Earth. Three of the horns will be plucked up by a further horn, which will grow up amongst them. This latter horn will replace the three and is identified as a man—blasphemous and mighty—who will wage war against the saints (true believers in God) and will rule up until the Messiah comes to establish His kingdom. This blasphemous man is clearly the Antichrist. The beast itself represents

FOOTNOTE CONTINUED ON THE NEXT PAGE

"And it will become unlawful for people to buy or sell without his mark on their foreheads or their right hands.[1] Isn't that correct?"

"Yes, that too. On the whole, it's going to be a truly dreadful time and even worse for the Jewish people. Very close to the end of the full seven years the Antichrist will move against Jerusalem, the capital of Israel.[2] He'll assemble his troops in Armageddon. Many have mistakenly thought that this is where the great battle will be, but actually it will be only the area in which his massive army gathers. The army will contain soldiers from all the Gentile nations of the world.[3] From Armageddon the Antichrist's forces will march to Jerusalem. The city will be captured, and the Antichrist and his army will then move against the remnant of Israel (those Jewish people who believe in Jesus the Messiah), who will have already retreated to the mountains over three years previously because they will have believed the warnings in the Bible about this time.[4] At that point Jesus will

CONTINUED FOOTNOTE PRESENT

---

the Roman Empire. As mentioned, this beast is the fourth in the passage from Daniel. It is preceded by three symbolic beasts, each of which represents an empire. The first represents the Babylonian Empire, and the second the empire of the Medes and Persians. The last of these three is a beast with four heads, which represents the Greek Empire, because after the death of Alexander the Great the empire split into four divisions. The Romans defeated and replaced the Greek Empire, becoming the next world empire.

[1] Revelation 13:16-18. The law will be implemented by the Antichrist's colleague, the False Prophet (for more information on this character see the first of two footnotes that accompany the main text earlier in this chapter pg 526 regarding the ancestry of the Antichrist). See Dispensations (6).

[2] Zechariah 14:1-15, Revelation 19:17-20.

[3] Zechariah 14:1-2, Revelation 16:13-16.

[4] Matthew 24:15-27, Mark 13:14-26, Revelation 12:6, 12:17 (see Chapter 21 pgs 455-460 for a comprehensive explanation of Revelation 12:1-17). The sign that they will need to retreat will be

FOOTNOTE CONTINUED ON THE NEXT PAGE

return, throw the Antichrist into the Lake of Fire and defeat the army. The faithful in Heaven will have returned with Jesus, except they won't participate in the battle." [1]

"And that's the end of the seven-year Tribulation period?"

"Yes. And as you said, after this will come the Millennium. Jesus the Messiah will start His thousand-year rule of the whole world from Jerusalem. Satan will be imprisoned in the Abyss for the entire thousand years. The faithful who came with Jesus from Heaven will rule with Jesus on the Earth.[2] The people of the world who survived the seven years and whom Jesus has selected for the Millennium will continue to exist on the Earth.[3] I suppose

CONTINUED FOOTNOTE PRESENT

---

the setting up of the idol (the abomination of desolation) in the Temple.

[1] Isaiah 34:1-8, Zechariah 14:1-15, Revelation 19:11-21.

[2] Revelation 20:1-6.

[3] Matthew 25:31-46. This judgement will take place after Christ's second coming. It will be a judgement of the living. The people of all the nations of the Earth will be gathered before Jesus to be judged as to who will inherit the Millennial kingdom. In this passage genuine Christians are represented as sheep. They will go into the Millenium alive. They will be Christians, because they will be judged to additionally inherit eternal life, that is, they will also eventually enter the New Heaven-New Earth. Non-Christians are represented as goats. They will be cast, presumably alive, into the everlasting fire, prepared for Satan and his demons. This is the Lake of Fire rather than Hell, as the latter is finite (see further on in this chapter pg 535). Eternal punishment in the Lake of Fire was promised for people who worshipped the Beast (the Antichrist) and his image, and received his mark during the Tribulation period, and this will, for some of them, be the fulfilment of that ominous guarantee (Revelation 14:9-11, see Dispensations [6]). Those like them in behaviour but who will have died before this judgement of the living and whose spirits will have descended to Hell will also eventually end up in the Lake of Fire (see Soul and Spirit). The Christians sealed for eventual eternal life in the New Heaven-New

FOOTNOTE CONTINUED ON THE NEXT PAGE

that we shouldn't be surprised that there will still be some resistance to the Messiah's rule during the thousand years from some of the people of the world, human nature being what it is. However, because of Jesus' strong rule[1] and the fact that the leader of the universal rebellion will be incarcerated during this period,[2] the world will be a very different place from what it was before; it will enjoy peace. It's about this era that the following saying applies: 'they shall beat their swords into plowshares, and their spears into pruninghooks: nation shall not lift up sword against nation, neither shall they learn war any more.'[3] After the thousand years are up, Satan will be released from the Abyss and once again deceive many people throughout the world. They will gather as a multitude to do battle against the encampment of those people loyal to God and against Jerusalem. Fire will come down from God out of Heaven and devour Satan's army. Satan will then be cast into the Lake of Fire for all eternity."[4]

"And what about after that?"

"All the residents of Hell will be judged by Jesus, then cast into the Lake of Fire to be punished for all eternity.[5] Following

CONTINUED FOOTNOTE PRESENT

Earth by Jesus' grace yet remaining alive on the Earth during the Millenium will have offspring, some of whom will become Christians and some who will not; the latter explains the rebellious element that will be present within the Millennial period.

[1] The Messiah will rule with a "rod of iron": Psalms 2:1-12, Revelation 12:5, 19:15-16.
See also His strong rule evident in Zechariah 14:16-21.

[2] Revelation 20:1-6.

[3] Isaiah 2:1-4, Micah 4:1-4. See Dispensations (7).

[4] Revelation 20:7-10.

[5] Revelation 20:11-15 (all judgement has been given by God the Father to God the Son—John 5:22-29). See Chapter 20 and relevant footnotes regarding Satan trying to lead people into the Lake of Fire (pg 398) and everyone one day standing alone before Jesus the Messiah to be judged (pg 442).

FOOTNOTE CONTINUED ON THE NEXT PAGE

the judgement, God will destroy the Heaven and the Earth and create a New Heaven and a New Earth. The New Jerusalem, God's sanctuary, will descend out of the New Heaven and come to rest on the New Earth. The vast city of New Jerusalem will not need the light of the sun in the day, the moon at night or any artificial light, because the Lord God will illuminate it continuously. And this is the eternal order in which the faithful live in peace and where there is no suffering."[1]

"The faithful? I interpret the faithful as those who've put their trust in Christ. How about the people who lived before Jesus' sacrifice?"

"Those who lived before His sacrifice were saved by their righteous faith in God; His saving grace was given to them for that reason, not because of their works.[2] Many of their faiths were amplified by the promise of the Messiah to come, the One who would be both man and God. Some of them had even met the eternal God Messiah in the form of the Angel of the LORD.[3] The Messiah's movements have been from everlasting.[4] Moses met the Angel of the LORD, who stated that He was God. The Angel of the LORD, God, gave Moses a special message to deliver to the Hebrews. God said that He'd come down to deliver them from affliction in Egypt and bring them to a land flowing

CONTINUED FOOTNOTE PRESENT

Although all the residents of Hell will be cast into the Lake of Fire, the following passages indicate that the judgement will be to determine the degree of punishment within the Lake of Fire: Matthew 10:15, 11:21-24, Mark 6:11. See Soul and Spirit.

[1] 2 Peter 3:7, Revelation 21:1-22:5. There will be both a sun and a moon; the passage merely states that the city will not need their light.

[2] Genesis 15:1-6, Psalms 32:1-11, Romans 4:1-25, Hebrews 11:1-40, Galatians 3:1-29. See Dispensations (1-5).

[3] See Chapter 1 pg 21 and footnote regarding "the Angel of the LORD".

[4] Micah 5:2.

with milk and honey. Moses asked God what name he should use when his fellow Hebrews asked him who'd sent him. God replied that Moses should tell them that 'I AM' had sent him.[1] Around one thousand five hundred years later, Jesus proclaimed in the Temple in Jerusalem that He existed before Abraham and was 'I AM'.[2] There were many other Old Testament characters who met the Angel of the LORD, including Abraham.[3] So they were not

---

[1] Exodus 3:1-17.

[2] John 8:2-59. There can be no mistake about Jesus' proclamations and admissions that He is God and the Messiah, the Son of God. In this passage alone Jesus stated that He was from above and not of this world and that He literally emanates from God. See also the following passages: Jesus declared that He and the Father are one—John 10:30-38, 17:21-26; Jesus declared that He is the Son of God—Matthew 18:19, John 3:13-18, 10:36-38, 11:1-4; and Jesus admitted to being the Messiah, the Son of God—Matthew 16:16-17, 26:63-65 (note the charge of blasphemy, confirming that Jesus' admission was understood).

Jesus also stated that He is the Son of man (select verses): Matthew 8:20, 9:4-6, 10:22-23, 19:28, 24:30, 26:63-65, Mark 8:38, 10:33-34, Luke 9:58, 18:30-33.

The following passages are of especial interest, as in each one Jesus states that He is the Son of man AND admits or states that He is the Son of God: Matthew 26:63-65, Luke 22:67-71, John 1:48-51, 3:13-18.

Of course, the rest of the Bible, which is completely inspired by God, also demonstrates that Jesus is God, the Son of God and the Son of man. The references are too many to list here, but many are presented and explained in Creation's Mutiny.

[3] Genesis 18:1-19:1, 22:11-18. Note that the angel of the Lord who visited mankind on Earth in the New Testament was not identified as being God. The most likely reason is that he isn't God, because the Messiah, Jesus, was then either on Earth or later at the right hand of God the Father during this angel's visitations. Matthew 1:20-2:13, 28:2, Luke 2:9, Acts 5:19, 8:26, 12:7-11, 12:23. Acts

FOOTNOTE CONTINUED ON THE NEXT PAGE

unfamiliar with the God Messiah, even though He'd not yet taken on flesh and sacrificed Himself for the world. They understood that through Him all the nations of the world would one day be blessed."[1]

Day 11

"What with all our enemies, at least we now know which group murdered Sol Kadmiel," Sol Hodaviah said.

"They don't know all your names yet," Sam replied.

"Four's enough, and it's only a matter of time before they know them all. We're going to need to change our approach. Since Sol Kadmiel's death there have been assassination attempts on two of the six remaining founding members—one on each."

"Attempts?"

"That's correct. Both were thwarted."

"What methods did the assassins employ against you?"

"I won't go into the details. Sam, you look so concerned. Don't worry about us. We're all prepared to die for the Gospel of Christ. Anyway, the power of the Throne isn't boundless. I will mention that one of the assassins died during his attempt. God's authority supersedes everything. We'll serve Him whether that means that we'll be killed for His sake or live to an old age and die of natural causes. Here are some pictures of various Turkish politicians and other Turkish VIPs."

Sam received the stack of pictures from Sol Hodaviah. He quickly identified the Guardian's brother.

"He's Azad Birand, the minister of transport," Sol Hodaviah said.

"And his dead brother?" Sam asked.

CONTINUED FOOTNOTE PRESENT

27:23 mentions the angel of God (rather than the angel of the Lord), who again was not identified as being God.

[1] Genesis 22:18.

"Your chief interrogator must have been Egemen. We haven't got a picture of him yet. Egemen was the elder of the two—a powerful industrialist but stayed out of the public eye."

Day 12

"We've identified only about a quarter of the members of the Throne. Today I want you to focus on two individuals. The first is the North American representative—the one who appeared to be more of a financier than a politician. The second is the Iraqi cleric. Tell me everything that you remember. I'll prompt you on specifics to jog your memory some more." There were no pictures for Sam to view. Sol Hodaviah held a small pad of paper and a pen to make notes.

"Before we do that, could you tell me some more about the future Babylon; they're both involved with its construction? It might help me to focus," Sam suggested.

"Very well. As I mentioned before, the Babylon of the end times will be a mighty city. It will effectively be the capital city of the world. It will trade with all the nations and become rich.[1] It won't just be secular but will also be the effective religious capital of the world. The false religions will unite into a single body.[2] The overwhelming impact of combining secular and religious elements at such tremendous heights of potency will be evident. The world will be seduced by the city's power and influence. The book of Revelation describes the city's ultimate destruction, the cause of which will be that 'she made all nations drink of the wine of the wrath of her fornication.' In this context the fornication is idolatry: people worshipping anything other

---

[1] See Chapter 18 pg 384 and footnote regarding Babylon as the political and commercial centre of the world.
[2] See Chapter 18 pg 384 and footnote regarding the false religions uniting in Babylon.

than their creator and sustainer is a gross form of infidelity. The city is described as 'THE MOTHER OF HARLOTS AND ABOMINATIONS OF THE EARTH.' It will be the greatest promoter of abominable idolatrous practices on the Earth. The city's deceiving influence will lead to the spiritual downfall of human beings the world over.[1] It's not surprising that the Antichrist will be its last king.[2] The city will kill many of us."

Sam looked surprised.

"Indeed, this city has been predicted to kill many genuine Christians. It will be drunk with their blood.[3] I expect that it'll be like a terrible form of Inquisition," Sol Hodaviah said.

"If Babylon is established again, then what of the Roman Empire; it's this empire that continues to exist until Jesus sets up his Messianic Kingdom?" Sam asked.

"The ancient city of Babylon at the time of Nebuchadnezzar[4] was once the centre of a vast empire named after the city.[5] However, after the city and empire fell, though the city continued to exist, it was considered to be only a part of the empires that conquered it. It was successively a part of the empire of the Medes and the Persians, and then the Greek Empire. The Roman emperor Septimius Severus seized the city in 198 AD, although

---

[1] See Chapter 18 pg 384 and footnote regarding the false religions uniting in Babylon (the "fornication" is idolatry, and the city will deceive all the nations with its sorceries).

[2] See earlier in this chapter pg 530 and footnote regarding the Antichrist as the king of Babylon.

[3] Revelation 17:1-6, 18:21-24. Note that everyone who accepts Jesus as his or her personal saviour is a saint (see Chapter 9 pg 213 and footnote regarding praying to Mary and other saints being wrong, as it is a form of idolatry).

[4] Nebuchadnezzar II.

[5] Daniel 4:28-30—the Kingdom of Babylon (Babylonian Empire), regarded today as the Neo-Babylonian Empire.

by that time it was in an abandoned state.[1] The new Babylon will be a part of the Roman Empire and not separate from it."

Day 13

"Tomorrow is your last day here," Sol Hodaviah said.

"Yes. There's still a lot to do though," Sam replied.

"We won't complete it all tomorrow. Based on your descriptions, we'll gather more pictures. I'll contact you myself. It will hopefully be in the next couple of weeks—while your mind is still fresh."

"One thing I'll never forget is how Satan appeared—so radiant."

"He tries to mimic God the Father and the Messiah God in so many ways. Bear in mind what Lucifer said in his heart: 'I will be like the most High.'[2] But his is just a physical light, whereas God the Father and the resurrected Christ each radiates both a physical and a spiritual light that illuminate both physical and spiritual darkness."[3]

Later that day

"I've been thinking about the Antichrist," Sam said. "There's another reason why he may be a Nephil rather than a normal man."

"Go on; I'm interested in your opinion on this," Sol Hodaviah replied.

---

[1] Dio Cassius' Roman History Epitome of Book 76 *chapter 9:1-4*. See Timeline.

[2] Isaiah 14:14.

[3] Job 12:4-22, 29:1-3, Psalms 18:28, 112:1-4, Luke 2:7-9, John 1:1-34, Revelation 1:11-16, 21:22-23, 22:5, 22:16.

"It seems that in the past these 'men of renown' have not just often been warriors but kings as well. In our reliable Bible Og was the king of Bashan,[1] and within Greek and Roman legends many of the Nephilim, as we define them, were kings such as Odysseus, the brothers Agamemnon and Menelaus,[2] Aeneas[3] and

---

[1] See Chapter 3 pg 64 and relevant footnotes regarding Og of Bashan.

[2] Homer's Iliad: Odysseus (Ulysses), Agamemnon and Menelaus—descendents reportedly of Zeus—were the Greek kings of Ithaca (Book 2 *lines 631-637*), Mycenae (Book 2 *lines 569-580*) and Sparta (Book 2 *lines 581-590*) respectively. Menelaus was greater in stature than even Odysseus (Book 3 *lines 203-224*). See also Apollodorus' The Library Epitome *chapters 2:16-3:12* (Agamemnon and Menelaus were full brothers), Homer's Odyssey Book 4 *lines 675-695*. See Chapter 14 pg 315 and relevant footnotes for the lineages of Odysseus and Agamemnon.

[3] Aeneas (one of the prominent Trojans who escaped from Troy after its defeat by the Greeks, around 1200 BC) was reportedly the founder and first king of Lavinium (in Italy) and a son of Anchises (six generations from Zeus) and Venus (identified with the Greek goddess Aphrodite, a daughter of Zeus or Uranus). Homer's Iliad Book 20 *lines 199-241,* Virgil's Aeneid Book 1 *lines 305-334*, see also Chapter 14 pg 314 regarding Aeneas having reportedly been a descendant of Zeus—the accompanying footnote contains his lineage.

Aeneas was the legendary ancestor of Romulus, who founded Rome (and reigned 753–716 BC): Homer's Iliad Book 20 *lines 288-308,* Virgil's Aeneid Book 1 *lines 223-277,* Livy's History of Rome Book 1 *chapters 1:1-8:7,* Dio Cassius' Roman History Book 1 *supplement by Tzetzes in Lycophron's Alexandra 1232,* Dionysius of Halicarnassus' Roman Antiquities Book 1 *chapters 59:1-5, 63:1-3, 65:1, 66:1-3, 70:1-2, 71:1-5.*

Approximate years of foundings of eminent cities in Italy by either Aeneas or his descendants: 1180 BC, Lavinium by Aeneas; 1152 BC, Alba Longa by Ascanius (son of Aeneas); and 753 BC, Rome by Romulus. See above references.

Romulus,[1] to name just a few. They were not just physically gigantic but also extremely ambitious. I doubt that global domination will be achieved by a normal man."

"For the sake of argument, I'd like to counter that with some examples of men who strove to conquer the world who were not suspect in that regard. Oh . . . Well . . . Now I think about it there are issues with even the first two who spring to mind. Alexander the Great[2] was reputedly a distant descendant of Achilles, a great-grandson of Zeus: the line of descent through Alexander's mother, Olympias. She was born into the Molossian royal house of Epirus, whose founding ancestor, Neoptolemus, was the son of Achilles.[3] Similarly, Julius Caesar . . ."[1]

---

[1] Romulus, reputed founder and first king of Rome, was reportedly a son of Rhea Silvia (a princess of Alba Longa [a city seeded from Lavinium] and a distant descendant of Aeneas) and Mars (Roman god of war, identified with the Greek god Ares). Not much is recorded of Romulus' stature. Plutarch mentioned that as a baby Romulus' size was beyond humankind. Livy's History of Rome Book 1 *chapters 3:1-16:8*, Virgil's Aeneid Book 1 *lines 223-277*, Dionysius of Halicarnassus' Roman Antiquities Book 1 *chapters 65:1, 66:1, 70:1-2, 71:1-5, 77:1-78:5* (a few possible fathers for Romulus are presented, including Mars), Book 2 *chapter 2:1-4*, Plutarch's Lives Romulus *chapters 3:1-4:3* (Mars is stated to have been the father, but an alternative father for Romulus is also presented).

For the approximate year that each of the above cities was founded see earlier in this chapter pg 542 and footnote regarding Aeneas.

[2] Macedonian king (reigned 336–323 BC). See Timeline.

[3] After the Trojan War, Neoptolemus reportedly travelled to Epirus (an area today shared by Albania and Greece), where he defeated a people called Molossians and became their king. With Hector's widow, Andromache, he had three sons: Molossus, Pielus and Pergamos. Pielus was reportedly the ancestor of Alexander the Great. 20 generations separated Alexander from Achilles. Apollodorus' The Library Book 3 *chapter 13:8*, Epitome *chapter 6:12-13*,

FOOTNOTE CONTINUED ON THE NEXT PAGE

"Sorry to interrupt, only I'm sure that I read that Alexander's father, King Philip of Macedonia, was a distant descendent of Hercules."[2]

"Yes, you're right. Alexander was reportedly doubly descended from Zeus: one line through Alexander's father and the other through his mother.[3] And Julius Caesar's family claimed that

CONTINUED FOOTNOTE PRESENT

Pausanias' Description of Greece Book 1 *chapter 11:1-3,* Library of History by Diodorus Siculus Book 17 *chapter 1:1-5,* Plutarch's Lives Alexander *chapter 2:1*, Strabo's Geography Book 7 *chapter 7:8* (states that the Molossians were ruled by the descendants of a son of Neoptolemus but names the son as Pyrrhus rather than any of the above three). See Chapter 14 and footnotes regarding the lineage of Achilles (pg 314) and the same chapter regarding Neoptolemus (pg 319).

Alexander also recognized Achilles as his ancestor during his lifetime: Quintus Curtius' History of Alexander Summaries Book 1 and Book 2, Book 4 *chapter 6:25-29,* Book 8 *chapter 4:21-26.*

[1] Lived 100–44 BC.

[2] The Macedonian kings were reportedly descendants of Hercules, a son of Zeus: Library of History by Diodorus Siculus Fragments of Book 7 *chapters 15:1-17:1,* Book 17 *chapter 1:1*, Plutarch's Lives Alexander *chapter 2:1.*

Alexander also recognized Hercules as his ancestor during his lifetime: Arrian's Anabasis of Alexander Book 3 *chapter 3:1-2,* Book 6 *chapter 3:1-2.*

[3] This is concluded in the preceding footnotes. Of further interest but can be dismissed—during the latter half of Alexander's life he proclaimed himself to be a son of Zeus (rather than Philip) and then later to be a god: the former was possibly triggered by a priest in Egypt who greeted Alexander as son of Zeus Ammon (Zeus Ammon is a deity representing the blending of two gods, one Greek and the other Egyptian) and the latter by Alexander's unbridled pride in his own achievements. Alexander was mortal, dying at the age of 33, and not an immediate descendant of Zeus, for Alexander was a man of normal height (see further on in this chapter pg 546

FOOTNOTE CONTINUED ON THE NEXT PAGE

their clan name 'Julian' was derived from one of their remote ancestors called Iulus, also known as Ascanius, a son of Aeneas. Therefore, the family was in fact making an even greater claim: that they were descendants of Jupiter (Zeus) because both of Aeneas' parents were reportedly descended from this supposed god."[1]

CONTINUED FOOTNOTE PRESENT

---

and footnote regarding this topic). Plutarch's Lives Alexander *chapters 27:3-28:3,* Quintus Curtius' History of Alexander Book 4 *chapter 7:5-32,* Book 8 *chapter 5:5-24,* Arrian's Anabasis of Alexander Book 3 *chapters 3:1-4:5,* Book 4 *chapter 9:7-9,* Book 7 *chapter 29:3,* Library of History by Diodorus Siculus Book 17 *chapters 49:2-51:4.*

[1] Livy's History of Rome Book 1 *chapters 3:1-4:3,* Virgil's Aeneid Book 1 *lines 223-296,* Strabo's Geography Book 13 *chapter 1:27.* Aeneas was reportedly doubly descended from Zeus: through his mother (Venus, Aphrodite) and father (Anchises)—see earlier in this chapter pg 542 and footnote regarding Aeneas.

Regarding the main text, a subtly different version of the story exists, which is that: Iulus (from whom the Julian clan was descended) was the son of Ascanius, rather than being an alternative name for Ascanius. After the death of Ascanius, Iulus contended with his uncle, Silvius (Silvius and Ascanius were both sons of Aeneas but by different mothers), for the rule of Alba Longa, which was a city that Ascanius had founded. Silvius acquired the throne and Iulus was made pontifex maximus. Library of History by Diodorus Siculus Book 7 *chapter 5:8.* See also Dionysius of Halicarnassus' Roman Antiquities Book 1 *chapter 70:1-4,* in which the high-priestly office held by Iulus is not named but described as being a powerful religious position that was later held by the descendants of Iulus in the time of the author (Dionysius): the descendants being Julius Caesar and Augustus Caesar, and the office therefore being of the pontifex maximus. This therefore sets the year of commencement of the office of the pontifex maximus to before 1000 BC and indeed before the foundation of Rome.

FOOTNOTE CONTINUED ON THE NEXT PAGE

"But Alexander and Julius Caesar were within the bounds of normal human physical stature.[1] The Bible defines Nephilim as beings who have a demonic-human ancestry **and** are gigantic,"[2] Sam said.

"Yes, I suppose that if these two conquerors were truly of demonic descent, then clearly the successive pairings of their ancestors with normal human beings through numerous generations over many hundreds of years meant that Alexander and Julius Caesar were themselves of normal height. Therefore, neither of them was a true Nephil. Approximately eight hundred

CONTINUED FOOTNOTE PRESENT

For the approximate year that each of the above cities was founded see earlier in this chapter pg 542 and footnote regarding Aeneas.

[1] Alexander was described as having been not tall but robustly built: Quintus Curtius' History of Alexander Summaries Book 1. King Alexander was shorter than his close friend Hephaestion, for when the mother of Darius (Darius was the last king of the Persian Empire) met them for the first time, she mistook Hephaestion for the king, because of the two men, Hephaestion was the tallest and the handsomest: Library of History by Diodorus Siculus Book 17 *chapter 37:3-6*. When sitting on Darius' throne, Alexander's feet were unable to meet the lowest step, unlike the throne's previous occupant, who was considered to be tall in comparison with his own troops: Quintus Curtius' History of Alexander Book 5 *chapter 2:13-15*, Plutarch's Lives Alexander *chapter 33:2-4*.

The inspiration that Caesar engendered in his troops was relayed by Plutarch. Within this account, Caesar's appearance is described. It is reported that he was lean and of poor health, but it was his bravery, ambition and stamina that far exceeded his appearance that impressed his troops. Plutarch's Lives Caesar *chapter 17:1-3*. A giant with tremendous physical presence is not described but rather a thin man of normal height. Moreover, within the many other ancient records of Caesar that are still in existence, there is no mention of giant proportions (a fact unlikely to be omitted).

[2] See Chapter 3 pg 67 and footnote regarding what the word Nephilim refers to.

and fifty years separate Alexander the Great[1] from Achilles,[2] and a greater number of years separate Alexander from Hercules.[3] Approximately one thousand one hundred years separate Julius Caesar[4] from Aeneas."[5]

"Maybe some of that Nephilic ancestry came through in their characters."

"That's one way of looking at it. A more-restrained view would be that seeing as neither was a true Nephil, then they can be regarded simply as normal men with tremendous ambition."

"So what's your conclusion?"

"Where something isn't completely clear, I think that it's commendable to speculate as long as we declare that that's what we're doing to ourselves and others. However, we should stay open-minded. It's only a matter of time before the Antichrist walks the Earth. His nature is going to be revealed!"

Day 14

"And what will you do with the secret of the throne of Satan?" Sam asked.

"We won't make this public yet. It's not the right time. If we do, then they'll take measures to conceal the Throne, and it will be buried by even deeper secrecy and more deaths. We want to find out who all the human players are. We want to know what they're doing and with whom they're interacting. For now, keep

---

[1] Born 356 BC.

[2] Achilles died in the Trojan War, around 1200 BC. For more information see Chapter 8 pg 178 and Chapter 14 pg 317, both with accompanying footnotes.

[3] Hercules died before the Trojan War. For more information see Chapter 14 pg 320 and relevant footnotes.

[4] Born around 100 BC.

[5] Aeneas fought in the Trojan War. For more information see Chapter 14 pgs 314-319 and relevant footnotes.

it to yourself. Discuss it with no one lest it be overheard by men as well as evil spirits."

"Don't you think that by now Satan knows that we know?"

"The Bible gives a location for Satan's throne. So in a way it's hardly a secret at all. It's also written how he starts religions on the Earth and how he controls the hearts and minds of humans. What you're asking is does he know that we know the exact location of his throne and that you've witnessed it with your own eyes. That I don't know. Satan and his demons are neither omnipotent nor omnipresent, but it's only a matter of time before they find out. They could even be listening to us now."

"What will he do when he finds out?"

"I honestly don't know. His greatest concern is what humans do with knowledge about him. And people are all different. With some, Satan prefers that they don't believe that he exists. Consequently, they have little understanding of the jeopardy to their eternal souls.[1] With others, he allows them to feel his presence and tempts them with rewards of power and glory, so that they embrace his world and the fleeting pleasures that it offers. The Bible gives us a profound knowledge about Satan. Christians are warned that they don't wrestle against flesh and blood but against the evil demonic powers of this world.[2] We're told this, so that we have the big picture in order to make the most informed decisions on how to act. Genuine Christians are the greatest human threat to Satan's ambitions. And with the extra knowledge that we now have, we're an even greater menace to him. Taking all these things into account, I think that when he finds out, he'll move to strike us with even more ferocity than before. Anyhow, I wouldn't worry too much about that, for we're allied with the only omnipotent being in existence,

---

[1] See Soul and Spirit.
[2] Ephesians 6:12.

God. We will be strong in the power of His might![1] Even if we die through Satan's devices, our eternal salvation is assured."[2]

"And what will you do with the knowledge that you gain about the activities of the human members of the Throne and their accomplices?"

"I can't discuss that with you, Sam." Sol Hodaviah paused to reflect. "Your mission is over. Rest your mind as well as your body. Let us deal with tomorrow's troubles."

"They're my troubles as well," Sam said in earnest. "You haven't got much time."

"Too true, although that can be said of any human living on the Earth."

Sam projected a thought that had been in his mind for a while: "I wonder how vain our efforts are to fight Satan. What I'm trying to say is that it's written in the Bible that before the Messiah returns to rule, the Antichrist will rule the world. What can we do to prevent this? Every prophecy in the Bible comes true."

"And should we do anything? That's also what you're asking, isn't it? We hope that the Messiah will return as soon as possible and establish His kingdom, because we'll be a part of it. Yet we also have a deep anxiety for those who haven't put their trust in Him. Our work is to tell people about their saviour, so that He can deliver them from Satan's kingdom.[3] This is the great spiritual battle, which goes on every day. The dissemination of lies has been one of Satan's key methods of destroying mankind's glorious future with God. There are so many false religions in the world. These united with a base in Babylon will be one of the most powerful deceiving forces the world has ever

---

[1] Ephesians 6:10-11.
[2] John 14:1-3, Acts 4:10-12, Romans 1:16, Ephesians 1:1-14, 2 Timothy 3:14-15, 1 Peter 1:1-9.
[3] Romans 6:17-23, 1 Corinthians 6:9-11, Colossians 1:1-29 (key passage), Titus 3:3-8.

known. We must reveal the truth about Babylon, the Antichrist and Satan. In this way, we can warn our fellow man about the present perils and those to come. This is part of that great battle."

"I understand. You've clearly thought deeply about this." Sam got up to leave. He had a small overnight bag that Sol Hodaviah had given him. It was already packed.

"Are you looking forward to seeing Rachel?"

"Again, I won't ask you how you know about her. I expect that you know that we never dated before I left for Turkey. We talked about it." Sam paused. "I just don't feel the same way about her anymore."

"Why?"

"I don't know. Something's changed."

Within Sam, an unintentional seed of love had formed for another. Unacknowledged and subconsciously suppressed, yet it survived. It dwelt in the core of his heart and had become a foundation that another love couldn't be built upon. But could the woman be turned? Perhaps so, since salvation is potentially for any of us, no matter what we happen to be involved in before we choose Jesus.

The following is advice for those who want to accept Jesus as their personal saviour, presented as the prayer of a person genuinely seeking salvation.

I believe that Jesus is God.
I'm a sinner, but I want to turn my life around.
I believe that Jesus died for my sins and ask His forgiveness for them.
I put my trust in Jesus that He will give me eternal life with Him.
Amen.

Important final comments

Creation's Mutiny is a combination of fiction and non-fiction. It is clear from the text as to which parts are fiction and which parts are non-fiction. Creation's Mutiny was written by M. W. Seymour (MWS) to motivate people to read and understand the Bible.

MWS has set the events of Creation's Mutiny in 2025 AD. He did this for convenience of narration and does not possess any knowledge as to when the biblical prophetic events will occur beyond that which is already revealed in the Bible. For example, he cannot state when the construction of the new city of Babylon will begin, but the Bible has revealed that the Antichrist will be at his most prominent for seven years and during this period the city of Babylon will feature significantly.

Regarding the Ark, MWS knows that it came to rest on the mountains of Ararat as stated in the Bible.

A throne is positioned in a chamber where a monarch can receive his (or her) subjects, discuss matters with them and deliver his commands to them. MWS does not know what the throne of Satan and the presumed accompanying chamber look like. The throne and the chamber could each be a natural object or a construction. MWS does not know exactly how Satan orchestrates his universal rebellion from the throne. MWS knows that the Bible states that Satan resides in Pergamos and that his throne is located there. The throne of Satan and the accompanying chamber must therefore be physical objects, because otherwise a location would not be given. MWS's opinion is that although what is stated was written approximately 2,000 years ago, it is very unlikely that Satan is no longer residing in Pergamos and that he has moved his throne from there.

SELECT BIBLIOGRAPHY

In each square bracket [ ] is the approximate year that the earliest original document was written—if a document is a compilation of works, then the year given is regarding the earliest work. If there are a collection of works in a single modern publication, then the one or those cited in Creation's Mutiny are in normal text, whereas if not cited, *italics* are used. When the work of an author has more than one volume that makes up a series, then the year of the edition presented is of the first volume of the series.

The Holy Bible [1446 BC]. English translation: Authorized Version of the Bible (The King James Bible), 1769 edition. Translation (excluding Apocrypha) by G. Abbot, J. Aglionby, L. Andrewes, R. Andrews, W. Barlow, W. Bedwell, T. Bilson, A. Bing, R. Brett, F. Burleigh, L. Chaderton, R. Clarke, W. Dakins, F. Dillingham, D. Featley, R. Fenton, J. Harding, J. Harmer, T. Harrison, T. Holland, L. Hutten, R. Hutchinson, R. Kilby, G. King, J. Layfield, E. Lively, J. Overall, J. Peryn, M. Rabbett, T. Ravis, J. Reynolds, J. Richardson, T. Sanderson, H. Saravia, H. Savile, M. Smith, R. Spaulding, J. Spenser, G. Thomson, R. Thomson, W. Thorne and R. Tighe.

Theogony [1000 BC], *Works and Days, Testimonia,* Hesiod, translated by G. W. Most, Loeb Classical Library, 2006 edition.

Iliad, Homer [1000 BC], translated by A. T. Murray, revised by G. E. Dimock, Loeb Classical Library, first published 1924, 2001 reprint.

Odyssey, Homer [1000 BC], translated by A. T. Murray, revised by W. F. Wyatt, Loeb Classical Library, first published 1919, reprinted with corrections 1998.

Homeric Hymns [700 BC, not considered to be works of Homer], *Homeric Apocrypha, Lives of Homer,* edited and translated by M. L. West, Loeb Classical Library, first published 2003.

Greek Epic Fragments [700 BC], edited and translated by M. L. West, Loeb Classical Library, 2003 edition.

The Shield, Catalogue of Women, *Other Fragments,* Hesiod [600 BC, not now considered to be works of Hesiod], edited and translated by G. W. Most, Loeb Classical Library, 2007 edition.

Olympian Odes [476 BC], Pythian Odes [498 BC], Pindar, edited and translated by W. H. Race, Loeb Classical Library, first published 1997.

Nemean Odes, Isthmian Odes [474 BC], Fragments, Pindar, edited and translated by W. H. Race, Loeb Classical Library, first published 1997, reprinted 2006.

Greek Lyric, Bacchylides [460 BC], Corinna, and Others, edited and translated by D. A. Campbell, Loeb Classical Library, first published 1992, reprinted 2006.

Persians, Seven against Thebes, Suppliants, Prometheus Bound [454 BC], Aeschylus, edited and translated by A. H. Sommerstein, Loeb Classical Library, first published 2008.

The Persian Wars, Herodotus [445 BC], translated by A. D. Godley, Loeb Classical Library, first published 1920, revised and reprinted 1926, 2004 reprint.

Cyclops, Alcestis, Medea [431 BC], Euripides, edited and translated by D. Kovacs, Loeb Classical Library, first published 1994, reprinted with changes and corrections 2001.

Children of Heracles, Hippolytus, Andromache [425 BC], Hecuba, Euripides, edited and translated by D. Kovacs, Loeb Classical Library, first published 1995, reprinted with revisions and corrections 2005.

Suppliant Women, Electra, Heracles [416 BC], Euripides, edited and translated by D. Kovacs, Loeb Classical Library, first published 1998.

Trojan Women, Iphigenia among the Taurians [414 BC], Ion, Euripides, translated by D. Kovacs, Loeb Classical Library, 1999 edition.

Helen [412 BC], Phoenician Women, Orestes [408 BC], Euripides, edited and translated by D. Kovacs, Loeb Classical Library, 2002 edition.

Bacchae, Iphigenia at Aulis [407 BC], Rhesus, Euripides, translated by D. Kovacs, Loeb Classical Library, 2002 edition.

Argonautica, Apollonius Rhodius [250 BC], edited and translated by W. H. Race, Loeb Classical Library, first published 2008.

The Histories, Polybius [167 BC], translated by W. R. Paton, revised by F. W. Walbank and C. Habicht, fragments edited and translated by S. D. Olson, Loeb Classical Library, first published 1922, revised 2010.

Library of History, Diodorus Siculus [56 BC], translated by R. M. Geer, C. H. Oldfather, C. L. Sherman, F. R. Walton and C. B. Welles, Loeb Classical Library, first published 1933.

The Library, Apollodorus [50 BC], translated by J. G. Frazer, Loeb Classical Library, first published 1921.

History of Rome, Livy [27 BC], translated by B. O. Foster, F. G. Moore, E. T. Sage and A. C. Schlesinger, index by R. M. Geer, Loeb Classical Library, first published 1919.

Eclogues, Georgics, Aeneid [19 BC], *Appendix Vergiliana,* Virgil, translated by H. R. Fairclough, revised by G. P. Goold, Loeb Classical Library, first published 1916, revised edition with new introduction 1999, 2004 reprint.

Apollodorus' Library and Hyginus' Fabulae [8 BC], translated, with introductions, by R. S. Smith and S. M. Trzaskoma, Hackett Publishing Company, Inc., 2007 edition. J. G. Frazer's translation of The Library by Apollodorus is cited in Creation's Mutiny.

Roman Antiquities, Dionysius of Halicarnassus [7 BC], translated by E. Cary, Loeb Classical Library, first published 1937.

Metamorphoses, Ovid [7 AD], translated by F. J. Miller, revised by G. P. Goold, Loeb Classical Library, first published 1916, third edition 1977.

Fasti, Ovid [8 AD], translated by J. G. Frazer, revised by G. P. Goold, Loeb Classical Library, first published 1931, reprinted with corrections 1996.

Geography, Strabo [18 AD], translated by H. L. Jones, Loeb Classical Library, first published 1917, 2005 reprint.

History of Alexander, Quintus Curtius [41 AD], translated by J. C. Rolfe, Loeb Classical Library, first published 1946, 2006 reprint.

The Jewish War, Josephus [75 AD], translated by H. ST. J. Thackeray, Loeb Classical Library, first published 1927, 1997 reprint.

Jewish Antiquities, Josephus [93 AD], translated by L. Feldman, R. Marcus, A. Wikgren and H. ST. J. Thackeray, Loeb Classical Library, first published 1930, 2001 reprint.

Lives, Theseus and Romulus, *Lycurgus and* Numa, *Solon and Publicola,* Plutarch [100 AD], translated by B. Perrin, Loeb Classical Library, first published 1914.

Lives, *Demosthenes and Cicero*, Alexander and Caesar, Plutarch [100 AD], translated by B. Perrin, Loeb Classical Library, first published 1919.

Histories*, Annals [116 AD], Tacitus, translated by **C. H. Moore* and J. Jackson, Loeb Classical Library, first published 1931.

Anabasis of Alexander [130 AD], *Indica,* Arrian, translated by P. A. Brunt, Loeb Classical Library, 1976 edition.

Description of Greece, Pausanias [170 AD], translated by W. H. S Jones, H. A. Ormerod and R. E. Wycherley, Loeb Classical Library, first published 1918.

Apology and De Spectaculis [200 AD], Tertullian, *Octavius, Minucius Felix*,* translated by T. R. Glover and **G. H. Rendall,* Loeb Classical Library, first published 1931.

Roman History, Dio Cassius [222 AD], translated by E. Cary, Loeb Classical Library, first published 1914, 2006 reprint.

History of the Empire, Herodian [247 AD], translated by C. R. Whittaker, Loeb Classical Library, first published 1969.

Ausonius [335 AD], translated by H. G. E. White, Loeb Classical Library, first published 1919.

The Fall of Troy, Quintus Smyrnaeus [370 AD], translated by A. S. Way, Loeb Classical Library, first published 1913, 2006 reprint.

Historia Augusta [395 AD], translated by D. Magie, Loeb Classical Library, first published 1921, 2006 reprint.

Zosimus: New History [500 AD], a translation with commentary by R. T. Ridley, Australian Association for Byzantine Studies, 1982.

Accounts of Medieval Constantinople, The Patria [550 AD], translated by A. Berger, Dumbarton Oaks Library, Harvard University Press, 2013.

On Buildings, Procopius [558 AD], translated by H. B. Dewing, Loeb Classical Library, first published 1940, reprinted with revisions 1954.

Decline and fall of Byzantium to the Ottoman Turks*, Doukas [1462 AD], an annotated translation of Historia Turco-Byzantina* by H. J. Magoulias, Wayne State University Press,

1975. *Modern descriptive designations—the earliest printed version of Doukas' work is known simply as Manuscript P.

The Histories, Laonikos Chalkokondyles [1464 AD], translated by A. Kaldellis, Dumbarton Oaks Library, Harvard University Press, 2014.

History of Mehmed the Conqueror, Kritovoulos [1467 AD], translated by C. T. Riggs, Greenwood Press, Princeton University Press, 1954 edition, reprinted 1970.

The Fall of the Byzantine Empire*, A Chronicle by George Sphrantzes, 1401-1477 [1477 AD], containing the Chronicon Minus by Sphrantzes *and part of the Chronicon Maius of probable multiple origins, including the writers Sphrantzes and Melissenos*, translated by Marios Philippides, The University of Massachusetts Press, 1980 edition. *A modern descriptive designation.

Ecclesiastical History, Eusebius [311 AD], translated by K. Lake and J. E. L. Oulton, Loeb Classical Library, first published 1926.

The Seven Ecumenical Councils of the Undivided Church [314 AD]. Their canons and dogmatic decrees, together with the canons of all the local synods which have received ecumenical acceptance. Edited with notes gathered from the writings of the greatest scholars by H. R. Percival (above written as presented). Published as the title Nicene and Post-Nicene Fathers, Second Series, Volume XIV, The Seven Ecumenical Councils, edited by P. Schaff and H. Wallace, Cosimo Classics 2007 edition. Relevant translators: W. A. Hammond, W. Lambert, J. Fulton, J. Mendham, McGarvey, F. A. Sanborn, J. Johnson, H. T. Bruns, Pusey and Buckley.

Documents of the Early Arian Controversy [318 AD]. English translations provided by the Fourth-Century Christianity Web site, sponsored by the History Department of Wisconsin Lutheran College and by Asia Lutheran Seminary, under the direction of G. L. Thompson. Translators of documents referenced: G. L. Thompson and A. J. West, and also referenced are their adaptations of translations found in Nicene and Post-Nicene Fathers: Second Series Volumes 2-4 (relevant translators: E.

Walford, B. Jackson and J. H. Newman). http://www.fourthcentury.com/urkunden-chart-2007/ last accessed 18th July 2013. The documents represent a collection of many ancient sources (sometimes more than one in a single document). There is more than one modern recognized method to reference the documents. The method used in Creation's Mutiny is based on Athanasius Alexandrinus, Werke, Band III/Teil 1: Urkunden Zur Geschichte Des Arianischen Streites 318-328 (Athanasius of Alexandria, Works, Volume III, Part 1: Documents for the History of the Arian Controversy 318-328), Hanns Christof Brennecke (Ed.) et al, published by De Gruyter, 2007 edition.

Life of Constantine, Eusebius [337 AD], translated with an introduction and commentary by A. Cameron and S. G. Hall, Clarendon Press, Oxford, 1999 edition, 2002 reprint.

Creeds, Councils and Controversies: Documents illustrative of the history of the Church A.D. 337-461 [337 AD], edited by J. Stevenson (translator of the Codex Theodosianus XVI 1.2: C. Pharr), first published by S.P.C.K 1966.

Socrates [439 AD] and Sozomenus [447 AD] Ecclesiastical Histories. Nicene and Post-Nicene Fathers Series II, Volume 2, published by Christian Classics Ethereal Library, Grand Rapids, Michigan (available online). Editorial supervision of P. Schaff. Socrates' and Sozomenus' works both translated by E. Walford, and revised by A. C. Zenos and C. D. Hartranft respectively.

Lives of the Popes, Volume I, Bartolomeo Platina [1474 AD], edited and translated by A. F. D'Elia, The I Tatti Renaissance Library, Harvard University Press, 2008.

Douay-Rheims Bible, an English translation (completed in 1609) of the Latin Vulgate (a Latin translation of the Bible), translated by G. Martin and W Allen, revised by R. Challoner (revision completed in 1752), published by Saint Benedict Press in association with Tan Books, 1899 edition.

Book of Mormon, Doctrine and Covenants, Pearl of Great Price, published by The Church of Jesus Christ of Latter-day Saints, Salt Lake City, Utah, U.S.A., 1981 edition, first English edition published in 1830.

The Mysterious Numbers of the Hebrew Kings, E. R. Thiele, Kregel Publications, 1994 edition, first published in 1983 by Zondervan Corporation.

Reasoning from the Scriptures, published by Watch Tower Bible and Tract Society of New York, Inc., 1989 edition.

The Elder Edda: A Book of Viking Lore [800 AD], translated and edited by A. Orchard, Penguin Classics, first published in 2011.

The Prose Edda, Snorri Sturluson [1220 AD], translated with an introduction and notes by J. L. Byock, Penguin Classics, first published in 2005.

Mesopotamian Chronicles [2200 BC], translated into French by J-J. Glassner (subsequent English translation from the French), edited by B. R. Foster, 2004, published under license from the Society of Biblical Literature by Koninklijke Brill NV, Leiden, The Netherlands.

Myths from Mesopotamia: Creation, The Flood, Gilgamesh and Others [1900 BC], edited and translated with an introduction and notes by S. Dalley, Oxford University Press, first published 1989, revised edition 2000, reissued 2008.

The Qur'an (Koran) [633 AD], a new translation by M. A. S. Abdel Haleem, Oxford University Press, first published 2004, first published with corrections as an Oxford World's Classics paperback 2005.

The Holy Qur'aan (Koran) [633 AD], with Arabic text, English translation by M. M. Pickthall, transliteration in Roman script by M. A. H. Eliyasee, published by Abdul Naeem for Islamic Book Service, 2008–2009 edition (above written as presented).

The Life of Muḥammad, a translation of Ibn Isḥāq's Sīrat Rasūl Allāh [740 AD], translated with an introduction and notes by A. Guillaume, Oxford University Press, first published 1955, 2012 reprint.

The Book of Idols, being a translation from the Arabic of the Kitāb al-Aṣnam by Hishām ibn-al-Kalbi [800 AD], translated with an introduction and notes by N. A. Faris, Princeton University Press, 1952 edition.

The Tombs and Moon Temple of Hureidha (Hadhramaut) by G. C. Thompson, printed at the University Press by John Johnson for the Society of Antiquaries, Burlington House, London, 1944.

Histoire Générale Des Religions (General History of the Religions), sous la direction de MM. Maxime Gorce et Raoul Mortier, containing the chapter Les religions Arabes préIslamiques (The religions of the pre-Islāmic Arabs) by G. Ryckmans, Libraire Aristide Quillet, 1947.

Cylinder Seals of Western Asia, by D. J. Wiseman, illustrations selected and photographed by W. and B. Forman, Batchworth Press Limited, London, 1958.

The Art of Mesopotamia, by E. Strommenger, photographs by M. Hirmer, Thames and Hudson, London, 1964.

The Rig Veda [1500 BC], An Anthology, One hundred and eight hymns, selected, translated and annotated by W. Doniger, Penguin Books Ltd, first published 1981.

The Mahābhārata [400 BC], 1. The Book of the Beginning, translated and edited by J. A. B. van Buitenen, The University of Chicago Press, first published 1973, paperback edition 1983.

The Mahābhārata [400 BC], 2. The Book of the Assembly Hall 3. The Book of the Forest, translated and edited by J. A. B. van Buitenen, The University of Chicago Press, first published 1975, Phoenix edition 1981.

The Bhagavadgītā in the Mahābhārata [200 BC], A Bilingual Edition, translated and edited by J. A. B. van Buitenen, The University of Chicago Press, first published 1981.

Bhāgavata Purāṇa [450 AD], translated and annotated by G. V. Tagare, edited by G. P. Bhatt and J. L. Shastri, Motilal Banarsidass Publishers Private Limited, Delhi, first published 1976, 2011 reprint.

The Minor Anthologies of the Pāli Canon Volume III: Chronicle of Buddhas (Buddhavaṃsa) [50 BC] and Basket of Conduct (Cariyāpiṭaka), translated by I. B. Horner, Pali Text Society, first published 1975, 2013 reprint.

Old Burma-Early Pagán, G. H. Luce, published for Artibus Asiae and the Institute of Fine Arts, Locust Valley, New York University, J. J. Augustin Publisher, New York, 1969 edition.

TIMELINE

DATES	EVENTS
Always existed	GOD (The Father, the Messiah and the Holy Spirit).[1]
Unknown	Heaven (the home of God) was created. The angels were created.[2]
4174 BC	The universe and the Earth were created.*
↑ The pre-Flood era ↓	Satan rebelled, and this event was followed by the temptation and fall of mankind, and the subsequent expulsion from Eden.[3] God observed the wickedness of mankind on the Earth. The pre-Flood giants were part of the corruption.[4]
2518 BC	The Flood began. The Flood ended in 2517 BC.*

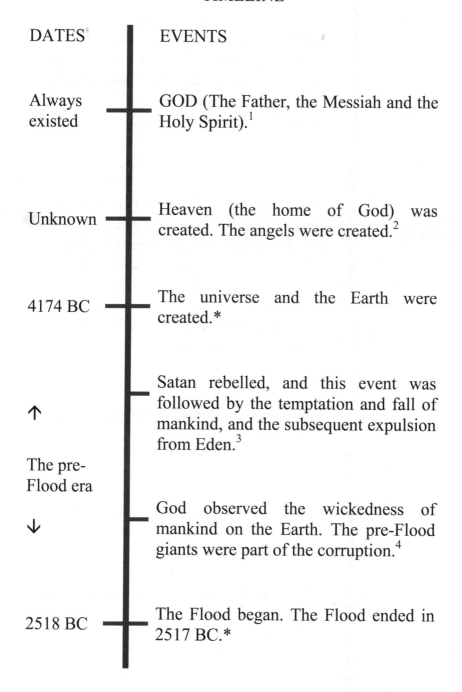

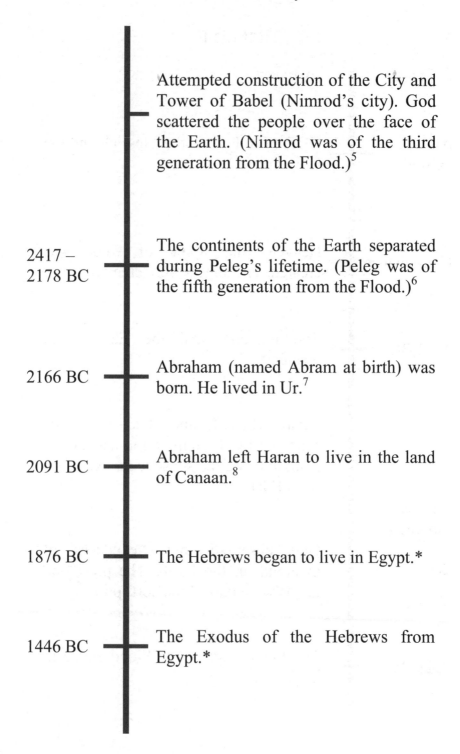

Attempted construction of the City and Tower of Babel (Nimrod's city). God scattered the people over the face of the Earth. (Nimrod was of the third generation from the Flood.)[5]

2417 – 2178 BC

The continents of the Earth separated during Peleg's lifetime. (Peleg was of the fifth generation from the Flood.)[6]

2166 BC

Abraham (named Abram at birth) was born. He lived in Ur.[7]

2091 BC

Abraham left Haran to live in the land of Canaan.[8]

1876 BC

The Hebrews began to live in Egypt.*

1446 BC

The Exodus of the Hebrews from Egypt.*

From 1406 BC onward the Hebrews fought with the inhabitants of the land of Canaan, some of whom were post-Flood Nephilim, for control of the Promised Land.[9] In approximately 1025 BC, David in his youth killed the Philistine giant Goliath.[10] The last recorded battle with the Philistine giants took place during David's reign as king, 1010–970 BC.[11]

966 BC

King Solomon (a contemporary of King Shishak of Egypt and King Hiram of Tyre) began to build the Temple in Jerusalem, known as the First Temple or Solomon's Temple.*

930 BC

The Kingdom of the Hebrews was divided into Judah and Israel.*

723 BC

Samaria (the capital of Israel) fell to the Assyrians led by Shalmaneser V. The majority of Israel's citizens were deported to the Assyrian Empire.[12]

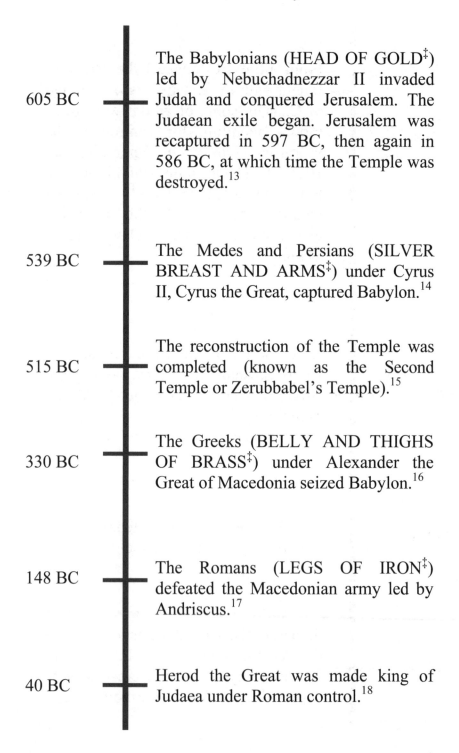

605 BC — The Babylonians (HEAD OF GOLD[‡]) led by Nebuchadnezzar II invaded Judah and conquered Jerusalem. The Judaean exile began. Jerusalem was recaptured in 597 BC, then again in 586 BC, at which time the Temple was destroyed.[13]

539 BC — The Medes and Persians (SILVER BREAST AND ARMS[‡]) under Cyrus II, Cyrus the Great, captured Babylon.[14]

515 BC — The reconstruction of the Temple was completed (known as the Second Temple or Zerubbabel's Temple).[15]

330 BC — The Greeks (BELLY AND THIGHS OF BRASS[‡]) under Alexander the Great of Macedonia seized Babylon.[16]

148 BC — The Romans (LEGS OF IRON[‡]) defeated the Macedonian army led by Andriscus.[17]

40 BC — Herod the Great was made king of Judaea under Roman control.[18]

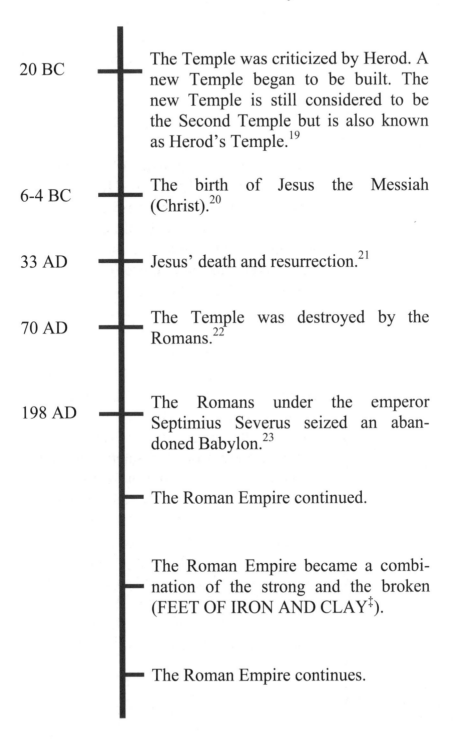

20 BC — The Temple was criticized by Herod. A new Temple began to be built. The new Temple is still considered to be the Second Temple but is also known as Herod's Temple.[19]

6-4 BC — The birth of Jesus the Messiah (Christ).[20]

33 AD — Jesus' death and resurrection.[21]

70 AD — The Temple was destroyed by the Romans.[22]

198 AD — The Romans under the emperor Septimius Severus seized an abandoned Babylon.[23]

The Roman Empire continued.

The Roman Empire became a combination of the strong and the broken (FEET OF IRON AND CLAY[‡]).

The Roman Empire continues.

The Rapture (the transfer of all Christians from the Earth to Heaven by Christ). People will become Christians after this event. The time of the Rapture is unknown, but the event is very likely to take place before the seven-year Tribulation.[24]

Future date: as yet unknown

The Tribulation will begin. During the Tribulation Babylon will be the political, commercial and religious centre of the world. Babylon will fall.[25] Toward the end of the seven-year Tribulation period Jerusalem will be defeated by the Antichrist's forces.[26] His army will then turn east to attack the remnant of Israel. The Messiah (THE STONE‡) will return and defeat the Antichrist and his army.[27] Not long after Satan will be bound in the Abyss (Bottomless Pit). The Millennium (1,000-year reign of Jesus the Messiah from Jerusalem) will begin.[28]

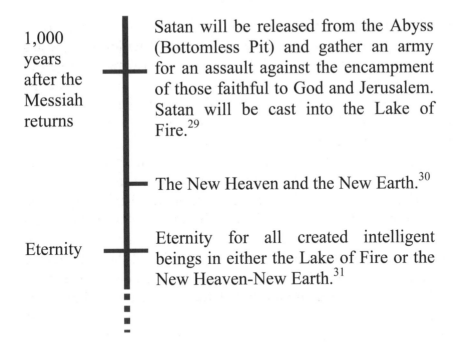

1,000 years after the Messiah returns — Satan will be released from the Abyss (Bottomless Pit) and gather an army for an assault against the encampment of those faithful to God and Jerusalem. Satan will be cast into the Lake of Fire.[29]

The New Heaven and the New Earth.[30]

Eternity — Eternity for all created intelligent beings in either the Lake of Fire or the New Heaven-New Earth.[31]

*See Timeline Method.
‡Relates to Nebuchadnezzar II's dream and the interpretation in Daniel 2:1-45 (see also Chapter 20 pgs 433-438).

Timeline Method

A suitable date was found on which precise sequential biblical chronology could be applied. That date is 930 BC, which was the year in which the Kingdom of the Hebrews divided and the first year of Rehoboam's reign over Judah. The majority of biblical chronologists place the division of the kingdom between 938 BC and 921 BC. However, E. Thiele has provided the finest answer by determining the date to be 930 BC. There are biblically recorded events during the reigns of the Hebrew kings that are connected with historical events documented by a nearby nation, Assyria, whose historical record has a precise chronology because it is conveniently linked to astronomical phenomena (e.g., total lunar eclipses), the exact dates of which can be confirmed with computers. Using the dates of the Hebrew-Assyrian connected events to assist him, he determined the dates of the beginnings and ends of the reigns of the Hebrew kings from their biblically stated lengths of reigns and the stated durations during which the reigns of kings of Judah overlapped with the reigns of kings of Israel. 930 BC was calculated to be the year of the division of the kingdom.[32]

The following contains specific lengths of time that the authors of the Bible (inspired by God) intended to be used to form a chronological record. The lengths of time serve this purpose as their primary function. The word "begat" can mean "was the father of" or "was the ancestor of". Every reference below using begat means "was the father of", because for all the individuals, excluding Noah and Terah, the age that the man begat his named male offspring is stated and it is stated that each man had other sons and had daughters. For Noah and Terah, begat still means the same thing, the specific reasons for which are detailed below. The Old Testament chronology is based on the Hebrew Masoretic text (used by the King James Version translators). The lengths of time were used to produce the timeline (dates and events) that preceded 930 BC. Working backward from 930 BC:

A. Rehoboam came to the throne when his father, Solomon, died. Solomon reigned for 40 years. In the fourth year of Solomon's reign the building of the Temple in Jerusalem commenced, 966 BC.[33]

B. The Exodus from Egypt of the Hebrews (the descendants of Israel, also known as Jacob) occurred 480 years before the initiation of the building of the Temple in Jerusalem. Therefore, the Exodus was in 1446 BC.[34]

C. The Hebrews stayed in Egypt for 430 years, the start of which was therefore in 1876 BC.[35] They were afflicted for 400 of those years whilst in Egypt.[36]

D. There were 642 years between the Hebrews moving to Egypt and the Flood, which makes the date of the Flood 2518 BC.[37]

At the age of 100 years Shem begat Arphaxad (which was 2 years after the Flood), after which Shem lived for 500 years. (Shem died at the age of 600 years.)
At the age of 35 years Arphaxad begat Salah, after which Arphaxad lived for 403 years. (Arphaxad died at the age of 438 years.)
At the age of 30 years Salah begat Eber, after which Salah lived for 403 years. (Salah died at the age of 433 years.)
At the age of 34 years Eber begat Peleg, after which Eber lived for 430 years. (Eber died at the age of 464 years.)
At the age of 30 years Peleg begat Reu, after which Peleg lived for 209 years. (Peleg died at the age of 239 years.)
At the age of 32 years Reu begat Serug, after which Reu lived for 207 years. (Reu died at the age of 239 years.)
At the age of 30 years Serug begat Nahor, after which Serug lived for 200 years. (Serug died at the age of 230 years.)
At the age of 29 years Nahor begat Terah, after which Nahor lived for 119 years. (Nahor died at the age of 148 years.)
It is stated that at the age of 70 years Terah begat 3 sons: Abraham, Nahor and Haran. But unlike many other passages that deliver similar facts, the relevant passage of the Bible does not then immediately state how long the begetter (Terah) lived after he begat one of these sons. However, the following can be reasoned from the Bible. In the early part of Terah's life he lived in Ur. Abraham, Sarah (Abraham's first wife, named Sarai at birth), Lot (Abraham's nephew) and Terah had intended to relocate together from Ur to the land of Canaan but ended up moving to and staying in Haran, which was on the way. Terah died in Haran at the age of 205. Abraham was 75 years old when he left Haran after the death of Terah. Therefore, Terah was 130 years old when Abraham was born. Terah's firstborn son when he was 70 years old was most likely Haran, as this man's son, Lot, was Abraham's contemporary and Nahor (the other son of

Terah) married Haran's daughter Milcah. Genesis 11:26-12:4. Compare this to Genesis 5:32, which has a similar arrangement. It is stated that Noah begat 3 sons when he was 500 years old; therefore, one of the sons was born when he was 500 years old, but it is not stated which. However, the firstborn son was not Shem. Shem was born when Noah was 502 years old, because at the age of 100 years, which was 2 years after the Flood, Shem had a son called Arphaxad (Genesis 11:10). See below for the note regarding the term "after the Flood".

At the age of <u>100 years</u> Abraham begat Isaac. (Abraham died at the age of 175 years.)

At the age of <u>60 years</u> Isaac begat Jacob and Esau, the twins. (Isaac died at the age of 180 years.)

Jacob lived for 147 years, 17 years of which were in Egypt; therefore, he moved to Egypt at the age of <u>130 years</u>.

Total (underlined numbers) = 642 years

E. The Flood lasted for 1 year and 10 days, which suggests that one needs to add a year to the above sequence of years to make the start of the Flood 2519 BC;[38] however, when the following passage states "after the Flood", it means after the Flood's commencement rather than after the end of the Flood. The reason is as follows. Genesis 9:28-9:29 states that after the Flood Noah lived 350 years and died at the age of 950 years; he was 600 years old (Genesis 7:11) when the Flood started and 601 years old (Genesis 8:13-14) when it ended, and therefore he would have died at the age of 951 years if "after the Flood" means after the end of the Flood. For consistency, one should deduce that the passage in Genesis 11:10 regarding the birth of Shem's son Arphaxad also means after the Flood's commencement. The above therefore means that the Flood began in 2518 BC and ended in 2517 BC.

F. The pre-Flood era lasted 1,656 years.[39] The universe and the Earth were created at the beginning of the pre-Flood era, 4174 BC.[40]

At the age of <u>130 years</u> Adam begat Seth, after which Adam lived for 800 years. (Adam died at the age of 930 years.)
At the age of <u>105 years</u> Seth begat Enos, after which Seth lived for 807 years. (Seth died at the age of 912 years.)
At the age of <u>90 years</u> Enos begat Cainan, after which Enos lived for 815 years. (Enos died at the age of 905 years.)
At the age of <u>70 years</u> Cainan begat Mahalaleel, after which Cainan lived for 840 years. (Cainan died at the age of 910 years.)
At the age of <u>65 years</u> Mahalaleel begat Jared, after which Mahalaleel lived for 830 years. (Mahalaleel died at the age of 895 years.)
At the age of <u>162 years</u> Jared begat Enoch, after which Jared lived for 800 years. (Jared died at the age of 962 years.)
At the age of <u>65 years</u> Enoch begat Methuselah, after which Enoch lived on the Earth for 300 years. But he did not die. Because of his special relationship with God, he was taken from the Earth at the age of 365 years.
At the age of <u>187 years</u> Methuselah begat Lamech, after which Methuselah lived for 782 years. (Methuselah died at the age of 969 years.)
At the age of <u>182 years</u> Lamech begat Noah, after which Lamech lived for 595 years. (Lamech died at the age of 777 years.)
The Flood started when Noah was <u>600 years</u> old. (Noah died at the age of 950 years.)

Total (underlined numbers) = 1,656 years

---

[1] Genesis 1:1-2, Micah 5:2, John 1:1-34, 1 John 5:7, Revelation 1:8-18.
[2] Job 38:4-7.
[3] Genesis 3:1-24, Ezekiel 28:12-17.
ENDNOTES

---

[4] Genesis 6:1-13.

[5] Genesis 10:6-10, 11:1-9.

[6] Genesis 10:25, 11:10-19, 1 Chronicles 1:19.

[7] Genesis 11:26-31.

[8] Genesis 12:4-13:4.

[9] Deuteronomy 1:1-7, 3:1-13, 9:1-5, Joshua 11:21, 15:13-14, Amos 2:9. See Chapter 3 pgs 65-71 and all relevant footnotes regarding this topic for a detailed explanation.

[10] 1 Samuel 17:1-58, 2 Samuel 5:4-5, 1 Kings 2:11.

[11] 2 Samuel 5:4-5, 21:16-22, 1 Kings 2:11, 1 Chronicles 20:4-8.

[12] 2 Kings 17:1-6, 18:9-11. Note that the ancient Assyrian Empire included areas that are now located in southeastern Turkey, Iraq and western Iran (the latter location is important to know, as the two passages mention cities of the Medes). See Chapter 14 pgs 312-313 with footnotes regarding the so-called "Ten Lost Tribes of Israel" and Chapter 19 pg 391 with footnote regarding neighbours for more information on the exile (deportation).

[13] 2 Kings 24:10-15, 25:1-12.

[14] Daniel 5:1-31, Mesopotamian Chronicles *26 Chronicle of Nabonidus (556-539)*. Belshazzar, king of Babylon (coregent with Nabonidus, who was away at the time of the invasion), was slain on the same night that his downfall was predicted by Daniel. Note that Darius the Mede was under the authority of Cyrus the Great.

[15] Ezra 3:8-6:15 (note that the Temple had a new foundation), Zechariah 4:9.

[16] Alexander had recently won a major battle against the king of the Persians, who had had mastery over Babylon. Not surprisingly, the Babylonians offered no resistance to Alexander and his troops entering and occupying the city. Diodorus Siculus' Library of History Book 17 *chapters 64:3-65:1,* Quintus Curtius' History of Alexander Book 5 *chapter 1:17-23 and 36-45,* Arrian's Anabasis of Alexander Book 3 *chapter 16:3-6.*

[17] The defeat of Andriscus (also known as the false Philip) repre-sented the final significant Macedonian resistance to Rome's conquering force: Livy's History of Rome Summaries Books 48-50,

---

Diodorus Siculus' Library of History Book 32 *chapter 15:1-7*, Dio Cassius' Roman History Book 21 *epitome by Zonaras 9.28*.

After this time, Rome slowly overcame the rest of the Greek Empire, whose last defeat was in 30 BC—the defeat of Ptolemaic Egypt: Livy's History of Rome Summaries Book 133, Dio Cassius' Roman History Book 50 *chapters 31:1-35:6*, Book 51 *chapters 1:1-3, 5:1-17:4*, Josephus' The Jewish War Book 1 *sections 386-397*, Josephus' Jewish Antiquities Book 15 *sections 187-201, 215-216*.

[18] Herod and his brother Phasael had previously been appointed by Mark Antony the shared rule of Judaea (42 BC). In 40 BC Herod was unanimously voted the king of the Jews (in actual fact, king of Judaea) by the Roman Senate; Octavian (future Augustus Caesar, emperor) and Mark Antony were especially supportive. Herod was later granted additions to his kingdom beyond Judaea by Octavian (these additions included Joppa, Samaria and Strato's Tower [became Caesarea]). Josephus' The Jewish War Book 1 *sections 242-244, 282-285, 359-360, 386-400*, Josephus' Jewish Antiquities Book 14 *sections 324-326, 381-389*, Book 15 *sections 187-201, 215-217*.

[19] According to Josephus, the foundation of Zerubbabel's Temple (also known as the Second Temple) was removed and another laid down, and if one compares Josephus' accounts with Ezra 5:2-6:3, one can see that the shape of Herod's Temple was different from Zerubbabel's Temple; however, as Zerubbabel's Temple was not destroyed by a foreign invader, Herod's Temple can still be considered to be the Second Temple, that is, a version of it. Jewish Antiquities Book 15 *sections 380-425*, The Jewish War Book 5 *sections 207-221*.

[20] The birth of Jesus occurred before the death of Herod. Before Herod's death, he tried to kill Jesus by ordering the killing of all the children (or possibly selecting all the males) in Bethlehem (and its borders) two years old and under based on what the wise men from the east had told him concerning the date of the appearance of the star that had coincided with Jesus' birth. Matthew 2:1-23. Herod

---

died in 4 BC (around March): Josephus' The Jewish War Book 1 *sections 665-673*, Josephus' Jewish Antiquities Book 17 *sections 190-192.*

If one assumes that there were merely a few days: between the issuing of the murderous order and its completion; and between the completion and Herod's death, then the earliest possible year of Jesus' birth was 6 BC. The main reason why this year cannot be firmly stated as the year of His birth, is that Herod, perhaps calculating that the star had been first observed one year previously or even earlier, rather than two years, might have increased the upper limit of his age selection, so that no relevant child would be missed through people tricking the assassins by exaggerating a child's age.

[21] For the year of Jesus' death and resurrection, the prominent contenders are the years 29 AD, 30 AD and 33 AD. 33 AD is the optimal choice; the preference for this year is derived from a prophecy in the book of Daniel (9:24-27), given to Daniel in either 539 BC or 538 BC (Daniel 9:1). The year that the Messiah was cut off, 33 AD, is obtained from a well-known calculation based on numbers in the prophecy and is summarized as follows:

Verse 24—seventy sevens (more literal translation than weeks), i.e., 490 units of time, are determined before the Messiah brings about everlasting righteousness (second coming—His return).

Verses 25-26—the time between the command to restore-and-build Jerusalem and the Messiah will be seven sevens plus sixty-two sevens, i.e., 49 + 434 = 483 units of time. At the end of the 434 units (which followed the 49 units, thus 483 in total) the Messiah will be cut off but not because He did anything wrong (an event during His first coming). The city (Jerusalem) and the Temple (Second Temple, Herod's Temple) will be destroyed by a people from whom a future prince (the Antichrist) will descend. The total 490 units of time are interrupted by the death of the Messiah. There are still 7 units to go. There is a period of time of unknown length before the 7 units restart. We are in this unknown length of time now.

Verse 27—demonstrates that the 7 units commence when the future prince (the Antichrist) makes a deal with many. In the middle of the 7 units he will set up an abomination in the Temple (this temple is known as the Tribulation Temple). At the end of these 7 units the Messiah will return.

The units of time are years. This is indicated by Daniel 12:11, which reveals that from the time that the abomination is set up to the Messiah returning will be 1,290 days, i.e., approximately 3.5 years (half of 7 years). Note that the 7 years will be the seven-year Tribulation period (Matthew 24:4-30, Mark 13:4-26).

Currently a lunar month is 29.5 days, and there are 365.25 days in a solar year. A solar year ensures that the seasons are aligned every year. The prophetic years are made up of 360 days. Early in the Earth's history the lunar month was 30 days and 12 months made up a solar year. This is demonstrated biblically—at the time of the Flood 5 months passed after exactly 150 days (Genesis 7:11, 8:3-4)—and is also evidenced by 360-day calendars of the earliest civilizations, which needed no adjustments (additions of days to the years) to ensure that the seasons occurred at the same time every year.

At the time of the prophecy (539 BC or 538 BC—Daniel 9:1) Daniel was aware that the times and seasons had changed (Daniel 2:20-21). That is to say, the seasons would no longer occur at the same time every year if the original 360-day year was followed. At the time of the prophecy 365.25 days made up a year.

The start of the 483 years is 444 BC (the command to restore and build Jerusalem came in the 20th year of the reign of Artaxerxes; his reign began in 464 BC—Nehemiah 2:1-6). 483 prophetic years (483 x 360) = 173,880 days. This number of days makes up 476 solar years (from the relevant time, which is 444 BC, and onward), the calculation being 173,880/365.25 = 476 years. There was no 0 BC; time passed directly from 1 BC to 1 AD. Therefore, the Messiah died, was cut off, in 33 AD.

[22] Josephus' The Jewish War Book 6 *sections 249-287,* Dio Cassius' Roman History Book 65 *chapters 4:1-7:1.*

---

[23] Dio Cassius' Roman History Epitome of Book 76 *chapter 9:1-4.*

[24] Matthew 24:31-51, 1 Corinthians 15:50-54, 1 Thessalonians 1:10, 4:13-18, 5:1-11, 2 Peter 3:10, Revelation 3:10, see also Chapter 9 pg 211 with footnotes regarding assumptions (people being taken up directly to Heaven) and Chapter 24 pg 529 with footnote regarding the seven-year Tribulation.

There is a debate concerning the time of the Rapture: whether it will come before, during or at the end of the seven-year Tribulation period. Before the Tribulation is the optimal choice for the simple reason that this is the time that best fits the biblical passages that relate to the Rapture and also best fits the rest of the Bible.

Matthew 24:31-51—this passage demonstrates that not even Jesus knows when the Rapture will occur; only God the Father knows. The Rapture will be a surprise. The Rapture cannot occur at the end of the Tribulation, because it is already written that Jesus will return precisely at the end of this seven-year period, and therefore this coming is not a surprise (Revelation 19:11-20:4). The passage from the book of Matthew proposes another type of coming.

1 Corinthians 15:50-54, 1 Thessalonians 4:13-18—the Rapture will occur with the sound of God's trumpet and the shout of the archangel. The Lord Jesus will descend from Heaven with the spirits of those believers who will have already died physically on Earth. Their spirits will be united with their dead remains, which will be raised as incorruptible living bodies to be caught up in the clouds. Believers who are alive at this time will be caught up to meet Jesus in the clouds (to be together with those who had died), their corruptible living bodies changed to incorruptible living bodies.

1 Thessalonians 1:10—Jesus will deliver believers from the "wrath to come", which is almost certainly the Tribulation (Zephaniah 1:14-18, Revelation 6:1-17). Therefore, the deliverance will most likely occur before the Tribulation (Revelation 3:10).

1 Thessalonians 5:1-11—Jesus will come like a "thief in the night": reiterating the surprise nature of this coming. Furthermore, we see again that the aim of the Rapture is to save believers from wrath

(almost certainly the Tribulation), i.e., the Rapture will most likely precede the Tribulation.

2 Peter 3:10—mentions the Lord coming as a thief in the night. This precedes terrible destructive events on Earth and in the heavens (space). There will be terrible destructive events on Earth and in space in the Tribulation period (Revelation 6:12-17) and the passage from 2 Peter is likely to be referring to them.

Revelation 3:10—living believers will be kept from the "hour of temptation, which shall come upon all the world" (almost certainly the Tribulation). Others will become Christians after the Rapture, evidenced by the fact that they will be in the Tribulation (Revelation 7:1-17).

In conclusion, Jesus' second coming will have two parts:

I. The first part is the Rapture, which will most likely occur before the Tribulation. Two groups will be caught up to the clouds to meet Jesus: (i) the dead believers—their spirits united with their dead bodies (transformed to be incorruptible and living), and (ii) those alive on the Earth who believe in Him. All these believers will then be transported to Heaven (those spirits of the dead, then united with their resurrected incorruptible bodies, will be returning), because Jesus will not settle on the Earth at this time but will go back to Heaven, where He will wait until His return to Earth (Revelation 19:11-20:4).

II. The second part is Jesus' return at the end of the Tribulation, at which time He will defeat the Antichrist and his army and then settle on the Earth to start ruling from Jerusalem (Zion): Zechariah 14:1-21, Revelation 19:11-20:4.

[25] See Chapter 18 pgs 383-385 and Chapter 24 pgs 530-531 as well as their relevant footnotes regarding these topics.

[26] See Chapter 20 pgs 406-408 and Chapter 24 pgs 529-534 as well as their relevant footnotes regarding these topics.

[27] The Antichrist and his army (made up of armies from all the Gentile nations of the world) will be defeated in Edom (today in Jordan), which is east of Jerusalem. The reason why they will be defeated in Edom is because they will seek to destroy the remnant

of Israel, who will have sought refuge there. Isaiah 34:1-10, 63:1-6, Micah 2:12, Zechariah 14:1-15, Matthew 24:15-22, Revelation 12:6, 12:14-17, 19:11-21.

[28] Revelation 20:1-6. See Chapter 4 pg 104 and footnote regarding the Abyss. See Chapter 24 pgs 534-535 and relevant footnotes regarding the Millennium.

[29] Revelation 20:7-10.

[30] Revelation 21:1-22:7. Jesus the Messiah will reign during the Millennium. Although the period will be a finite 1,000 years, His reign can be thought of as eternal, because when the New Jerusalem has descended, He will reign from there forever in the New Heaven-New Earth. His reign will be continuous. Even Satan's assault on Jerusalem at the end of the Millennium will have no influence on the Messiah's reign. See Chapter 14 pg 312 and footnote regarding all the twelve tribes still represented in the Jewish people today.

[31] Revelation 20:11-15, 21:1-22:21. See Soul and Spirit.

[32] The Mysterious Numbers of the Hebrew Kings *chapters 1-5*. Within this book, E. Thiele explained that 931 BC was also valid for the year that the Kingdom of the Hebrews divided and the first year of Rehoboam's reign over Judah.

[33] 1 Kings 6:1, 11:42, 2 Chronicles 3:1-2, 9:30.

[34] 1 Kings 6:1.

[35] Exodus 12:40-41.

[36] Genesis 15:13.

[37] Genesis 11:10-32, 12:1-5, 21:5, 25:7-8, 25:26, 35:28-29, 47:28.

[38] Genesis 7:11, 8:13-14.

[39] Genesis 5:1-7:6, 8:13-14, 9:28-29.

[40] Genesis 1:1-5.

DISPENSATIONS

A dispensation is the character within a certain period of time of God's behaviour toward mankind as well as His expectations of our behaviour toward Him and to one another. Since creation there have been multiple dispensations, which have changed from one to another at discrete times, thus making a series. We are in the fifth, and there are three yet to come, making a total of eight dispensations.[1] Although the entire Bible is valuable for edification, some passages instruct a certain action given a certain circumstance and may not be directly applicable to our

---

[1] 1 Corinthians 9:16-17 demonstrates one aspect of dispensation, which is the delivery of God's message.

Ephesians 1:3-10 explains that in the last dispensation all things in Heaven and Earth will be gathered under the authority of the Messiah (Christ), who died for our sins, and that this is the will of God the Father. This passage also indicates that there is more than one dispensation.

Ephesians 3:1-12 demonstrates that there is a dispensation of grace—grace being salvation through faith in the Messiah, which is an unmerited gift. Although this dispensation was God's plan since creation, it was not revealed until certain ages had passed.

Colossians 1:23-29 reveals that the Gospel of the Messiah marks an era of God's behaviour toward man, that this era was hidden from previous ages and that we can preach the Gospel to others.

The last two passages also indicate that there have been multiple dispensations before the Messiah's dispensation of grace.

The above passages contain the four occurrences of the English word dispensation in the King James Version (all in the New Testament). In these four instances dispensation has been translated from the Greek word "oikonomia". This Greek word appears four more times in the New Testament, but in these instances oikonomia has been translated as "stewardship" three times (in Luke 16:1-8) and as "edifying" once (in 1 Timothy 1:4). Neither of these passages (in brackets) significantly adds nor takes anything away from the definition of dispensation in the main text.

lives today. For example, some passages state that sins need to be atoned for with animal sacrifice. This form of sacrifice is not applicable today, as Jesus ended the necessity with His sacrifice, but these passages help us to understand the need for sacrifice to atone for our sins. An understanding of the dispensations gives us the ability to place passages from the Bible in their contexts and enables us to determine if we should or shouldn't directly apply the passages to our lives. Many incorrect doctrines come from misapplication of the Scriptures. An understanding of the dispensations helps to avoid this. The dispensations cover the entire Bible, and a multiplicity of messages can be gained from each. It would be impossible to list all the messages, so at the end of each summarized dispensation one or a few short messages have been placed. The dispensations are as follows.

1. The Pre-Flood Utopian Era (4174 BC – ?*)

The law given to Adam and Eve was basic. Do be fruitful and multiply. Do dominate all creatures on the Earth. Do eat from the Tree of Life. Do not eat from the Tree of the Knowledge of Good and Evil or death shall result. A man should marry one woman, and together they shall be one. Adam and Eve ate the fruit of the Tree of the Knowledge of Good and Evil, which was the fall.[1] Messages: God's utopian plan is revealed. We can never accuse our creator of not giving humanity an opportunity for a perfect deathless ageless society on Earth. We should obey God.

*This date is definitely before 4044 BC, because Cain and Abel were born before Seth, who was born when Adam was 130 years old. Adam and Eve had their first son after the fall.[2]

2. The Pre-Flood Fallen Era (?* – 2517 BC)

The previous laws continued, except mankind no longer had access to the Tree of Life and therefore could no longer eat its

---

[1] Genesis 1:27-29, 2:9-17, 2:21-25, 3:1-24.
[2] Genesis 3:1-4:2, 5:1-3.

fruit, and with regard to the Tree of the Knowledge of Good and Evil, the damage had already been done. Mankind's sins could be atoned for with animal sacrifice; offerings of crops were not respected by God. Although the law do not murder was almost certainly already in the heart of man, this law was declared.[1] Messages: Sin creates problems, including death. Even after sin was in the world, mankind could still have a relationship with God.

3. The Post-Flood Pre-Mosaic Law Era (2517–1446 BC)

(Mosaic Law simply means law given by God to Moses.) During this era (which was before the Mosaic Law) the previous laws continued. Additional laws were added, given by God to all mankind through Noah and his three sons. In summary, the additional laws allowed the eating of meat of any creature but not the blood, and murder would be punished with the death penalty. God promised not to destroy the Earth again with a flood.[2] During this era God dealt blessings and punishments directly onto individuals and nations. Examples: God directly blessed Abraham; God directly punished Sodom and Gomorrah for the cities' wickedness; and God directly punished the Egyptians for their cruelty toward the Hebrews.[3] Furthermore, God dealt blessings onto individuals and nations through other individuals and nations. Examples: God blessed Egypt through the interpretation of Pharaoh's dreams by Joseph (a future widespread famine was predicted in the dreams, and so provision was made for it); and God blessed the Hebrews through the Egyptians, as Pharaoh allowed the Hebrews to stay in Egypt during the

---

[1] Genesis 2:17, 3:3, 3:11, 3:21, 4:2-16 (Cain didn't initially confess to the murder of Abel, which demonstrates that Cain knew that he'd sinned).

[2] Genesis 8:20-9:17.

[3] Genesis 13:14-17, 15:1-6, 18:20-19:28, Exodus 1:8-22, 3:6-9, 5:1-11:10.

famine.[1] Messages: God maintained a relationship with mankind after the Flood. God judged individuals directly and indirectly during their lifetimes on Earth. God judged nations directly and indirectly.

4. The Post-Flood Mosaic and further God-given-Laws Era (1446 BC – 33 AD)

Laws were given by God to Moses, after which they were disseminated to the other Hebrews. The giving of the laws started and they began to be followed prior to the Exodus from Egypt, just before the first Passover. There were many laws.[2] After Moses, additional laws were given by God through other men.[3] The Hebrews spread the laws to non-Hebrews by contact with them while wandering, while in the Promised Land and also while the Hebrews were exiled in other lands,[4] which sounds restricted; however, the laws were written by God in the hearts of mankind, made evident by the fact that the laws were instinctively known by the other nations, the people of which judged one another according to the laws.[5] The Ten Commandments were given prominence amongst all the laws. In summary, the Ten Commandments can be divided into two groups: the first four[6] are regarding how we should behave toward God and the last six[7] are regarding how we should behave to one another.

---

[1] Genesis 41:1-57, 42:1-47:27.

[2] Exodus 12:1-40:38 (some of the laws were directly received from God by Moses and Aaron together), Leviticus 1:1-27:34, Numbers 1:1-36:13, Deuteronomy 1:1-34:12 (some of the laws were heard by the Hebrews while Moses was receiving them from God).

[3] Joshua 1:1-18, 1 Kings 6:12-13, Ezra 6:14, Proverbs 6:20, Jeremiah 7:1-7, Malachi 2:1-5.

[4] Joshua 8:32-35, Esther 8:1-17, 9:27, Jeremiah 35:2-19, Daniel 2:1-4:37, see first footnote of this dispensation.

[5] Romans 2:11-15.

[6] Exodus 20:1-11.

[7] Exodus 20:12-17.

Animal sacrifice continued, but offerings of crops were then also acceptable to God.[1] During this era God dealt blessings and punishments directly onto individuals and nations. Examples: God directly blessed the Hebrew nation; God directly punished Korah and his followers for their rebellion; and God directly punished and blessed Nebuchadnezzar II.[2] Furthermore, God dealt blessings and punishments onto individuals and nations through other individuals and nations. Examples: God used the Hebrews to punish the inhabitants of the land of Canaan for centuries of evil (in fact, there were special laws made for this specific time for the inheritance of the Promised Land); God punished Israel and Judah with the Assyrian and Babylonian Empires respectively; and God blessed Judah through Cyrus the Great (king of the empire of the Medes and Persians), who ordered the Second Temple to be built.[3] Messages: God's love and patience is shown but also His judgement. Don't mimic those individuals and nations who were punished by God (either directly or indirectly). Because God's laws are written in our hearts, we are in error if we believe that we shall be better off on the Day of Judgement if we don't read the Bible to seek the will of God during our lives (especially if given ample opportunity). We are all aware that we are sinners and that we need God's forgiveness.

---

[1] Offerings of crops either alone or with an animal sacrifice— Exodus 29:2-25, Leviticus 2:1-16, 5:11-13, Numbers 18:12 and many more.

[2] Exodus 3:7-17, 14:12-31, 16:4-26, Numbers 16:1-50, Daniel 4:1-37.

[3] 2 Kings 17:1-23, 24:1-25:21, 2 Chronicles 36:5-23, Ezra 1:1-11. For the punishment of the inhabitants of the land of Canaan see Chapter 3 pg 68 and footnote regarding the Hebrews inheriting the Promised Land.

5. The Messiah's Era of Grace (33 AD – beginning of the Tribulation)

(Grace can mean an unmerited gift.) We have been given a New Covenant, which is salvation through belief in the Messiah. The unmerited, merciful gift known as "grace", which is this salvation through belief in the Messiah, was made accessible to the entire world by God the Father through Jesus the Messiah's perfect sacrifice.[1] This Good News was initially mostly spread by Jewish people to other peoples.[2] Regarding the Law (God's written laws), it was summarized by Jesus in the following statements when He was asked, "which *is* the great commandment in the law?" Jesus replied, "Thou shalt love the Lord thy God with all thy heart, and with all thy soul, and with all thy mind. This is the first and great commandment. And the second *is* like unto it, Thou shalt love thy neighbour as thyself. On these two commandments hang all the law and the prophets."[3] Jesus said, "If a man love me, he will keep my words"; in other words, if you love me, then obey what I teach.[4] To obey Him is to put your trust in Him, for salvation is through the Messiah alone.[5] The Law is something that shows us our sins and the need for salvation through Christ. It is impossible to achieve salvation by following the Law.[6] This doesn't mean that if we've accepted Jesus and received His salvation, that we can live lives ruled by

---

[1] John 3:13-21, 14:1-11, Acts 3:1-26, 4:10-12, 5:29-31, 13:33-38, 20:32, 26:15-18, Romans 3:24, 4:16, 5:1-21, 11:1-6, 1 Corinthians 15:42-58, Galatians 3:1-29, Ephesians 1:2-14, 3:1-12, Colossians 1:12-14, 1:23-29, Titus 2:11, 3:3-7, 1 Peter 1:3-4, Revelation 21:1-27.

[2] Entire New Testament.

[3] Matthew 22:36-40.

[4] John 14:15-23 and something similar in John 15:7-15.

[5] Psalms 2:1-12 and see previous footnotes in Chapter 9 pg 213, Chapter 13 pg 294 and Chapter 20 pg 426, all regarding salvation through Christ (Messiah) alone.

[6] Acts 13:33-38, Romans 3:19-26, 7:1-25, Galatians 3:1-29, 5:1-6.

sin, but we should live righteous lives, which reflect our faith in Him.[1] Before the Messiah's grace, salvation was through righteous faith in God; His saving grace was given to men and women for that reason, not because of their works. In this way, God's saving grace was present through all the previous eras, but His saving grace was later made universally accessible through Jesus' sacrifice.[2] Message: Put your trust in Jesus.

6. The Messiah's Era of Grace extending into the Tribulation (a future 7 years)

The above previous New Covenant will continue but with the additional law that if anyone worships the Beast (the Antichrist) and his image, and receives his mark, then they will be punished during the Tribulation period and will ultimately be condemned eternally to the Lake of Fire.[3] Messages: Put your trust in Jesus. Although there will be only one person known as the Antichrist, who will be the king of Babylon during the Tribulation period, the New Testament reveals that there are and will be many antichrists, defined by anyone who: denies that Jesus is the Messiah and therefore rejects both the Father and the Son;[4] and/or denies that Jesus the Messiah came to the Earth as a man[5]—those who espouse this often state that Jesus was only in a divine form or an angel, therefore disregarding the fact that God

---

[1] John 8:1-12, Romans 6:1-18, 7:18-8:15, Philippians 1:2-11, 1 Timothy 6:3-11, 1 John 1:1-10.

[2] Genesis 15:1-6, Psalms 32:1-11, Romans 4:1-25, Hebrews 11:1-40, Galatians 3:1-29, see also Chapter 24 pg 536 and footnote regarding righteous faith in God.

[3] Revelation 13:11-18, 14:9-11, 16:1-2, 19:20, 20:4-15.

[4] 1 John 2:22-29.

[5] 1 John 4:3, 2 John 1:7-13.

put on flesh, so that He could die for our sins. Jesus is 100% man and 100% God.[1] Don't follow antichrists.

7. The Millennial Era (a future 1,000 years)

Satan will be imprisoned in the Abyss during this era. Jesus the Messiah will reign over all the nations of the Earth from Jerusalem (Zion) with a rod of iron. Some people will resist Him, but because of His strong rule, the world will be at peace. Keeping the Feast of Tents (Succot) will be law for the entire Earth. The nations that will not keep this festival will be punished. After the 1,000 years are complete, Satan will be released from the Abyss to lead his final rebellion. He will lead many people against the encampment of those faithful to God and against Jerusalem. Satan and his army will be defeated.[2] Messages: Put your trust in Jesus. He will return as the King of kings. He has great plans for the Earth.

8. The New Heaven and the New Earth (a future eternity)

God will do away with the Heaven and the Earth, and He will create a New Heaven and a New Earth. The New Jerusalem will descend from the New Heaven and come to rest on the New Earth. God the Father and Jesus the Messiah will reign from the New Jerusalem. The New Heaven-New Earth will be occupied by the faithful. Those judged to not reside in the New Heaven-New Earth will be cast into the Lake of Fire, where they will remain for all eternity.[3] Messages: Put your trust in Jesus. Trusting in Jesus means that you will be in the New Heaven-New Earth for all eternity.

---

[1] See Chapter 8 and relevant footnotes regarding the same topic (pg 185) and God born into this world as mortal flesh to be a true sacrifice for our sins (pg 185).

[2] Psalms 2:1-12, Isaiah 2:1-4, Micah 4:1-4, Zechariah 6:12-13, 14:1-21, Revelation 12:5, 19:11-20:10.

[3] Ephesians 1:3-10, 2 Peter 3:7, Revelation 3:12, 20:10-22:21.

SOUL AND SPIRIT:
HOW ARE THEY DEFINED, ARE THEY ETERNAL AND WILL THEY BE UNITED WITH A RESURRECTED BODY?

The following are the biblical Hebrew and Greek words that have been translated into the English words soul and spirit:

Nephesh (Hebrew)—soul
Psuche (Greek)—soul
Ruach and ob (both Hebrew)—spirit
Pneuma and phantasma (both Greek)—spirit

Although every relevant biblical passage has been examined for each definition, the listed references are not always complete. However, those listed serve as examples from which the definitions were derived. Those biblical references omitted add nothing or little further to the definitions. A reference may be cited in more than one definition, because there is more than one meaning of the relevant word in the context that it is found. In square brackets [ ] are the Hebrew and Greek words that have been translated into soul or spirit. If a word is in the plural form, then it was also considered.

What are the Old Testament definitions of a soul?

1. *An eternal (in one direction, future), motivating force of a human that together with a body makes up a human being. [Nephesh.] Examples: Genesis 2:7—God breathed life into the lifeless man, whom He'd formed from the elements of the Earth. The man then became a "living soul", a "living nephesh", that is, a soul contained within a physical body, both together function-ing as a living human being. Genesis 35:17-19—Rachel died and her soul departed. 1 Kings 17:21-22—Elijah was aware that the soul is eternal and prayed to God that the soul of a dead child

would return. God returned the child's soul, and he revived. Job 33:14-22—soul is used three times in this passage. Verse 18 indicates a different fate for the life of a man and his soul: destruction and the pit respectively. In this context the pit is a place for the unrighteous dead (the punishment section of Sheol, which is Hell: see Chapter 7 pg 152 regarding Heaven—the accompanying footnote explains Paradise, Sheol, Hades and Hell). In verse 20 soul means definition 3 (below). In verse 22 soul means the present definition, and the grave, a translation of the same Hebrew word (shachat) translated as pit in verse 18, is where the man's soul is headed. Psalms 16:10—the soul can descend to Sheol (in this instance translated incorrectly as Hell in the King James Version). This verse is a prediction regarding the Messiah: that at His death His soul would go to Sheol (the Paradise section—see Chapter 7 pg 152 as suggested above) but not be left there, and neither would His body have time to decompose before the reunification of his soul and body. Christ's soul is eternal in both directions, past and future (His soul is excluded from the one direction in the definition, because He is God). Other examples: Psalms 49:15, 86:13, Proverbs 11:30, 23:14, Isaiah 38:17.

2. Existence as a living human being, a living person. [Nephesh.] Examples: Genesis 12:13—Abraham referred to his soul as his existence as a human being, capable of death. Genesis 46:22—the number of male descendants from Jacob and Rachel at the beginning of the Hebrews' stay in Egypt was 14 souls: souls simply meaning persons. Other examples: Genesis 12:5, 17:14, 19:20, Exodus 12:15, Leviticus 4:2, 7:21, 20:25, 1 Samuel 17:55, 2 Samuel 14:19, Job 7:15, Proverbs 19:16, Isaiah 3:9.

3. ‡A motivating force that feels. [Nephesh.] Examples: Leviticus 26:13-30—in verse 30 God spoke about His own soul, which has the ability to experience deep displeasure. Deuteronomy 11:13—in this passage the soul is a motivating force that can

drive a person to love, and yet is distinct from the emotional heart. Other examples: Genesis 27:4, 34:3, Leviticus 23:32, 26:43, Numbers 21:5, Deuteronomy 11:18, 12:15, 30:6, Judges 10:16, Jeremiah 5:29.

4. Morale. [Nephesh.] Example: Numbers 21:4—the soul of the people was discouraged. This demonstrates a group-motivating force that feels. Other example: Numbers 21:5.

The Hebrew word nephesh has also been translated as (note that where relevant, English words and phrases in quotes are not necessarily direct quotes from the King James Version; they have been given generalizability):

a) Creature, thing (living), beast, and in combination with the Hebrew word "behema" (translated as "beast") together they mean "beast". Genesis 1:21, 1:24, Leviticus 11:10, 24:18.

b) In combination with the Hebrew word "chay" (translated as "life") together they mean "life". Genesis 1:20.

c) In combination with the Hebrew word "kol" (translated as "all") together they mean "in all". Numbers 31:35.

d) Life, mortally. Genesis 9:5, Deuteronomy 19:11.

e) Person, man, any, (any) one, yourself, him, himself, they, he, myself, themselves. Genesis 14:21, Exodus 12:16, Leviticus 2:1, 4:27, 11:44, Deuteronomy 19:6, 1 Kings 19:4, Job 36:14, Psalms 105:18, 131:2, Isaiah 46:2.

f) Mind. Genesis 23:8.

g) Lust. Exodus 15:9.

h) Heart (emotional). Exodus 23:9.

i) Dead, body, dead body. Leviticus 19:28, 21:11, Numbers 9:7, Psalms 17:9.

j) Let me, as one wants, over unto the will, so would one have it, unto the will, unto one. Numbers 23:10, Deuteronomy 21:14, Psalms 27:12, 35:25, 41:2, Proverbs 6:16.

k) In combination with the Hebrew word "ratzach" (translated as "kill") together they mean "slayeth". Deuteronomy 22:26.

l) At one's own pleasure, at one's pleasure, one's own, given to appetite, appetite, of the desire. Deuteronomy 23:24, Psalms 105:22, Proverbs 14:10, 23:2, Ecclesiastes 6:7, 6:9.

m) In combination with the Hebrew word "mar" (translated as "bitter") together they mean "discontented". 1 Samuel 22:2.

n) Ghost. Job 11:20.

o) In combination with the Hebrew words "min" and "etza" (translated as "from" and "advice" respectively) together they mean "hearty counsel". Proverbs 27:9.

p) In combination with the Hebrew word "bayit" (translated as "house") together they mean "tablet". Isaiah 3:20.

q) Fish. Isaiah 19:10.

r) In combination with the Hebrew word "'az" (translated as "strong") together they mean "greedy". Isaiah 56:11.

What are the New Testament definitions of a soul?

1. *An eternal (in one direction, future), motivating force that together with a body makes up a human being. [Psuche.] Examples: Matthew 10:28—in essence, Jesus explained that we should fear the destruction of body and soul in Gehenna (a permanent place of everlasting fiery torment and therefore specifically the Lake of Fire [Mark 9:43]: Gehenna is inaccurately translated throughout the King James Version as Hell— explanation below) over that of the death of the body on Earth. In the context of the entire Bible the destruction of the unrighteous soul will be eternal as will be the body, for even the unbelieving dead will be resurrected to have a living body but one that can receive everlasting punishment. The sequence of events: at death the unbelievers' punishment starts as fiery torment of the soul in Hell (the punishment section of Hades); after the Millennium the bodies of unbelievers will be resurrected and united with their souls to appear before the Great White Throne of Judgement; and then the unbelievers will be cast into the Lake of Fire for eternity

(Matthew 18:4-8, 25:31-46, Mark 3:29, 9:43-48, Luke 16:19-31, John 5:26-29, Jude 1:7, Revelation 14:9-11, 20:11-15, 21:8, 22:15, see Chapter 7 pg 152 as suggested above, see Chapter 20 and accompanying footnotes regarding the Lake of Fire [pg 398] and judgement by Jesus the Messiah [pg 442]). Acts 2:22-33—in verses 27 and 31 the soul of Christ was not left in Hades (the Paradise section: in this instance Hades incorrectly translated as Hell in the King James Version—see Chapter 7 pg 152 as suggested above), clearly demonstrating that the soul is eternal. Christ's soul is eternal in both directions, past and future (His soul is excluded from the one direction in the definition, because He is God). Other examples: Matthew 16:26, Mark 8:36-37, Luke 12:19-20, Hebrews 10:39.

2. ‡A motivating force that feels. [Psuche.] Examples: Matthew 12:15-18—God (presumably the Father) declares that He has a soul that delights in Jesus (this passage from Matthew quotes Isaiah 42:1). Matthew 22:37—the soul, capable of love, is distinct from the reasoning mind and the emotional heart. Other examples: Mark 12:30, John 12:27, Hebrews 10:38, 2 Peter 2:8, Revelation 18:14.

3. Existence as a living human being, a living person. [Psuche.] Examples: Mark 14:34—Jesus remarked that His soul was so sorrowful that it could die. Acts 2:43—fear came on every soul who witnessed the work of the Holy Ghost. Other examples: Acts 3:23, 1 Peter 3:20.

The Greek word psuche has also been translated as (note that where relevant, English words and phrases in quotes are not necessarily direct quotes from the King James Version; they have been given generalizability):
a) Life. Matthew 2:20.

b) In combination with the Greek word "kakoo" (translated as "injure") together they mean "make one's mind evil affect". Acts 14:2.

c) Mind. Philippians 1:27.

d) In combination with the Greek word "ek" (translated as "from") together they mean "heartily". Colossians 3:23.

What are the Old Testament definitions of a spirit?

1. A supernatural being who exists eternally (in one direction, future, unless God, then both directions). [Ruach.] Examples: Genesis 1:2—during the creation of the Earth the Spirit of God moved upon the face of the waters. The Spirit of God is eternal in both directions, past and future. Genesis 41:38—the Spirit of God can be inside a human being. Pharaoh wanted a man "in whom the Spirit of God *is*" to direct the food storage to counter the impending famine. Joseph was that man. 1 Samuel 16:14-23, 19:9—the Spirit of God departed from Saul, and God sent an evil spirit to enter Saul. The evil spirit was clearly a demon, thus demonstrating that God still has ultimate authority over Satan's demonic cohort: an authority that He exerts when He chooses (see also 1 Kings 22:19-23, 2 Chronicles 18:18-22). Psalms 104:4—angels loyal to God are a category of spirits. Other examples: Numbers 11:29, 24:2, 27:18, Judges 3:10, 14:6, Isaiah 11:2, 59:21, Zechariah 6:5.

2. ‡A motivating force that feels and is part of a person. [Ruach.] Example: Genesis 41:8—the spirit of Pharaoh was troubled by his dream. Other examples: Genesis 45:27, Deuteronomy 2:30, Joshua 5:1, 1 Samuel 1:15, Psalms 51:17, Proverbs 16:2, Ezekiel 13:3, Haggai 1:14.

3. An attribute that can be infused into a person by God. Although not directly stated, it is implied that the attribute

acquired by the person comes about from the person being infused by the Spirit of God. [Ruach.] Examples: Exodus 28:3— God filled various individuals with the spirit of wisdom to make Aaron's priestly garments. Other example: Deuteronomy 34:9 (see Numbers 27:18-23). Support: Exodus 31:3—the infusion of the Spirit of God was accompanied by the attributes: wisdom, knowledge, understanding and workmanship.

4. A feeling that can come over a person. [Ruach.] Example: Numbers 5:14—the spirit of jealousy can come upon a person. Other examples: Numbers 5:30, Hosea 4:12, Micah 2:11.

5. An attribute that can be infused into a person by God, but the person does not receive the attribute by receiving the Spirit of God. [Ruach.] Examples: Isaiah 19:14—God can mingle a corrupt spirit into the people of a nation to cause them to make mistakes. Isaiah 29:10—God can pour out a negative spirit of deep sleep onto prophets, rulers and seers.

6. Morale. [Ruach.] Joshua 5:1—the Amorite and Canaanite kings lost their spirit, because they were fearful of the Hebrews and what God had done for them.

7. An evil spirit. [Ob.] Example: 1 Samuel 28:8-25—demonic spirits can enter individuals, giving them supernatural insight and ability; the human in this case was the witch of Endor. Other examples: 2 Chronicles 33:6, Isaiah 19:3.

The Hebrew word ruach has also been translated as:
a) Cool. Genesis 3:8.
b) Breath. Genesis 6:17.
c) Wind. Genesis 8:1.
d) Mind. Genesis 26:35.
e) Blast. Exodus 15:8.
f) Courage. Joshua 2:11.

g) Anger. Judges 8:3.
h) Quarters. 1 Chronicles 9:24.
i) Vain. Job 15:2.
j) Air. Job 41:16.
k) Tempest. Psalms 11:6.
l) Side. Jeremiah 52:23.
m) Spiritual. Hosea 9:7.

The Hebrew word ob has also been translated as bottle. Job 32:19.

What are the New Testament definitions of a spirit?

1. A supernatural being who exists eternally (in one direction, future, unless God, then both directions). [Pneuma.] Examples: Matthew 3:16—after Jesus' baptism, the Spirit of God descended onto Jesus. The Spirit of God is eternal in both directions, past and future. Matthew 10:20—the Spirit of God can enter a human and control what that person says. Matthew 12:43—an unclean spirit can possess a human being. 1 Corinthians 12:3-13—the Spirit of God can be infused inside a person to give gifts such as wisdom and prophecy. Hebrews 1:7—the angels who are loyal to God are a category of spirits. Other examples: Matthew 22:43, Mark 1:23, 3:11, Luke 4:18, 4:33, Acts 2:4, 8:39, Romans 8:27, Ephesians 2:2, 2 Timothy 1:7, Revelation 2:11, 16:14.

2. *An eternal (in one direction, future), motivating force of a human that together with the body makes up a human being. [Pneuma.] Examples: Luke 23:46—just before Jesus died, He presented His Spirit to God. Jesus' Spirit is eternal in both directions, past and future (His Spirit is excluded from the one direction in the definition, because Jesus is God). Acts 7:59-60— just before Stephen died he asked God to receive his spirit. 1 Corinthians 5:5—the flesh can be destroyed, but the spirit is

eternal. The suffering of the flesh can lead to an individual mending his or her ways, so that he or she receives Christ and the eternal spirit can be saved through Him. Note that this suffering of the flesh is not self-inflicted. 1 Peter 3:19-20—there are spirits in prison (Hell, punishment section of Hades) of unrighteous people who died before the Flood while the Ark was being prepared and of unrighteous people who died at the time of the Flood (see Chapter 7 pg 152 as suggested above—the accompanying footnote interprets in detail 1 Peter 3:18-20). Other examples: 1 Corinthians 7:34, Galatians 5:17, 1 Thessalonians 5:23.

3. ‡A motivating force that feels and is part of a person. [Pneuma.] Example: Colossians 2:5—Paul's spirit experienced joy. Other examples: Matthew 5:3, 26:41, Mark 8:12, Luke 1:17, John 4:23, 1 Corinthians 2:11 (the spirit of man).

4. A phantasm, a ghost visibly manifesting itself. [Pneuma.] Luke 24:37-43—after Jesus' resurrection, He appeared to His disciples, who thought that He was a phantasm. He reassured them that it was Him and proved it.

5. A phantasm, a ghost visibly manifesting itself. [Phantasma.] Example: Matthew 14:26-27—the disciples were afraid, because they thought that they were witnessing a phantasm walking on the water. Jesus reassured them that it was Him. Other example: Mark 6:48-50.

The Greek word pneuma has also been translated as:
a) Ghost (as in Holy Ghost or gave up the ghost). Matthew 1:18, 12:31, Luke 12:10, John 19:30.
b) Wind. John 3:8.
c) Spiritually, spiritual. Romans 8:6, 1 Corinthians 14:12.
d) Life. Revelation 13:15.

The Greek word phantasma has not been translated as anything else.

With regard to humans, are there any definitions of soul and spirit that are similar?

Two different definitions are each derived from very similar biblical (Old and New Testaments) uses of the words soul and spirit:

I. * An eternal (in one direction, future), motivating force of a human that together with the body makes up a human being [nephesh, psuche, pneuma].

II. ‡ A motivating force that feels and is part of a human being [nephesh, psuche, ruach, pneuma].

From all the definitions already presented in the previous sections one can see that there are other similar definitions derived from similar uses of the words soul and spirit, e.g., morale and mind; however, it is beyond the scope of Creation's Mutiny to comment further on them.

If each of the above two definitions (I and II) represents such similar biblical uses of the words soul and spirit, then is the soul the same as the spirit?

Regarding definition I, both the soul and the spirit are eternal. Both are motivating forces. Whilst on the Earth, both are combined with the body. Both leave the body at death. Both will be united either with an incorruptible resurrected body (in Jesus' case, already occurred) or with a resurrected body that can endure everlasting punishment. Despite this, there are indications that soul and spirit are not exactly the same, found in the following passages.

1 Thessalonians 5:23. And the very God of peace sanctify you wholly; and *I pray God* your whole spirit (pneuma) and soul (psuche) and body be preserved blameless unto the coming of our Lord Jesus Christ.

The context of the passage (see entire chapter) does not exclude both the spirit and soul meeting definition I. If they both meet the definition, then they are different as each is presented as a separate part of a person.

Hebrews 4:12. For the word of God *is* quick, and powerful, and sharper than any twoedged sword, piercing even to the dividing asunder of soul (psuche) and spirit (pneuma), and of the joints and marrow, and *is* a discerner of the thoughts and intents of the heart.

Again, the context of the passage (see entire chapter) does not exclude both the spirit and soul meeting definition I. Indeed, they are likely to meet the definition, as the distinction between soul and spirit is clearly something hard to discern and it is the Word of God who is able to achieve the distinction. The Word of God, being sharper than a double-edged sword, is needed to separate soul and spirit, thus indicating that they are close together and adherent to one another. Soul and spirit are so intertwined that although not the same, each serves an extremely closely related function, and they do this together.

From a practical point of view either word, soul or spirit, can be used individually when expressing to others: the eternal (in one direction, future), motivating force of a human that together with the body makes up a human being; the motivating force of a human that departs from the body at death to go to either Heaven or Hell; the motivating force of a human that will one day be united with an incorruptible resurrected body to live eternally in the everlasting epoch of the New Heaven-New Earth (first through the Millennium if the individual died before this period—Revelation 20:1-6);[1] and the motivating force of a human that will one day be united with a resurrected body that can endure eternal punishment in the Lake of Fire.[2]

Regarding definition II, both the soul and the spirit are motivating forces that feel and are part of a person. The following two passages indicate that in both, the soul and the spirit meet definition II.

1 Samuel 1:15. And Hannah answered and said, No, my lord, I *am* a woman of a sorrowful spirit (ruach): I have drunk neither wine nor strong drink, but have poured out my soul (nephesh) before the LORD.

Isaiah 26:9. With my soul (nephesh) have I desired thee in the night; yea, with my spirit (ruach) within me will I seek thee early: for when thy judgments *are* in the earth, the inhabitants of the world will learn righteousness.

However, the soul and the spirit are different, as each is presented as a separate part of a person. Nevertheless, they are

---

[1] If a living human is raptured (assumed) to Heaven, then there is no period of separation of soul and spirit from the body; the body is simply transformed to be incorruptible. See Timeline regarding the Rapture and the accompanying footnote.

[2] If a living human is cast directly into the Lake of Fire, then there is no period of separation of soul and spirit from the body; the body is simply transformed to one that can endure everlasting punishment: Revelation 19:20 and see Chapter 24 pg 534 and footnote regarding selection for the Millennium.

clearly very similar and serve an extremely closely related function. They, as definition II, are probably also being referred to in Hebrews 4:12 and are likely to be similarly intertwined.

From a practical perspective either word, soul or spirit, can be used individually to relate to others the motivating force that feels and is part of a person.

SELECT INDEX OF SUBJECTS AND PROPER NOUNS

The listed page numbers can refer to words in the main text, footnotes, timeline and glossary.

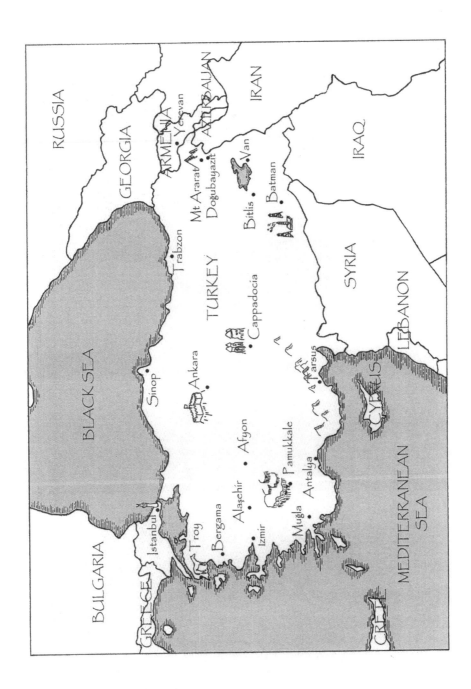